Designing TCP/IP
INTERNETWORKS

Other VNR Business Technology/Communications Books. . . .

Designing TCP/IP
INTERNETWORKS

Geoff Bennett

VAN NOSTRAND REINHOLD
I(T)P™ A Division of International Thomson Publishing Inc.

New York • Albany • Bonn • Boston • Detroit • London • Madrid • Melbourne
Mexico City • Paris • San Francisco • Singapore • Tokyo • Toronto

Copyright © 1995 by Van Nostrand Reinhold

I(T)P ™ A division of International Thomson Publishing, Inc.
The ITP logo is a trademark under license

Printed in the United States of America

For more information, contact:

Van Nostrand Reinhold
115 Fifth Avenue
New York, NY 10003

International Thomson Publishing GmbH
Königswinterer Strasse 418
53227 Bonn
Germany

International Thomson Publishing Europe
Berkshire House 168-173
High Holborn
London WCIV 7AA
England

International Thomson Publishing Asia
221 Henderson Road #05-10
Henderson Building
Singapore 0315

Thomas Nelson Australia
102 Dodds Street
South Melbourne, 3205
Victoria, Australia

International Thomson Publishing Japan
Hirakawacho Kyowa Building, 3F
2-2-1 Hirakawacho
Chiyoda-ku, 102 Tokyo
Japan

Nelson Canada
1120 Birchmount Road
Scarborough, Ontario
Canada M1K 5G4

International Thomson Editores
Campos Eliseos 385, Piso 7
Col. Polanco
11560 Mexico D.F. Mexico

1 2 3 4 5 6 7 8 9 10 QEBFF 01 00 99 98 97 96 95

Library of Congress Cataloging-in-Publication Data

Bennett, Geoff.
    Designing TCP/IP internetworks / by Geoff Bennett.
        p.   cm.
    Includes bibliographical references and index.
    ISBN 0-442-01880-0
    1. TCP/IP (Computer network protocol)   2. Internetworking
(Telecommunication)   I. Title.
TK5105.585.B46   1995   94-46461
004.6'5--dc20   CIP

*This book is dedicated
to the memory of my dad
George Bennett*

Table of Contents

Section 2: THE NETWORK INFRASTRUCTURE

5   LAN Technology   111

6   WAN Technology   147

7   Bridging Overview   193

8   Traditional Bridging   207

9   Token Ring Bridging   233

10   Translation Bridging   265

11   Routing Principles   279

16 Designing for Resilience 461

17 Designing for Security 487

18 Designing for Performance 527

Section 4: APPENDICES

Designing TCP/IP INTERNETWORKS

Section 1

DESIGN AND TECHNOLOGY REVIEW

CHAPTER 1

Design Overview

> *For any project we may identify three major variables; cost, scope and delivery time. The specification of any two of these will cause variation in the third.*
>
> *The Heisenberg Extended Uncertainty Principle*

1.1   What is Design?

Networks and Internetworks are living things. They never really become stable, although they can reach what scientists call a "steady state." When you begin the design process, you may think that it has an end point. It hasn't, because real systems simply move from one design phase to another. An example of this is drawn in Figure 1.1.

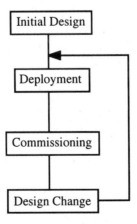

Figure 1.1:   Ongoing Design

This chapter presents a personal approach to design. I've listed two reports that may be interesting as comparative reading in the references [1, 2].

1.1.1   The Users and The Providers

One of the key philosophies to remember is that an internetwork is as much of a company resource as the buildings, the computers and the office furniture. The design process, the selection of equipment, the installation and the ongoing maintenance are all part of the service that the network provider offers to the network users. Decide from the outset to make this process a team effort. Throughout the rest of this chapter, I'll be describing methods and documentation to help you in the design process. However, each stage will require decisions. You must judge whether a particular decision can be taken on your own initiative, or passed to the Management Team for agreement. Remember that an oversight committee will generally sign off on technical decisions providing you give them a clear reason for the decision. Think ahead. If you can't give yourself clear reasons for a particular decision, don't expect to convince anyone else.

Use the Management Team as an arbitration committee between you (the provider of the network) and the users of the network. Remember that the systematic approach will work in your favor.

1.1.2   Using Documents as Tools

For some, documentation is a chore. It's like filing, or writing up meeting minutes. The problem for most people is that they don't know *what* to write, so they end up writing the wrong thing at the wrong time. They include too much useless information, and leave out all the important stuff. Good network documentation should read more like a Tom Clancy novel than an IEEE standard! (Note: My rationale here is that you read an IEEE standard and fall asleep before you learn anything, whereas after reading "Red Storm Rising," I'm now a fully qualified gunner on an M1A1.)

I hate paperwork. The problem is that most large projects simply cannot happen without paperwork and the related procedures. As a designer you've got a simple choice. You can fight the paperwork issue, or you can work with the system to make sure that the paperwork and procedures can be kept to a minimum. In this chapter I'll be suggesting that you create and maintain the following documents:

- The Network Proposal
- The Request for Proposal (RFP) or Request for Information (RFI)
- Service Level Definitions and Agreements
- Site and Network Logs
- Network Maps

And all this from a guy who hates paperwork? There are two things you should consider. First of all, not all these documents need to be created for all possible networks. Smaller networks don't need a formal RFP or RFI stage. Larger networks may be obliged by law to have them. A Network Map can be as simple or complex as you decide. Service Level Definitions and Agreements are the main point of argument. My experience shows that they can be the best way to clarify what the network is supposed to do and whether it's actually doing it. These documents are the best protection for a Network Designer.

I have to draw on experience again when I say that the Network Proposal ends up saving us paperwork. For small networks, the proposal can start as a two page memo. However, the innovation in this process is that we keep the original Proposal and build onto it during the lifetime of the network. By creating this single document at the start, we can avoid repetitive memos and descriptions during the life of the network. Having the proposal on line is doubly efficient; we can save a few trees by simply referring to specific parts of the document, or using cut and paste features in electronic mail packages.

1.1.3 A Structured Method

Despite the increase in internetworking experience, it still isn't possible to publish an internetworking recipe book. I can suggest a formal methodology that you might like to follow in your design process. This methodology is based on the standard Systems Analysis approach used to design a software system, and it is adapted to the needs of the internetwork. You may decide that some of the stages in the process are too formal for your case. The larger your internetwork project becomes, the more formal the process should be. For large internetworks, the process that I describe will be too general, and specialized project planning and management methodology will be necessary.

In Figure 1.1 I showed a box marked "Initial Design." Figure 1.2 shows a more detailed view of this box.

I'll now cover the steps in the Design Process in a little more detail. At various stages I'll be referring to the documents that I describe above.

1.2 The Design Process

This section is really an expansion of the flow chart I drew in Figure 1.2.

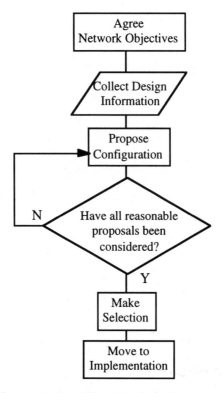

Figure 1.2:   The Design Process

1.2.1   Establish The Internetwork Objectives

The overall design objective for an internetwork is to allow electronic communication to take place. For a given application in a given budget range, the internetwork must offer the highest levels of performance, reliability, and security. However, no internetwork will involve just one person, and so establishing the true objectives of the internetwork will involve a little research. The following questions should be asked:

- Who are the target users of the internetwork?

- What are the applications that must be supported?

- Does the internetwork replace an existing communication system? If so, what migration stages must be considered?

- How do individual corporate objectives effect the internetwork? (e.g. for corporate locations, for mergers and acquisitions, is the internetwork part of the core business?)

- What are the performance requirements? Note that these can be stated for different parts of the internetwork at different times of day, for different applications over the internetwork, and for combinations of these sub groups.

- What are the reliability objectives? These can also be stated for the same sub groups as performance.

- Who will be responsible for managing the internetwork? Does it make sense to subdivide the internetwork for management purposes?

- What is the life expectancy of the internetwork?

- Finally, and most importantly, what is the budget?

There are many abstract goals that you can set out to achieve in a network design process. Some of these goals such as performance, capacity, security, resilience and reliability can be expressed in more quantitative terms. In other words, these are services that we can measure.

1.2.2   Defining Service

Any router can be described as "high performance," any line as "high capacity" and any system as "highly reliable." Our expectations change from year to year, and part of the art of salesmanship is to interpret the specification for your own equipment in the most favorable light. When we set out to design a network, we'll encounter inconsistency and surprises every day, and so whatever we can do to set up some points of reference must be a good thing.

We can measure many different things about a network. We can even measure the same thing in many different ways. One of the more useful administrative tools in network design is the *Service Level Definition*. Some of you may be more familiar with the term *procedure*. In management terms a procedure is a documented method that describes what to do in a well-defined circumstance. In an office environment, we are surrounded by procedures, for example fire drill instructions, first aid drills. We have procedures when someone is hired or fired.

To give you a general idea, a Service Level Definition should define:

- WHAT we are measuring
- HOW we should measure it

In other words, a Service Level Definition is a procedure that allows us to define a service quality test for a stated network property, like performance, reliability, or response time. Examples of poor Service Level Definitions include:

- The network will be secure.

- The network will offer high performance levels at all times.

These definitions are not only useless from a design aspect, but they're also incredibly dangerous for you, if you're the network administrator. If the network is performing below par, then these definitions can't be used to decide how bad the problem is. On the other hand, if the network is exceeding the design goals, they can't be used during your salary review to show your boss how good a job you've been doing!

Later in this chapter, I give some more specific samples of Service Level Definitions.

1.2.3   Agreeing on Service Goals

When you create a Service Level Definition, you don't commit to a level of service. Rather you define what you're measuring and how you should measure it. *Service Level Agreements* are the documents that you can regard as a quality contract between you and the network user.

The word *agreement* is the important one here. As the "technical guru" for the internetwork, you essentially have control over Service Level Definitions. You can choose the parameter to be measured, and the measurement technique to suit the capabilities and resources at your disposal.

However, the actual quality levels *must* be *agreed*.

Service Level Agreements are "living documents." They should continually evolve as the needs of the users and the capabilities of the network provider change. By using the Service Level Agreement, you can prevent excessive demands on the network. For example, let's say you've previously agreed to a specific quality of service for 25 users on a specific site. The number of users increases to 50, and they start to complain about poor response times. You see that the leased line connecting this site with the central site is overloaded. You can now negotiate the strategy in two ways. First of all the users on the remote site must accept a lower quality of service because they have broken the original Service Level Agreement. Alternatively, you can be given budget to buy data compression devices, or an ISDN overflow connection, or more bandwidth on the leased line. Without the documentary backup of the Service Level Agreement, you will need to be much more of a politician to argue the case for your internetwork.

Cover Your Anterior!

Although it's normal to express this homily as "cover your ass," I prefer to protect other parts of my body from management abuse. You may feel that I'm being needlessly pedantic about the formality of the Service Level Agreement. However, I think you'll agree with me once you've experienced your first redesign committee meeting. The internetwork will be a new and wonderful corporate resource for around 12 months. It should go through the following stages in its life cycle:

1. Interest from all parties during the specification and design process.

2. Hassle for the network administrator during the installation and commissioning process.

3. Initial euphoria that this thing seems to work.

4. Some departments complaining that some of their equipment no longer works properly since this damned internetwork was installed. These problems are usually caused by poor configuration of legacy applications or hardware. The internetwork just causes the existing problem to surface.

5. The mature phase when the internetwork is working. You've now learned how the internetwork operates. You're familiar with the products you've installed. You've got the most irritating bugs out of the hub/bridge/router/NMS code (delete as applicable).

6. A growing feeling that the internetwork is overloaded, is being displaced by newer technologies, or is incapable of supporting new applications.

Up to and including Stage 4, you may find that you can get away with most reasonable requests to modify Service Level Agreements or Definitions. Errors will be forgiven (providing they don't cause crashes on the corporate mainframe, or involve too many passengers' bags being sent to Cleveland). So up to this point, your Service Level Agreement document should include plenty of leeway. Scientific tests are difficult to make on an internetwork, so you'll need to refine your Service Level Definitions constantly. Renegotiating Service Level Agreements may be more difficult. So, if you have to do it, you need to know you're right, and have evidence to back it up. Psychologically, however, you have the upper hand within this phase.

At the end of Stage 5 and into Stage 6, when users start taking the network for granted, you need to have established your position. Your Service Level Definitions and Agreements should be in place. You should also feel confident of meeting the criteria and standards you have set for the internetwork.

If you have managed the situation correctly, you should now welcome Stage 6. With the correct presentation, the dissatisfaction of the internetwork users can be translated into career progress for you (i.e. more staff, more resources). I'd like to inject a note of cynical realism here. In an ideal world, business would accept the arguments of an experienced network administrator to justify expansion of the internetwork. In reality, I've seen some companies take their networks to the brink of collapse before they accept the financial arguments for expansion. The formality of the Service Level Agreements may give you the evidence you need to make expansion decisions before the crisis breaks.

If you are a high level manager taking a sneaky look at this book, you should remember that good network administrators are worth their weight in gold. Most of them are not only motivated by money, they also need to feel that they are learning and growing. If you don't appreciate the person in charge of your successful internetwork, you can be sure that some other company will!

1.2.4   Gathering Information

While we can regard the establishment of design objectives as the most critical stage of the design process, gathering information to formulate the objectives is certainly the most difficult. The challenges we face in the gathering process include the following.

Accuracy of Information

One of my favorite bureaucratic quotations comes from Sir Josiah Stamp (1849-1941), who was Her Majesty's Collector of Inland Revenue for Queen Victoria. He stated "The government is extremely fond of amassing great quantities of statistics. These are raised to the nth degree, the cube roots are extracted, and the results are arranged into elaborate and impressive displays. What must be kept in mind, however, is that, in every case, the figures are first put down by a village watchman, and he puts down anything he damn well pleases."

In more scientific terms, we can use two terms to describe the quality of data: *accuracy* and *precision*. Accuracy essentially describes how close we are to getting the real answer. If we measure the weight of 1 liter of pure water at room temperature, we *should* find that it weighs 1kg. The closer our measurement is to 1kg, the more accurate it is. In contrast, if we ask a class of students to all take the same measurement (possibly with different sets of scales), we may get answers ranging from 0.9kg to 1.1kg. The average measurement might be 1kg, and so we still achieve an *accurate* result. If another class makes the same measurement the next day and gets values between 0.5kg and 1.5kg, they may still end up with the same average answer, and be just as accurate as the first class. However, their *precision* is lower, because their range of readings is wider. Remember the golden rule: network designers should state their traffic growth forecasts to two decimal places to prove that they have a sense of humor.

Format of Information

Assuming we can get the information we need, will it arrive in the right format? Typically any data you receive will always be expressed in the least convenient units, and the frame of reference may also be different (in the benchmarking business one of the most common variables is packet size, for example). Assuming measurement procedures and units are standardized, the presentation format may vary. If you are a Lotus 123 user, you may not appreciate being sent two weeks worth of network load data on a Macintosh disk that is prepared in Excel. Similarly, in the Customer Service labs at Wellfleet we use Sniffers and

W&G LAN analyzers so that we can interpret packet traces from customers using either machine on their network.

As the policy maker you have at least three alternatives.

- You'll be collecting all the data yourself, so you can be assured of consistent, appropriate format.

- You can impose a range of data formats as part of the Design Proposal Document.

- In a large network, or where extensions to an existing internetwork are planned, you may have the luxury of a dedicated NOC team (Network Operations Center). Part of the NOC workload might be to reformat data received from corporate sources for use in planning or maintenance operations. To be realistic, the NOC team should publish a list of supported formats for specific data types.

Investigative Resources

One of the easiest things to underestimate is the amount of time that's necessary to take measurements. If we have an existing internetwork that we'd like to extend, we might take measurements at different parts of the internetwork to see where we should provide more bandwidth or additional connections. In these cases our job is relatively simple; we connect an analyzer for a few days and record traffic load. But then someone suggests that we might like to test for overloads and failures on the network, and so we start adding some tests (having constructed or captured the appropriate packet types). After a couple of weeks of a one month study period, we are still on the first segment of a 20 segment network and we still don't have the data we thought we needed in the first place!

In the planning stage for a totally new network, the task is more complex. In this case we need to model the network so that we can locate possible bandwidth bottlenecks, or to design more resilient routing. Bandwidth data is easy because the only acceptable policy to adopt in a modern client/server network is to support worst-case loading levels. This means that most bandwidth calculations can be done on a simple spreadsheet.

For routing design we may need to resort to modeling techniques. Modeling programs allow us to input the behavior of individual network elements (like routers and bridges), and then to perform dynamic testing on the resulting system. Most Modeling packages were developed to decide if telephone exchanges could support enough subscriber extensions. Many of the assumptions they make are not directly valid for connectionless, packet-switched systems like IP. To model just a few seconds of real LAN traffic may require hours of processing time on a fast PC. However, the problem that I find most disturbing about Modeling packages is that they make assumptions about the behavior of IP routers that the manufacturers themselves could not begin to guess at. Unlike PABXs operating with 64kbps channels, a high performance router does not have a "non blocking backplane," and can never know how much data the next frame will contain.   My own feeling is that Modeling packages may again be useful if the world chooses ATM LAN technology, and high performance routing can be achieved with fixed length cells, but that time is a long way off.

Document Your Assumptions

During the Design Process, you will be making many assumptions. In all cases, I strongly suggest that you document these assumptions, explain their significance, and have the assumptions agreed in committee. This has three possible benefits for you. First, if you're making an incorrect assumption, there may be someone with direct experience of the specific subject who will spot your mistake before it's too late. Remember that you are an *internetwork architect*, and you shouldn't be expected to have the same level of detailed knowledge about end-user applications as the Data Processing Manager would have. Second, in the worst-case you are covering your rear. Third, you are showing an open approach to the design process and involving all levels of management in the project process. You may be glad of this team spirit in the future, so cultivate it wherever possible.

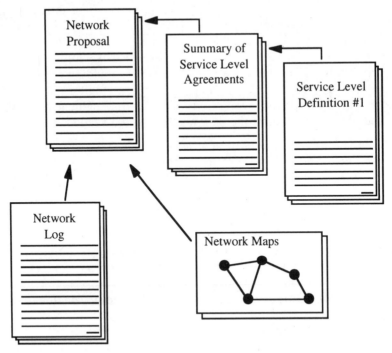

Figure 1.3:   Relationship of Network Documentation

The document you should use for recording assumptions and agreements etc. is the Network Proposal. This begins its life as an upbeat description of why the company needs the network, and how the system will develop. This original document then becomes an introduction for the ongoing record of the network design. I show the relationship between these documents in Figure 1.3.

Think About Network Management NOW!

It's never too soon to think about network management. In most good quality NMS packages, you will find mapping tools, inventory databases and even some Modeling capabilities. By using the NMS as part of your design process, you will avoid duplicating information entry at a later stage.

The Internetwork Log

The most valuable document in your internetwork is the Site Log. Obviously this must be kept on a computer somewhere, but it must also exist on paper. Network operators will fill in details by hand initially, and then transfer the results to the computer-based log. Log information should be very detailed for those parameters that don't change quickly: for example, the street addresses of corporate sites, road directions to reach unmanned switching stations and locations of keys. For information that may change more quickly, you need to use some judgment. Actual network addresses may change quite often, especially while the network is in the commissioning stage. Contact names for various network sections are vital pieces of information. Remember, the more important a given location, the more contact names must be established, and the more widespread your training program should be.

1.3 What Kind of Information?

So what kind of information do we need about the network? Although each installation will have subtle differences, I can summarize the major types of information as follows:

- Site Information
- Traffic Analysis
- Anticipated Growth
- Performance Goals
- Reliability Goals
- Other Constraints
- Equipment Specifications
- Training Requirements
- Costing Information

1.3.1   Site Information

In a mainframe centric network, sites can be divided into "Processor Sites" and "Terminal Sites." In general the former required special facilities and staff, the latter did not. For a while in the 1980s the trend was away from these centralized networks and towards distributed peer networks. Today the trend has swung back because traditional SNA functions are being replaced by internetworks. However, the new role of the mainframe is as the LAN "Super Server." The result is that, while there is more intelligence out on the remote sites, the traffic flow patterns are more like an SNA network. I've tried to illustrate this by showing the locations of processing power, session concentration or network routing intelligence in Figure 1.4.

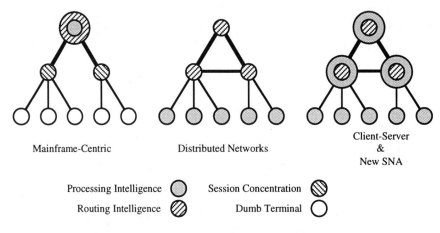

Mainframe-Centric   Distributed Networks

Client-Server
&
New SNA

Processing Intelligence ◉   Session Concentration ◍

Routing Intelligence ◍   Dumb Terminal ○

Figure 1.4:   The Evolution of Internetworks

1.3.2   Traffic Analysis

Traffic volume, the type of traffic, and the pattern of traffic flow in the network are the most critical factors influencing the overall performance of the network. Modern network analyzers can measure a range of pre-defined functions such as:

- Percentage utilization

- Packets per second

- Errors per second

- Kilobytes per second

- Most active stations

Traffic analysis can be used to define a performance *baseline* for each LAN segment. In this context, a baseline is simply the level of normal LAN activity. Baseline measurements allow us to set thresholds for alarms, or Network

Management traps. Most analyzer manufacturers suggest that alarm thresholds
are set at 5% higher than *peak utilization.*

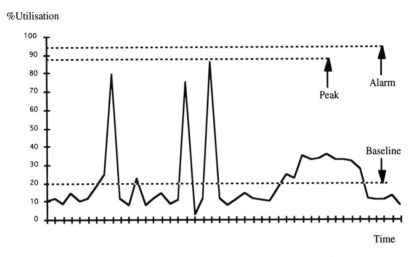

Figure 1.5:   Traffic Utilization Graph

Traffic volume is easy enough to measure in an existing network, but requires
careful discussion and calculation for a completely new network. The best way
to predict loading is to characterize the type of workstations on the network, and
then to find an existing LAN segment that is similar. Alternatively, you can opt
for the predictive approach and try to calculate the traffic pattern from a single
workstation, then extrapolate to the number of workstations on the proposed
segment.

Traffic Type

It's also important to determine traffic type. The performance tuning procedure
that I discuss in Chapter 15 is based on a knowledge of the Transport Layer
protocols that are operating over your IP traffic. In addition, you need to take
inventory of the other protocols that are in use in the network: do these
protocols need to be supported over the backbone? Try to make sure the answer
is "no" for as many protocols as possible.

For TCP/IP networks traffic will typically take the form of TCP, UDP, or NFS
over UDP traffic. Another major aspect is to determine whether traffic is
interactive or batch. The classic generalization is that interactive traffic requires
very short response time form the network but may not need a lot of bandwidth.
This is becoming less valid; interactive traffic size often follows a probability
distribution. Batch traffic is insensitive to response time but may need a lot of
bandwidth.

The pattern of traffic can be easy to determine, and is really just an
interpretation of Figure 1.2. One of the confusing factors is that client/server

and peer to peer traffic is often mixed over the same internetwork. The classic example is a site that has its own local server, but connects to a single, central site for access to a corporate database.

For traffic analysis, a map is essential. It is even more useful if this map is computer based, so that changes can be made quickly and copies sent electronically so they can be edited and updated by colleagues. I talk more about drawing packages below.

Load statistics can be measured using a variety of network analyzers. This is a useful feature for networks that already exist because the impact of expansion and additional connections can be calculated or extrapolated. For new networks, analysis data is also important. Using analyzers, you can measure existing network segments that are performing the same task with the same equipment as your proposed network. You can estimate internetwork traffic loads and get some idea of the burst characteristics of the application environment.

Token Ring Analyzers - Warning!

It's widely known in the industry that Token Ring LAN analyzers are simply not in the same quality league as their Ethernet and FDDI counterparts. An independent test performed by Data Communications [5] seems to give quantitative confirmation of this opinion. Remember when you read this test report, however, that most of the analyzers will deliver enough performance to stress the network at average packet sizes. Hopefully, the next generation of Token Ring analyzers will benefit from the new chipsets (like IBM's LANstreamer).

1.3.3   Anticipated Growth

Edgar Feidler, of the Conference Board, proposed a series of light-hearted rules for economic forecasts in the Board's magazine *Across The Board* in June 1977. Two of my favorites are: "If you have to forecast, forecast often.," and "If you're ever right, never let 'em forget it."

Forecasting growth in networks is just as difficult as predicting changes in the stock market, and it can bring you just as much trouble if you're wrong. In past years, user estimates of growth rate have generally been low. This is because internetworking products are required when companies grow, *and* when they downsize (since the management expects the same amount of work to be done by fewer people). Growth planning is one of the few processes that becomes more accurate due to committee involvement. Overestimates in one department *can* be offset by underestimates in another. Historical trend information is useful, but only as a guide. New applications (such as client/server) can cause a step increase in network utilization. The appearance of new application types cannot be predicted from history.

Remember, if you made the wrong choice of hardware, you can still change your mind. I've known three Network Administrators that were promoted after they'd decided to throw out their old routers and buy a different brand. All of them were able to argue (correctly as it happens) that they made the correct choice given the situation at that time.

1.3.4   Performance Goals

These form the basis of a Service Level Agreement between the internetwork providers and its customers. We have a three stage process here that you'll be seeing for other Service Level issues:

- Define a specific performance test, and write a Service Level Definition. Assess the performance of the system under test conditions, and a variety of loads.

- Use the test data to formulate the Service Level Agreement for Performance.

- Agree on a measurement policy to check if the Service Level Agreement is being met, and what to do if it isn't.

While I was writing this chapter, I had to make a visit to a customer site because the network administrator was not happy with his new router network. This was the first time the company had used dedicated routers, and so the managers had no experience to help them decide if they'd made a wise decision. When I spoke with the network administrator, his first remarks were that the network performance (they were using IPX) was not as good as they'd expected. Users were complaining about response times. A little more detail then emerged. It seemed that one of the department managers (a very influential voice at management meetings) was complaining because performance has not *improved* since the router was installed. I must admit I'd promised an overall improvement in an earlier pre-sales visit because at that time the customer was using a single bridged Ethernet segment with a couple of hundred users attached. The big problem was that the network administrator had not performed any performance measurements *before* the routers were installed, so he had no quantitative basis on which to argue with his colleague. When I looked at the workgroup in question, it seemed they were using an overloaded Novell File Server, *and* they were doing some spooky stuff with multiple Novell encapsulation types. It turned out that the File Server was the bottleneck because of poor configuration. Installing the router had no effect whatsoever on this workgroup, and that's what they were complaining about!

Performance levels have to be defined in very simple terms that both sides can easily understand, and are unlikely to be misinterpreted.

Earlier in the chapter I promised I'd give you some more examples of Service Level Definitions. Here are three possible definitions of network response time:

| Definition #1: | Response time is defined as the time interval between a client process initiating a transaction request and the receiving of the transaction acceptance. |

| Definition #2: | Response time for a terminal is defined as the time between the SEND key being pressed and the keyboard being freed for the next character to be typed. |

| Definition #3: | Response Time for an asynchronous terminal is defined as the time between any keypress and the return of the remote echo for that character by the final destination host. The test configuration is shown in the attached diagram[1]. The measurement will be taken by hard wiring a network analyzer into the terminal connection marked SOURCE and recording the timer interval between the TX and RX pulses for the first bit of the character byte. The Response Time will be measured 100 times. All measurements will be retained for future analysis, but the average of these measurements will be expressed in milliseconds and will be defined as the "Average Async Terminal Response Time." Response time measurements will be taken with the Network Load parameter at 0%, 10%, 50%, 80% and 100%. |

Each of these definitions is becoming more specific, but I think they are also becoming easier to understand. In the final definition we are saying what we're measuring (and we're giving it a name we can use as reference), where and how we should measure it, and how we should present the results. However, we also need to come up with suitable tests for block mode terminals, PC terminal emulations, client/server applications and so on. The most accurate tests will be the most specific. This is something you need to decide during the Service Level discussions.

Performance levels must be agreed. For example, let's say that we are interested in an asynchronous terminal attached to a terminal server. In the past we've made our 10%, 50%, 80% and 100% measurements of response time. The results are shown in Table 1.2.

---

[1]Don't expect to see a diagram here; it'll be in your document!

Table 1.2:   Measured Response Times

Network Load (%)	Response Time (ms)
0	4.2
10	10.3
50	12.7
80	23
100	220

On the basis on this information, we need to define a single figure that represents the Service Response Time for an asynchronous terminal attached to a terminal server. Let's assume first of all that if the Network Load (another defined parameter) ever exceeds 80%, we will assume that this is a "bad thing." In other words, it should only happen in the event of temporary rerouting, and we may have contingency plans to provide additional emergency bandwidth (e.g. ISDN or Switched-56 Dial on Demand). This means that we should always be able to say that 23ms is a worst-case response time when the network is operating correctly. Let's double this value to give ourselves some leeway, and round up to the nearest ten milliseconds. We can then propose a Service Level Agreement that is worded as follows:

"90% of all transactions in a one hour measurement period will have a response time that will not exceed the Service Response Time of 50ms."

1.3.5   Reliability Goals

Like the Performance Goals, Reliability Goals will become the subject of Service Level Agreements. However, in this case we have an established set of metrics from which to base our measurements. These are the Mean Time Between Failure (MTBF), Mean Time To Repair (MTTR) and Spare Holding Recommendation concepts. For an individual internetwork element like a router or a workstation, we can calculate the likelihood of its failure. However, using resilient routing techniques, we can create an internetwork that is tolerant to the failure of individual elements within the system.

For WAN links, Service Level Agreements within the corporate internetwork must be applied as back to back agreements with the WAN provider. For example, it would be foolish for us to commit to a 99.5% availability of a particular WAN link if the PTT will only commit to a 99% availability.

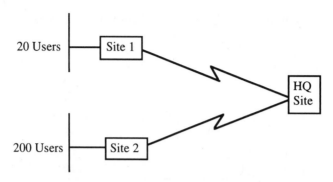

Figure 1.6:   Which Site is More Critical?

In addition, you should use a sensible metric to measure downtime.   For example, Figure 1.6 shows two remote sites linked to a central HQ. Site A has 200 users who download database information from HQ. Site B has 20 users. If the WAN link to Site A fails for 10 minutes, does it have the same cost to the company as if the link to Site B failed for the same period? Assuming that the terminal populations are performing equally important tasks, we can say that Site A is more important. A quantitative measurement unit might be "user hours" of downtime. Measuring downtime in this way allows us to agglomerate data from multiple sites, and to handle the concept that different carrier circuits may have different reliability levels.

Reliability of internetworks has a direct and proportionate effect on cost, and so it's vital to get the internetwork customers to allocate a cost of downtime. Most of the customers I've dealt with are reluctant to name a figure simply because if they were honest, any salesman could cost justify twice as many WAN links and twice as much internetworking equipment (in other words most user under-value their own businesses).   Banking and finance establishments are a refreshing exception. These guys have a good idea of what downtime in their network costs, so they are prepared to invest in resilience features and additional equipment.

1.3.6   Existing Constraints

There is a wonderful myth in the business world: the *Green Field Site*. The term is supposed to describe an environment with no existing constraints, nothing already decided.

In the real world, we must work with a range of existing decisions, policies and other constraints. For example, even if your company is moving to a completely new site, you may be obliged to use existing office PCs, minicomputers, mainframes, and most importantly, applications. Your internetwork will be the vehicle to support a variety of departmental and corporate applications, and this may be the biggest single constraint you have to face. I can only give very general advice here.

First, avoid the temptation to support legacy applications using customized gateways or protocol converters, especially if this traffic is supposed to pass over the internetwork backbone. These devices may seem like a great idea at first, but this technology can get out of hand. I once saw a communications room with shelves full of protocol converters for 5250 terminals. The boxes were "good value" when they were first chosen, but a few years later buying additional converters cost three times more than a PC network adapter, cable connection, and hub combined.

Second, make sure you are aware of the impact of the constraint. The customer with the protocol converters was unaware that AS/400s can be fitted with an IBM-supported Ethernet interface that would have allowed a much cleaner bridged connection for the PCs. There was a cost impact to migrating the AS/400s, but this was easily justified compared to the cost of the protocol converters. For really major issues, it may be time for the company to think about migrating some of the legacy applications onto Open Systems hosts (i.e. UNIX machines).

Finally, remember to document these constraints carefully as they could save your life later when you need to explain why on earth you ever decided to support SDLC or LAT over the backbone!

1.3.7   Equipment and Site Specifications

You should keep documentation updated for all of the equipment in the internetwork. Manufacturers will be happy to give you all the brochures you need, but you should also make sure that you obtain copies of Application Notes, or any other tips that the manufacturers provide. Some of this material may be in electronic format. Manuals may be available in CD-ROM format, for example. There are certain documents you need to make sure are up to date:

- Warranty and support contract information. If you're obtaining your equipment from multiple sources, you need to track the appropriate support contacts.

- Software Release Notes. These documents are becoming much more important as manuals move to the CD-ROM format. You'll find that manufacturers may produce software releases quarterly, but only update their CDs annually. Keep *all* Release Notes, even older versions.

- Current equipment brochures and specification sheets. Products that you chose for your internetwork two years ago will have "evolved." Even if the outside box is the same shape and color, the chips inside will have changed to keep pace with cost effective components.

- Building plans and maps. Building plans are important for all internetworks, but you'd be surprised how useful maps will become. If you are part of a large corporation, some of your "troops" may not be familiar with all of the sites. Directions to reach a specific location, with building plans, etc. are incredibly useful.

- An Equipment Numbering Plan. This is a centralized identity scheme for all of the equipment in your network, and is absolutely vital as soon as the internetwork extends beyond a single room. A Numbering Plan can usually be included in the Network Management System, and is essentially an Inventory Database.

1.3.8   Training Requirements

There are many forms of training that you can consider for the internetwork.

- Outside training on generic technologies (e.g. TCP/IP, X.25, FDDI, Cabling Systems)

- Outside training on generic applications used by the MIS team (e.g. Word, Excel, CAD Packages)

- Outside training on specific products (manufacturer courses).

- Internal training.

The range of internal training is pretty broad, but has one common theme. It is customized to the characteristics of your internetwork. You can hold courses on the procedures you've defined in the Service Level documents, on an overview of the internetwork itself, and for specific network applications.

Internal training is very important. It makes users feel more comfortable with the internetwork, especially if you arrange follow up sessions three months or so after the original course. Take these sessions seriously because they are a good chance to listen to *your customers* without their input being "filtered" through layers of management.

I Don't Have The Time

OK, I agree that these courses don't just write themselves. They require preparation and time to present them. But wait! How long do *you* think such a course should last? My advice is that an Overview session could last less than 2 hours. You could hold the course over lunch time if you have some tasty snacks brought in.

Course materials may be obtainable from manufacturers themselves. Most of the companies I've worked for (and most of their competitors) offer excellent introductory booklets on generic networking technology. If their documentation is not suitable, ask them for *seminar materials*. Most manufacturers send representatives to conferences (like Interop, CIBET, and NetWorld) to give presentations on generic topics. These presentations are sitting on a file server in a Powerpoint or Persuasion file format just waiting for someone to love them. Get everything you can. You may be able to use the materials directly, or if you ask for diskettes, you can adapt the format to your own requirements. Remember that all of the Diskette Tutorials are in a Powerpoint format that you can use too.

The bigger the scale of your internetwork, the more important your training effort should become. Build in the cost of training for yourself, your staff, and your customers to the running cost of the network.

User Groups

User Groups have been around for quite some time now. Cisco, Proteon and Wellfleet have active User Groups, and the information exchanged at these meetings is usually well worth the effort of attending. User forums are also active on the Internet and on electronic bulletin board services such as CompuServe. You can get valuable information from these sources. Sensible manufacturers usually assign support staff to monitor the interactions on the User Forums to make sure that if a user reports a known bug, they can get immediate help and advice. In addition, there are occasions when a well meaning user can give bad advice, and hopefully the manufacturer techies will step in to assist.

1.3.9   Costing Information

Cost is the final arbiter in any design process. At the start of this chapter I quoted from Heisenberg's Extended Uncertainty Principle. When you think about this "unnatural law," it seems to be obvious. As soon as you define the exact scope of a project, and nail yourself down to a timescale, you lose control of the cost. This is because things go wrong, project timescales slip, and accelerating the project will cost money. For most businesses today, the cost element and delivery time of a given project may be more important than the scope. Using the Service Level concept, you can express the degree of compromise to the internetwork service due to changes in scope, timescale or cost.

There are some important considerations to bear in mind when calculating costs for network designs.

- Always obtain costing estimates in writing. Verify the time limits on such quotations and mark them in your diary. Request time extensions to quotations if you're running close to the deadlines and get these extensions in writing.

- Inflation is still a big problem outside the US. Make sure you build in inflation to the projected running costs of the network. Remember that equipment costs may go down, but labor costs will continue to rise.

- Separate one-time charges (purchase cost, installation cost, etc.) from ongoing costs (support contracts, line rentals, etc.).

- Does the vendor have a trade in policy for new equipment? This is rare in the internetworking business because the cost of modern equipment is so much lower than older units.

- Get advice from your own purchasing department. Form good contacts in this department, and make sure you're familiar with your company's purchasing policy.

Real costing analysis is beyond the scope of this book. I have suggested two studies that will give you somewhere to start [3, 4], but you'll find that these will lead you through a trail of accounting and economic references.

1.4   Internetwork Specific Design Issues

There are many possible design considerations that you might like to favor. I've chosen five specific areas:

- Designing a network to run IP

- Optimizing for performance

- Optimizing for resilience

- Optimizing for security

- Designing to support SNA

In Section 3 of the book, I'll be covering each of these areas in a dedicated chapter.

1.5   A Review of Design Documentation

This is a quick review of the documentation that I've described in the Design Process.

The Network Proposal

The proposal document is the first thing you should write. In it you should summarize the situation in your organization today. You should identify problems with the current situation that improved communications can address. The proposal should summarize the reasons why your organization needs an internetwork. At this stage, you should not attempt to predict the nature of the internetwork. For example, why should you pre-suppose that this will be an IP internetwork (even though I just gave you a few good reasons)? Other protocols are equally valid, and you will probably end up with a multiprotocol internetwork for the next few years. The proposal may discuss the logic of an integrated voice/data network, for example.

Overall, you should state what the goals are for the internetwork, and position the goals with relation to the strategic goal of your corporation. For example, you might write down one or more of the following objectives:

- Maximize profit for the corporation.

- Improve revenue rate. For example, a utility such as an electricity supply company might install direct network connections to its subscribers. The billing accuracy will be dramatically increased, with a consequent improvement in service quality and revenue return.

- Reduced risk of loss. This could be applied to any business if the internetwork will be used for systematic backup purposes. For mission critical applications, the internetwork may make it easier to implement disaster recovery plans.

- Improve service quality for network users with consequent increase in efficiency. Again, this can be applied to any business type.

- Reflect the high prestige of the corporation. An interesting tactic, but it has been known to pay off. I have known cash rich customers to select FDDI where Ethernet would have been OK, or a top of the range router where a mid range model could have done the job. I advise you not to put this objective in writing unless you're certain of the reaction of your colleagues.

Remember the Golden Rule for this part of the design process: your Proposal *must* be signed off by the Management Team. As long as you have consensus, you are in an excellent position to negotiate changes in the network or its goals.

The RFP

You can now decide if you would like to go out to tender for the internetwork project. Most people believe that the tender process increases competition and means a good deal for the end-user, but I don't think there's any real evidence to suspect that this is the case. Tender responses are deliberately written to present a given product in the best possible light, and can be very misleading.

There are some definite disadvantages to the tender process. An open tender may produce a large number of competing responses. The amount of information coming back may take a long time for you to assimilate. If you're a government agency, you may be obliged to go out to tender for projects that exceed a certain value, but beware; by those same rules, you may also be obliged to accept the lowest tender regardless of your own opinion of the competing solutions.

In general, you will find that it's the system integration capability of a particular supplier that will be the real difference between competing tender responses, and unfortunately ISO hasn't found a way to measure that yet.

I once was involved with a multi-million-dollar deal that was won simply on the strength of one man who had a good project management reputation. They were right, too!

Today the leading few manufacturers in any given product type are so closely matched, that system integration expertise can be the deciding factor.

If you *really* think you want to go to through the RFP process, I've tried to offer some hints throughout the book.

RFPs are not that easy to write. I'd advise you to consider using an external consultant if you've never done something like this before. Also, you can use the proposal as an introductory overview for the RFP, but remember to trim out company confidential information. RFPs are very sensitive documents, and you should be confident that your supplier will treat the document as confidential. You may like to get the respondents to sign a *non-disclosure agreement* (NDA) for this purpose. Check with your organization's legal department.

The RFI

There is an alternative document you might consider using. This is the *Request For Information* (RFI). You should consider the RFI as a way to obtain information on a specific vendor's product line, but where the information is specifically tailored to your design task. For bridges, you might include questions on Learning Table size, for example. The RFI is a vital opportunity for you to express more abstract questions about product behavior given a specified set of conditions.

In an RFI, you can also ask for manufacturers' opinions and future strategy, and their design suggestions.

The Service Level Definitions

The question is, should you write the definitions *during* or *after* the RFP process? The answer depends on how open your RFP is. If you've just sent out a tender to see how cheap you can buy a Cisco or Wellfleet router, then you can write the definitions before you get the response. However, with an open RFP, you don't even know the form of the internetwork you'll be getting. For example, you may get a proposal for a *Value Added Network* (VAN), where you don't own the router equipment at all. You may even have your entire computer systems equipment *Facilities Managed* (FM). With a total FM solution, it's possible that the only thing about your computer system that you'll "own" is the data you produce. Everything else is leased from the FM provider.

The Service Level Agreements

Once the Service Level Definitions have been written, you can start to discuss the quality levels to be met by the network, and formulate the Service Level Agreements. Revision of these agreements should occur on a regular basis (maybe quarterly), to reflect the changing requirements of the users, and the capabilities of the internetwork.

The Site Logs and Network Log

These documents are written histories of everything that happens in the network. Network watch operatives will enter problem information into a local Site Log. This information can then be transferred to a central Network Log. Obviously this process is made easier if the logs are written in a well-defined format, and are stored electronically.

Network Maps

There are many tools we can use to make maps of our networks. Many users that I've met favor the low tech solution of pencil and paper. In the past this solution was inevitable because changes in the network topology were being made on the edge of the network, away from any management stations. Today, the portability of computer power means that we can rediscover the benefits of a computer based drawing package in network mapping. The big problem is to decide what kind of package to use. Here are some suggestions.

Pencil and paper may seem attractive to the busy network administrator. You might promise yourself that you really will transfer the changes to the NMS when you have the time, but will this happen? In large networks, hand-drawn maps are impractical. I once visited a ship design office, and they produced superb maps that were drafted over the building blueprints. At first it was fun for them to do, but soon grew to be a chore, and they switched to a PC.

The next question concerns the format of the map. Users who have artistic talent often favor bit-mapped drawing packages (Windows Paint, PC Paint, MacPaint). For the rest of us, bit-mapped packages are a nightmare. We opt for vector driven packages, such as the normal PC and Mac drawing programs (Corel Draw!, Designer, MacDraw). Drawing packages are a big improvement over paper for many reasons. However, you should look for certain features that will help you:

- Does the package have architectural scaling and automatic measurement?

- Can the package import a wide range of graphic formats? This is useful for importing maps or building blueprints. Also useful for importing symbols of your network components.

- Can the package export to your NMS?

- Does the package have a layer capability? This is useful to separate geographical features (like a wall) from infrastructure (like a duct) and network features (like a cable).

- What degree of zoom is available? Is the zoom feature "intelligent." Zoom intelligence involves the ability to automatically display groups of objects with a group symbol if we zoom out beyond a certain level. Also, if we zoom out beyond a certain point, the package should suppress text labeling.

You may then decide to go a stage further (and higher in price). Today there are many drawing packages that are designed to help you map networks. These packages contain sophisticated layering functions, include spreadsheets and databases that can be linked to specific network components, and can talk directly to popular NMS packages. Examples include netViz (Quyen Systems), GrafBASE (Network Dimensions) and NodeMap (Haven Systems). Such packages also contain intelligent line drawing capabilities. An example is if you draw 20 workstations attached to a 10BASET hub. With an ordinary PC drawing package, if you decide to move the hub, you have to manually redraw all the connections. With an intelligent line drawing system, connections are automatically redrawn as you move the associated objects.

The final level of map integration is where the NMS can "see" the map. In these integrated systems, alerts from the NMS will be transmitted to the map. At the crudest level this might involve a color change for the icon.

1.6   Summary

- Network Design is an active process. We can look on it as a series of negotiations between the provider of the network and its users.

- The Designer must take control and adopt a structured procedure.

- The most powerful negotiating tools for the Designer are the documents that describe the goals of the network, and the Design Process that is trying to achieve these goals.

- Documenting the Design Process is essential. This chapter suggests several formal documents: The Network Proposal, the RFP or RFI, Service Level Definitions, Service Level Agreements, Site and Network Logs, and Network Maps.

- The Network Proposal is the original concept document for the network. I describe this document as having multiple parts (sections that can be distributed internally and externally).

- The Network Proposal is a "living document." It should be the ultimate, up to date description of the network that can be understood by management.

- The RFP is a formal document that may involve legal obligations on the part of a supplier, or user.

- The RFI is a less formal document that is an important aid in the information gathering process.

- Objective for the network should be expressed in terms of Service Level Definitions, and Service Level Agreements.

- A Service Level Agreement is a contract between the Network Provider and the Network User. It states the goals of the network in terms of one or more Service Level Definitions.

- A Service Level Definition is a written description of a selected network parameter, and a test method. The Definition does not contain goals.

- Site and Network Logs are much more technical documents. They represent the day to day history of the network.

- Gathering information for these documents is an active and time consuming process. This stage is very important in a successful design.

- Maintaining the documents is also time consuming. However, designers must modify their expectation level for the documents to suit the size of the network and the staff resources they have available.

- Tools exist to help the designer. These range from word processors, through computer-based drawing packages to full Modeling systems.

1.7 References

[1]   *Re-Engineering The Network,* July 1993. The Yankee Group, 200 Portland Street, Boston, MA 02114.

[2]   *Open Systems Transitions Scenarios*, January 1993. Datapro Report. McGraw Hill, Datapro Information Service Group, Delran, NJ 08075.

[3]   Nathan J. Muller. *Financial Planning for Network Managers*, November 1992. Datapro Report. McGraw Hill, Datapro Information Service Group, Delran, NJ 08075.

[4]   D. Minoli. *Network Cost Analysis Methods*, March 1992. Datapro Report. McGraw Hill, Datapro Information Service Group, Delran NJ, 08075.

[5]   K. Tolly, D. Newman. "How Accurate Is Your LAN Analyzer?." *Data Communications International*, January 1994. McGraw Hill.

CHAPTER 2

Networking Overview

> *Don't lose heart*
>
> *...they may want to tear it out*
>
> *...and they'll want to avoid a lengthy search.*
>
> **White's Statement**

2.1   Introduction

Internetworking devices are key components in any organization's communication strategy. The purpose of this book is to try to offer some advice on how to go about designing large networks and internetworks.

However, I do have to justify my choice of TCP/IP as a protocol to discuss. In the eyes of many, TCP/IP is an outdated protocol, stretching back 20 years. Surely this protocol cannot hope to address the requirement of modern networking? So many communication concepts have been discovered during this time. In fact, TCP/IP is growing old rather gracefully. While it's true that the IP and TCP protocols are "mature," more modern protocols such as OSPF (1989), PPP (1990) and SNMP2 (1993) continue to demonstrate the evolving nature of TCP/IP. The other contestants in this battle are SNA and the GOSIP protocols defined by ISO.

The marketplace has refused to allow its communication strategy to be tied to a single proprietary architecture. In 1986, it was assumed that TCP/IP would soon give way to open standards. These were different from earlier architectures in that they existed on paper in a fully standardized form *before* they were ever implemented in a real system. In addition, committees must be seen to be fair and so if a vendor grouping wants a field to be inserted into a specific address for example, the address gets a bit bigger. This pattern was followed for most ISO protocol developments and therefore ISO addresses are bigger and contain a more complex structure than any other address type.   Software implementations of ISO protocols take up more RAM and use more CPU power than their industry developed cousins.

TCP/IP has become the "protocol that wouldn't die." Developed by users in co operative environments, new protocols within the TCP/IP suite can be deployed in experimental environments to assess their likely impact on the network. Assuming the trials are successful, the protocols are published, source code is made available (typically under UNIX) and interested parties start to use it. There are two immediate differences I can call to mind between the TCP/IP and ISO views of the world. The first is the method of obtaining standards. To obtain an Internet RFC, you simply log onto an Anonymous FTP server (I describe how later) and an electronic copy of the file is sent to you. To obtain an ISO or IEEE standard is expensive. Like TCP/IP standards, ISO documents contain frequent cross-references, so buying a single document doesn't do you much good.

The second is the saga of ISO management ; the CMIS/CMIP initiative. After almost 10 years of effort, CMIS/CMIP is still a "future direction" for virtually every mainstream communication company. In contrast, in the TCP/IP world, the first management protocol, SGMP, was written and implemented within 6 months. It has since been developed into SNMP and now SNMP2. While the ISO fans were wondering what management was like, the TCP/IP pioneers were finding out.

TCP/IP is far from perfect. It is a motley collection of standard written by professionals and amateurs alike. It is over-extended in some fundamental areas such as address space. However, TCP/IP is here now and it achieves its purpose; multi vendor communication. The problems that exist today with TCP/IP will be worked out, because they always have been in the past.

Quoting marketing statistics in a textbook is always dangerous but a recent report[1] showed that there were currently 65,000 *commercial* TCP/IP networks operating today, compared with around 400,000 IPX networks. However, the same report offered some statistics about the volume of company traffic carried by TCP/IP and IPX. This is summarized in Figure 2.1.

Of course, TCP/IP is already the dominant protocol in academic and research networks. The key factor in the relationship between IP and IPX is that IP is capable of internetworking on a large scale. Today, IPX does not have this capability. Even with Novell's efforts to implement IPXWAN [18] and NLSP [17], IPX will continue to be an *intra*networking, rather than *inter*networking protocol in the medium term. TCP/IP will consolidate its position as the de facto internetworking protocol, while encapsulation technologies to support heterogeneous intranetwork groups will become more widely adopted.

---

[1]Source: Network World 27/12/93-3/1/94.

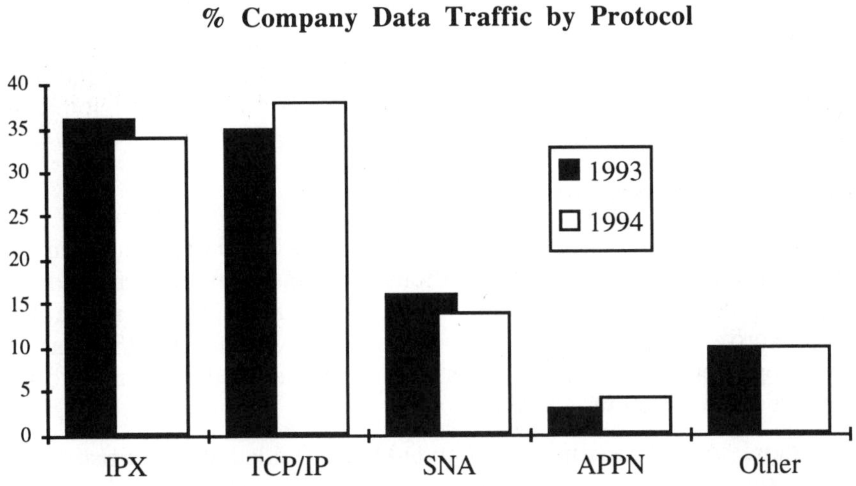

% Company Data Traffic by Protocol

Figure 2.1:   The Changing Importance of LAN Protocols

2.2   IP History

Speaking about the past, it seems right to lay out a brief history of TCP/IP. You often find that several world class ideas come from a single source. A good example in the data processing industry is the Xerox PARC laboratory. From this non-commercial environment came the mouse, windowing and graphical interfaces and Ethernet. In the data communications business, the equivalent source is the Defense Advanced Research Projects Agency (DARPA). In 1969 DARPA began funding a development project for a high speed, packet switching communications network to links its laboratories and research centers. The system became known as the ARPANET and this network was one of the first communication systems to make use of a layered architecture that I describe below. In fact, the ARPANET model preceded the ISO OSI reference model by almost a decade. Backed by government funding, with the opportunity to pursue "blue sky" technologies, ARPANET pioneered many of the communication methods used by today's peer oriented and packet switched networks. As the ARPANET grew, it faced the same kind of problems that we do today ; eventually you'll connect two systems from different manufacturers. In the case of the ARPANET, there were installations from virtually every major computer supplier (and remember, there were a lot more of them in those days). The designers in the ARPANET faced the general problem of how to transfer information between multivendor systems and how to pass this information over wide area circuits in a reliable and efficient fashion. ARPANET solved the problems using a variety of protocols and technologies. Many of these were too expensive to implement in the commercial or academic marketplace, but the exception was the Transport and Internetwork portion of the ARPANET called the Transmission Control Protocol / Internet Protocol (TCP/IP). TCP and IP are two protocols that exist within a wider suite of protocols, known by various names: the DoD protocol or the Internet protocol suite. I will use the term "IP protocol," or "the IP stack" because in the context of this book, it is typically the internetworking protocol that will concern us.

TCP/IP Becomes Commercial

Why was TCP/IP so successful? As the problems of host interconnection become more critical, there were far fewer solutions available than there are today. The major alternative was the Xerox Networking Systems (XNS) protocol stack. However, Xerox didn't open up XNS soon enough, whereas TCP/IP was always seen as an open protocol. XNS was used as the basis for the Novell and Banyan Network Operating Systems (NOS).

Another more logical reason was that DARPA funded the integration of the TCP/IP protocols into the University of California's Berkeley Software Distribution (BSD) version of UNIX. This had far reaching consequences as UNIX became the operating system of choice on the minicomputer and workstation, TCP/IP was assured of a wide following. Version 4.2 of the BSD UNIX (released in September 1983) was the first to include TCP/IP protocols in the generic operating system and this was eventually carried over into commercial "OEM" versions of UNIX. Later on in the 1980s Sun Microsystems published their Open Network Computing (ONC) standards. These are better known as the Network Filing System (NFS) and they are designed to operate over a TCP/IP stack. NFS has since been licensed by virtually every major computer manufacturer that builds something bigger than a PC.

Why Is TCP/IP an *Internetworking* Protocol?

TCP/IP and XNS were evolving at pretty much the same time. In many ways, XNS had the opportunity to see where TCP/IP was going wrong and correct the problem.   In one area, however, TCP/IP became inherently stronger: internetworking.   The growth of the ARPANET and   its evolution into the Internet forced two consequences onto the TCP/IP protocol:

- A centrally administered address allocation was required so that no two users of the Internet could be given the same IP address.

- Hierarchical routing protocols were developed to allow one organization to "protect" itself from other organizations. In a router network, it's possible for one user to misconfigure equipment, causing routing "anomalies."

In contrast, the XNS (and later, IPX) had no centralized address allocation and no hierarchical routing capability. In other words, we owe most of TCP/IP's functionality to the real world requirements of the Internet.

2.3 Development of the Internet

Although the ARPANET was a general success, its first generation protocols were expensive to implement, slow and prone to crashes (both of individual stacks and of the networks themselves). Around 1974, a new set of core protocol definition documents were proposed by Vinton Cerf and Robert Kahn [1]. This proposal was the basis for the development of the IP and TCP protocols. Over the next three years, the ARPANET host systems converted over to the new protocols. In 1984 the ARPANET was divided into two parts: one retained the name ARPANET and the other became known as MILNET. MILNET still exists today and is an unclassified military communication network.

During the 1980s the ARPANET acted as the backbone for a range of new regional networks that were funded and operated by public, private and academic institutions. Collectively these became known as the Internet. In the late 1980s a new backbone network was constructed with funding from the National Science Foundation (NSF). The NSFnet gradually replaced the ARPANET as the Internet backbone. In 1990 the old ARPANET was formally shut down.

What Is the Internet?

The Internet started out as a Wide Area Network that allowed various US universities and research organizations to communicate. It was based on leased lines and X.25 networks. Locally, LAN connections were implemented on Ethernet at first and then on other LAN technologies as they evolved. The Internet has grown into a world-wide communication network. This data highway carries information from academic, commercial and military institutions. Just about any information that is available in the public domain (and some that isn't) can be found on the Internet [2]. In Table 1.1 I list the major events that occurred during the lifetime of the ARPANET. I obtained these dates from a variety of sources and so I'd give some of them a +/- of one year. More than anything I think you can begin to appreciate the tremendous changes that have taken place in the communications industry during the lifetime of the ARPANET.

The concept of all this communication between "Internet Buddies" is heart warming of course, but there are a few questions that people ask when they first encounter the Internet:

- Who pays for it all?
- Who designs the protocols?
- Who makes the decisions?
- How do I join?

Table 2.1: The Life and Times of The ARPANET

Date	The Communication World	The Data Processing World
1969	DARPA begins funding of ARPANET.	
1974	SNA introduced. Design started on ARPANET core protocols by Cerf and Kahn.	
1975	DCA assumes responsibility for ARPANET. Status of network changes from experimental to operational.	Zilog announces Z80. MOSTech announces 6501 and 6502. Microsoft founded.
1976		Apple Computer founded. TI announces 16 bit TMS9000.
1977	ISO publishes OSI Model.	Apple II, TRS-80 and Commodore PET launched. DEC announces Vax and VMS.
1978		Intel announces 8086.
1979	Proteon founded. DIX consortium publish Ethernet V1.0 specification.	Sinclair announces ZX80.
1980		Apple goes public. Apple launches doomed Apple III.
1981	Proteon ship software based router operating on PDP-11 platform. Corvus introduce OmniNet. Hayes introduce Smartmodem 300.	IBM introduces the PC.
1982	IBM introduce LU6.2. DoD policy statement chooses ARPANET protocol as strategic standard. DDN created to oversee process.	Compaq introduces PC compatible Portable computer. Intel announces the 286.
1983	BSD UNIX 4.2 includes TCP/IP protocols as standard. Novell launch Netware. DoD adopts TCP/IP suite as a formal standard.	Microsoft announces Windows (doesn't ship for 2 years).
1984	ANSI X3T9.5 committee begins work on FDDI. Cisco Systems Founded. ARPANET splits into ARPANET and MILNET. Term "Internet" coined.	Motorola introduces the 68020. Apple introduces the Mac. IBM introduces the PC/AT.

1985	DoD requires GOSIP conformance for large projects (users then find ways to bypass the requirement; the "commitment statement" was born). IBM launch 4Mbps Token Ring.	Atari announces the 520ST. Commodore announces the Amiga. Intel announces the 386. Microsoft ships Windows.
1986	Wellfleet Communications founded. Cisco AGS, first customer shipment.	IBM introduce the short lived RT/PC (6150), a RISC based UNIX workstation. Sperry and Burroughs merge to form Unisys. Motorola announce 68030.
1987	IBM announces SAA. Microsoft and 3Com announce joint development plans for LAN Manager.	IBM introduce the PS/2 and OS/2. Apple launch the Mac II.
1988	Wellfleet CN, first customer shipment. ARPANET "worm" creates havoc on over 6000 computer systems[1]. Proteon demonstrates first SNMP router and management station at Interop. ATM is adopted as a strategic direction by CCITT.	MIPS announces its RISC CPU. IBM ships OS/2 Presentation Manager. AMD introduces 29000 RISC chip. Intel announces 386SX. NeXT computer announced.
1989	OSPF specification published. Cisco, Proteon, and Wellfleet compete to ship first FDDI router. IBM announces 16Mbps Token Ring.	Sun announces SPARC workstation. DEC announces MIPS RISC based DECstation 3100. HP announces intention to buy Apollo computer. Intel announce the i486 CISC and i860 RISC.
1990	Proteon ships RISC based CNX500 router. 3Com withdraw from LAN Manager project and sell all rights to Microsoft. ARPANET formally dissolved.	Motorola announces 68040. Microsoft ships Windows 3.0.

---

[1]The worm is discussed in more detail in Chapter 17.

2.4   Administration

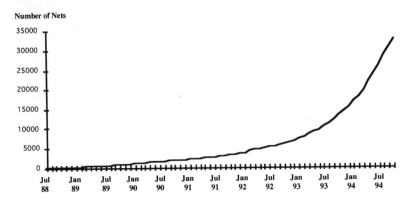

Figure 2.2:   The Growth of the NSFnet

Who Pays?

The Internet is not just a single network. University and other research networks make up the vast majority of its available bandwidth. World-wide, there are several commercial ventures to provide Internet access and many of these are operating in Europe [3]. If you are an academic institution, then some form of connection deal is normally available through some centralized academic organization. In the UK, for example, this is the Joint Networking Team (JNT). During 1994 the Super JANET network will start to offer Internet connections to private companies in order to fund some of the massive infrastructure investment of the network (Super JANET is based on multiple 34Mbps technology over SMDS). In Turkey, various universities are accessing the Internet through the Technical University of Istanbul[1]. So the simple answer to the questions is that local connection to the Internet is funded by the user organization. The Internet backbone is comprised of a collection of centrally funded data networks.

Who Designs the Protocols?

Protocols like TCP and IP have already been designed, of course, but they need to be updated and maintained. In fact TCP was the subject of some major updates during 1988 with the Van Jacobsen "Slow Start" enhancements. In addition, new protocols and methods must be continually added to allow the Internet to meet modern communication challenges. One such addition is the OSPF routing protocol described in Chapter 11. Each of these protocols is actually proposed, described, and eventually defined in documents called Requests for Comment (RFC). At the very least, an RFC is the Internet equivalent of an ISO standard document, but RFCs are also formalized

---

[1]Some of these connections make use of the IP-in-SNA tunnelling technology described in Chapter 17.

discussion documents and can be used to contain information or tutorials. Today there are over 1500 RFCs, although only a fraction of these will be current, or relevant to an individual user. Routers typically need to support the most RFCs, hosts the fewest. A typical example of RFCs that are relevant to an internetwork router are shown in Table 1.2.

Table 2.2: Some of the RFCs Supported by a Typical IP Router

Protocol	RFC Number(s)
IP	RFC 791
IP Subnetting	RFC 950
ICMP	RFC 792
ARP	RFC 829
Proxy ARP	RFC 1027
RIP	RFC 1058
OSPF	RFC 1247
EGP	RFC 827, 904
BGP3	RFC 1267
PPP	RFC 1548, 1332, 1333, 1334
Telnet	RFC 854 and many others
SNMP	RFC 1155, 1156, 1157, 1213 (et al.)

Table 1.2 represents a reasonable subset of RFCs for a modern entry level router. Typically there would be another five or ten RFCs that describe "value added" functions, or for special connections to X.25, Frame Relay, SMDS, or ATM.

How Do I Obtain an RFC?

There are several ways you can obtain an RFC. The most obvious way is to download the appropriate file over the Internet. This can be done by good old surface mail (at a charge), or by using the File Transfer Protocol (FTP) over the Internet.

The postal address for the NIC is currently:

DDN Network Information Center
14200 Park Meadow Drive
Suite 200
Chantilly, VA 22021

For inquiries, there are two telephone numbers for the Government Systems NIC, where you will find someone on duty between 07.00 and 19.00 hours Eastern Standard Time.

1-800-365-3642

or outside the US:

Int + (1) 703-802-4535

For Internet file transfer, you should make the choice a little more carefully. Remember that you'll be downloading information over an IP internetwork that may pass over multiple administrative zones, over widely different line speeds. Several Internet locations now offer RFCs online, as well as vast amounts of other useful information. Most of them operate as *anonymous FTP servers*. FTP is one of three common file transfer protocols that you'll find on any TCP/IP host. FTP includes security features and forms a session with the operating system of the target host (so the password information can be synchronized with the security mechanism of the host operating system). The term "anonymous FTP" is simply a convention that any user who logs into the host will be allowed some minimal access rights under the user name "anonymous" (the associated password is usually "guest," or can be your Internet mail address).

The "traditional" source of RFCs is the NIC's own Anonymous FTP host, **nic.ddn.mil**. My experience over the past few months is that this host offers a slower service than many other hosts. This may not be the fault of the NIC, but could be the route I'm using to get to the host. If you use FTP to get into the NIC, in the directory **netinfo** you'll find a short information file called **how_to_get_rfcs**. This file contains an updated list of Anonymous FTP servers on the Internet. It really is worthwhile for you to "shop around."

A really useful file on the RFC server is the RFC index. On the NIC, this can be found in the directory **/netinfo/rfc-index.txt**, while the RFCs themselves can be found in **/rfc**. Before you attempt to connect to the NIC, it is worth spending a few moments refreshing your memory on the way that the FTP command works. Most of the RFCs are stored as simple ASCII text files, but some of the best are stored with diagrams in Postscript (PS) format. Sidnie Feit [12] gives an example FTP dialogue with the NIC in her book. The first time you download an RFC, it's worth choosing a short one (try RFC877) to give you an idea of the speed of your Internet connection. After the FTP transfer has completed, FTP will tell you the speed of transfer in kBps, but remember this will vary from day to day and on the time of day.

Who Makes the Decisions?

The development of Internet protocols is administered by an independent organization called the Internet Activities Board (IAB). Within the IAB there are two "task forces": the Internet Engineering Task Force (IETF) and the Internet Research Task Force (IRTF). In short, the IETF solves immediate problems, the IRTF looks at longer-term issues. The IETF has over 40 working groups that are coordinated by the Internet Engineering Steering Group (IESG). The relationships are shown in Figure 2.3.

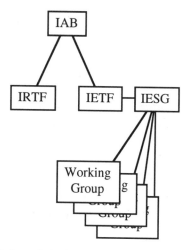

Figure 2.3: Administration of the Internet

How Do I Join In?

You can ask this question from two perspectives. First there is the issue of physical connection to the Internet, and second how an individual user can get the best from the information and services offered by the Internet. Connecting to the Internet varies from country to country. The connection procedure in the past was divided into two stages; first ask for an Internet address, second make the physical connection. As the Internet becomes larger and more complex, the two stages are logically connected. Outside of the academic environment, service companies are providing Value Added Network (VAN) or Virtual Private Network (VPN) access into the Internet fabric. In Finland, for example, the PTT operate a nationwide Frame Relay service which can optionally provide Internet access. Such network providers obtain blocks of IP address space to allocate to their subscribers. In effect they become local NICs.

If you don't know who your local Internet provider is, then the NIC in Virginia can give you details.

The process of accessing Internet information is much more varied. In the beginning, network "benefactors" would advertise the addresses of FTP servers (offering RFCs, for example) that they would maintain. Today the sophistication of Internet offerings has grown in proportion to the spread of this communication highway. News distribution utilities allow individual Internet users to subscribe to specific discussion groups. The Worl-wide Web (WWW) is an ambitious project to share extremely high quality information between academic or research groups.

The Internet is now being used to transfer videoconferencing information for IETF meetings, and a range of multimedia experiments are being developed. The overall effect is to increase the pressure for more bandwidth on the Internet, as well as more sophisticated protocols to cope with the new information types.

Several good books are available to help you understand Internet services [17, 18, 19]. As a Network administrator, you should be aware that the privilege of access to the Internet can be abused. When first connected to this vast source of information, your users may waste hours looking around. Rather than forbid this discovery process, it is often better to give informal presentations on how to use the Internet services and what these services contain. Access controls can also be applied, some of which are described in Chapter 17.

2.5   The OSI Model

When a systems analyst first begins to plan out an application, he or she must develop a model of the way that the application will operate. The model may be based on data flow between different parts of the application, or it may be based on an object-oriented approach where code modules can be easily modified or reused in other projects.

Communication software is a very good example of a large, generic application. This software has the additional requirement that it must interoperate with implementations from other vendors. Application interoperability has still not been achieved between Excel and Lotus, for example. In fact, until the introduction of generic windowing environments, program writers were obliged by law to make their products appear to be different. Finally, communication software differs from most other applications in that different parts of the application may be operating on different CPUs or computers.

As a result, communication software has been the target of structured design techniques from its very early days. Initially, different vendors developed different models of their communication systems, but very early on, a vendor independent model was developed. This is known as the Open Systems Interconnect (OSI). The model is defined and maintained by ISO, the Organization for International Standardization[1].

The OSI Model doesn't have to be applied to ISO standard systems. It can be applied with equal success *within* a proprietary communication system like Novell IPX, or a pre-ISO system like TCP/IP. So, it's possible to say that a suite of software, or a communications device, is OSI-based, when it doesn't comply to any specific ISO standards.

---

[1]"ISO" is not an acronym, it is a word. In ancient Greek, "iso" means "equal" and is the stem of words like isobar, and isosceles triangle.

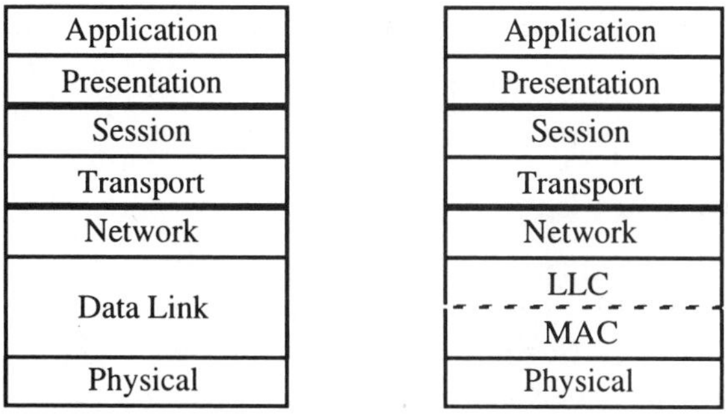

Application
Presentation
Session
Transport
Network
Data Link
Physical

Application
Presentation
Session
Transport
Network
LLC
MAC
Physical

(a): Basic OSI Model

(b): Multi-Access
OSI Model

Figure 2.4:   The OSI 7-Layer Model

The OSI model is classically divided into the seven layers I have shown in Figure 2.4(a). When LANs were introduced, the Data Link Layer was divided into two, as I show in Figure 2.4(b). You should think of this "8-Layer" model as applying to any multi access network such as Frame Relay, X.25 or ATM, as well as traditional LANs. For these technologies, the lower part of the Data Link Layer became known as the Media Access Control (MAC) sublayer and the upper part the Logical Link Control (LLC) sublayer).

The OSI model is based on a couple of simple assumptions:

- A set of rules or operational procedure operates at each layer. These are called *protocols*.

- The protocols operating at each layer are only allowed to communicate with the OSI layer directly above, or directly below their own layer.

These two assumptions allow us to compartmentalize and structure our communication software. By building our architectures around the OSI model, we offer guidelines to Systems Analysts when they design the software. By adhering to standards, we can even achieve interoperability between software written by different vendors; whether that software operates at the same, or different layers in the OSI model.

Each layer in the model is responsible for different functions. Here is my version of the OSI functionality. You can read alternative descriptions in [4, 9]. It's traditional to start at the bottom of the model and work up. Just for a change I'll take the "top down" approach. I'd like you to focus on the objective here: two applications are trying to communicate over a collection of networks.

Layer 7: Application Layer

Application Layer functions within the protocol stack allow programs to access specific network services, such as File Transfer, Terminal Emulation and so on.

Layer 6: Presentation Layer

The Application Layer function will receive the data from the Application. It then decides how it will format this data so that it can be "presented" to the network. Some of this formatting is a bit obscure, but two obvious functions that you might perform at this stage are compression (for videoconferencing, for example) or encryption (for sensitive data). It is the Presentation Layer protocols that will perform this formatting.

Layer 5: Session Layer

Now that our data is in the right format, it'd be nice if we had some way to achieve a logical connection with the other machine. Different applications will choose different ways to make this happen. File Transfer is one of the more complex, because we would normally like to achieve a secure file transfer. If this is the case, we'd normally expect to establish a formal *session* with the other machine. Sessions involve a connection request, with some form of identification and password exchange. These functions are performed by Session Layer software.

Layer 4: Transport Layer

Protocols at the Transport Layer form a duplex (two way) data pipe between the programs that are communicating with each other. Since several programs may be accessing the network within a single computer, it would seem that a process specific addressing scheme is required. In UNIX this address that an individual communication process uses is called the *port*. In today's UNIX, a port is a 16 bit value (it will get bigger).

A second Transport Layer function is that of end to end *error detection* and possibly *error correction*. There are Transport Layer protocols that provide a *reliable service*, where errors are corrected. There are also Transport protocols that provide an *unreliable service* (sometimes called a *datagram service*). When unreliable protocols are used, higher layer process may be used to decide if error has occurred, and if they subsequently need to be corrected. Some file transfer applications may require a reliable service. However, other file transfer applications may implement an internal error detection and retransmission protocol and do not require a reliable Transport service.

The third thing we need to do at this layer is to provide *flow control*. The concept of flow control is simple. It's a messaging system that operates across the network that allows the receiver to ask the transmitter to slow down. The transmitter/receiver flow control can operate end to end, or can operate on a hop by hop basis for a multihop route. In Figure 2.5, each double-ended arrow shows a flow control relationship.

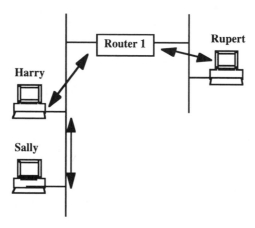

Figure 2.5: Examples of Flow Control Relationships

If Harry is sending a file to Sally, flow control would operate directly between the two hosts. If Harry is sending a file to Rupert, there is one flow control relationship between Harry and Router 1 and another relationship between Router 1 and Rupert.

The fourth thing to do at this layer is *fragmentaton* and *reassembly* of the message. The messages that we send over LANs and WANs are typically longer than the network can process in a single transmission unit. Transport Layer protocols will, therefore, break down a message into an appropriate transmission entity. These entities are different for different Transport Services. In UDP (a connectionless service), the entity is called a *datagram*.

Layer 3: Network Layer

The Network Layer performs four basic functions.

Addressing. Yes, more addressing. The Transport Layer addressing that we used will allow the data from the file transfer to reach the appropriate program on the remote host. But how do we get it to the right machine in the first place? This function is carried out in the Network Layer addressing scheme. In the IP scheme, a 32-bit IP address is used to deliver information to a specific machine.

Routing. Network Layer addressing is always designed to allow easy routing of traffic around the network. In particular, the concept of hierarchical addressing is key at the Network Layer.

Error notification. Since the path of our message may span many individual networks, it seems like a good idea to have the ability to notify the transit devices that something was wrong with an individual link.

Fragmentation and Reassembly. The Transport layer performs end to end fragmentation and reassembly. This function needs to be repeated on a hop by hop basis across the network because of the variation in MTU size for different network technologies. I offer some advice on how to avoid Network Layer fragmentation in Chapter 14.

Layer 2: Data Link Layer

Our file is now fully addressed for internetwork transit and is passed from the Network Layer to the top of the Data Link Layer. As the Chinese say "even the longest journey begins with a first step." The first step for our file transfer information is to be successfully transmitted across the first LAN cable. To achieve that we need to format the information for the appropriate LAN technology. At this layer, the data unit is known as the *frame*. Frames contain very specific features such as a preamble, addresses and a field which allows the integrity of the frame to be verified (the *checksum* or *CRC*).

When the OSI model was first devised, only WAN links were considered. In a serial connection, the concept of addressing is irrelevant; you simply push the bits in at one end of the cable and they *will* fall out the other end! For LANs, this assumption cannot apply because they are multidrop, or multi-access technologies. These terms basically mean that many end stations share the same cable and a frame sent by one station can potentially be received by all attached stations. To allow messages to pass between specific end stations, addresses are used.

To allow the OSI model to operate more effectively for LANs, the Data Link Layer was divided into two sublayers: the *Logical Link Control* (LLC) sublayer and the *Media Access Control* (MAC) sublayer. The LLC sublayer protocol can be used to define logical connections over a multidrop network such as a LAN. The main example of LLC protocols are the IEEE 802.2 set, Class 1, Class 2, and Class 3 [10].

The MAC sublayer protocols define the frame format and the way in which a station is allowed to access the multidrop channel. Examples of MAC protocols are Ethernet, IEEE 802.3, 802.4, 802.5 and FDDI [11, 12, 13, 14].

Layer 1: Physical Layer

The MAC sublayer passes an entire frame, represented as binary digits, to the Physical Layer. Protocols in this layer are responsible for the correct representation of the digital information over a transmission medium. One of the biggest challenges in this respect is the ability to carry the clock timing along with the data. Physical Layer encoding schemes such as Manchester Encoding, NRZ and 4B5B are used to make this happen [9]. Network speed, voltages, connector types, and pin outs are also defined at this layer.

2.5.1 Frame Construction and Reduction

Using a layered protocol stack offers a number of advantages to Systems Analysts and programmers, but it seems to have the effect of increasing the overhead on the frame that actually travels over the network. This is because each protocol layer must add its own marker, as a *header*, or a *trailer* or both. The process of building a network frame from the Application Message is called *frame construction*. The reverse process is called *frame reduction*. The cycle is shown in Figure 2.6. The first time I saw this particular representation was in Radia Perlman's book [4], so I've reproduced the diagram here. Other representations tend to be more complex.

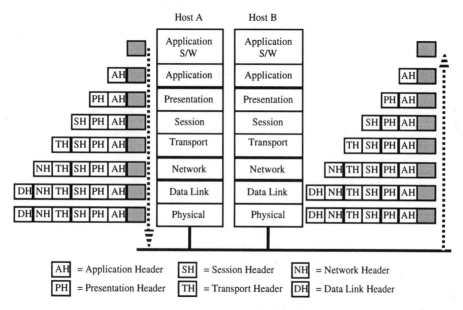

Figure 2.6: Frame Construction and Reduction

As frames move "down" the model, the software operating at each layer appends its own marker information around the data unit. For any given layer, the information it receives from above is regarded as "data," even though it may contain overhead already. Framing overhead is something you should get used to, because you'll see it appearing often within the TCP/IP protocols. Moreover, frame overhead is becoming increasingly common in Wide Area Networks. This is a subject I discuss in more detail in Chapter 6.

2.5.2   The TCP/IP Protocols

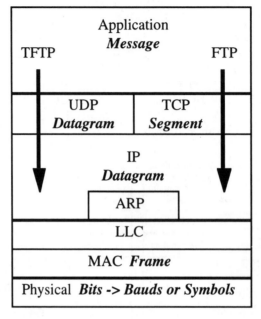

Figure 2.7:   Protocols in the TCP/IP Suite

Figure 2.7 shows the actual protocol that operate in a TCP/IP stack. You'll find all of these acronyms explained in the Glossary. There are two arrowed paths that I've marked through the stack. The right hand arrow shows the stack used by the File Transfer Protocol (FTP), and the left hand arrow shows the stack used by the Trivial File Transfer Protocol (TFTP). In this case the difference is that FTP uses the TCP protocol, a reliable Transport Layer. TFTP uses the UDP protocol, an unreliable Transport Layer. TFTP file transfers can still be made over unreliable layers because there is a simple error detection and correction mechanism built into TFTP.

This diagram highlights the fact that at any layer of the OSI Model there may be more than one protocol operating. Higher level protocols may be able to use more than one of these protocols, but more often, this is not the case. For example, FTP always operates over TCP and TFTP always operates over UDP. In contrast, NFS almost always operates over UDP, but could be implemented over TCP if necessary.

2.6   So Many Addresses?

One of the most frequent comments that I hear about LANs concerns addressing. Why are there so many addresses inside a LAN frame? In my description of the OSI model I covered the basic reasons why addressing is necessary at each layer; let me now talk about who administers these addresses.

Port addressing is determined within the operating system and by the applications themselves. To return to the file transfer example, both communicating end systems need to agree on a suitable port address. So it seems logical for different applications to be allocated the same port number. These are called *well known* ports. Port number 15h is used for the File Transfer Protocol (FTP), for example. Allocation of well known port numbers is made by the *Internet Assigned Number Authority* (IANA) and the results published in an RFC called Assigned Numbers. At the time of writing this RFC had recently changed from 1060 to 1340 and is regularly updated. Port numbers are re-used from host to host. In other words, the FTP port 15h should be the same on all hosts in the network[1].

IP addresses can be assigned by the designer of the network, using methods that I outline in Chapter 13. However, an IP address is like a telephone number: it should be unique across the entire internetwork. If you decide to attach to the Internet, you need to ensure that no other host or network is using the addresses that you have chosen. This is quite a feat today, as there are more than one million hosts attached to the Internet! To save you the trouble, there is a centralized allocation body called the Network Information Center (NIC). At one time there was only one NIC and you simply sent a mail message or fax describing your network and asking for a suitable address. Today the job of address allocation has to be decentralized and so regional NICs are appointed by the NIC, with their own address blocks pre-allocated. This allocation scheme will have future benefits for the Internet as it imposes a geographical significance for the addressing, as well as allowing faster and more local response form the addressing authorities.

MAC addresses were originally intended to be globally unique. A 48 bit value was chosen to allow enough addresses to be allocated. In fact when the original Ethernet network was being designed by the DEC Intel Xerox consortium back in 1980, the team wanted to use 64 bit addresses because with this size of address a station could select an address at random and the odds of address conflict are "vanishingly small." However, a 48 bit scheme was eventually adopted for Ethernet, the IEEE LANs and for FDDI. With 48 bits, some form of centralized address administration is required. Initially this was done by Bob Printis at Xerox, but then control passed to the IEEE. MAC address administration is done by assigning each interface manufacturer a block of addresses. The manufacturer is then responsible for assigning unique addresses within this range. MAC addresses are "burned in" to interface cards, and they are contained in a chip somewhere on the card. Most LAN protocol stacks (IP, XNS, IPX, Banyan, AppleTalk) use the addresses that are already on the card. DECnet uses a different mechanism and overwrites the burned-in address [19].

---

[1]If this wasn't the case, FTP simply wouldn't work.

Local MAC Addressing

In fact, the MAC address has a little more structure to it. The two least significant bits of the first byte of the MAC address are given specific functions:

- Bit 0 of the MAC address is known as the *group/individual* (G/I) bit. If this bit is set, the MAC address refers to more than one possible host on the LAN (a broadcast or multicast). If the bit is clear, then this frame is addressed to one possible host on the LAN (a unicast).

- Bit 1 of the MAC address is known as the *global/local* (G/L) bit. Originally, if this bit was set, it meant that a vendor has purchased a group of addresses from IEEE. If the bit was clear, then the manufacturer or the user was using non-assigned addresses and the responsibility for unique addressing is passed to the user.

Unicast, Multicast, and Broadcast

LAN adapter chipsets were designed with a few simple assumptions in mind. First of all, the host where the LAN adapter is installed will have a single unique identity given by its MAC address. This is the *unicast address* of the host.

> *Only one host must use a given unicast address on any single LAN segment, or multiple segments connected by MAC transparent devices such as Repeaters or Bridges. Unicast addresses are valid entries in the MAC Source or MAC Destination address fields of a network frame.*

For some chipsets, there may be the capability to allow the workstation to belong to a group address. For example, it might be useful to be able to send out one LAN frame that would be received by all Spanning Tree Bridges, or all OSPF routers. This function is called a multicast address.

> *Multiple hosts on the same LAN segment may belong to the same multicast address group. In addition, a given host may belong to more than one multicast group. Multicast addresses are valid entries in the MAC Destination address field of a network frame, but are invalid addresses in the MAC Source address field.*

The final type of address is the broadcast address. In IEEE terms, a broadcast is an "all ones" address, in other words all 48 bits of the address are set to binary 1.

> *Any frame which has its MAC destination address set to the broadcast address will be received by all hosts on the same LAN segment. A host does not need to belong to a broadcast group in order to receive a broadcast frame. The broadcast address is a valid entry in the MAC Destination address field of a network frame, but is an invalid address in the MAC Source Address field.*

Multicast and Broadcast Use in IP

TCP/IP doesn't make very much use of multicasts (unfortunately). ARP, RARP, IGRP, RIP and many of the first generation of IP protocols used the broadcast address instead. To be fair, the designers had no real option since at that time the multicast feature was not available, for a variety of reasons:

- Some early Ethernet chipsets were not able to support multicasting.

- Non-IEEE LAN technologies, like ProNET-10, and ProNET-80 used a simple 8 bit MAC address that didn't have the room for multicasting.

- The first and second generation of Token Ring chips were "brain damaged" and their multicasting didn't work. This bug was caught early enough for IBM to devise a standard kludge called *functional addressing* [13, 16].

Newer IP protocols such as OSPF use multicasting and include workarounds to support multicast deprived technologies. In addition, many vertical market applications are starting to use multicast technology, which has lead to a demand for IP multicast and the routing of multicasts [15]. The main objection to broadcast traffic is that, on a multiprotocol LAN, hosts that are not running IP are continually being interrupted by IP traffic such as ARP and RIP.

Bit Order

One of the more embarrassing disagreements in the LAN industry is that of bit order representation on LANs. Just like family secrets, bit order is usually mentioned quickly in a low and mumbled voice in the hope that nobody will notice. To make matters worse, I always see bit order explained differently, with the "blame" laid on Ethernet or Token Ring depending on the author's current employer. I'm going to try and keep it simple and hopefully without bias.

LANs are bit serial transmission systems. If we send a byte of information, we need to decide if we want to transmit the low order (Least Significant) bit first, or the high order (Most Significant) bit first. To illustrate the importance of this decision, think of the number 123 decimal. In binary this number (including all leading 0s in the byte) is written 01111011. If we transmit this binary in the order LEAST significant bit first we'll transmit 1, 1, 0, 1, 1, 1, 1, 0. If the station at the other ends thinks we're transmitting MOST significant bit first, it will interpret this bit stream as the binary value 11011110, which is the decimal value 222. There are some values for bytes where the bit order interpretation doesn't matter; 10000001, 11000011, 11100111, 11111111, 01111110 etc. These binary values are symmetrical. The problem is that we'd be very limited in our address choice if we used only symmetrical bytes. Moreover, the IEEE has already defined bits 0 and 1 of the first byte of the MAC address for the G/I and G/L functions, so this restricts the symmetry choices even more.

But wait! Why don't we just agree on an interpretation order? Yes, of course that's the sensible thing to do. The first thing that the IEEE 802.1 committee did was to define that the first bit of a MAC address that was transmitted "on the wire" is the G/I bit. This is a useful step because it alerts the chipset hardware very early on in the address recognition process. The G/I bit is the MOST significant bit of the MAC address and so all IEEE LANs transmit their MAC address fields in MSB-first order. Since the Ethernet standard predated the IEEE decision, there was no way to change the fact that Ethernet transmits all other parts of the frame in LSB-first form.

When Token Ring was introduced, the designers decided to transmit the entire frame in the same format. Since the MAC addresses must be transmitted MSB-first, the entire Token Ring frame is transmitted MSB-first.

When the remainder of the frame is received by the host or router, the internal software always interprets the bits correctly and always transmits the bits in the same sequence.

MAC bridges always connect the same LAN technologies and so they couldn't care less about bit order. Except that some bridges do connect different technologies; Ethernet/FDDI Translation bridges and the IBM 8209 Translation Bridge. I discuss the consequences of the bit order problem for Translation Bridges in Chapter 3. For routers, this is simply not an issue because if you're transmitting an IP datagram between an Ethernet and a Token Ring through a single router, the IP packet is "stripped" of its frame "identity" as part of the routing process.

A Note on FDDI. The bit order for FDDI follows the IEEE 802.5 guidelines and so FDDI is conceptually an MSB LAN. However, FDDI doesn't represent bits directly on the wire (or fiber). Instead, each byte is divided into two four-bit nibbles and each nibble is coded into a five bit symbol [14].

2.7 Connections and Communication

Imagine you're making a telephone call. You pick up the phone, dial a number, and the person at the other end answers. When you finish the conversation, you hang up. In telephone communication, when the number is dialed and the phone picked up, a connection is made. This connection is maintained for the duration of the call and then it is cleared. This mode of communication is known as *connection-oriented*. While the call is in progress, the users at each end don't need to keep on using telephone numbers because the connection between the two of them is dedicated to this call.

Contrast this with the way we send letters and post cards to each other. Each letter has a full address on it. Even if you send a letter regularly between the same two addresses every day, the Post Office doesn't keep a note of this or allow you to abbreviate the address in any way.

Both of these connection modes are used in popular communication technologies.

2.7.1   Connection-Oriented Mode

Connection-oriented communications are usually used by Wide Area services, but is also used in SNA networks. The telephone network, ISDN and public X.25 services are good examples. Future ATM services will also be connection-oriented. Each of these technologies uses connection-oriented mode for a slightly different reason. Here are some properties of connection-oriented communication:

Three Phases

Message transfers consist of three distinct phases. The CALL REQUEST, DATA TRANSFER and CALL CLEAR phases. The CALL REQUEST phase is the only part of the transaction that needs to contain full addressing. The DATA TRANSFER phase can use an abbreviated addressing scheme (in the case of X.25 and ATM), or no addressing at all (in the case of telephones or ISDN).

Maintaining The Session

Distinct sessions are formed between the two communicating stations of a connection-oriented system. To keep these session in place is very important. In circuit-switched networks like the telephone system (and possibly ISDN) we can use electrical measurements to judge if the session is still OK. In packet or cell-switched systems like X.25 and ATM, we need session maintenance information to flow around the network. You can read in more detail how these processes work [7, 8]. Different network technologies refer to these protocol in different ways and so in this book I'll be referring to the session maintenance protocols as ."keep alives."

No Rerouting

Abbreviated addressing is a great idea to conserve Wide Area line bandwidth, but if one of the lines in the connection path is broken, there isn't enough information inside the DATA TRANSFER phase packets to allow the switches to reroute around a problem. Classic X.25 networks suffered from this problem. In the event of a break in communication, the user had to send another CALL REQUEST packet. This allows the network to perform rerouting if an alternative path is available. At the time of writing, ATM networks don't allow dynamic call allocation (they implement permanent connections) and so it isn't clear how ATM will cope with rerouting.

Reliable Delivery

A big benefit of connection-oriented systems in the past has been that at each hop in a transit path across the network, messages are checked to see if they made it across the link without any kind of corruption. In the old days of low speed analog circuits, this allowed worl-wide X.25 links to be made over some pretty nasty circuits. Today, satellite connections and digital circuits make these protocols less necessary. Most US and European networks are reliable enough to allow only end to end data checking.

2.7.2   Connectionless Mode

Connectionless communication is used by non-SNA LAN protocols like TCP/IP, IPX and DECnet. In this mode, every packet in the network contains full end to end addressing. There is no distinct CALL REQUEST or CALL CLEAR phase. In addition, there are no specific Network Layer keep alives.

Packet Address Overhead

Connectionless messages are obviously more bulky than connection-oriented messages because of the full addressing on each packet, but the presence of these addresses allows the network to automatically reroute traffic around congested or failed links.

Performance Considerations

Connectionless protocol packets must be individually routed. In other words, if a stream of packets for Destination X enters a router, the software inside the router does just as much work on the last packet as it did on the first. The router cannot "learn" anything useful from the data stream. In contrast, a connection-oriented data stream has already been allocated a virtual route through the network. Each of the switches in the path have already allocated buffer space and code paths for the data. You would think that connection-oriented systems would be faster than connectionless, wouldn't you?

That actually depends on the specific connection-oriented protocol. For X.25, the switching rate is around 20 times slower than for IP, for the same CPU power. This performance drop is more attributable to the LAPB protocol used to verify point to point transmission in X.25 systems [7].

2.7.3   End Systems and Intermediate Systems

I've described the concept of communication modes. I've mentioned the word "internetwork." Internetworks actually consist of two kinds of device; an *End System* and an *Intermediate System*. ES and IS are ISO terms. The equivalent TCP/IP jargon is *host* and *router* respectively.

At one time it was easy to explain the difference between a host and a router, but as processing power and RAM became cheaper and software became "free," the distinctions have started to blur. I'll give you the simple definition and then explain the exceptions.

Host systems are computers that have only one LAN or WAN interface installed. Because there is only one way into or out of the host, there is no opportunity for the device to make routing decisions.

Routers are computer systems that have more than one LAN or WAN interface installed. By using appropriate software, the router can make switching decisions and move traffic from one interface to the other.

If you use these simple definitions, you'll be OK in more than 90% of cases. Here are some exceptions:

- Hosts that are running UNIX can run a background task called *routed* (route demon). This allows then to act like a single port router. There isn't much point in them doing this in a "normal" environment. Adding a second or third interface to the unit will allow it to act as a conventional, single protocol router.

- It is possible to add more than one IP address to the same interface. This process is called multinetting and is often used in a transitionary phase between a private IP addressing scheme and an Internet registered scheme. In some circumstances, a single port router with a multinetted interface can be useful (Chapter 17 gives one example in a secure network environment).

- Routers may be set up for example, to route DECnet and IPX, but not IP. IP may be needed for management purposes and so a "Host Only" IP stack can be turned on in the router.

2.8 Summary

- TCP/IP is an open networking protocol.

- Unlike some other networking protocols, TCP/IP is well suited for internetworking for two unique reasons. First of all its addresses were always globally allocated, so duplicates can only be the result of an error. Second, it has a defined routing hierarchy that allows large internetworks to be managed in a structured way.

- It is possible to build a private TCP/IP network, or to attach to a global TCP/IP network called the Internet.

- The TCP/IP standards are defined in RFC documents that are administered by the IETF.

- Although there are thousands of RFCs, only a couple of dozen will apply to a typical internetwork.

- TCP/IP is well suited to internetworking because it has always been used with a global addressing scheme and has a mature capability for hierarchical routing.

- In the opinion of the author, TCP/IP has already become the de facto internetworking protocol and TCP/IP will gradually dominate local networking environments in the next few years.

- Communication systems are broken down into layered models. Rules and procedures that operate with a given layer are called protocols. The most common model in use today is the ISO OSI 7 Layer Model.

- Communication software at each layer of the OSI Model adds its own overhead.

- LANs are shared communication channels, and addresses are used to direct frames from one host to another.

- MAC addresses deliver frames to the appropriate host on the same wire. Network Layer addresses deliver packets to the correct host, even if the packet must pass over several networks between source and destination. Port addresses deliver the message to the correct program running in the destination host.

- Three overall types of MAC address exist: unicast (one station), multicast (multiple stations) and broadcast (all stations).

- MAC addresses are assigned by the manufacturer of the interface. Network addresses are assigned by the network operator (in the Internet, addresses must be within the assigned address block). Port addresses are agreed by the operating system and application designers.

- Ethernet is an LSB LAN, Token Ring is an MSB LAN. FDDI is conceptually an MSB LAN, but doesn't transmit "raw bits" on the wire.

- Thanks to the established conventions, Routers don't care about the bit order of a frame; Translation Bridges do.

- Communications can logically occur using a connection-oriented mode, or a connectionless mode of operation. Both modes are in common use and both have their pros and cons. IP is a connectionless protocol.

2.9   References

[1]   Cerf, Vinton G. and Kahn, Robert E. *A Protocol for Packet Network Interconnection*. IEEE Transactions of Communications, May 1974.

[2]   Ed Krol. *The Whole Internet*. (O'Reilly & Associates, 1992).

[3]   Mark A. Miller. *LAN Troubleshooting Handbook*. (M&T Books, 1993).

[4]   Radia Perlman. *Interconnections*. (Addison-Wesley, 1991).

[5]   Stan Schatt. *Understanding Local Area Networks.* (Macmillan, 1989).

[6]   Seifert, Rich. *"Ethernet: Ten Years After."* Byte, January 1991.

[7]   R. J. Deasington. *X.25 Explained.* (Ellis Horwood, 1989).

[8]   Martin de Prycker. *Asynchronous Transfer Mode.* Ellis Horwood, ISBN 0-13-178542-7.

[9]   *Handbook of Data Communications.* NCC Publications, ISBN 0-85012383-1.

[10]   Institute of Electrical and Electronic Engineers. *Carrier Sense Multiple Access with Collision Detection (CSMA/CD), ISO/IEC 8802-3.* ANSI/IEEE Std 802.3, 1990.

[11]   DEC, INTEL and XEROX. *The Ethernet, A Local Area Network-Data Link Layer and Physical Layer Specification, Version 2.0.* Document number AA-K759B-TK, November 1982.

[12]   Network General Corporation. *Sniffer Network Analyzer Operations Manual.* Publication 20028-001, May 1990.

[13]   Institute of Electrical and Electronic Engineers. *Token-Ring Access Method and Physical Layer Specification,* IEEE Std 802.5, 1989.

[14]   Floyd E. Ross et. al. "FDDI, A LAN Among MANs." *Computer Communication Review* (July 1990).

[15]   Douglas E. Comer. *Internetworking with TCP/IP.* (Prentice Hall, NJ 1991).

[16]   Mark A. Miller. "Troubleshooting Token Ring," *LAN Technology Magazine* (June 1989).

[17]   Mark Dickie. *Routing in Today's Internetworks.* (Van Nostrand Reinhold, 1994).

[18]   M. Allen, "Novell IPX Over Various WAN Media (IPXWAN)," *RFC 1634.* May 1994.

[19]   Digital Equipment Corporation. *DECnet Digital Network Architecture (Phase IV) General Description.* Order number AA-N149A-TC, May 1982.

CHAPTER 3

Communicating Over an IP Network

If you think the problem is bad now, just wait until we've solved it.

Epstein's Law

3.1 Introduction

In this chapter I'll give a brief overview of TCP/IP and in the next a look at the mechanics of IP communication. Since there are entire books that cover just these subjects, these chapters will contain frequent cross-references to RFCs and other works for additional detail. Ill look at:

- The TCP/IP Programming Interface; the API

- A comparison of the two major Transport protocols: UDP and TCP

- The structure and function of the two main Network Layer protocols: IP and ICMP

- The Address Resolution Protocol (ARP) and its derivatives, RARP and Proxy ARP

3.2 Application Programming Interfaces

To the casual observer, it may seem that there are thousands of communication applications performing all sorts of arcane and interesting functions. In most networks today, the tasks we perform consist mainly of:

- File transfer

- Terminal emulation

- Electronic messaging

- Running programs remotely

- Network management

Whatever we try to do over a network requires software to make things actually happen. Software needs to access a generic set of commands and functions that apply to the network. This type of software interface is known as an *Application Programming Interface* (API). APIs are used throughout the software industry today. When you buy a PC, there is a built-in API called the ROM BIOS that allows us to write the same code to run on PC-compatibles from many different vendors. More relevant today is the API for the higher level operating systeMs. Microsoft Windows and Apple's System 7 both have well documented APIs.

TCP/IP implementations are available on DOS, UNIX, System 7, VMS, various IBM mainframe systems and many other proprietary operating systeMs. Do all these systems use the same API? Originally TCP/IP was developed for a UNIX environment and an API called the *Socket Interface* was devised. When TCP/IP was ported to other environments, the socket interface was not always applicable. With second and third generation implementations, UNIX-like socket interfaces are the norm. The most recent convert to sockets is Microsoft Windows, which now offers the *Winsock API*.

Within the PC world, the most popular API is certainly the Network Basic I/O System (NetBIOS). This was originally developed by Sytek back in the early 80s and then backed by IBM for its initial networking product offerings.

3.2.1   The Socket Interface

The *socket programming interface*, or just *socket interface* was first introduced with the BSD 4.1c version of UNIX in 1982. Many modifications and updates to the socket interface have been proposed and implemented since that time.

The original socket interface was not dedicated to TCP/IP use. In fact it's a generic *process to process* API. In a network environment, the processes will generally be located on different host computers. In addition, BSD was intended to be able to support XNS and X.25 as communication protocols in addition to TCP/IP. However, when the ISO Transport Layer protocol specifications were completed it became clear that the basic socket interface would not be adequate to support generic applications over all of these protocols. AT&T introduced an enhanced Transport Layer Interface (TLI) for their derivative of UNIX (System V) in 1986. In recent years, there have been ongoing attempts to bring together the two UNIX hemispheres: BSD and System V. As you may be aware, these attempts have not been fully successful. This is one of the reasons that the socket interface remains the de facto API for TCP/IP today. During 1993, Microsoft announced a socket-compatible programming specification for its Windows 3 graphics interface for DOS. I assume that this API specification will be migrated to Windows 4 (which will include an operating system instead of relying on DOS) which may become available in the 1994 timescale. Windows/NT already uses a socket style API.

IBM support TCP/IP on all of their current platforms and has a socket API available for all of these implementations. However, since these APIs are actually emulations of UNIX functions, you should check the appropriate IBM documentation before committing to application features. In general, the IBM TCP/IP implementations I've encountered have been extremely stable and quite rich in functionality.

As Figure 3.1 shows, the socket interface provide three TCP/IP services:

- TCP streams
- UDP datagrams
- Direct (raw) datagram connection to IP

Examples of TCP/IP applications that use each of these services are Telnet (uses TCP), NFS (uses UDP) and OSPF (uses the raw interface).

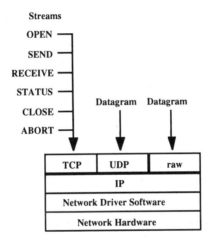

Figure 3.1:   Socket APIs

The TCP Streams Interface

The most complex of the socket services is TCP StreaMs. TCP is a connection-oriented service which involves a multistage connection process, with reliable data transfer and a clean connection termination. During data transfer, there is flow control, as well as error detection and correction. A detailed description of these stages goes beyond the scope of this book. Sidnie Feit [2] gives a more detailed overview. Application developers should use the TCP interface if they require reliable data transfer (and don't want to write their own error checks) with the capability to resequence packets.

The UDP Datagram Service

UDP is a much more basic and simple interface. As a connectionless protocol, the UDP interface simply sends data or receives data.

Hosts that run simply as UDP clients will open UDP process as they need to send information. However, if you expect to receive *unsolicited* UDP datagrams, you must set up a "listening" process that will await some form of communication. Listening processes must operate in a known location, because no prearranged addressing has been agreed between the two hosts. This leads us to the concept of Transport Layer addressing and *Well Known Ports*.

Application developers should choose the UDP interface if they want to optimize their application for performance. UDP leaves them free to develop error detection *if necessary*, error correction *if necessary* and packet resequencing *if necessary*. UDP timers were originally defined for local use and applications that are targeted at WAN operation should include the ability to change timer values on a per-application basis.

Port Addresses

In Chapter 2 I discussed the OSI model and described the concept of addressing. In Figure 3.2 I summarize the function of these addresses. We use MAC addresses to allow many hosts to share the same network channel, yet be sure that traffic can be sent from one specific host to another. Network Layer addressing allows us to move information packets between two hosts, regardless of the type of network they are connected to and the number of intermediate networks we need to cross.

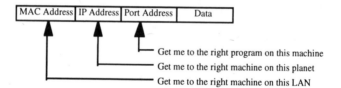

Figure 3.2:   Do We Have Enough Addresses Yet?

The combination of MAC and Network Layer addresses allows us to move information from one machine to another, whether these machines are on the same LAN segment or connected to the Internet on different sides of the planet. But host computers may be running more than one communication program. How do we ensure that the information is reaching the right one? This is where Transport Layer addressing comes in. In the TCP/IP world, the Transport Layer addressing entity is called the *port*. A port address is 16 bits long and has no specific substructure. The combination of an IP address and a port is known as a *socket address*. Socket addresses give us all the information we need to direct traffic to the correct program running on any host computer connected to our IP internetwork.

Some of the higher level programs that need to communicate are standard protocols in their own right like Telnet or FTP. The Application Layer protocols are called *well-known services*. They use the same port numbers in all implementations; and these are called *well-known ports*. The port numbers are specified in the relevant RFC and are summarized in Assigned Numbers. Table 3.1 shows a short list of the most common well-known ports:

Table 3.1: Well-Known Port Numbers

Application Protocol	Well-Known Port (decimal)
TCP Port Service Multiplexer	1
FTP	20 (data) 21 (control)
TELNET	23
TFTP	69
SNMP	161 162 (trap)

Port numbers 0 to 255 are reserved for well-known ports. User-developed applications should use port numbers above 255. Port number collisions by concurrent applications on the same host are administered by the operating system. In effect, application programs request the next available port number from TCP/IP.

3.2.2 NetBIOS

There is one other popular API that I should mention: NetBIOS. NetBIOS was first introduced as a complete protocol stack for the IBM PC Network adapter.

NetBIOS is an extension of the *Basic Input/Output System* (BIOS) chip of an IBM-compatible Personal Computer. When early PC networking application were written, the only APIs that were available were proprietary interfaces provided by each LAN interface supplier. Two of these APIs struggled for dominance: the Novell API and NetBIOS. In this case, NetBIOS was provided as a pure API, with other protocol stacks providing the Transport functions. NetBIOS emulators exist over an IPX stack, for Banyan VINES and over TCP/IP. Even the "native" NetBIOS that operates today over IBM Token Ring adapters is actually an emulator. The only original NetBIOS is the version that operates over the IBM PC Network adapters.

NetBIOS is defined as an API for TCP/IP networks in RFCs 1001 and 1002. Originally, NetBIOS was designed to provide groups of PCs, sharing a common broadcast medium, with simple mechanisms to locate resources (applications) and send and receive data with an application peer. The collection of all of these capabilities is more commonly known as the NetBIOS Services.

NetBIOS Services

NetBIOS Services are broken down into three general categories:

- NetBIOS Name Service
- NetBIOS Session Service
- NetBIOS Datagram Service

Each NetBIOS service defines the functions which provide end nodes with application access over a common broadcast medium.

NetBIOS Node Types

In addition to the NetBIOS Services, RFC 1001 and 1002 also define three types of end nodes which reside in a NetBIOS network:

- Broadcast nodes (B nodes)
- Point-to-Point nodes (P nodes)
- Mixed nodes (M nodes)

B nodes communicate using a mix of UDP datagrams and TCP connections. B nodes may freely operate with each other within a *broadcast area*. and always rely on broadcasts to locate resources. In the context of a router internetwork, a broadcast area does not extend *through* the router. NetBIOS broadcasts are issued as MAC broadcasts and these will not pass through the router.

P Nodes communicate using a mix of UDP datagrams and TCP connections. P nodes neither generate nor listen for broadcast UDP packets. P nodes do, however, offer NetBIOS level broadcast and multicast services using the capabilities of NetBIOS Name Servers (NBNS) and NetBIOS Datagram Distributors (NBDD). In theory, for router internetworks, P node behavior offer the best option to extend NetBIOS communication beyond the immediate LAN segment. Hosts on the LAN segment (or even the router itself) could act as an NBNS or NBDD and convert the service request to a *directed broadcast*. A directed broadcast is a fully addressed IP datagram, which can then be routed in the conventional way to the required NetBIOS server.

M nodes (Mixed mode nodes) are P nodes which have certain B node characteristics. M nodes use both broadcast and unicast. M nodes rely on NBNS and NBDD servers. However, M nodes may continue limited operations should a NBNS or NBDD become unavailable.

In practice only B nodes are used in NetBIOS networks today (including NetBIOS over IP) because the applications running on these machines do not support the use of NBNS or NBDD services.

NetBIOS Name Service

NetBIOS resources are referenced and accessed by end nodes using the corresponding NetBIOS name of the resource. NetBIOS names allow applications and the PCs on which they reside to be known by the other applications and PCs on the network.

NetBIOS names are 16 bytes long and consist of alphanumeric characters. Each NetBIOS host on the network maintains a list of all known NetBIOS names within a local name table. Hosts access NetBIOS applications by requesting the NetBIOS name for the application they want to use. As a result, lower-layer address information is not available to NetBIOS applications or to the PCs accessing the applications. All NetBIOS name-to-MAC addressing cross-references are achieved via a series of request/response broadcasts packets between the requesting end node and the node on which the application resides.

NetBIOS names are also used to identify nodes on the network. All nodes participating in a NetBIOS network are assigned a permanent node name consisting of 6 bytes of address followed by 10 zeros. When a new NetBIOS application or host is added to a network it must first register its name with the other applications and PCs on the network.

NetBIOS name registration has two aspects: first, name registration is used to ensure other applications and PCs know that the new application or host exists. Second, name registration is used to insure that the name for the new application or PC is unique from all other names already present on the network.

Names can be used to refer to unique applications or hosts, or to represent a group. These are known as *exclusive names* or *shared names* respectively. It is important to note that NetBIOS over IP relies on a broadcast method to register a new NetBIOS name on the network. NetBIOS name registration packets are always broadcast to UDP port 137 and are registered as either exclusive or shared names.

The area across which the NetBIOS name is known is called the *NetBIOS Scope*. Each NetBIOS Scope has a "Scope Identifier" which is a string of characters meeting the requirements of the Domain Name System (see Chapter 13). All NetBIOS names are represented in a manner consistent with the definition for "compressed name messages" outlined in the Domain Name Service Specification, RFC833.

The NetBIOS Name Service offers three basic functions:

- Add Name
- Delete Name
- Find Name

The *Add Name* packet (also referred to as *Name Claim* or *Add Name Query* packets) is broadcast by any new NetBIOS resource to verify the NetBIOS name they are using is unique. If no response is received to the Add Name packet after (typically) six successive broadcasts the name is assumed to be unique and will be used by the name server.

The *Delete Name* packet is used when a NetBIOS application no longer requires the use of its name. Exclusive NetBIOS names are assumed active unless the NetBIOS name is explicitly deleted from the network.

The *Find Name* packet (also referred to as *Name Query Requests* or *Name Request*) is used by NetBIOS clients to obtain the network address of a NetBIOS Name for a service that the client is trying to reach. Find Name packets are answered by the host (or hosts for a shared name) on which the service resides. The response to the Find Name is called a *Name Query Response* packet. Note that the Find Name packet is a broadcast, whereas the Name Query Response packet is a unicast to the destination node who originally sent the Find Name. As you'll see later, this is analogous to a conventional TCP/IP ARP request/response transaction. Both the Find Name and Name Query Response packets are directed to UDP Port 138.

NetBIOS Session Service:

A session is a reliable message exchange conducted between two NetBIOS applications. Sessions provide two-way communications, they are sequenced, reliable and transmit data using messages that can be up to 131,071 bytes long.

NetBIOS sessions use the Name Service to identify the IP address and the TCP port of the node or applications with which a session is desired. This phase is known as sessions establishment. NetBIOS sessions are established using TCP port 139.

When two NetBIOS applications are communicating the session is considered having reached a steady state and closed when either has gone down.

NetBIOS Datagram Service:

NetBIOS datagrams always have a named destination and source address. The destination name/address may be specific (exclusive name/IP address pair) or broadcast (multicast to a group). NetBIOS Datagram Service establishes communications using UDP port 138.

Like NetBIOS sessions, the host that wishes to send NetBIOS datagrams first broadcasts a Find Name to learn the IP address of the destination NetBIOS name. NetBIOS nodes with matching names respond by sending Name Query Response packets back to the requesting node including their IP address for the requested NetBIOS name. When a Find Name packet is broadcast attempting to establish communications with a shared name, only one node within the group should respond.

An example of a datagram broadcast to a group is seen during the login process used in a Microsoft LAN Manager network. LAN Manager client PCs broadcast a login request to a group name (the group includes the resources the client has access to within that domain). Upon receiving the broadcast, all members of the group defer their response to the NetBIOS server identified as the one responsible for performing login authentication. Once a response has been received and the login process has completed, the requesting client PC is able to send and receive messages with each entity within that group/domain.

A NetBIOS UDP datagram has a maximum size of 1064 bytes. The smallest possible IP datagram MTU is 576 bytes. When the UDP datagram exceeds the maximum amount of data allowed in a UDP packet, the NetBIOS datagram must be fragmented before transmission and reassembled when received. This is done in the same way as any other IP fragmentation and reassembly operation.

Figure 3.3 shows the structure of an IP-encapsulated NetBIOS datagram.

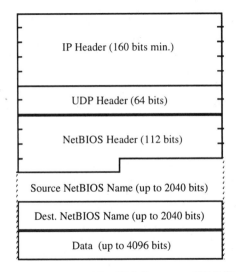

Figure 3.3: NetBIOS over UDP/IP

NetBIOS Summary

NetBIOS was designed for PC LANs, at a time before internetworking PC LANs was even considered. As a result, many of its basic features are based on a broadcast principle which is in direct opposition to the goals of structured internetworking. The efforts to operate NetBIOS over routeable stacks such as IP have done virtually nothing to solve this problem. However, you may find yourself obliged to implement NetBIOS support in your internetwork. Many older applications are written to this API and even today most applications with a pure PC-heritage tend to use NetBIOS.

If your internetwork design process involves the specification of new applications, I strongly advise you to have these written to a socket interface.

3.3   The Internet Protocol (IP)

IP is designed to move information packets from one host to another, with the assumption that the internetwork between the hosts can involve multiple network sections using different technologies and offering no guarantee of safe delivery. The basic IP protocol provides three services:

- Connectionless delivery, sometimes called a *datagram* service

- A mechanism for fragmentation and reassembly

- Packet addressing and routing

Session-oriented traffic that uses IP should not assume that datagrams will arrive in the same order that they were transmitted, or that the datagrams will arrive in an uncorrupted form.

IP networks can span the world and so the intrepid IP datagram may encounter Ethernets, Token Rings, FDDI and various WAN technologies on its journey as well as being switched by routers from different manufacturers with different capabilities. Some sections of the journey may require that the original datagram is broken down into smaller components and then reassembled either at another router in the path, or at the receiving host.

The IP Address

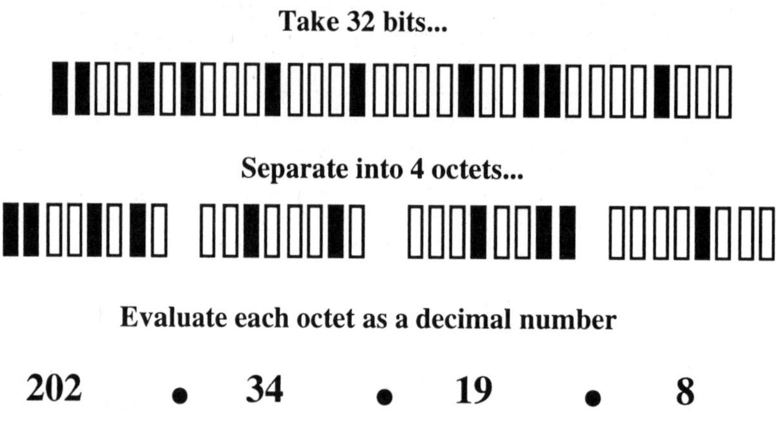

Take 32 bits...

Separate into 4 octets...

Evaluate each octet as a decimal number

202   •   34   •   19   •   8

Figure 3.4:   Representing an IP Address

IP addresses are always 32 bits long, although they may not always look that way thanks to a written convention called *dotted decimal notation*. In Figure 3.4 I show a 32-bit IP address written in binary form and separated into four 8-bit fields. Each field is evaluated independently and the resulting four numbers are converted to decimal. This may seem like a strange way to write an address, but it has a couple of advantages. First of all, addresses can be discussed using the decimal number base, which is very familiar to humans, but not much good to computers. Second, by separating the address into fields, we have left ourselves the opportunity to apply a hierarchy quite easily. Three additional concepts are woven into the IP address:

- Network ID and Host ID
- IP Address Class
- IP Subnets

3.3.1   Network ID and Host ID

When IP addresses are used by software, they are obviously used in their binary format and the addressing scheme has a few properties that only show up if you think of the address in this way.

For example, I've already spoken about the way that Network Layer devices like routers are able to view entire LANs using a single address, and don't have to keep track of every host on the network. To do this, the router identifies some part of the IP address to represent the *Network ID*. How much of the address is used for this purpose? When IP addresses were devised, nobody really knew that networks would grow the way they have, but the original designers of the addressing scheme were canny enough to leave scope for flexibility in addressing structure. So IP addresses include the concept of *Address Class*. The "class" of an IP address decides how much of the address will be interpreted as the Network ID.

- Class A addresses have an 8-bit Network ID
- Class B addresses have a 16-bit Network ID
- Class C addresses have a 24-bit Network ID

All IP addresses are 32 bits long and so the subtraction of the Network ID portion of the address leaves the following address space for hosts. This part of the address is called the *Host ID*.

- Class A addresses have a 24-bit Host ID
- Class B networks have a 16-bit Host ID
- Class C networks have an 8-bit Host ID

3.3.2   Deciding Address Classes

So how do we tell if an IP address is Class A, B or C? Obviously we have to use a technique so that software can make the decision very quickly. Typically this means a binary comparison technique. The designers of IP chose to use the first few bits (the Most Significant Bits) of the most significant byte of the IP address. In binary terms, I summarize the principle in Figure 3.5.

1st Byte Bit Pattern	1st Byte Value (Decimal)	Address Class
0 X X X X X X	1...127	Class A
1 0 X X X X X	128...191	Class B
1 1 0 X X X X	192...223	Class C
1 1 1 0 X X X	224...239	Class D

Figure 3.5:   Binary View of IP Address Classes

From the human viewpoint, Class A addresses always "begin" with a number between 1 and 127; Class B addresses between 128 and 191; Class C addresses between 192 and 223.   Only these three address classes are used for host addresses, Class D addresses are used for IP multicast purposes (two Class D addresses, 224.0.0.5 and 224.0.0.6, are allocated to OSPF, for example) [8].

A Quick Word on Multicast

In the last Chapter I explained the concepts of unicast, multicast and broadcast. In the context of the IP address, multicast has a specific meaning. An entire address block, the Class D address range, is reserved for multicast purposes. When somebody thinks of a special purpose for a group, they can apply for a Class D address to describe the group.   The Assigned Numbers RFC [10] describes the current reserved addresses. These include:

- All IP Hosts
- All IP Routers
- All OSPF Routers
- All OSPF Designated Routers

Perhaps a more pictorial way of looking at IP addresses is shown in Figure 3.6. This illustrates the relative sizes of Class A, Class B, and Class C address space. In the extreme cases, a Class A network can support almost 17 million hosts, but only 126 of these networks can ever be interconnected. Class C networks can only support 254 hosts, but there are 2 million possible unique network IDs. Class B addresses offer the best compromise, especially when used with appropriate subnetting as we'll see below.   The problem is that only around 16,000 Class B addresses are available and most of these have been allocated. At the time of writing, it is estimated that Class B address space will be exhausted by 1996, but the range of estimates for Class B address exhaustion varies dramatically from "tomorrow" to "ten years."

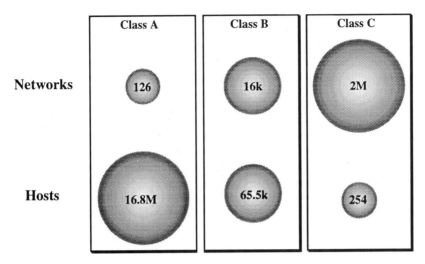

Figure 3.6: Pictorial View of IP Address Space

3.3.3 Centralized Address Allocation

If you decide to build an IP internetwork, you can, of course, choose the class, subnet structure and individual address numbers in complete freedom. However, if you ever want to connect your internetwork to another internetwork, how can you guarantee that the addresses chosen by both internetworks are unique? Networks that attach to the Internet have always been obliged to comply with Internet addressing schemes allocated by the Network Information Center (NIC). Originally there was only one NIC, which was set up to serve the original ARPANET and operated by a company called SRI. Today, NIC address allocation is regionalised, with authorized NIC representatives in various geographical (outside of the US, this is usually national) locations. Anyone that would like to become an Internet member simply sends an E-mail or official letter to the NIC requesting address space and describing the network they would like to build. The NIC has a set of guidelines that it will use to allocate an appropriate number of Class C addresses, or, in very rare instances, a Class B address. It's possible for non-registered users to connect their networks into Internet address space, but this must be done using specially designed addressing schemes and potentially using *address translation gateways* to ensure addressing consistency.

For routers, the concepts of Network ID and Host ID are very convenient. These classifications are not always so convenient when we are trying to devise an address structure that fits a corporate organization.

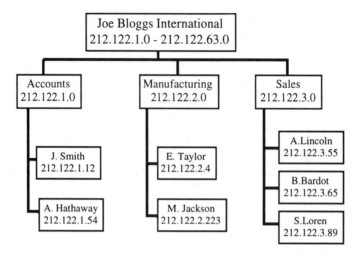

Figure 3.7:   Class C IP Addressing in a Corporate Structure

In Figure 3.7 I show a typical situation today. Joe Bloggs International decides to set up a corporate IP internetwork. The company applies for an IP address and is allocated a block of Class C addresses; from 212.122.1.0 to 212.122.63.0. The NIC guarantees that no other Internet-attached company has been allocated these addresses and Joe Bloggs are themselves responsible for address allocation within their organization.

Following an internal addressing structure, Joe Bloggs allocates addresses 1, 2 and 3 to the Accounts, Manufacturing and Sales departments, respectively. Each department can support up to 254 machines.

Look at the way that I've described the Accounts department; 212.122.1.0. The Host ID of 0 is actually an illegal value. This address is an administrative convention used to refer to the entire "local wire" address space. Hosts numbered 212.122.1.1 to 212.122.1.254 will assume that they are on the same local wire and can reach each other directly. I give some more examples of address identification in the Diskette Tutorials.

3.3.4   IP Subnets

If two hosts have the same Network ID, then they assume that they are on the "same wire." Conversely if they have *different* Network IDs, they will assume that they are on "different wires," in other words, they must use an IP router to reach each other.

This reliance on the Network ID is very strong, so let's have a look at a specific Class B address.

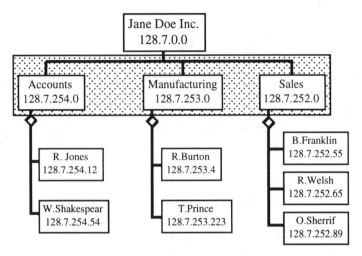

Figure 3.8:   Class B IP Addressing in a Corporate Structure

In this addressing scheme, each department has the *same* Network ID. Each host will assume that is on the same wire as all of the other hosts. This may be the case for a small network, or a network connected by bridges, but it's not the case for a router network. If the shaded rectangle in Figure 3.8 is a multiport bridge and the diamonds represent connections to the bridge, then this addressing scheme will work fine. If the shaded device is a router, this addressing scheme will not work.

This is not a very satisfying situation. After all, Jane Doe had to try very hard to persuade the NIC that her organization needs a Class B address and it seems a shame not to use it fully. If fact there is a way around this type of problem. The concept is known as *IP Subnetting*. If we subnet an IP address, we use part of the Host ID space to represent an additional layer of address hierarchy.

Figure 3.9 shows the logical view of Jane Doe's Class B network. The overall network can be addressed using its Network ID of 128.7.0.0. Unless they are told about subnetting, all hosts with an address beginning 128.7 will believe that they are on the same physical wire. Once the subnet mask is configured in the hosts and routers, each subnet is seen as a logically separate network. Each of the subnets in this diagram are connected using a router. Figure 3.10 shows the basic principle behind subnet addressing. Part of the Host ID field is used to represent the Subnet ID, which allows us another level of hierarchy in our addressing scheme. Using the Subnet ID to differentiate the different LAN segments, a router can now allow the kind of connections shown in Figure 3.8.

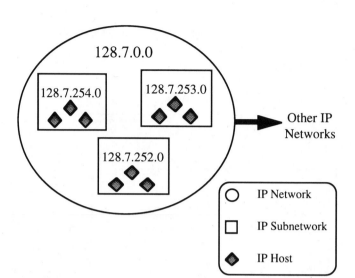

Figure 3.9:   Logical Views of Class B Network

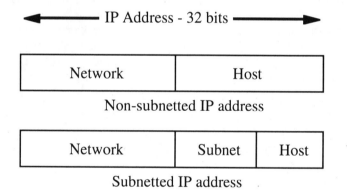

Figure 3.10:   Subnetting an IP Address

Hosts *and* routers must be told about subnetting and the descriptions of subnets must be consistent. Remember that routers and hosts both need to decide which part of an IP address refers to the Network ID and which part refers to the Host ID. Using the Class structure described in Figure 2.3, we can use binary comparison to decide if the Network ID is 8, 16 or 24 bits of the address. When we subnet, we actually *extend* the length of the Network ID. To indicate how far we would like to extend it, we use a binary *subnet mask*. For each bit in the IP address that we would like to use to indicate the Network or Subnet ID, we set a bit in the subnet mask. By default, the non-subnetted address classes have the following masks:

Table 3.2:   Default Subnet Masks

Address Class	Default Mask (binary)	Default Mask (decimal)
A	11111111.00000000.00000000.00000000	255.0.0.0
B	11111111.11111111.00000000.00000000	255.255.0.0
C	11111111.11111111.11111111.00000000	255.255.255.0

How Do Subnet Masks Work?

Imagine that in Figure 3.8, Mr. Burton in Manufacturing wants to send a message to Ms. Welsh in Sales. The IP software in their respective computers needs to decide if they are on the same network, or different networks. The software takes the IP addresses (in binary) of the source and performs a binary AND with the subnet mask. The software then takes the destination IP address and performs a binary AND operation with the subnet mask. The two resulting 32-bit numbers are compared. If they are the same, then the source and destination are on the same wire. If the results of the AND operations are different, the destination host is assumed to be on a different wire. The exact details of this are described below.

Mr. Burton's IP address is 128.7.253.4. The address mask has not been changed and so is the default mask for a Class B address; 255.255.0.0. The result of (128.7.253.4) AND (255.255.0.0) is 128.7.0.0.

Ms. Welsh's IP address is 128.7.252.65. Again, she is using a default address mask of 255.255.255.0. The result of (128.7.252.65) AND (255.255.0.0) is 128.7.0.0.

The two results are the same and so the IP software has been able to numerically verify what we can see with our own eyes; logically these two machines are on the same network 128.7.0.0.

To use her address more effectively, Jane Doe needs to change the subnet mask from its default value. In Chapter 13, I discuss the factors you need to consider when you decide how much subnet space is needed. For this introduction, let's assume that we can use 8 bits of the Host ID field for subnetting and let's assume we decide to use the same length of subnet for the whole network. The subnet mask now becomes 255.255.255.0.

Mr. Burton's software now calculates (128.7.254.4) AND (255.255.0.0) and the result is 128.7.254.0 for the source host. For the destination host, the comparison is (128.7.253.65) AND (255.255.255.0) and the result is 128.7.253.0. These are no longer the same and so Mr. Burton's software will assume that the source and destination are on different networks. Hosts that believe that they are different networks will also assume that they can only reach each other by using an IP router.

Subnetting can be used with all classes of IP address, but subnet address space must always be "stolen" from the Host ID field. This means that the size of subnets that are possible will vary between Class A, B and C addresses. Unfortunately, the most common address allocated today, Class C, offers us the least opportunity to subnet since it has only 8 bits of Host ID even in an unsubnetted address[1].

> *When an IP host compares the destination address with its own IP address, it is performing the first stage routing decision, i.e. are the two hosts on the same local wire? For this reason, it's absolutely essential that hosts and routers on the same internetwork agree on the size of all subnets.*

Choosing Subnet Numbers

In Figure 3.8, you might have noticed that the subnet numbers used in Jane Doe's network begin at 128 and seem to work downwards in a random fashion. This numbering scheme is the one recommended in RFC 1219 and I discuss the reasons for it in Chapter 13.

Byte Boundaries

In introductory descriptions of IP subnetting, it's always tempting to select subnet masks that align nicely with byte boundaries, such as 255.255.255.0. This isn't mandatory, however. Subnet masks are used as binary values within the IP software and we just represent them in decimal for our own convenience. For example, a mask of 255.255.252.0 applied to a Class B network ID would indicate a Subnet ID length of 6 bits and a Host ID length of 10 bits. When subnets don't align on byte boundaries, it can be difficult to decide *visually* if two IP addresses are on the same subnet or not.

Variable Length Subnets

In all of my subnet examples I have made the assumption that the subnet masks are identical. This doesn't have to be the case. An 8-bit subnet on a Class B address, as used in Jane Doe's internetwork allows up to 254 hosts to be installed on each subnet (subnet 0 and subnet 255 reserved). Consider two extreme situations. First, an Ethernet LAN workgroup has 500 hosts installed on it. Ideally we should reduce the size of the Subnet ID to 7-bits using a mask of (255.255.254.0). This leaves a 9-bit Host ID field, allowing up to 510 hosts. If I use this mask throughout my Class B address space, I could only configure 126 of these subnets (7-bit Subnet ID). This may seem like a good number and it may even satisfy the needs of this network, but perhaps not if point-to-point WAN circuits are used. The WAN link between routers needs to be given IP addresses. Each end of the link will have its own IP address and will be using the same 7-bit mask as the LAN segments. However, the WAN segment will only

---

[1]To make matters worse, an "all zeros" and "all ones" subnet number value is reserved.

ever have 2 hosts attached, which means that 508 possible IP address have been wasted. If we have 20 such WAN connections in the network, then over 10,000 IP addresses will be wasted! Although point-to-point links are the most extreme example, we can also think in terms of different sizes of workgroup requiring different sizes of subnet mask.

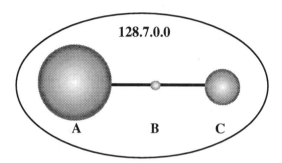

Figure 3.11:   Variable Length Subnets in Action

In fact it is possible to assign different sizes of subnet mask to different LAN segments, although this feature is not supported in all routing protocols (see Chapter 14). In Figure 3.11 I show how the Class B Network ID 128.7.0.0 can be divided up into a "large" subnet (A), a "medium" subnet (C) and a "small" subnet (B). The reason we'd do this is simple. As IP address space begins to run out, we need to be able to use address space more economically. If we'd applied a mask of 255.255.255.0 to this Network ID, each of our subnets could support up to 254 hosts. If subnet B were a serial line with just two end points, we would have wasted 252 addresses straight away.

Unfortunately, the use of variable length subnets is hampered by three factors:

- The current state of the RFCs is such that they don't fully define whether or not variable length subnetting should take place [5, 6, 7].

- Routing protocols such as RIP and IGRP do not support variable length subnetting. OSPF does in theory, but only the "best quality" implementations actually support the feature in practice [7, 9].

- Because there's so much binary comparison work, variable length subnets are stunningly difficult for most humans to understand and certainly make the internetwork design process more difficult.

Non-Contiguous Subnet Masks

Another assumption I made during this introduction to subnetting is that the binary mask used to define the size of the subnet is *contiguous*. In other words, all 8 bits of an 8-bit subnet mask are grouped together AND they begin directly after the final bit of the Network ID. Because routers work totally in binary for subnet resolution purposes, non-contiguous subnet masks will work, but are really not advised. I've shown some examples in Table 3.3. To make the issue a bit clearer, I've underlined the "host zeros" that are trapped between the "subnet ones" and make the subnet mask non-contiguous.

Table 3.3:   Contiguous and Non-Contiguous Subnet Masks

Mask (Decimal)	Mask (Binary)	Subnet Type
255.255.255.0	11111111.11111111.11111111.00000000	Contiguous
255.240.240.0	11111111.11110000.11110000.00000000	Non-Contiguous
255.255.240.0	11111111.11111111.11110000.00000000	Contiguous
255.255.207.0	11111111.11111111.11001111.00000000	Non-Contiguous

When you come to design an IP addressing scheme and select subnet sizes, possibly with variable length subnets, I think you'll agree that non-contiguous masks are just too complex and they have no real added value. This philosophy is shared by the Internet community, as RFC 1219 recommends the use of contiguous subnet and host ID fields.

Non-Contiguous Subnets

A rather different concept with a similar name is that of non-contiguous subnets. In Figure 2.6, I've shown all the subnets in Jane Doe's internetwork joined together within the 128.7.0.0 address space. In other words, these subnets are *contiguous*. Now consider the situation I've shown in Figure 2.9.

Two Jane Doe sites are interconnected over a different IP Network ID. This situation could occur, for example, in a typical Internet installation where traffic would pass over the NSFnet backbone. This addressing scheme is perfectly legal. However, in order for a router to correctly pass traffic from one subnet to the other, it needs to know about the subnet structure on each site. In Chapter 4 I'll be covering the standard router algorithm, but you can get a taste of the problem right now. Think about the situation of Router_1. He's receiving traffic from Site_1 and needs to decide where to send it. A host in the same position would use the subnet mask to extract the Network and Subnet ID from the destination address. In this case Router_1 might receive a packet from subnet 128.7.243.0 that is trying to reach subnet 128.7.253.0. To human eyes, an obvious route exists over network 177.12.0.0, but Router_1 can only know if Router_2 supplies the information. In Chapter 4 you'll read about dynamic routing protocols and Autonomous SysteMs. In this case, we need to ensure that Router_2 is sending subnet level detail to Router_1, otherwise the packets will never get through. The most common routing protocol today, RIP, is not allowed to pass this information (stated in a slightly ambiguous way on Page 21 of [10]). In contrast, OSPF must allow this information to pass in order to allow variable length subnetting. So the situation illustrated in Figure 3.12 is illegal for a RIP network, but would be legal in an OSPF network.

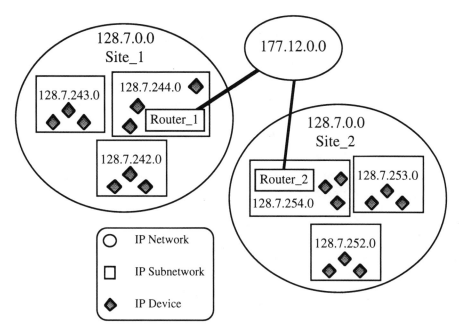

Figure 3.12: Non-Contiguous Subnets

Proxy ARP

What happens if hosts are not able to understand subnetting? Or the Network Administrator doesn't want to go around changing host subnet masks? In fact, because subnetting was an *addition* to the normal IP addressing scheme, there were many early IP implementations that did not implement it. The technique of Proxy Address Resolution, or Proxy ARP, was devised to solve this problem. However, since I haven't discussed normal address resolution, I'll leave Proxy ARP until later in this chapter.

3.4 IP Packet Formats

IP addressing is essentially straightforward and is a published standard. The Network Layer of IP is independent of any underlying communications network. In other words, when the packet is processed by the network Layer software, this software does not care if the information has come from, or is going to, for example an Ethernet, Token Ring, FDDI, etc. However, IP packets do have to be represented correctly at the Data Link Layer so that they can "exist" on the specific LAN technology.

In effect, an IP packet will be encapsulated by an appropriate LAN Data Link Layer, looking something like this:

Data Link Header
Protocol Multiplexing
IP Packet
Data Link Trailer

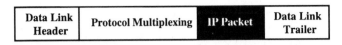

Figure 3.13: Generic IP Packet Encapsulation

- The Data Link Header and Trailer exist to allow the IP datagram to be carried safely over a LAN or WAN. These parts of the frame are specific to a particular network technology, so an Ethernet frame looks different from a Token Ring frame.
- The Protocol Multiplexing field is designed to allow frames from different protocol stacks (eg. TCP/IP, Novell, AppleTalk, etc.) to be carried over the same wire. I'll be referring to this as the "Type Field."
- The IP Packet format will always be the same, regardless of the LAN technology and is described below.

Now, in theory we could have a different encapsulation for every LAN technology: Ethernet, Token Ring, FDDI, etc. In practice, however, there are really only two kinds of encapsulation: *Ethernet* and *SNAP*. To understand why there are just two varieties, I need to give you some background on the development of Ethernet and the IEEE LANs.

3.4.1 IP Packet Format

An IP packet, or *datagram*, is at least 20 bytes long and looks something like this:

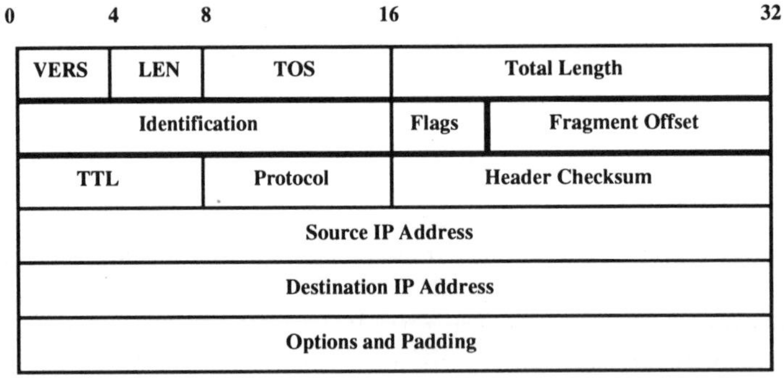

0
4
8
16
32
VERS
LEN
TOS
Total Length
Identification
Flags
Fragment Offset
TTL
Protocol
Header Checksum
Source IP Address
Destination IP Address
Options and Padding

Figure 3.14: Format of an IP Datagram

The notation I have used here is pretty standard in the literature and RFCs for the representation of packet formats and will be used throughout this book.

VERS: Version number. The current version is 4 and the next version is supposed to be 6 (IPng, or IP Next Generation).

LEN: The length of the IP header measured in 32-bit units (double words). This field does not include the data field and so is really a measure of the length of the Options field, since all other fields within the IP header are fixed in length.

TOS: Type of Service. This field has a rather complex structure and is not currently implemented by host IP software. However, in theory a host can use this field to specify the *Delay*, *Throughput* and Reliability of the communication path. The OSPF routing protocol described in Chapter 14 supports the concept of TOS, although most router manufacturers do not yet implement the feature because host software does not set these bits.

Total Length: The total length of the IP datagram measured in bytes. This length includes the header and data fields.

Identification: Used in packet fragmentation and reassembly.

Flags: Control flags that are used to indicate whether this datagram can be fragmented or not and whether this datagram is the last in a sequence of fragmented datagraMs.

Fragment Offset: Contains the number of 64-bit pieces (excluding IP header bytes) in previous fragments. In theory this field allows datagram fragments to arrive at reassembly points out of sequence and to be temporarily held in the correct buffer location to await remaining fragments.

Time to Live (TTL): A very useful field which can be used to eliminate permanent packet loops. This field contains the number of seconds that the packet can exist on the internetwork. In theory each router that processes the packet will subtract the time required for the packet to pass from this field. Since routers take much less than one second to switch a packet and this field does not allow fractional entries, the convention is for a router to decrement the TTL field by one. Router must discard packets whose TTL is zero. The recommended starting value is 32.

Protocol: Indicates the higher level protocol (eg. 6=TCP, 17=UDP) to which the software should deliver the datagram. A complete list of the values can be found in RFC 1060.

Header Checksum: This checksum is only calculated on the IP header and not on the data field. Since the checksum process cannot actually include the checksum itself, this field is assumed to be zero.

Source IP address: The 32-bit IP address of the sending host.

Destination IP address: The 32-bit IP address of the host for which this datagram is intended.

Options: The options field is itself optional! The options available include Kerberos Security, Loose Source Routing, Strict Source Routing, and Record Route. Hosts don't have to put anything in this field, which would make the IP header length only 20 bytes, but they do have to be capable of processing Options fields in order to correctly estimate the start of the data field.

Padding: Since the length of the IP Options field is variable, padding bytes (containing zeros) are inserted up to the next 32-bit boundary. Thus, an IP datagram which includes Options will always have a header that is at least 24 bytes long.

3.4.2   Serial Lines

IP packets must be encapsulated to be sent over serial lines. At this time there are four likely encapsulation formats, depending on the nature of the connection:

- A vendor-proprietary router-to-router connection.

- Serial Line IP (SLIP) over an async line.

- The Point to Point Protocol (PPP) over a synchronous line.

- Frame Relay encapsulation.

The easiest way to keep these methods clear in your mind is to ask yourself what we are trying to connect together:

- If we're trying to connect two routers together, then we can use Vendor Proprietary, PPP, or Frame Relay.

- If we are connecting two *different* vendors' routers together, we must use either PPP or Frame Relay. We don't need to use a Frame Relay network in order to benefit from the protocol.

- If we want to connect an host to another host over a dial-up link we would normally use SLIP, but asynchronous PPP is becoming .more popular.

- If we want to connect an host to a router over a dial-up link, we would again normally use SLIP, but asynchronous PPP is gaining popularity here too.

- If we want to connect an host to a router or another host over a *synchronous* leased line or ISDN, we have to use PPP. Note that ISDN may define another encapsulation in the future, but at the time of writing, PPP is the standard choice.

I'll be dealing with WAN connection in detail in Chapter 6.

3.5   Address Resolution Protocol (ARP)

In Chapter 1 I introduced the concept of addressing. On a LAN, all stations share the communication channel and decide if a specific message is intended for them using *MAC addresses*. MAC addresses do not have any direct relationship to IP addresses . In other words if I know a host's IP address I cannot mathematically calculate its MAC address[1]. The problem is that to communicate with another IP host, we normally know the IP address (or can derive it from a name) and so we need to determine the MAC address. To allow us to do this, IP implementations normally include the *Address Resolution Protocol* (ARP).

ARP allows an end station on a LAN segment to find the MAC address of any other active host on the same LAN segment, assuming the IP address of the desired host is known.

ARP works in a very simple way and involves a 2-stage exchange of information: the *ARP request* and the *ARP response*. The sequence of the exchange between two hosts called the SENDER and RECEIVER is as follows:

- The SENDER knows the IP address of the RECEIVER. To determine the RECEIVER's MAC address the SENDER transmits an ARP request.

- The RECEIVER receives the ARP request, recognizes its own IP address within the request and sends an ARP response.

This is really all there is to an ARP request. However, I illustrate an ARP transaction in detail between hosts Porgy and Bess below.

When a host has completed a successful ARP transaction, it stores the results in a table of IP addresses and MAC addresses called the *ARP cache*. The next time that the station needs to send a message, it doesn't need to send out an ARP request, it can simply consult its ARP cache. Line 9 of the IP Transmission Algorithm shows this lookup process.

3.5.1   Aging the ARP Cache

ARP allows hosts to learn about IP and MAC address relationships. Once a hosts has learned about a particular relationship, does it ever need to "forget" it? How about in the situation where a LAN interface fails in a particular host. The interface is replaced with a new one, which of course has a different MAC address from the old one. All the of the other hosts on this LAN who have cache entries for the failed interface now have incorrect information. This problem is solved using an aging procedure. Every few minutes (in the case of OS/2 LAN Manager every 5 minutes, for example), the ARP cache is processed and the age of each entry is decremented by 5 minutes. In Table 3.3 I show the state of a typical ARP cache.

---

[1]The only exceptions I'm aware of to this statement are the ProNET LANs (10Mbps and 80Mbps proprietary Token Rings) that use an 8-bit MAC address. In this case, the lowest 8 bits of the IP address become the MAC address.

Table 3.3:   Intermediate State of ARP Cache

	Dest.IP Address	Dest.MAC Address	Timestamp	SR RIF
1			5	
2			Static	
3			0	
4			15	

Whenever an ARP cache entry is used, its timestamp is returned to the default starting value, e.g. 15 minutes. If an entry's timestamp reaches zero, it can be removed from the cache, forcing the host to send a new ARP request. Since it will take longer than 15 minutes for a user to discover they have a defective LAN interface and have it replaced, the issue of changing MAC addresses is solved. To stay with the example of LAN Manager, a cache entry is only removed if the cache is at full capacity and this can lead to some unexpected results if interfaces are replaced.

Table 3.3 is an ARP cache for a Token Ring host, since the final column contains Source Routing information, the RIF (Routing Information Field) for this destination. Note that entry 3 may be removed on the next update of the table. However, entry 4 has just been used by this host and its timestamp is set to 15 minutes, the default for this host. Entry 2 is a static entry.

> RFP Question: ARP implementations vary dramatically, especially in aging strategies. In a mission-critical network, a good understanding of the ARP implementation will <u>always</u> pay off during diagnostic work. This information should be provided by host and router vendors and by the vendors of any other devices that need to use ARP (e.g. , Terminal Servers, Gateways).

ARP caches allow "static" entries (i.e. entries that are manually inserted) that are not aged. This type of entry is useful to cut down on the amount of ARP traffic on the LAN. Another way to achieve this that requires much less effort is to increase the default value to hours or even days before an ARP entry is removed. This should only be done if you're sure that interfaces don't fail very often.

3.6   Internet Control and Messaging Protocol (ICMP)

If something goes wrong with IP or ARP, we need to signal the error. This is where the Internet Control and Messaging Protocol (ICMP) comes in.

ICMP, defined in RFC 792, must be included in every IP implementation. Originally ICMP was intended as an error-reporting protocol to inform end systems that a particular router, host or network couldn't be located. Over the past few years, however, ICMP has expanded to offer a range of other useful services to IP hosts and routers. I can summarize the most popular ICMP capabilities as follows:

- To inform hosts and routers that a given host or network is unreachable (HOST UNREACHABLE, NETWORK UNREACHABLE).

- In the PING utility to test routes across the network (ECHO REQUEST, ECHO REPLY).

- To request flow control from the sending host (SOURCE QUENCH).

- To tell a host that a better route exists (REDIRECT).

- To tell a host what the subnet mask is for this network segment (ADDRESS MASK REQUEST).

- To allow hosts and routers to discover each other dynamically (ROUTER DISCOVERY).

I don't have space for a comprehensive set of examples of ICMP, but other authors [1, 2, 3] do give a good selection. The examples I've chosen focus on two aspects of ICMP usage. First, how to interpret ICMP messages in a diagnostic scenario. Second, the implications of new forms of TCP/IP (such as IPAE, CIDR and IPv6) on the ICMP paradigm. I'll be using Figure 3.15 as the setting for these examples.

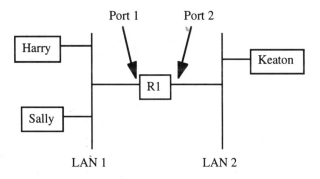

Figure 3.15: An ICMP Test Bed

A couple of reminders about this diagram: first, each of the hosts (Harry, Sally, and Keaton) have unique IP addresses. Second, each of Router R1's interfaces has a unique IP address. Third, each LAN segment's address must be part of a different IP Network ID.

An example addressing structure that fits these requirements would be:

Host	IP Address
Harry	192.32.44.5
Sally	192.32.44.6
R1, Port 1	192.32.44.10
R1, Port 2	201.88.17.10
Keaton	201.88.17.4

Example 1

In Figure 3.15, let's assume that the LAN cable into R1, Port 2 has fallen out, or the Ethernet port is down for some other reason. Within the Routing Table, the route entry for this port will be marked as down.

If Harry sends an IP datagram to Keaton, the router will see that the required destination can be reached out of Port 2, but Port 2 is down. Without an error protocol, the router would drop the packet, and say nothing to Harry. Harry's application software would timeout on the packet and retransmit several times before some error message is passed on to the human operator. This message might be the equivalent of the DOS "Abort, Retry, Ignore?" message and the user might decide to keep trying. The outcome is additional useless traffic load on the network. In pure LAN environments this may be no big deal, but WAN connections can soon be overloaded by this type of traffic.

ICMP is particularly useful in this case because as soon as the router realizes that Port 2 is down, it can send a message back to Harry. The ICMP message is known as a "NETWORK UNREACHABLE."

If Harry's message had to traverse several networks before it reached R1, the ICMP message will always be passed back along the line to the originating host.

Example 2

Let's now imagine a different fault with the Test Bed. Harry sends the same datagram to Keaton. The datagram is getting through the router OK, but this time something is wrong with Keaton so that he can't reply. In this case, we can't say for certain if an ICMP message will be generated for the following reason: if R1 has already sent an ARP to Keaton and resolved the IP/MAC address relationship, then no ICMP message will be generated by the router. This is because IP is a connectionless protocol. As far as the router knows, it has done its job by passing the datagram onto LAN 2. The fact that Keaton isn't able to receive it is irrelevant. In this case, application timeouts are the only way to resolve the problem.

However, if Keaton hasn't yet been attached to LAN 2, or if Keaton hasn't transmitted for some time (so that his entry has been aged out of the ARP cache), then the router *does* have a way to determine of Keaton is alive: the ARP request will timeout. In this case, R1 will generate an ICMP message called a "HOST UNREACHABLE."

Example 3

This time, the test bed's working fine. No faulty cables or dead hosts. However, there is still a place for ICMP. Let's say that Sally is transmitting to Harry. Sally has a super new Pentium machine with a high performance Ethernet adapter while Harry has the old office '286. Sally's machine can transmit a lot faster than Harry can receive. In this situation, Harry's software should be written so that if buffer space falls below a certain threshold, a special type of ICMP packet is sent to Sally. This packet is called "SOURCE QUENCH" and basically means "slow down please."

Example 4

Keaton is also lucky enough to have a Pentium machine. In this example, Keaton transmits at full speed to Harry. A modern router has no problem keeping up with this sort of traffic flow, so poor old Harry's buffers start to fill up again. This time Harry regards the router as the culprit and sends SOURCE QUENCH traffic to Port 1 on R1. *The router will almost certainly ignore this message.*

When internetworking gurus get together and decide to have a few beers, the subject of Flow Control through routers used to be a favorite topic. There are a few arguments in defense of R1's behavior, but let me just give you the simplest and most convincing. R1 is forwarding IP traffic, but it is almost certainly forwarding at least one other protocol stream. This could be IPX, DECNet, or it could be acting as a bridge. All of these protocol streams are competing for the bandwidth on any given exit port. IP happens to have defined a good flow control protocol. Other protocol stacks differ in their flow control implementations. Bridges don't get involved with flow control in any way. So the argument goes that since IP is a connectionless protocol stack, flow control can only be clearly justified on an intranetwork basis. In other words, in a multiprotocol system IP might be well behaved and end up suffering bandwidth starvation because of it.

The leading router vendors have not abandoned the concept of flow control. Instead, they just don't achieve it using ICMP. Wellfleet and Proteon for example, offer a bandwidth reservation system for WAN connections. With this feature, a given percentage of a WAN line's bandwidth can be reserved for a specific protocol type. The protocol can use more than this percentage if there is additional bandwidth available, but it will never get less.

The reachability and flow control messages are the original ICMP functions. However, this useful protocol is growing additional functions all the time. I discuss some of the other uses of ICMP elsewhere in the book.

3.7   Summary

- IP Communication is used by Application PrograMs.   These programs use an API to enable communication.

- Currently the two most popular APIs for an IP internetwork are the NetBIOS interface and the Socket Interface.

- Communication passes between end stations using the Internet Protocol.

- IP is a Network Layer protocol that includes a hierarchical addressing paradigm.

- The basic IP hierarchy starts with the concept that an entire network segment, or broadcast domain can be addresses using the Network ID. Individual end stations in the broadcast domain are uniquely addressed using the Host ID.

- Three IP address classes were defined: Class A, B, and C. These differ in the relative sizes of Network ID and Host ID.

- All IP addresses are 32 bits long, regardless of class.

- An additional level of addressing hierarchy can be applied by allocating some portion of the Host ID to be interpreted as a Subnet ID.

- The size of the Subnet ID field is indicated in the Hosts and Routers using a binary mask, the Subnet Mask.

- IP addresses were intended to be allocated uniquely across the world. The Network Information Center has this responsibility.

- IP internetworks can be built using privately allocated addresses, but address duplication may occur when these internetworks are connected.

- IP is designed to be a media-independent addressing scheme. Standards exist that define how the IP packet structure is represented on Ethernet, Token Ring, FDDI, Serial Lines, X.25 and a range of other transport networks.

- Individual transport networks have their own MAC Layer addressing. This addressing generally bears no mathematical relationship to IP and so an Address Resolution Protocol is used to translate from a known IP address to an unknown MAC address.

- IP also defines a messaging protocol, ICMP to allow status and errors to be signaled across the network. ICMP has been extended in scope to include such functions as Router Discovery.

3.8 References

[1] Douglas E. Comer. *Internetworking with TCP/IP.* (Prentice Hall, NJ 1991).

[2] Feit, Sidnie. *TCP/IP; Architecture, Protocols and Implementation.* (McGraw-Hill 1993).

[3] Washburn, K. Evans, J.T. *TCP/IP; Running a Successful Network.* (Addison-Wesley 1993).

[4] J. Postel. "Internet Protocol." *RFC 791.* September 1981.

[5] P. Tsuchiya. "On the Assignment of Subnet Numbers." *RFC 1219.* April 1991.

[6] J. Mogul. J. Postel. "Internet Standard Subnetting Procedure." *RFC 950.* August 1985.

[7] J. Moy, "OSPF Version 2", *RFC 1583.* March 1994.

[8] S. Deering, "Host extensions for IP multicasting." *RFC 1112.* August 1989.

[9] Dickie, M. *Routing in Today's Internetworks* (Van Nostrand Reinhold, 1994).

[10] Reynolds, J. Postel, J. *ASSIGNED NUMBERS.* RFC 1340.

CHAPTER 4

The Mechanics of IP Communication

> *Network Bandwidth is INFINITE, FREE and has ZERO DELAY*
>
> *6th Rule of Application Development*

4.1 Introduction

What is host communication? The simplest way to look at this is to imagine we're sitting at a terminal and we type the name of a communication application, for example:

telnet

Telnet will allow us to connect as a terminal to some multi-user host. The problem is that we haven't told telnet *where* we want to connect. Let's say we need to enter some payroll information, so we might have set up something like this:

telnet payroll

The "payroll" parameter is some kind of name that will mean something to telnet. In Chapter 13 I describe how naming system can be designed for our internetwork, but their actual function is simple. All hosts on an IP network are addressed by the *numerical* IP addresses I described in the previous chapter. Names are first converted to IP addresses by a lookup procedure. So the actual telnet command will somewhere be converted to:

telnet 192.32.60.1

IP addresses don't actually mean too much to LAN adapters. As I'll describe in Chapter 5, LANs normally work on a 48-bit MAC address that's assigned by the manufacturer when the interface is made. The numerical IP address has to be related to a MAC address at some stage so that we can deliver the packet to the correct host.

In this chapter I look at how this process occurs and how it varies with the nature of connecting devices between the source and destination IP hosts.

4.2   An IP Transmission Algorithm

When we design an internetwork, the issues involved are essentially scaled up from individual end station communication. The way that this communication works will vary. A highly simplified IP *Transmission Algorithm* is shown below.

The IP Datagram Transmission Algorithm

```
1:      w = my_IPaddress
2:      W = my_MACaddress
3:      x = destination_IPaddress
4:      X = destination_MACaddress
5:      y = my_subnet_mask
6:      z = my_default_router_IPaddress
7:      Z = my_default_router_MACaddress
8:      IF (w AND y) = (x AND y) THEN
9:      LOOKUP_MAC(x)
10:     IF found THEN
11:       SEND_PACKET(X, x)
12:     ELSE
13:       SEND_ARP (x)
14:       SEND_PACKET(X, x)
15:     END IF
16: ELSE
17:     LOOKUP_MAC(z)
18:     IF found THEN
19:       SEND_PACKET(Z,x)
20:     ELSE
21:       SEND_ARP (z)
22:       SEND_PACKET(Z, x)
23:     END IF
24: END IF
```

I'll be using this algorithm to describe how IP hosts communicate in the following environments:

- On the same cable
- On the same cable, but separated by a REPEATER
- Separated by a bridge
- Separated by a router

4.3 IP Communication over a Piece of Cable

When Porgy and Bess are first installed, they are actually a couple of PCs used in a single small office. The workgroup is small and it is connected on the same Thick Ethernet segment using traditional cable taps. I have drawn out this configuration in Figure 4.1.

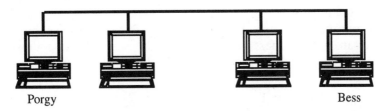

Porgy   Bess

Figure 4.1: IP Host Systems on the Same Ethernet

To describe what happens here, I need to assign some addresses to the hosts.

Table 4.1: Example MAC and IP Addresses

Host Name	Ethernet MAC Address	IP Address
Porgy	AA2233445566	212.144.17.5
Bess	CC6655443322	212.144.17.189

Look at the IP addresses I have chosen. The part of the address I have underlined, 212.144.17, is identical in both cases. As I described earlier, the address format is Class C and so the first three bytes of the address represent the Network ID. I know I'm repeating myself here, but this is a vital point: if two or more stations are on the same LAN and you would like them to be able to communicate directly, they must have the same Network ID. If the Network IDs were different, these stations would assume that they are on different networks. In the Transmission Algorithm, take a look at line 8. This line of code allows the host to decide if an ARP broadcast can reach the destination network.

Let's assume we are sitting at Porgy and we want to transfer a file to Bess. What do we know about Bess? To make things a little bit easier, let's assume that we already know that the IP address of Bess is 212.144.17.189. The software running in Porgy also knows that his own IP address is 212.144.17.5. The subnet mask for the network is the default value for a Class C address: 255.255.255.0. Having performed the appropriate AND, Porgy knows that he is on the same LAN as Bess.

Earlier I mentioned that Ethernet LAN adapters have no idea about IP addresses and must use 48-bit MAC addresses in order to exchange frames. To find out Bess's MAC address, Porgy will send out an ARP request. The ARP request contains the following information:

> *"THIS MESSAGE IS BROADCASTED. I am an ARP request. I am looking for a station with IP address 212.144.17.189. I was sent by a station with IP address 212.144.17.5 and a MAC address of AA2233445566."*

Because an ARP request is a broadcast, all the stations <u>on the same LAN segment</u> receive the packet. Stations that are running TCP/IP can recognize that the broadcast is an ARP request and will check to see if their address is being requested. Stations which are not running TCP/IP will ignore the ARP request, BUT their CPUs will have been interrupted by the broadcast nevertheless.

When Bess receives the ARP request, it recognizes its own IP address and that Porgy is requesting its MAC address. Bess now sends an *ARP response*. ARP responses do not need to be broadcasted because Bess knows the MAC address of Porgy and can send the ARP response directly. The ARP response would contain this information:

> *"THIS FRAME IS ADDRESSED TO CC6655443322. I am an ARP response. My IP address is 212.144.17.189. My MAC address is CC6655443322."*

This is a complete ARP transaction. Porgy and Bess can now associate an IP address with a specific MAC address. Both End Stations store the list of IP addresses and MAC addresses they have learned through ARP. The storage area is called an *ARP Cache*. When the two stations need to communicate at a later stage, they do not need to send ARPs. Instead they simply consult the ARP Cache. In the Transmission Algorithm, this can be seen in the "IF" clause beginning at line 9. Each time an host uses an existing ARP Cache entry, it refreshes a timer for this entry. If ARP Cache entries become "too old," they are removed from the table. This process is known as *aging out*, or simply *aging*. I haven't shown this directly in the Transmission Algorithm, but you can imagine the refresh function being a part of the "LOOKUP" routine.

Once the workstations have established the Address Resolution, then the file transfer can begin. The file is broken down into message blocks which are small enough to be transmitted over the LAN. In the case of Ethernet, this limit is 1500 bytes. Each message block will be inserted into a LAN frame for transmission.

In the case of traffic from Porgy to Bess, the LAN frame will look something like this:

Figure 4.2: Example Frame, Porgy to Bess

There are a couple of things to notice about this frame:

- The frame is directly addressed to Bess at the MAC Layer. No other devices (such as routers or bridges) need to be involved in this information transfer.

- As a dirty trick designed to confuse the beginners in the LAN business, MAC layer addresses appear in the order DESTINATION-SOURCE. In contrast, IP addresses appear in the order SOURCE-DESTINATION. Get used to it, it won't be the last time.

Assuming that Bess is switched on, running IP software and the cable connection is OK, the message will get through. Bess will reply to Porgy with frames that look like this:

Figure 4.3: Example Acknowledgment Frame

4.3.1   The File Transfer Process

The exchange of IP packets over the LAN may be more complex than I have described. A primary requirement, for example, is that these packets reach Bess without being corrupted. Real file transfer programs (not just IP-based programs) use different procedures for data transfer, but the overall effect is that a stream of packets containing the file, or small parts of the file, are moved between the hosts and some form of acknowledgment packet is sent back.

As our little LAN grows, it may have to be laid over a longer distance. Using the configuration guidelines provided by the manufacturer, we may find that we need to install *Repeaters* to amplify the signal strength and to ensure reliable reception by all of the hosts on the LAN. Different LAN technologies use different distance guidelines for their operation, but one of the most common distances is the "magic" 100m limit for operation over Unshielded Twisted Pair (UTP) cable. The story goes that AT&T, with its vast experience of telephone structured cabling, calculated that almost all of its telephones were within 100m of a wiring closet. When the 10BASET standards were developed, this figure was used as a goal for the component developers. Some UTP Ethernet vendors claim much longer distances from the closet, partly due to the improved UTP cables which are now available.

4.4   IP Communication over a Repeater or Cabling Hub

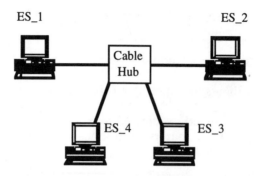

Figure 4.4: Communication through a Cable Hub

For Token Ring and FDDI, there are currently no standards for UTP operation, but there are plenty of products operating de facto encoding schemes and standards are in process.

Sooner or later, as LANs grow in size, we will need to install repeaters. What is the effect on the communication mechanism I described above?

4.4.1   Repeater Operation

When communication signals pass down a cable, they become gradually weaker the further they travel. This effect is called *attenuation*. As the attenuation of a signal gets worse, it becomes more and more difficult for end stations to *reliably* receive the signal. If cables are too long, the number of errors on the LAN will become unacceptable. These problems can be a direct result of poor cable design when the LAN is installed. As LANs grow, cable design rules may be broken for any number of reasons. For LANs with low traffic levels, users may not actually notice the effects of excessive cable attenuation. In higher demand environments, the result of excess attenuation is that the response time from the network will become longer, although the LAN may still operate.

For 10BASE2 systems, the longest *unrepeated* cable length is defined as 185m. For 10BASET systems, it is 100m. Fiber optic based Ethernet systems can have unrepeated cable lengths up to 2 000m.

To help users extend their LANs over longer distances, a device called a *repeater* is used. This is simply a signal amplifier, it extends the distance that a signal can be passed over an individual cable.

What will happen to the communication scenario I have just described if we install a repeater between the source and destination hosts? Well, in simple terms, nothing. A repeater is installed in a cable connection when the transmission signal needs to be amplified. Repeaters have no effect on the MAC or IP addressing of workstations.

4.4.2   Cable Hub Operation

A Cabling Hub is a specialized form of Repeater, which allows a network signal to be repeated out of many ports attached to the same hub. Hubs are essentially cable management devices and may offer very sophisticated configuration, management and diagnostic features. Figure 4.4 shows a simple Cable Hub. Each connection to an individual End Station is actively repeated. In fact, early "hub-like" products were nothing more than multiport repeaters. For that reason, the IP communication scenario I described above operates in exactly the same way for a Cable Hub. All of the End Stations shown in Figure 4.4 are on the same physical Ethernet, Token Ring or FDDI segment.

What's The Difference?

...between a Repeater and a Cabling Hub? Well nothing really, especially in terms of IP communication. Both devices are totally transparent to the host systems. Hubs were a development of multi-port repeaters that seemed such a great idea that they became products in their own right. Today cabling hubs contain many value added features that make them much more functional and expensive than repeaters. Hubs may contain or routing modules and in these cases you have to identify the LAN segments that are bridged or routed and treat the hub as the appropriate connection device. For management purposes, hubs may also be hosts because you can Telnet into them, or they can run SNMP management processes. To some, hubs also seem to be a good location to install server or gateway functions.

4.5   IP Communication over a Local Bridge

If the LAN keeps growing, we may need to install a bridge. Unfortunately, bridging technology varies dramatically between Ethernet, Token Ring, and FDDI. For the purposes of this description, I will concentrate on Ethernet Transparent Bridging.

For Ethernet, bridges are useful for two main reasons. First, if we keep on adding repeaters, we also add delay (the active circuits of the repeater cause a delay on the signal. If there is too much delay in the network, the rules say that we must use a "store and forward" device to cancel out the delay. This can be achieved by using a bridge, or a router.

Second, as bridges became more sophisticated, new capabilities were added. In particular, the concept of the "Learning Bridge" was introduced. A Learning Bridge acts as a traffic separator. Each Ethernet segment which lies between two bridges has its own 10Mbps of bandwidth. The bridge keeps purely local traffic from "leaking" onto other LAN segments.

How do our workstations communicate when the Connecting Device is a Bridge? In simple terms, they operate in exactly the same way that they do for a cable, repeater or hub. In other words Porgy and Bess can again use the same addresses that I described in Table 4.1.

So, Porgy and Bess have identical network numbers in their IP addresses and communicate directly using the ARP protocol to resolve end station MAC addresses.

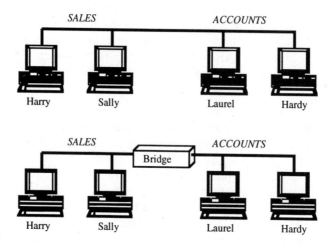

Figure 4.5:   Workgroup LAN and Bridge Positioning

In the upper part of Figure 4.5 I show two separate workgroups. Porgy and Bess are in the "Sales" workgroup. Laurel and Hardy are in the "Accounts" workgroup. As you would expect, most of the traffic on the Ethernet is addressed between workstations in the same workgroup, or from workgroup hosts to their local file server. For example, if the Ethernet frame shown in Figure 4.2 is transmitted by Porgy, it would be nice if we could prevent it from using up bandwidth on the Accounts workgroup Ethernet. One possible way to do this is with a bridge.

The bridge shown in the lower part of Figure 4.5 does not need to have its own MAC address (or IP address). Instead it operates in *promiscuous mode*. This means that the Ethernet interfaces on each side of the bridge will receive all of the traffic that is transmitted on each of their Ethernet segments, regardless of the MAC destination addresses on these frames. Promiscuous mode allows the bridge to monitor the <u>source</u> MAC address on each frame it receives. The bridge begins to build a table of addresses like this:

Sales Workgroup Segment (Port 0)	Accounts Workgroup Segment (Port 1)
AA2233445566 (Porgy)	3FEACBA98765 (Laurel)
CC6655443322 (Bess)	ACBA98765432 (Hardy)

Note that the Bridge doesn't actually know that there is an "Accounts" or "Sales" workgroup. I have just used these terms for clarity in the table. The Bridge does know, for example that an End Station with MAC address AA2233445566 is located on the LAN segment which is connected to the Bridge's Port 0. In contrast, the End Station with MAC address 3FEACBA98765 is attached to the LAN segment which is connected to the Bridge's Port 1.

If the bridge has built the table, it can decide that traffic from AA2233445566 to CC6655443322 does not need to be copied onto the Accounts workgroup segment. However, traffic from CC6655443322 to ACBA98765432 *does* need to be copied onto the Accounts workgroup segment.

There are two additional rules for bridges. First, if the table is incomplete and an unknown address is received, then the bridge must copy the frame to the other segment. Second, if a broadcast frame is sent (such as an ARP), the frame must be copied onto the other segment.

This second rule means that we can treat bridges as though they were just extensions of an Ethernet cable. Communication will occur in the same way as for repeaters and pieces of cable. However, bridges may solve some of the distance limitations imposed by Ethernet and may help with traffic congestion by separating workgroup traffic.

4.6   IP Communication through a Router

Bridges are useful devices for the short-term extension of LANs, but most people in the industry and users communities do not really regard them as true internetworking devices. The main reason for this is that a bridged internetwork cannot be scaled indefinitely. The exact reasons for this will become clear as you discover more about the demands of internetworking. In addition, I cover some of the basic reasons in Chapter 15 when I discuss ways to maintain internetwork performance and protect network bandwidth.

In Figure 4.6, I show Device X as a router. The rules for IP addressing state that the two network segments must have unique *network* or *subnetwork* numbers. So, in this case our address list looks like this:

Station Name	Ethernet MAC Address	IP Address
Porgy	AA2233445566	212.144.17.5
Router_A	DD9988776655	212.144.17.201
Router_B	EE8877665544	212.144.18.201
Hardy	CC6655443322	212.144.18.189

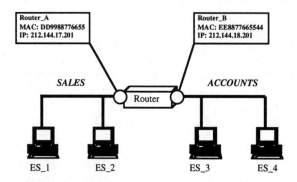

Figure 4.6: IP Communication through a Router

The MAC and IP address formats follow the guidelines I gave in Chapter 3.

If we want to transfer a file from Porgy to Hardy, the software in Porgy is able to determine that Hardy is on another network segment (using line 8 of the Transmission Algorithm). In this case Porgy's own network number is 212.144.17 and Hardy's network number is 212.144.18. This type of traffic is called *internetwork* traffic (because it passes *between* networks).

Having decided that Hardy is on another network segment, Porgy needs another piece of information, the IP address of the *Default Router* for Porgy's local network segment. In the Transmission Algorithm, I show this as being assigned a value in Line 6. In an actual host, these values will be set up using the installation utilities provided with the IP software. Where IP is a native part of the operating system, such as UNIX, well known utilities are provided to set and examine these values. Typically in a BSD-derived UNIX, the two appropriate utilities are known as *ifconfig* and *ipconfig*.

Let's now look at a file transfer operation between Porgy and Hardy.

4.6.1   File Transfer Through a Router

This process occurs in several stages.

Stage 1

The human operator of Porgy types in the instructions for the file transfer. The instruction includes the IP address of Hardy, in this case 212.144.18.201.

Stage 2

As we can see in Line 8 of the Transmission Algorithm, the TCP/IP software in Porgy compares the IP network numbers of Hardy with its own network number. The numbers are different and so Porgy decides that it must send this frame to its default router. The *IP address* of the default router has already been configured manually in ES-1, it is in fact 212.144.17.201.

Stage 3

Porgy looks in its ARP cache to see if the MAC address for 212.144.17.201 (the default router) is already known. In this example, let's assume that it does not already know this address.

Stage 4

Porgy sends out an ARP request for the default router (212.144.17.201), in exactly the same way that it would do for any other host on its own LAN segment. The frame looks like this:

Figure 4.7:   ARP Request from Porgy

Stage 5

The default router answers the ARP request.

Figure 4.8:   ARP Response from Router_A

Stage 6

Porgy can now send the first block of the file transfer. The frame looks like this:

| Router_A MAC
DD9988776655 | Porgy MAC
AA2233445566 | Type=IP
0800 | Porgy IP
212.144.17.5 | Hardy IP
212.144.18.189 | File Transfer
Message Block | CRC
(Check) |

Figure 4.9: First file transfer block from Porgy.

Notice that the MAC destination address on this frame is the default router address, but the IP destination is Hardy.

Stage 7

The router receives the frame. It strips off the Ethernet framing and examines the source and destination IP addresses. It decides that it knows where the final IP destination is and reconstructs another frame for transmission out of the Router_B port. This port is connected to the same LAN segment on which the final destination of the packet is located (the router can tell this by comparing the network number of the destination IP address with the network number on its own output port.

Stage 8

The router examines its own ARP cache for the output port to see if there is an entry for the IP address 212.144.18.189. Assuming this is the first time Router_B has had to transmit to Harry, it must first send out an ARP Request:

| Broadcast MAC
FFFFFFFFFFFF | Router_B MAC
DD9988776655 | Type=ARP
0806 | Router_B IP
212.144.18.201 | Hardy IP
212.144.18.189 | ARP Request
Message Block | CRC
(Check) |

Figure 4.10: Communication from Default Router to ES_4

Stage 9

Hardy sends an ARP response to the Router_B:

| Router_B MAC
DD9988776655 | Hardy MAC
CC6655443322 | Type=ARP
0806 | Hardy IP
212.144.18.189 | Router_B IP
212.144.18.201 | ARP Response
Message Block | CRC
(Check) |

Figure 4.11: Hardy's ARP Response

Now the router has the IP and MAC addresses of both hosts and can deliver the IP traffic from Porgy:

| Hardy MAC
CC6655443322 | Router_B MAC
DD9988776655 | Type=IP
0800 | Router_B IP
212.144.18.201 | Hardy IP
212.144.18.189 | File Transfer
Message Block | CRC
(Check) |

Figure 4.12: File Transfer frame from Router_B to Hardy

Traffic which passes back from ES_4 to Porgy via the router will follow the reverse route. Here are the frames:

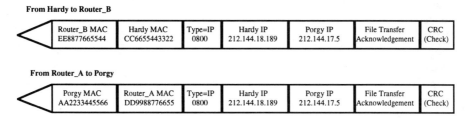

Figure 4.13: Acknowledgment from Hardy to Porgy

4.6.2   Reverse ARP (RARP)

ARP is a useful and mature protocol, but it is designed to find the MAC address for a specified IP address. What happens if you know the MAC address and need to find the IP address? Well, first of all, let's think how that might happen. Imagine a diskless workstation. This device has no means of storing any kind of configuration information; it doesn't have an operating system and it doesn't have a disk to store anything. All it has is a bootstrap ROM and a burned in MAC address on its LAN interface. The bootstrap ROM will probably contain the code for a protocol called BOOTP, that I describe in Chapter 13. However, you can think of BOOTP as a boot file transfer protocol if you like. Since BOOTP is designed to work over internetworks, the diskless workstation needs to obtain an IP address before it can use BOOTP. For this, it will use *Reverse ARP* (RARP). Unlike ARP, where we broadcast a request for a particular IP address, RARP requires a *RARP server* to be configured on the same LAN segment as the discless workstation. The RARP server contains a centralized ARP cache of IP addresses against MAC addresses that has been entered manually by the Network Administrator. When the discless workstation sends out a RARP request it has the format:

> *"THIS MESSAGE IS BROADCASTED. I am a RARP request. I am looking for my IP address. I was sent by a station with a MAC address of AA2233445566."*

4.6.3   Proxy ARP

Proxy ARP is also known as *ARP Subnet Routing*, *Promiscuous ARP* and *The ARP Hack*. I described the use of subnets earlier in the chapter, that both hosts and routers must agree on the size of the subnet mask, or things will go horribly wrong. Since subnetting was an additional feature of IP, some of the early implementations did not include subnet support. In Figure 2.7, the network has been subnetted with an 8-bit mask and is logically divided into subnets 254, 253, and 252. Let's assume that the hosts are not aware of subnetting and they don't realize that they are located on logically separate subnets. A host with IP address

128.7.254.17 wanting to send a message to 128.7.253.1 will apply a mask of 255.255.0.0 in Line 8 of the Transmission Algorithm and will come to the decision that it is on the same LAN segment as its desired destination host. This would be true if the two hosts were connected by repeaters, the same cable hub or even a bridge. However, their respective LAN segments are actually connected by a router, as shown. Routers are "forbidden" to copy ARP broadcasts onto other segments and so the two hosts in Figure 4.14 will never find each other.

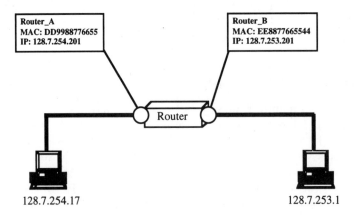

Figure 4.14:   Proxy ARP Application

If routers support Proxy ARP, they will respond to the ARPing host as though they were the final destination host. Note that the ARP request is not forwarded by a Proxy ARP router. To control the way that ARP responses are sent by the router, Proxy ARP defines a set of conditions which must *all* be satisfied. These conditions are:

- Proxy ARP is switched on for the receiving interface.

- The router knows the location of the destination Network ID or Subnetwork ID. Note that the router does not need to know the MAC address of the requested host (i.e., it doesn't need to have the destination MAC address stored in its ARP cache). This feature allows Proxy ARP to operate successfully over a multi-hop router network, but prevents the router responding to requests for Martian Hosts.

- The direction of the destination Subnet ID must not be the same as the physical interface on which the ARP request was originally received. This rule avoids the router responding to ARP requests that would have been answered by a "legitimate" host.

Originally Proxy ARP was used to support the older, "subnet-ignorant" IP implementations. Modern IP implementations are fully aware of subnetting and don't need Proxy ARP's help. However, there are two important applications for

Proxy ARP even in a modern network. First, Proxy ARP can be used to assist in migrating a bridged network over to full routing. In essence, the feature buys the Network Administrator some time to modify host configurations to suit the subnetting scheme. Second and more important, Proxy ARP can be used to implement traffic load balancing across multiple routers, or to provide a resilient routing scheme. Both of these techniques are discussed with examples in Chapters 15 and 16.

4.7 IP Tunneling

In this chapter I've described how two or more IP devices can exchange information over a network such as Ethernet or FDDI. Because LANs don't directly use IP as their addressing scheme, an additional protocol, ARP, is used to dynamically resolve addresses.

It isn't possible to use ARP with all multi-access network technologies. Some of these, such as X.25, Frame Relay, or ATM, don't support the vital first step in an ARP transaction: the broadcast. For these systems, a variety of encapsulation techniques are used to transport LAN frames over the WAN. Since each of these techniques is optimized and specialized to the specific WAN technology, we need a way to describe the transport technique. Within the industry, *tunneling* has become the accepted term.

In Table 4.2, I show the major address formats for the most popular WAN services you are likely to encounter.

Table 4.2: WAN Address Formats

WAN Technology	Address Format
X.25 (1980)	X.121 DTE Address, 15 decimal digits
X.25 (1984, 1988)	ISO NSAP
Frame Relay	10-bit DLSI for PVC Service
SMDS	E.164 address, 15 decimal digits
ATM	E.164 or ISO NSAP
ISDN	E.164

X.25, ISDN and ATM are totally connection-oriented services. This means that no logical communication channel exists until a call has been placed. Frame

Relay is currently a Permanent Virtual Circuit (PVC) service, which means that multiple permanent connections exist between any two subscribers on the WAN. SMDS was actually designed for LAN interconnection and contains a multicast and broadcast emulation capabilities. Let me present you with the three "magic questions" for any tunneling device:

- How do we associate a destination IP address with an appropriate WAN address?

- How do we open, monitor and tear down the WAN connection?

- How do we encapsulate the LAN traffic for transport over the WAN?

Address Resolution over Tunnels

I'm ashamed to say that most address resolution over tunneling systems is done using static tables. Using X.25 as an example, let's take a look at the WAN in Figure 4.15.

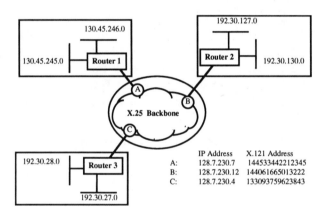

Figure 4.15:   An IP over X.25 Addressing Scheme

For this example, imagine the world from the point of view of Router 1. This box has two directly attached Ethernet LANs and an X.25 connection to several other sites.

Let's imagine that a device on a network that is directly attached to Router 1 wants to talk to a device on LAN 192.30.130.0. The device will use the same IP Transmission Algorithm that I outlined earlier; in other words, the transmitting host has absolutely no idea that it is communicating over a WAN rather than a LAN.

The host decides that it's on a different network than its destination and so sends the packet to the default router (in this case, Router 1). Router 1 has a conventional Routing Table in which we see that to get to network 192.30.130.0, the Next Hop is address 128.7.230.12. This is the IP address assigned to the X.25 connection in Router 2. Since the network 128.7.230.0 is *directly attached*, Router 1 would *normally* ARP for the MAC address of the next hop router. In this case, the next hop is over an X.25 network, which does not support ARP.

To take the place of ARP, routers use a second table. In this table, which was manually entered into Router 1, the IP address 128.7.230.12 is matched against an X.121 address of 144061665013222.

Router 1 now makes a standard X.25 call and sends the information. When all of the buffered information is sent, Router 1 will hold the connection open for a short period (several tens of seconds) to see of any more information is supposed to go to this network. If the timer expires, then the X.25 call is cleared.

A similar procedure is adopted for ISDN, ATM SVCs and Frame Relay SVCs. Three things change depending on the WAN technology,

- The WAN address format
- The call signaling protocol and facilities
- The encapsulation format for the IP datagram

The Next Hop Resolution Protocol

The concept of static address mapping is fine for small networks, but there are many X.25-connected routers with hundreds of static entries in their mapping tables. These are incredibly difficult and very tedious to maintain. Every time a new device is added, every router that expects to communicate with the device must be updated.

While the problem was confined to X.25 or ISDN, the router community was not too bothered about the situation because these transport technologies are rare in the USA. However, since ATM is a connection-oriented transport system, operating is almost the exact same way as X.25, suddenly we are seeing some action to solve the problem.

There is a draft proposal for an alternative approach to address mapping called the *Next Hop Resolution Protocol* (NHRP). Since this is a draft, I'll just sketch out the basic idea of the protocol.

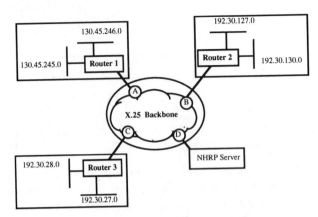

Figure 4.16: NHRP Principle

In Figure 4.16 you can see the same X.25 network as before. The routers on this network have the same addresses and the same issue with finding the next hop. In this case, however, each router is configured as an NHRP client. When Router 1 receives a packet that it must send to address 128.7.230.12, it still knows that this packet must traverse the connection-oriented WAN. Instead of consulting a large table of X.121 addresses, the router look for just one entry: the X.121 address of the NHRP server. Router 1 then makes an X.25 call to the NHRP server and asks what the X.121 address is for the corresponding IP address 128.7.230.12 and the server responds (assuming such a match is found). The address mapping tables that were previously distributed around all of the routers in the network are now centralized at the server. The network administrator still has the job of setting up the server, but when adds and changes are made to the network under NHRP, only the server entry needs to be changed.

It's likely that NHRP will contain some equivalent domain hierarchy and a backup mechanism similar to DNS, but at this time the details are still being discussed.

4.8 Summary

- TCP/IP is a sophisticated communication stack that has been continuously developed over two decades.

- The key to the scaleability of IP internetworks is the use of a hierarchical addressing scheme that allows us to limit the scope of broadcast domains.

- In IP communication, the hosts themselves make the first decision as to whether the conversation is *intra*network (i.e., between two hosts within the same broadcast domain) or *inter*network (i.e., between hosts in different broadcast domains).

- Communication on the same wire, or over a MAC Layer interconnection device, is within the same broadcast domain.

- Communication through a router allows interconnection between broadcast domains.

- Sometime we need to pass IP traffic through a non-IP intermediate network. For this purpose we use a tunneling device. Tunneling is a feature of most modern routers.

4.9 References

[1] D. Plummer.. "Ethernet Address Resolution Protocol: Or converting network protocol addresses to 48-bit Ethernet address for transmission on Ethernet hardware," *RFC 826*. November 1982.

[2] J. Postel. "Internet Protocol," *RFC 791*. September 1981.

[3] R. Braden. "Requirements for Internet hosts - application and support," *RFC 1123*. October 1989.

Section 2

THE NETWORK INFRASTRUCTURE

CHAPTER 5

LAN Technology

> *A man with one watch knows what time it is...a man with two watches is never sure.*
>
> *Segal's Law*

5.1 LAN Overview

LANs are obviously a key component in internetwork design. In this chapter I'd like to concentrate on the specific aspects of LAN technology that will be important in the design process. These are:

- LAN frame formats

- Transmission characteristics

- Address resolution

- Cabling schemes

- Special design features

5.2 LAN Frame Formats

I discussed the concept of LAN frames in Chapter 3, and now I'd like to look in a little more detail at the specific characteristics of the most common LANs.

Frames have a special job to do. For this reason we can imagine a mythical beast called a *generic LAN frame*, and I've tried to draw this beast in Figure 5.1.

Starting Delimiter	Destination Address	Source Address	Protocol Multiplexing	Data	CRC	Ending Delimiter

Figure 5.1: The Generic LAN Frame

The generic LAN frame begins with a *frame delimiter* whose job is to allow the LAN chipset to distinguish the beginning of the frame from idle signals, or mid-frame signals. Some LAN technologies (like Token Ring and FDDI) are able to use special signal patterns for frame delimitation, whereas other technologies use a combination of "silence" followed by "improbable" bit patterns.

Frames must also contain addresses for the destination source stations. These MAC level addresses have only local significance in a router internetwork.

The frame must contain a protocol multiplexing field. I described this field in Chapter 3, as the *Type* or *SNAP* field, and allows receiving hosts or routers to determine the Network Layer protocol being used within the frame.

Next in the frame is the "data" portion. Since frames are Data Link Layer entities, any Network Layer (or higher) protocol is seen as data.

After the data comes some form of error check, followed by an ending delimiter. Let's have a look at LAN frames in detail, assuming that they will be carrying IP traffic.

5.2.1   CSMA/CD LANs

There are two CSMA/CD LANs that are in common use today: Ethernet and IEEE 802.3. Although these LANs are very similar in many ways, their frame structure is very different.

Ethernet

Figure 5.2 shows the format of an Ethernet frame.

The Starting Delimiter for Ethernet is an 8-byte series of alternating binary "1" and binary "0." In the last byte of the sequence, the final two bits are set to binary "1" to indicate that this is the end of the Starting Delimiter. The alternating binary sequence helps the clock circuits of the Ethernet adapter lock onto the signal more effectively, since Ethernet is transmitting its clock as a part of the data stream.

The Destination address is a 48-bit value that is administered as I describe in Chapter 2. Ethernet follows the IEEE 802.1 convention that the first bit transmitted on the wire is the *U/I* (Universal/Individual) bit. If the bit is set, then this frame is either a broadcast or a multicast. If the bit is clear, the frame is a unicast. Since this bit is conventionally thought of as the most significant bit of the address, Ethernet transmits MAC addresses in MSB order.

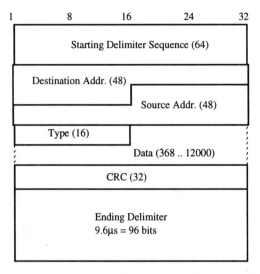

Figure 5.2: Ethernet Version 2 Frame Format

The protocol multiplexing field in Ethernet is known as the *Type* field. It is 16 bits long, and I list some of the common Ethernet type numbers in Table 5.1. For IP, the three most likely numbers that you'll find in this field are 0800h (IP), 0806h (ARP), and 8035h (RARP).

Table 5.1: Examples of EtherType Values

EtherType (hex)	Protocol
0600h	XNS IDP
0800h	DoD IP
0805h	X.25 PLP
0806h	ARP
8035h	RARP
0200h	Xerox PUP
0201h	PUP Address Translation

The data field for Ethernet is up to 1500 bytes long and is followed by a 32-bit CRC. Finally the Ethernet and IEEE 802.3 standards specify a minimum "quiet" period of 9.6μs (the equivalent of 96 bits) before the start of the next frame. This is called the *inter-frame gap*.

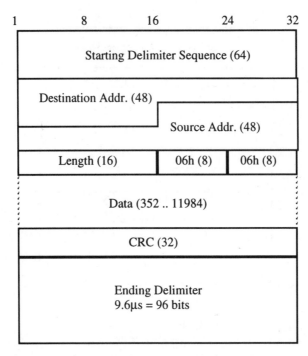

Figure 5.3:   Obsolete LSAP Frame Format for IP

IEEE 802.3

For some reason, the IEEE 802.3 committee decided to fool around with the Ethernet specification. The most important change they made was to change the Type field into the Length field. Right after the Length field would normally be the 802.2 Link Service Access Point (LSAP) field, consisting of the Destination Service Access Point (DSAP) and the Source Service Access Point (SSAP).

Each of these fields is only 8 bits long, so the range of LSAPs available is limited. Initially an LSAP of 06h was reserved for IP with a frame structure like the one shown in Figure 5.3. When it became clear that the size of the LSAP field was just not enough for practical purposes, a new encapsulation scheme was devised: SNAP.

IEEE 802.2 defined a workaround (or "kludge") known as the Sub Network Access Protocol (SNAP). Using SNAP encoding, both LSAPs are set to the value AAh. The next byte is the standard IEEE 802.2 Control field, which in the SNAP encoding scheme is set to the value 03h (actually this indicates a connectionless, "un-numbered information" frame in IEEE 802.2). The next 24 bits are, in theory reserved for the Universal Organization Identifier, which is the 24-bit address block assigned by the IEEE to any LAN interface manufacturer. Since UOI only has local significance, RFC 1042 indicates that these bits should be set to 0 when representing IP traffic. The next 16 bits represent the same Ethernet Type field value that we would have had if 802.3 had never fooled with the standard in the first place.

SNAP

Table 5.2:   Assigned LSAP Values

LSAP Value (hex)	Description
00	Null LSAP
02	LLC Management (Individual)
03	LLC Management (Group)
04	SNA Path Control (Individual)
05	SNA Path Control (Group)
06	DoD IP (obsolete)
42	IEEE 802.1 Spanning Tree
AA	IEEE 802.2 SNAP
E0	Novell Netware
F0	NetBIOS
FE	ISO 8473 CLNP
FF	Global DSAP

Ethernet / 802.3 Interactions

Ethernet and 802.3 can happily co-exist on the same LAN segments, but there must be some way to distinguish between the formats. The 802.3 Length field counts the remainder of the frame, including the CRC. The maximum value for this Length is actually lower than the lowest minimum legal Ethernet Type value (0600h for XNS is 1536 decimal).

The two EtherTypes used by PUP in Table 5.2 are obsolete Types that should never appear on modern LANs. These were the original Type numbers defined by Xerox for Ethernet, and the choice of numbers predates the need to differentiate between Ethernet and 802.3.

A few other quirks arise because of the differences between Ethernet and 802.3. These are often made more serious because Ethernet and 802.3 frame formats can coexist on the same LAN segment. Sometimes I think life for the designer would be a lot easier if coexistence weren't possible!

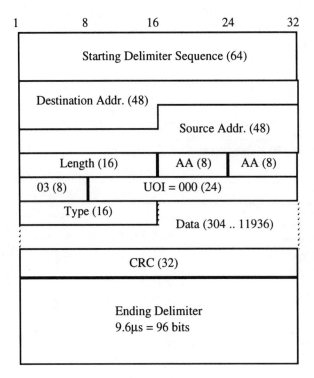

Figure 5.4:   IEEE 802.3 Frame Format

- IP can be represented in either form. In Ethernet format, the appropriate RFC is 894. For IEEE 802.3, it's RFC 1042.

- The two formats can coexist on the same LAN. However, an Ethernet host cannot communicate with an 802.3 host.

- Routers are able to receive both formats. In their ARP cache, a router will store the frame format fro the specific hosts on each directly attached CSMA/CD LAN segment.

- The first time a router needs to ARP for an end station on a CSMA/CD LAN, it doesn't know if that end station is running Ethernet or SNAP. The router can send ARPs in both formats, and the required host will only respond to the format that it recognizes.

- Transparent Bridges should not perform any kind of format conversion.

- Translation Bridges will perform a format conversion since all other LAN technologies apart from Ethernet use the SNAP format. On a CSMA/CD LAN, a Translation Bridge must be configured with a default transmission format, since it cannot learn formats using ARP.

- Using Ethernet format, the data field can be up to 1 500 bytes long, whereas with SNAP the data field is only up to 1 492 bytes long. When IP datagrams are routed from an Ethernet format segment to a SNAP format segment, fragmentation may result. This will reduce performance of the router.

- Translation Bridges should not perform fragmentation.

Where possible, hosts should be configured for the same format throughout the network. Just because routers are capable of format conversion doesn't mean that it's desirable. It seems wise to select SNAP encapsulation since this is used by all other IEEE LAN technologies, and will be used by Fast Ethernet LANs when they emerge.

Multiprotocol Operation on CSMA/CD

Other protocol stacks are fairly evenly split between Ethernet, LSAP, and SNAP encoding. Table 5.3 summarizes the most common forms of protocol encapsulation.

5.2.2   Token Ring

Token Ring uses SNAP format exclusively, so RFC 1042 applies here. The frame format is shown in Figure 5.5. A possible problem in heterogeneous LANs is that the Token Ring data field is much larger than Ethernet. For 4Mbps Token Ring, the data field is up to 4,434 bytes, whereas on 16Mbps Token Ring the figure is 17,938 bytes.

In Chapter 9 I describe the interaction between Source Route Bridges used on Token Ring, and routers. Token Ring is able to send out Explorers that include an MTU negotiation parameter. Used correctly, this can prevent fragmentation.

Unlike Ethernet, Token Ring uses encoding violations within the data stream to signal frame delimiters, so the long preamble and inter-frame gap of CSMA/CD LANs is avoided. In addition, Token Ring has no minimum frame size that is decided by the access technique. Instead, the minimum frame size is decided by the smallest valid protocol data unit.

If small IP packets (e.g. single character Telnet) are passed from Token Ring to Ethernet or 802.3, the packet will be padded to bring it up to the CSMA/CD minimum frame size.

Table 5.3:   Typical Multiprotocol LAN Encapsulations

Protocol Type	Typical CSMA/CD Encapsulation(s)	Other LAN Encapsulations
IP	Ethernet (RFC 894) SNAP (RFC 1042)	SNAP (RFC 1042)
Novell IPX	Novell (Global DSAP) LSAP Ethernet	SNAP
AppleTalk Phase 1	Ethernet	N/A[1]
AppleTalk Phase 2	SNAP	SNAP
Banyan VINES	SNAP	SNAP
XNS	Ethernet	N/A[2]
DECNet IV	Ethernet	SNAP
DECNet V / ISO 8473	LSAP	LSAP
Native NetBIOS	LSAP	LSAP

Note 1:   AppleTalk Phase 1 was only ever defined on LocalTalk and EtherTalk. Other LAN technologies (e.g., Token Ring, FDDI) must use AppleTalk Phase 2.

Note 2:   XNS was only officially defined on Ethernet. Proprietary implementations form 3Com and Ungermann-Bass use SNAP encapsulation for other LAN technologies.

5.2.3   FDDI

FDDI uses basically the same frame format as Token Ring, with SNAP encoding according to RFC 1042. Unlike Token Ring, however, FDDI does not normally make use of a Routing Information Field (RIF) for Source Routing. FDDI frames do carry RIF information when native Source Route Bridging is performed between Token Ring and FDDI. Currently this form of bridging is not the subject of an independent standards document.

5.3   Cabling   Schemes

Cabling is a fundamental requirement in all conventional LAN systems. The topic of cabling is far too detailed for anything more than a brief overview.

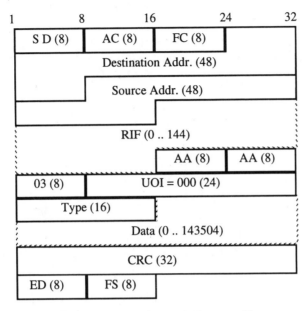

Figure 5.5: IEEE 802.5 Frame Format

5.3.1 IEEE 802.3 10BASE5

The original Ethernet style technology is now more accurately described as IEEE 802.3 10BASE5. The 10BASE5 designation describes a 10Mbps, Baseband LAN with 500m between repeater elements.

10BASE5 uses a thick coaxial cable backbone, usually colored yellow for normal office grade (plenum, or other special grades of cable use different color coding). This is the derivation of the term "yellow cable Ethernet," or "Thick Ethernet."

Figure 5.6 shows the basic layout of this kind of network.

10BASE5 Drawbacks

The 10BASE5 cabling scheme is actually still popular in industrial installations, where the immunity of the cable to external interference can override some of the other difficulties. These can be summarized as:

- Thick coax cable is expensive.

- Thicker cables are always more difficult to install, with larger permitted bend radii than other cable. Thicker cables need larger free space in ducting, which is in short supply in existing installations.

- Drop cables are expensive compared to UTP, and the permitted distance is short.

- External taps are active devices (although they take power from the cable itself). They are expensive and tricky to install and are an additional point of failure. A faulty tap may bring down the whole trunk.

- The 10BASE5 scheme doesn't suit modern structured cabling.

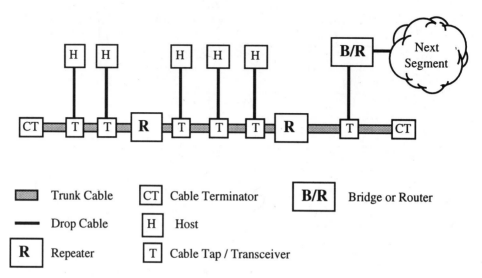

Figure 5.6:   IEEE 802.3 10BASE5 Cabling System

Table 5.4:   10BASE5 Design Rules

Parameter	Value
Taps per segment	100
Max Node Separation	5 segments, 4 repeaters
Max. Segment Length	500m
Network Span	2,500m
Min. Separation Between Transceivers	2.5m
Max. Drop Cable Length	50m

5.3.2   IEEE 802.3 10BASE2

Also known as CheaperNet and ThinNet. The 10BASE2 system uses a thinner coaxial cable to economize on conduit space, and because it costs much less than thick coax cable. Thin coax also has a much tighter bend radius than the 10BASE5 coax.

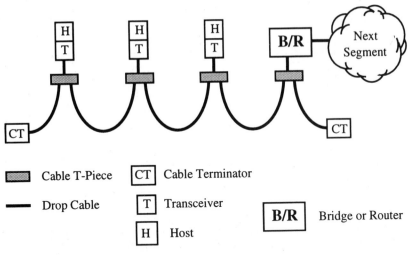

Figure 5.7:   IEEE 802.3 10BASE2 Cabling System

Table 5.5:   10BASE2 Design Rules

Parameter	Value
Taps per segment	30
Max Node Separation	5 segments, 4 repeaters
Max. Segment Length	185m
Network Span	925m
Min. Separation Between Transceivers	0.5m

10BASE2 integrates the transceiver element onto the LAN interface, so saves on component costs and offers higher reliability. However, the lower quality of cable means that only 200m of cable can be laid between repeaters.

10BASE2 Drawbacks

The 10BASE2 system is an excellent system that was a tremendous boost to Ethernet popularity during the 1980s. It is a very simple system to install for a handful of PCs in a small office location.

The coax cable is simple to terminate, and the BNC bayonet connection easy to attach. Another advantage of the system is that all the cable are the same; you can't mix up male and female connections, and with a coax cable it's difficult to mix up the pinouts.

The big problem is the daisy chain topology. This is ideal for an unplanned office layout, but doesn't suit the structured cabling systems that are so popular today. The problem with coax cable is that you can't run telephones over it, which is the whole point of structured cabling.

10BASE2 can be laid out in a star topology using *multiport repeater* (MPR) equipment. However, the main thrust for the development of these devices went towards twisted pair cabling rather than coax. Thus MPRs for coax tend to be expensive compared with modern 10BASET hubs.

In addition, coax cable is *normally* associated with Ethernet. As shown, Token Ring is more likely to operate over twisted pair cabling.

So by choosing coax, you have already chosen to use Ethernet.

Probably the biggest single drawback to the 10BASE2 system is something I call MTS; ."Missing Terminator Syndrome." This condition can cause serious damage to your nerves! It can be caused in several ways. An uninformed user simply disconnects their station from the daisy chain. The chain is broken, and stations on each side cannot communicate. Much more serious is that the "broken" ends of the chain are not terminated correctly, so the effect is that the entire Ethernet segment is down. In general, moves and changes in a 10BASE2 network can be tricky in a working LAN segment.

5.3.3   Ethernet FOIRL

During the history of Ethernet development, several initiatives have been taken to operate the system over a fiber optic connection. All of these systems are proprietary. However, recent efforts have converged upon an accepted standard called the *Fiber Optic Inter-Repeater Link* (FOIRL).

In simple terms, FOIRL components now exist to replace virtually any copper cable in an Ethernet network.

Typically these components use multimode fiber, with a connection length up to 2km. However, single mode links can extend the link beyond this distance. Due to the timer sensitive CSMA/CD algorithm, the total distance covered by the Ethernet depends on the delay of the cable and any active components within the collision domain.

5.3.4   IEEE 802.3 10BASET

The 10BASET standard is responsible for the fortunes made by several companies in the late 80s and early 90s. Up to the launch of this standard, Ethernet was under a serious threat from the emerging Token Ring network. Only two years after the launch of 10BASET, it seems that Token Ring is restricted to die-hard SNA users only.

Figure 5.8 shows the basic 10BASET layout.

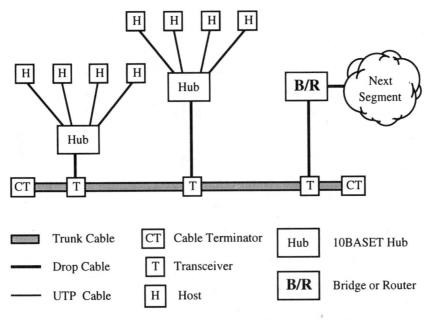

Figure 5.8:   IEEE 802.3 10BASET Cabling System

In a 10BASET system, the hubs act as ordinary Ethernet hosts, using either 10BASE5, 10BASE2 or FOIRL.

10BASET doesn't suffer from Missing Terminator Syndrome for the attached hosts, but the hubs themselves are subject to MTS. Luckily we fool around with hubs less often than hosts, so the vulnerability is less strongly felt.

10BASET Design Rules

The design rules for 10BASET are identical to either 10BASE2 or 10BASE5 for the inter-hub spacing. Connections from the hub to the host can be up to 100m of UTP cable. Up to 4 hubs can be placed in sequence. Check with your specific supplier because different vendors' equipment is capable of different transmission distances.

10BASET Drawbacks

In general, 10BASET represents the logical limit for Ethernet cabling. Using this system, designers can choose between coax (thick or thin), twisted pair (shielded or unshielded), or fiber.

Cabling hubs are active components, and will have an associated price tag, but the volume sales of these devices coupled with the competitive nature of the market helps to keep this incremental cost low.

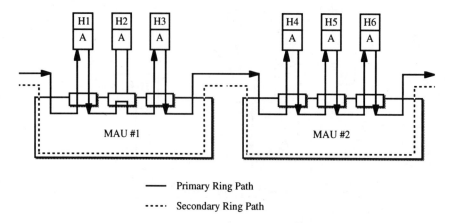

— Primary Ring Path

----- Secondary Ring Path

Figure 5.9:   The Token Ring MAU System

The real drawbacks to 10BASET are due to the limited bandwidth and shared nature of Ethernet. More about this below.

5.3.5   Token Ring

In the late 80s, I was actually working for a Token Ring manufacturer, and we had great hopes that Token Ring would become as popular as Ethernet.

In many ways, Token Ring is superior to Ethernet in a shared LAN technology. Today, the trend is towards switched LANs, as I describe below, and quite simply Ethernet is much more suited to this technology than Token Ring.

For cabling purposes, Token Ring was a great improvement on both 10BASE5 and 10BASE2. As I show in Figure 5.9, Token Ring was designed around a cabling system that was fundamentally suited to structures cabling systems.

The heart of this cabling system is the *Multistation Access Unit* (MAU). Host computers attach to MAUs physically and electronically. When their adapter circuits are activated, an electrical signal is sent to the MAU to open a relay that allows the host to join the ring. This technique means that when stations are disconnected physically (i.e., we pull their cables out), they remove themselves from the ring by default, and do not disturb its operation.

Additional benefits for Token Ring come from its more sophisticated access control technique. Unlike Ethernet, Token Ring has no fundamental distance limit caused by CSMA/CD, and its transmission scheme is more suited to separate, unidirectional transmission/reception. This last aspect means that it's much easier to develop fiber optic Token Ring systems than equivalent CSMA/CD systems. Ironically, although the technical difficulties are greater, fiber optic Ethernet components are more readily available, and usually cheaper than Token Ring.

Token Ring was first shipped in a 4Mbps version, and this version has always been able to operate with Category 3 (or better) UTP. Unfortunately, IBM never bothered to ask early Token Ring pioneers like Proteon about transmission schemes, so higher speeds over UTP suffer from significant "technical challenges." Basically, 16Mbps Token Ring over UTP is vulnerable to accumulated jitter. Jitter is when the synchronization between consecutive stations in the ring is not good enough to ensure reliable synchronous communication. Since Token Ring has only one clock master in the ring (the Active Monitor), the timing error accumulates as the signal passes from host to host. The lower the quality of the cable, the greater the jitter.

During the period from 1990 to the present day, various (non-standard) improvements have been made in 16Mbps over UTP. Unlike 10BASET, these improvements are vendor-specific and are not always complementary. For this reason, many users prefer to build Token Ring segments from single-vendor components.

Token Ring Design Rules

The design rules for Token Ring are complex. Originally, IBM published comprehensive tables to show the design requirements. Back in 1989, Dave Bird and I reverse engineered IBM's tables to publish a Proteon design guide. Having determined a perfectly valid formula that would reproduce the tables, we found that the Proteon MAUs actually imposed more loss in the cable because they included transformer components, whereas IBM MAUs didn't bother to use transformers on all their ports.

When we came to 16Mbps, we didn't even bother trying. As far as we could tell at that time, the design rules for Token Ring would be "fluid" for several years.

Most of the top Token Ring vendors now publish design guides for their own equipment, so my advice is to contact your intended vendors.

RFP Question:	The supplier will include a design guide that is valid for both 4Mbps and 16Mbps operation for the proposed Token Ring components. If the supplier intends to quote for cabling, it will relate specific cable types to the terms used in the Design Guide.

5.3.6   FDDI

Design of the Fiber Distributed Data Interface (FDDI) was originally begun in 1984 by the ANSI X3T9.5 committee. The saga of standardization almost warrants a book in its own right (except that it's incredibly boring). Suffice to say that FDDI took a long time to become a standard. Modern FDDI systems have been essentially stable and interoperable since 1990.

FDDI is a Token Ring system, and uses a similar frame structure to IEEE 802.5. Unlike Token Ring, however, true MAC Layer multicasts operate correctly.

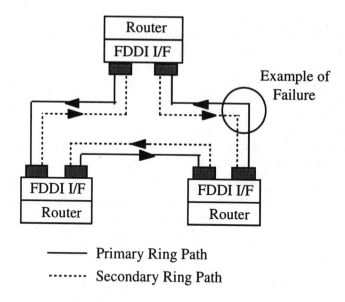

Figure 5.10:   The Original FDDI Cable Layout

Cable Topologies

In cabling terms, FDDI was intended for operation over fiber optic cable, but because this media is several times more expensive to purchase and install than copper, there have been several incremental developments.

Figure 5.10 shows the original FDDI cabling system. A duplex fiber cable (i.e., a cable with two fiber filaments) is used to interconnect FDDI devices. FDDI is designed to operate at 100Mbps over the Primary Ring Path. If cable connections are lost, a continuous path is maintained by allowing the FDDI data to flow back over the Secondary Ring Path. Note that normal FDDI products *do not* make use of both rings paths at once; in other words, FDDI doesn't *normally* operate at a 200Mbps aggregate data rate. Some FDDI hubs do offer dual-MAC operation (two MAC entities are required, one to run each ring), so deliver an aggregate 200Mbps for the rings.

The first development to come in this cabling scheme was the introduction of the *Optical Bypass Switch*. Imagine the problem in Figure 5.11. If you decide to disconnect the upper router, you immediately out the ring into failure mode. Bypass switches are rather crude mechanical devices that prevent ring failure if devices are disconnected.

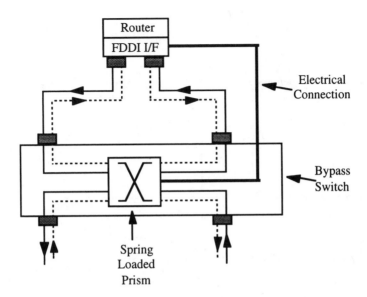

Figure 5.11:   FDDI Optical Bypass Switch

Figure 5.11 shows the "low tech" solution. The bypass switch is actually a spring-loaded prism. In its normal state, and electrical connection from the FDDI device keeps the prism in place so the optical path passes out onto the main ring. If electrical power is lost, the spring forces the prism into its bypass position, and the FDDI device is simply taken out of the optical path. Crude but effective. Unfortunately bypass switches tend to absorb a fairly large amount of optical signal because of the misalignment of the prism components with repeated use.

The most sensible, but expensive, solution is to turn FDDI into a structured cabled LAN using hub technology.

Figure 5.12 shows three modes of connection for an FDDI host into a hub. The Single Attach Station (SAS) uses one duplex cable (a single cable with two fiber paths, one connector at each end). A Dual Attach Station (DAS) uses two duplex cables and operates in the spirit of the original FDDI scheme. If a DAS cable breaks, then the alternate cable path can be used. The ultimate level of security is provided by the Dual Homed connection. With Dual Homing, a DAS station connects each cable to a different FDDI hub. To make Dual Homing work, there is an obvious restriction, but I'd like to spell this out clearly:

- Both hubs *must* be on the same backbone ring.

- The *same* FDDI Token must circulate through both hubs, so you cannot separate the dual homing hubs with a bridge.

RFP Question:	Describe the options for SAS, DAS and Dual Homing connection for the proposed FDDI equipment.

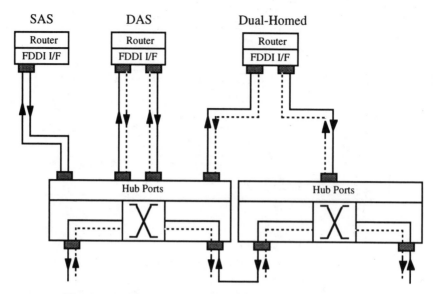

Figure 5.12:   FDDI Hub Connection Options

Cable Distances

FDDI was designed to use multimode fiber cable with a size of 62.5/125 µm. The signal transmitters for this type of fiber are red light emitting diodes (LED) operating at wavelengths of 850nm, or 1300nm. At FDDI speeds, multimode fiber can transmit signals up to a conservative distance of about 2km. However, with an optical system the actual transmission distance depends on the purity of the optical path. Patch connections and fiber splices will attenuate signal.

Using stronger transmitters doesn't really solve the problem of multimode distance. Instead, long distances can be achieved using monomode (alias single mode) fiber. Single mode signals must be introduced to the cable using a coherent light source such as a laser. FDDI lasers operate at 1300nm. In general, there are three categories of laser transmitter. Class I lasers are the kind used in CD players or laser pointers and are medically harmless. Class II lasers are strong enough that they could cause vision damage after long exposure (perhaps tens of seconds). For this reason, Class II lasers may be subject to health and safety regulation in some countries. Class III lasers go all the way up to industrial cutting tools and are definitely subject to regulation.

Typical FDDI single mode products use Class I lasers and can operate at unrepeated distances of around 10-12km. Class II lasers are generally used by carriers and PTTs and installed in specially contained cabinets by trained personnel. Readily available products can operate up to 30km and some specialized systems go even further.

Switching Hubs

Regardless of the LAN technology, cabling hubs have evolved to offer an extremely efficient and flexible mechanism to build LANs. This evolution has passed through several discrete stages:

- Multiple Backplane Hubs

- Software Configured Backplane Hubs (configuration switching)

- Port-Switched Hubs

- Virtual LAN Hubs

Multiple Backplane Hubs

In a "physical" network, the segment is defined by the cable. If two hosts are on the same cable, they hear each other's broadcasts and multicasts. We say that the hosts are within the same *Broadcast Domain*. In conventional LAN hubs, the Broadcast Domains are defined by connecting the cards in the hub chassis to one of the LAN backplanes in the hub. This concept is shown in Figure 5.13, where the port interfaces in Slots 1, 2 and 3 are associated with Backplane 1, whereas the interface in Slot 4 is associated with Backplane *N*. Hosts that are attached to ports in Slots 1, 2 and 3 are in the same Broadcast Domain. The hosts attached to Slot 4 are in a different Broadcast Domain. Since a pure hub offers no bridging or routing function, the Broadcast Domains are separate.

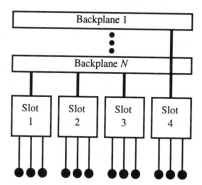

Figure 5.13:   Physical LAN Hub Topology

A more flexible hub technology is the *Port Switching Hub*. In this architecture, any individual port can be *logically* assigned to a given LAN backplane. By controlling the number of ports assigned to each LAN segment, the conventional LAN congestion problem can be avoided.

Because the composition of the LANs is created by the logical configuration of the hub rather than the physical cable layout, such systems are known as *Virtual LANs*.

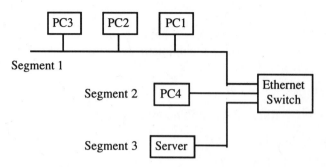

Figure 5.14:   Ethernet Switching

5.4   Getting More Bandwidth from LANs

One of the problems with conventional Ethernet technology is that the probability of collisions on the wire can rise dramatically as the loading on the LAN increases and when the number of active stations increases. This effect is known rather melodramatically as "Ethernet Meltdown." Until recently, the phenomenon was just an irritation for the most heavily loaded LAN segments. Everyone accepts that real Ethernet throughput is around 3-4 Mbps. Power users could move to FDDI, assuming they could justify the cost. Today, however, we have several additional choices, as well as enjoying a drop in FDDI prices:

- Switched Ethernet
- Fast Ethernet
- Full Duplex Ethernet
- ATM LANs

Since all of these technologies are still developing rapidly at the time of writing, I can only give an overview of the individual technologies.

5.5   Switched Ethernet Overview

Ethernet is at its most efficient when there are only two stations on the LAN segment. In this case, there really is a half-duplex 10Mbps throughput available. Ethernet switches act just like multiport bridges. They allow the number of stations on an individual segment to be reduced, even down to the limit of a single station per port. I show the principle in Figure 5.14.

In this example, Segment 1 is a medium-demand segment where some peer-to-peer traffic passes directly between PC1, PC2, and PC3. These three machines share the 10Mbps bandwidth in the conventional way. Segment 2 has a high demand workstation, PC4 and Segment 3 has the Server. Segments 2 and 3 offer dedicated, *half-duplex* Ethernet bandwidth to the attached stations.

The Switch acts as a true MAC Layer Bridge and learns the MAC address(es) on each segment. It can then prevent traffic from "leaking" onto other segments and reducing the overall bandwidth.

If we measure the performance of a connection between two workstations, we will always find that the connection has a lower delay by using a switch than if we use a router.

Broadcasts and Multicasts

Like any Transparent Bridge technology, Ethernet Switches must pass broadcast and multicast traffic. Because they are multiport devices, this will result in "flooding" of broadcasts and multicasts throughout the extended bridge domain. For a single switch, this will be annoying, but not serious. If switches are installed in a "cascaded" topology, as shown in Figure 5.15, the results can be much more serious. In this diagram, a broadcast or multicast on any LAN segment will result in multiple copies of the broadcast being spread around the LAN. In other words, you really don't want to use these things with NetBIOS!

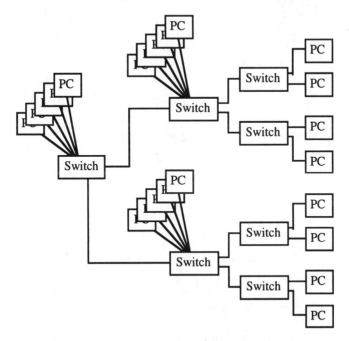

Figure 5.15:   Cascaded Switch Topology

This topology is made much worse if Spanning Tree bridges are installed on any of the switched segments. The default timer for the Spanning Tree protocol transmission is only 2 seconds, which means one multicast flooded to each switched segment per Spanning Tree bridge. Other possible problem protocols are DECNet (end station and Level 1 hellos), AppleTalk (continuous RTMP and Zone traffic), and VINES (lots of StreetTalk database updates).

Switches and Routers In Perfect Harmony

Some industry analysts have pointed to the appearance of Ethernet switches as a threat to the role of the router. In fact, switch technology may prolong the life of the conventional router by offloading desktop LAN frame "routing." By using a high performance, low delay bridge to front-end a router, it should be possible to build higher performance local LAN segments while protecting backbone and WAN bandwidth. I show a typical synergistic installation in Figure 5.16.

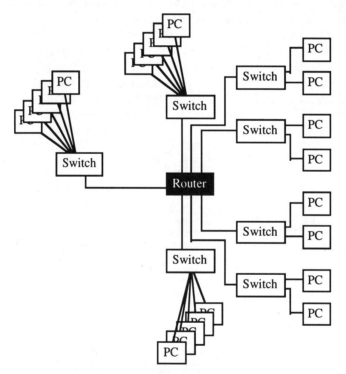

Figure 5.16:   Ethernet Switches and Routers Working Together

In this topology, a broadcast sent from any PC will only be flooded *within* any individual switch. Since all switches are interconnected through the router, then the broadcast will be stopped.

If WAN connections are involved, the case for a router is even stronger since the WAN bandwidth disappears under a flood of useless broadcast and multicast traffic.

Fast Packet vs Store-And-Forward

Ethernet switches can be divided into two variants: Fast Packet and Store-and-Forward. Conventional bridges and routers are store-and-forward devices. They wait for the entire LAN frame to be received into the device, verify the CRC and then transmit the frame. Fast packet devices only clock in the first few bits of the frame (remember the destination MAC address is one of the first fields of the frame).

In March 1994, Data Communication magazine benchmarked a range of Ethernet switches. As you'd expect, the lowest latency switch was the "fast packet" Kalpana Etherswitch at 40μs for a 64 byte frame. The next lowest latency was for the "store-and-forward" Lannet LANswitch at 51.2μs. An average latency for the other devices tested was around 100μs. Both switches were capable of forwarding wire speed Ethernet for all packet sizes, at all applied loads. For practical purposes, the difference between the two forwarding modes is usually irrelevant, for a couple of reasons.

First, if we operate in a client/server environment, the server is attached to the same switched LAN port as the clients. When clients contend for the server bandwidth, even a fast packet device will kick into store-and-forward mode. The Catch-22 is that real environments that demand LAN switching will *usually* operate with some server contention, so a fast packet switch will *usually* operate in store-and-forward mode.

Second, the solution to the server connection bottleneck is to use a Fast Ethernet, or FDDI connection and perform Translation Bridge conversion in the switch. Translation *requires* a switch to operate in a store-and-forward mode.

My own feeling is that the latency improvement between routers and switches is so great that the *incremental* improvement of fast packet isn't worth the effort, especially since the switch will usually default to a store-and-forward operating mode.

5.6 Full Duplex Ethernet Overview

A full-duplex connection is one in which we can transmit and receive on the same connection at the same time. WAN connections are usually full-duplex, but historically LAN connections have been half-duplex.

An Ethernet bus LAN must be half-duplex, since any attempt at full-duplex behavior will result in collisions, as you can see in Figure 5.17.

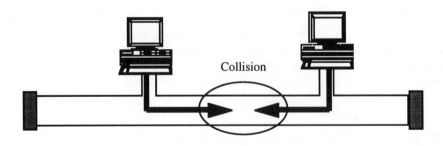

Figure 5.17:   Full Duplex Operation on a Bus LAN

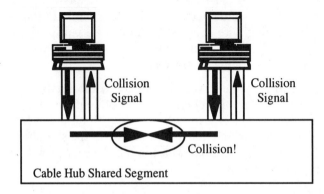

Figure 5.18:   Collision Signaling on 10BASET

In 10BASET LANs, the stations are connected to the cable hub with two pairs of cables: one for transmit and the other for receive. Is full-duplex operation possible here? The answer is "no" because according to the 10BASET specification, stations must "listen" on the receive pair to detect collisions while they are transmitting. The 10BASET hub is responsible for the collision signal on the receive pair, as I show in Figure 5.18.

However, if we're using switched Ethernet with one station per port, there can be no collisions. This means that we could change the use of the receive pair to allow full duplex operation. It is this capability that is now being made available in LAN interfaces and hubs.

What Do I Need to Use Full-Duplex Ethernet?

Full-duplex Ethernet requires a special adapter and cable hub. At the time of writing, these are being shipped by Cabletron, Hughes, Kalpana, and Netwiz. Adapter cards are available from Cabletron, Cogent, Compaq, DEC, IBM and Seeq. In addition, Intel has stated that standard Ethernet adapters that use their 82596 LAN controller should be able to operate full-duplex using a software upgrade.

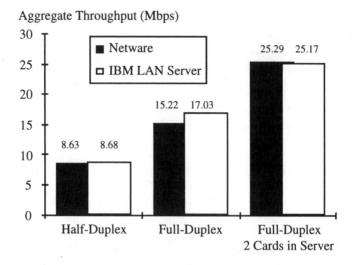

Aggregate Throughput (Mbps)

Figure 5.19:   Interlab Benchmarks of Full-Duplex Ethernet

Performance benchmarks from Interlab indicate that full duplex is an attractive technology for file servers, while workstations can remain on conventional half-duplex Ethernet. The key to the efficient use of full-duplex is that file server operating systems are inherently multitasking, allowing concurrent transmission and reception of data streams.

From these early results with full-duplex Ethernet, I see the technology as a good way to extend existing LAN lifetimes for a minimum of additional investment. However, if the cost of Fast Ethernet adapters and hubs drops as forecast, then I think that many users will opt instead for this higher performance technology.

5.7   Fast Ethernet Overview

Using switched Ethernet and full-duplex Ethernet, we can squeeze more bandwidth out of existing technology. By moving to FDDI at 100Mbps, we can get at least 10 times the performance of switched Ethernet. However, FDDI is expensive as a technology. Back in 1988 when "real" FDDI product first started leaking onto the market, interface cards cost around $4,000, while an average quality Ethernet card cost around $400. Today the prices of both technologies have dropped, but the differential remains the same. You can buy an FDDI interface for a PC for around $1,000, while an average Ethernet card costs around $100.

A couple of years ago, the industry started kicking around the idea of boosting Ethernet performance to 100Mbps. Somehow the industry was able to convince everyone that 100Mbps components for "Fast Ethernet" would be cheaper than 100Mbps components for FDDI, even though FDDI chips have been in production for several years and manufacturers have had time to recoup development costs.

5.7.1   Two Approaches

To extend Ethernet architecture to support 100 Mbps transmission speed, two new LAN technologies have been proposed. Both technologies are now in the process of becoming IEEE standards, one in the IEEE 802.3u subcommittee and the other in the IEEE 802.12 subcommittee. Both technologies use a star topology, with workstations attaching to a dedicated cabling hub over a choice of copper or fiber optic media. Both technologies also use a shared bandwidth approach. That is, the 100 Mbps network bandwidth is shared among all the users of the LAN. However, the Ethernet CSMA/CD algorithm will not operate efficiently at 100Mbps with a *shared* cable. This is because the back-off period after a collision equates to 10 times more lost bandwidth at 100Mbps than it does at 10Mbps. For this reason, I believe that the most useful 100Mbps Ethernet products will be based on switched LAN technology.

100BASEVG-AnyLAN (IEEE 802.12)

A catchy name. The two key features of this proposal are that it uses an algorithm called *Demand Priority Architecture* (DPA) to control access to the network and that it can use voice grade (hence the "VG") cable for transmission. Strictly speaking, voice grade cable can't even be used for UTP Ethernet at 10Mbps which is why the DPA signaling technique is so important. An additional feature of DPA is that it may be possible to utilize the technique for isochronous traffic streams. However, since frame-based transmission techniques are still retained, it will not be possible to interleave voice and data transmission from the same workstation. The most serious drawback to the VG approach is that operation over Category 3 cable requires 4 cable pairs for each host. Users who already have Category 3 cable may not have 4 pairs available for dedicated data use (two of the four pairs normally pulled to the desktop are used by telephone connections). For newer sites, who are deciding on the type of cable, the "politically correct" choice today is Category 5 cable. This higher quality cable requires only two pairs to operate at 100Mbps, or even 155Mbps ATM speeds.

At the time of writing, only Hewlett-Packard are continuing to push this technology, while the mainstream hub vendors such as 3Com, Cabletron and Synoptics have chosen the alternative, IEEE 802.3u technology.

100BASE-T (IEEE 802.3u)

The 802.3u technique uses the same CSMA/CD algorithm as regular Ethernet, but uses a different signaling technique to allow 100Mbps signals to be run over copper cable. The 802.3u system was originally targeted at Category 5 UTP cable (two Category 5 cable pairs per host). However, the VG-Any-LAN signaling scheme has been adopted by the IEEE 802.3u developers, so this technology can also be operated over Category 3 cable. Like VG-Any-LAN, four Category 3 cable pairs are required for each host connection.

Both 802.12 and 802.3u are valid, 100Mbps approaches. Like other LANs, they transmit data in frames, with SNAP-encapsulated IP packets. Broadcasts and multicasts operate normally, so ARP and Routing Protocol updates need no modification.

Assuming they survive as commercial techniques, both technologies will eventually appear in switched form. Full duplex versions are also possible and have already been designed into Synoptics products. However, many users are already becoming bored with the bickering between the two Fast Ethernet camps. With the continuing confusion, there is a possibility that a completely new alternative for high speed desktop connectivity will steal the lead: ATM LANs.

5.8 ATM LAN Overview

ATM was designed as an efficient, high speed multiplexing technique for WANs. However, since it is such a high speed technique, it has been adapted to desktop operation.

5.8.1 Frames and Cells

All of our current generation of LAN applications generate data as variable length message blocks, which are mapped into variable length LAN *frames*. In contrast, ATM networks can only carry *cells*. The conversion from frames to cells is called *segmentation* and the return from cells to frames is called *reassembly*. The two-way process of segmentation and reassembly (SAR) can (indeed, must) be implemented in hardware.

In Figure 5.20, the device drivers for the operating system simply "catch" outgoing IP traffic and pass it to the adapter card.

On the adapter card, LAN emulation techniques (such as ARP emulation) and VC signaling allow a connection to be made from Harry to Sally. IP traffic passed from the device driver is segmented into cells. High speed circuits cut the LAN frames up into fixed-length ATM *cells*. The cells are transmitted over the cable connection into the ATM Hub/Switch. Within the switch, a dedicated channel is allocated to the link between Harry and Sally. This is a full duplex connection operating a quite high speeds. Currently available products operate at the following line rates and after each line rate I indicate the cable types supported:

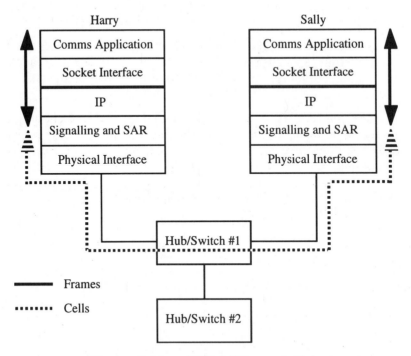

Figure 5.20: ATM LANs and Hubs

- 25.6Mbps. An IBM initiative that was turned down by the ATM Forum, but has been pushed by IBM outside of the standards arena (does this sound familiar?). At the time of writing, 25 companies had stated intention to support this line speed. UTP, STP, MM, SM.

- 51.8Mbps. This is the "official" ATM LAN speed promoted by the ATM Forum. UTP, MM, SM.

- 100 Mbps. This line speed re-uses PMD components from FDDI (the AMD TAXI chipset clocked at 125MHz). However, pure ATM cells are transmitted over the cable connection. UTP(5), MM, SM.

- 140 Mbps. If we clock TAXI chips at 175MHz, we end up with 140Mbps line rate. UTP(5), MM, SM.

- 155Mbps. This is a true ATM/SONET/SDH speed (in SONET it is known as OC3). In LANs, this line rate reuses Physical Layer components from the FibreChannel system. UTP(5), MM, SM.

- 620Mbps. This is the next logical step up and is known as OC12 in the SONET scheme. No *production* adapters are available at this speed, although it's just a matter of time. Media currently unknown.

Figure 5.21:   Address Translation Concepts

5.8.2   Address Translation

ATM is a connections-oriented, switched network with its own addressing structure. This structure is based on the ISO *Network Service Access Point* (NSAP) addressing scheme, which looks very different from IP. To move IP information over the ATM network therefore requires an Address Translation phase. One of the interesting challenges to an ATM LAN is that ATM cannot support broadcast or multicast techniques such as ARP, RIP, OSPF, or Router Discovery.

Figure 5.21 illustrates the problem. Within a single IP Address Domain (let's assume this is a single Ethernet segment), broadcast address discovery like ARP can spread over the entire domain. However, with ATM "in the way," broadcasts cannot cross the network.

For information to be transmitted over an ATM network, logical connections called Virtual Channels must be set up. VCs are exactly analogous to X.25 Virtual Circuits, or an ISDN telephone call. By the end of 1994, the signaling protocol (Q.2931) will be harmonized (it currently exists in two flavors) and at the Las Vegas Interop in May '94, a broadcast/multicast emulation technique called LAN Emulation was demonstrated.

LAN Emulation

ATM LAN Emulation is defined as an extension to the ATM Forum *User-Network Interface* (UNI). The UNI defines the interface between the ATM "host" and the first ATM switch in the network. It defines the physical and logical interface and the call signaling protocols.

To support "legacy" devices[1], the initial approach of the ATM Forum is to create a software device driver that will make the ATM network appear to be an Ethernet or Token Ring LAN. Figure 5.22 shows the basic approach of LAN Emulation.

---

[1]Legacy devices are what most of the world is running its data communications on. So, when an ATM evangelist refers to a "legacy device," you can substitute the words "essential," "vital," "indispensable."

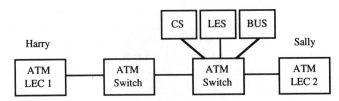

Figure 5.22:   ATM LAN Emulation

In this example, we have two hosts, Harry and Sally, who want to exchange regular IP traffic. If they were on an Ethernet, then they would ARP for each other's MAC address, just as I described in the previous chapter. However, the ARP protocol relies on broadcast operation, which is simply not possible on a connection-oriented network such as ATM.

Each of these hosts has an ATM interface installed, with the appropriate device driver software. This software supports a *LAN Emulation Client* (LEC) function. The LEC software "catches" the broadcast and sends it to another ATM device called a *LAN Emulation Server* (LES). The LES is just an ordinary computer that stores the ATM and IP addresses of all of the hosts attached within this LAN Emulation Domain. When the LES receives the "ATM ARP" request, it consults its existing cache of address entries. If the requested IP address is in the cache, the LES will send the corresponding ATM address (an ISO NSAP address) back to the LEC.

If the address is not in the cache, the LES may consult another device called a *Broadcast Unknown Server* (BUS). In theory, the BUS can poll all the attached ATM hosts to determine "unknown" IP addresses.

ATM workstations determine the ATM address of the LES and BUS for their LAN Emulation Domain by consulting a *Configuration Server* (CS). The ATM address of the CS is statically defined in the host when the ATM interface is installed, or if no address is configured, can be found on a "well known" ATM channel number.

LAN Emulation also allows communication to pass between a native ATM workstation and a conventional LAN-attached device. In Figure 5.23 I show how this can happen.

In this case, Sally is connected to a conventional Ethernet, whereas Harry is on an ATM LAN. Let's assume that all the hosts are configured to be within the same Network ID. This means that ARP will be used to establish MAC addresses. When Sally sends out an ARP broadcast, the ATM SAR Device acts as the LAN Emulation Client. This means that existing Ethernet adapters do not need to be modified to communicate with new ATM LAN segments.

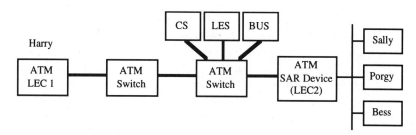

Figure 5.23: Support for Legacy LANs over ATM

Non-Blocking = Non-Scaleable

One of the big misunderstandings in the ATM LAN world is the concept of bottlenecks and backplanes. Most of the first generation ATM hubs are built with matrix backplanes or shared memory busses. This means that when a VC connection is established, its bandwidth is assured. The concept is known as a *non-blocking* architecture. A shared memory bus is a *blocking* architecture, because contention for bus resources will cause congestion. Shared memory devices are particularly vulnerable to contention problems caused by congestion buffering, especially at ATM speeds.

The point is that even the non-blocking character of the matrix switch is lost as soon as we connect one hub to another. The interhub connection can only be made at the same speed as the workstation connections. Because ATM is already operating at such high speeds, a single inter-hub VC can totally occupy the link and will lead to serious congestion problems. Ironically, because ATM fundamentally depends on instant, infinite bandwidth, it reacts rather badly if it doesn't get it.

How Do I Connect My ATM LANs to Legacy LANs?

ATM LAN marketing people have coined the term *legacy LAN*. A simple definition of legacy LAN is the communication channel that your company uses for its core business today. If legacy LANs were less important than this, we could throw them away and start again with ATM (only to repeat the process in three years time when the next gee-wiz technology appears).

The real way to approach this issue is to decide where and how ATM will be used in the LAN environment. Today there is just one reason to use ATM LANs; BANDWIDTH. For groups that require very high bandwidth, ATM LANs can be installed. For the remaining 99% of the typical enterprise, some form of "legacy LAN" can be used.

High performance routers are the ideal connection platform from frame and packet based LANs into ATM. In the near future (1995 time frame), an important concept will be that of "AAL5 Routing." This is where a high speed router will accept a stream of ATM cells that are carrying a routeable protocol such as IP or IPX. These cells are re-assembled into complete LAN frames, at which point buffering and flow control can occur (ATM has neither of these features today). The frame may then be segmented back to cells and exit the router on another ATM connection. Does this sound crazy? Well it's not. While we're still generating data in bursty, variable length blocks (frames, packets, whatever we call them), some form of buffering is needed.

5.9   Non-Physical Media (Wireless LANs)

LAN hosts need to be able to send their signals over some kind of connection medium. Laying cable can be expensive and one of the big issues facing many companies today is the need to move employees from one part of the organization to another, known as *adds and changes*.

Some installations are difficult to cable. When I visit my bank, I see marble-floor splendor paid for by my ancestors, no doubt. The plaster molding on the wall would be destroyed by cable installers and would be uneconomical to replace in today's business climate.

Non-physical LANs have been under development for several years now. They fall into three categories:

- UHF and microwave radio

- Microwave

- Infrared

. Figure 5.24 shows the portions of the Electromagnetic Spectrum occupied by Infrared and Microwave communications.

5.9.1   Signal Characteristics

You can see that the Electromagnetic Spectrum is a busy place. Not all of the radiation types are suitable for office use. At very low frequencies, we wouldn't be able to insert high frequency information (e.g., 10Mbps Ethernet) into the signal. Even starting at the 100kHz point, the frequencies are occupied by long distance communication such as short wave radio.

In fact, there are two strategies we can use to select a suitable frequency:

- Allocate frequencies to subscribers assuming that interference can avoided by unique allocation. This is a bit like the NIC IP address allocation.

- Design a low power system so that LAN signals do not extend beyond the local area.

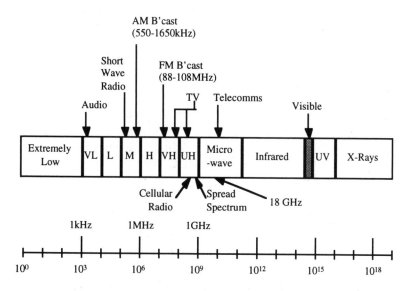

Figure 5.24:   The Electromagnetic Spectrum

Both techniques are used. The first is used by point-to-point microwave communication, which requires a case-by-case approval from local authorities. The second technique is used in LAN systems.

Wireless LAN frequencies range from the top end of the UHF band (900 MHz), through the microwave band and into the infrared. As the frequency gets higher, we can insert more information per second into the beam. At the same time, the propagation characteristics change. Electromagnetic waves interact with solid matter, like us, or the buildings we work in. As we move up the frequency scale, the radiation starts to behave more like visible radiation. So, instead of passing through matter as we expect from radio, signals are absorbed or reflected.

At the bottom end of the radio LAN frequencies, 900MHz to 1.8GHz, these signals are beginning to be strongly absorbed by solid matter. In fact, above 300MHz, we can reflect or focus radio signals just like we would with visible radiation.

At the top end with infrared, you can try your own experiments with your TV or VCR remote controls. Some units can control TVs from another room, bouncing signals off doors or ceilings to get to the target.

Spread Spectrum

One of the benefits we pick up from the end of the Cold War is access to former military technology. Spread Spectrum communications systems were designed to find clear channels among enemy jamming and to hop from one frequency to another to confuse eavesdroppers. In the frequency range 902MHz to

908MHz, 2.4GHz to 2.5GHz and 5.8GHz to 5.9GHz, commercial spread-spectrum devices are now available. These units have a range of about 250m, they offer speeds of up to 2Mbps and they require no explicit licensing. Some units are equipped with sockets for encryption chips such as DES.

Microwave

At 18-19GHz, low power microwave systems are available. These have a longer range, with one system quoting a coverage of 5,000 m^2. They can now deliver LAN-like speeds of around 3-4Mbps. Explicit licensing is required, although some manufacturers have acquired corporate licensing that can be passed onto customers.

Infrared

This is a rapidly growing area of the market. The signals are blocked by any IR-opaque barrier (some types of "transparent" plastics are opaque to IR). This means that multiple systems can be deployed within a building without interference problems. These systems require no licensing and commercial systems exist that emulate Token Ring directly (data rate of 4Mbps). Conversion boxes are available that allow routers to participate in the IR LAN using standard Token Ring or Ethernet ports.

5.10 Which LAN Should I Install?

If you are in the position of deciding which LAN to install in a totally green-field site, the recommendations and arguments have never changed.

First, look at the applications. Find out what your users need and look at the APIs and communication stacks that are used to implement the applications. By moving from a bandwidth hog API to a more conservative system, by eliminating fancy and unnecessary graphics for remote applications, by matching LAN access speeds to WAN access speeds, you may be able to make drastic bandwidth economies.

The majority of new installations today will be more than happy with conventional, shared Ethernet. It's true that the ATM market is healthy and booming, but it is still dwarfed by the sales of conventional Ethernet and Token Ring. I'm assuming that I'll have a chance to write at least a second edition of this book before the situation changes dramatically.

For higher demand users, switched Ethernet and Full Duplex Ethernet allow you to structure your bandwidth much more finely than before. Switched Ethernet is achieved by simply changing the hub; the existing LAN adapters, driver software and cabling remains untouched. The change may improve performance by a factor of ten or more over typical shared segments. In addition, Virtual LAN switched systems will begin to displace conventional routers for LOCAL interconnection.   Routers will reign supreme when it comes to remote interconnection.

Conventional FDDI is still the most mature of the high speed technologies, although it is more expensive to implement than Fast Ethernet. Some conservative designers still prefer to install this established and robust technology.

For the highest demand applications, where cost is no issue, I'd look at ATM LANs combined with a high performance router to connect them into the corporate data highway.

Wireless LANs will hold a niche market position, but will never be able to offer the bandwidth that conventional cabling can.

5.11 Summary

- LAN technologies operate at the Physical and Data Link Layers of the OSI Model.

- LANs are designed to operate as shared media communication channels. To share the cable, LANs implement access control mechanisms and use hardware addressing to allow stations to send information to each other.

- Most LANs today use the same, 48-bit hardware addressing system which was defined by Xerox for Ethernet, but which is now administered by the IEEE.

- Hardware addresses and IP addresses are related using ARP.

- Standards or agreements are in place defining how IP traffic appears on different LAN types.

- Most LAN types use the SNAP encoding method defined in RFC 1042, but pure Ethernet LANs use an older encapsulation method defined in RFC 894.

- Ethernet and SNAP encapsulated frames can coexist on the same LAN segment. Workstations running different encapsulations should not normally be able to communicate directly.

- Routers should be capable of understanding different encapsulation schemes on the same LAN port. However, this is not recommended as it will reduce router performance.

- LANs transmit information as variable length frames. LAN technologies differ in the maximum frame size they can support. This value is called the MTU.

- If possible, a single IP datagram will be carried in a single LAN frame. However, fragmentation and reassembly protocols exist within IP so that larger datagrams can be split up over several frames.

- LANs offer relatively high speeds of connection, but they share this connection between many hosts.

- By reducing the number of hosts on a given LAN segment, the bandwidth available to any host can be increased.

- The ultimate bandwidth increase on a conventional LAN is to have a single workstation connected to a given LAN segment. This is the mechanism used in Switched LAN products.

- LANs such as Switched Ethernet can be operated in a Full Duplex mode. Full Duplex connections only make sense for multitasking hosts such as UNIX machines, or LAN servers.

- Several initiatives are under development allowing 100Mbps connections to the desktop at lower costs than current FDDI products.

- ATM has been developed for deployment in LAN environments. At the time of writing, there are many questions still to be answered about the ATM technique.

- Wireless LANs offer an interesting option in niche environments. However, these products are not currently interoperable, so potential users will have to be prepared for single-vendor dependence.

5.12 References

[1]   DEC, INTEL and XEROX. *The Ethernet, A Local Area Network-Data Link Layer and Physical Layer Specification, Version 2.0.* Document number AA-K759B-TK, November 1982.

[2]   IBM. *Token Ring Network Introduction and Planning Guide.* Document number GA27-3677, 1986.

[3]   Digital Equipment Corporation. *A Primer on FDDI: Fiber Distributed Data Interface, Version 2.0.* Document EC-H1580-42/92, June 1992.

CHAPTER 6

WAN Technology

> *It doesn't matter if you fall down as long as you pick up something from the floor as you get up.*
>
> *Avery's Observation*

6.1   Introduction

This book is intended for an international audience so it's particularly difficult to write a generic chapter on WAN interconnection. Having thought about it for a while, I've come to the conclusion that there are really five hot topics:

- Bandwidth
- Connectivity
- Address Translation and Resolution
- Interoperability
- Security

6.1.1   Bandwidth

This is the obvious factor when we interconnect LAN applications over a WAN. In simple terms, WANs are slower than LANs and application designers do not make any allowance for this fact.

TCP/IP is certainly the best LAN protocol for WAN use, vastly superior to Netware and AppleTalk for its bandwidth economy (I'm thinking particularly of acknowledgment and routing protocol behavior), better than DECnet for addressing and better than OSI because it's actually available.

Nevertheless, application developers have been remarkably imaginative in their quest to fill up WAN bandwidth. While protocol developers have been economizing on bandwidth using protocols like OSPF, application developers have discovered X-Windows and Client/Server architectures.

Protecting WAN bandwidth is something that routers are very, very good at. It's probably the biggest single reason for the success of the router over the past five years. The advent of ATM WANs will not change this situation at all, because there are two extreme scenarios for the ATM-capable future:

- ATM bandwidth levels may only be available in urban, highly developed areas. Urban ATM clusters may be interconnected over more limited inter-area bandwidth. With the increased demand on the overall network, each user will end up with about the same bandwidth they have today.

- At the other extreme, everyone might have access to LAN-like bandwidth over the WAN. However, application developers will continue to devise more sexy ways to use up this bandwidth. The overall effect is that WANs continue to be a bottleneck and routers continue to do their job.

This job can be summarized as to:

- Limit broadcast domains

- Process and summarize route discovery traffic

- Be the vehicle for caching features such as DLSw or NetBIOS/IP Name Caching.

- Offer management focus and potential management summarization

6.1.2   Connectivity

Internetworks are spreading to organizations that are typically more familiar with modem or X.25 connections schemes. A good example is the banking industry. Figure 6.1 shows a typical banking network. Two centralized HQ sites (one for disaster recovery) feed a number of regional sites in a meshed backbone of permanent, leased lines.The branch site (of which there may be hundreds or thousands), cannot each have a dedicated line, even into the regional site because of port limits. Let's say there are 400 branches and 4 regional sites. Each router at the regional site would need 100 ports if each branch was singly connected. The Cisco 7000 has 5 slots and Cisco ship an 8-port serial interface, a total of 40 serial ports. Not enough. Wellfleet's top end BCN has 13 slots, with an 8-port serial interface and that gives up to 104 ports. Just enough. But wait a minute. We may need to connect regional to the HQ over a higher speed link, maybe a High Speed Serial Interface (HSSI, operates up to 52 Mbps) or an OC-3 ATM. The Cisco and Wellfleet HSSI and ATM interfaces are single port and take up a whole slot. That knocks the BCN back down to 96 branch connections, which isn't enough.

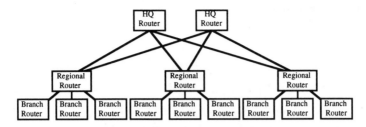

Figure 6.1: Hierarchical Branch-Office Internetwork

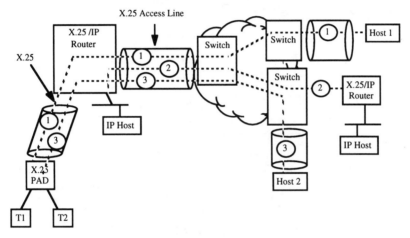

Figure 6.2: Virtual Circuit Concepts

Looking at the problem another way, in Figure 6.2. Why can't we use a WAN connection like a LAN? In other words, put addressing information onto the WAN frame so that we can multiplex connections from many branch sites into a single physical port at the regional site? These connections are called *Virtual Circuits* (VC). VC technology can be used with X.25, Frame Relay, SMDS and ATM.

The Figure shows physical connections (my poor artistic talents have tried to represent transparent tubes), with dotted line VCs passing through them. The physical cable is identical to a leased line and has a specific bandwidth limit; e.g., 64kbps, 1.544 Mbps etc. The traffic on the VCs *shares* the bandwidth on the cable in the similar way that LAN users share the bandwidth on an Ethernet or Token Ring. Traffic for the physical connection is simply put into a transmit queue and sent in turn. Like IP or IPX packet switching, VC switching is a form of *statistical multiplexing* and makes very efficient use of the line bandwidth.

VCs require a *switched WAN*. In other words, we don't have a dedicated cable running between us and our destination. Indeed, we may not always connect to the *same* destination.

6.1.3   Address Translation and Resolution

Think back to Chapters 2, 3 and 4. In these Chapters I described the way that LAN workstations communicate with each other using TCP/IP, even though the underlying LAN actually used a totally different 48-bit addressing scheme.

For WANs, address resolution may be trivial, or it may be quite complex.

In the case of Leased line WANs, we simply apply Bennett's Law, push the bits in one end of the pipe and they fall out the other end. For switched WANs like X.25, ISDN, and ATM, it isn't so easy. All of these WANs have their own addressing scheme. Until the address is defined and the connection made, we haven't got anywhere to push the bits!

Table 6.1:   WAN Address Formats

WAN Technology	Address Format
X.25 (1980)	X.121 DTE Address, 14 decimal digits
X.25 (1984, 1988)	ISO NSAP
Frame Relay	10-bit DLSI for PVC Service
SMDS	E.164 address, 15 decimal digits
ATM	E.164 or ISO NSAP
ISDN	E.164

Table 6.1 shows the various WAN addressing schemes that are in use today. As I discussed in Chapter 4, the router must have a mechanism to convert the LAN addresses to WAN addresses.

6.1.4   Interoperability

Interoperability on WANs is gaining in importance. At one time, we could be sure that all the routers in our internetwork would be from the same vendor. Today, multivendor buying policies are much more common and interconnection over WANs to different companies is becoming the norm. WAN interoperability standard really began with the *Point to Point Protocol* (PPP) and went on from there. As each new WAN technology comes to market, the IETF are quick to define connection and encapsulation standards.

6.1.5   Security

The WAN is the place where the network leaves our premises. It is a potential entry point for unauthorized personnel. The WAN is probably the most popular point at which security measures will be applied.

In Chapter 18 I discuss the ways we can secure our internetworks.

6.2   Leased Lines

Leased line are a natural internetworking option for Wide Area connections. To the LAN, a leased line is a simple extension of the LAN. The issue with leased lines is that they are expensive to operate; you pay for the line even when you're not using it. In addition, a leased line is a point-to-point technology and it becomes even more expensive to produce meshed internetworks using leased lines. The pricing differential between North American and European leased line rate produces the biggest single problem for Product Marketing. Today, most routers lack the simple features that really suit them for WAN internetworking outside of North America, because the product management decisions are made in the US.

6.2.1   Logical Representation

A Leased Line is the simplest form of WAN from a logical point of view. It can be regarded as a single, fixed, duplex data pipe operating between any two locations. The PTT uses Time Division Multiplexing (TDM), or *Digital Access Cross Connect Switch* (DACS) technology to deliver smaller "packages" of line bandwidth that have been taken from a much higher backbone line. In North America, the location of the multiplexing equipment is normally known as the *Point of Presence* (POP) for the local carrier. Line rentals are charged on a distance and bandwidth basis, although many discount offers are available if the two ends of the line are connected to the same mux or DACS exchange.

6.2.2   Physical Interfaces & Speeds

Table 6.2 shows the most common physical interface and line speeds offered by leased lines. Typical low speed synchronous leased lines operate over the venerable RS232

6.2.3   Physical Layer Framing

Low speed leased lines up to 64kbps are presented as a single channel of bandwidth, with no additional framing imposed on the line.

Table 6.2: Maximum Line Rates for Serial Interfaces

Physical I/F	Line Speed
RS232, V.24/V.28 (synchronous), X.21bis	Up to 19.2kbps
V.35	Up to 8Mbps
X.21	Up to 10 Mbps
HSSI	Up to 52 Mbps

If we look at a leased line that is operating at more than 56/64 kbps, we see that the connection is not presented as a single data pipe. Instead, the connection is *channelized*. In the US, a T1 connection is divided into 24 channels. In the rest of the world, a 2.048Mbps E1 connection is divided into 32 channels of 64kbps each. One channel is always used for signaling and another channel may be used by the carrier for management purposes. Framed interfaces like E1 are presented to the user on a special interface called *G.703*. A single G.703 duplex connection uses two BNC connectors (the same size as CheaperNet, 10BASE2). Framing and signaling conventions for this interface are defined by two CCITT other standards, *G.704* and *G.732*.

Why is T1/E1 Channelized?

The T and E carrier services are channelized because of a historical quirk. When telephone services were first digitized, the technique used was called Pulse Code Modulation (PCM). The way that PCM is implemented by most non-US carriers (based on a logarithmic digitizing algorithm called A-Law), a single voice channel requires 64kbps of bandwidth. When the digital infrastructure for most of the world's telephone services was implemented, it was designed around the magic 64kbps concept. High level digital lines were, therefore, multiplexed as chunks of 64kbps bandwidth. This is generically termed the Plesiochronous Digital Hierarchy (PDH). In North America, a different digitizing algorithm was used (μ-Law) which required only 56kbps of bandwidth for a single voice channel. The T1 and E1 line connections offered today are designed to support PABX equipment and *drop and insert multiplexers*. They are not ideally suited to LAN routers or bridges.

Nevertheless, a few router vendors, like Cisco and Wellfleet, support direct G.703 connection to the router. The physical connection is either a dual mini-BNC (the same as an Ethernet 10BASE2), or a single 4-wire connection terminated in a DB-9 Sub D connector. Overall the G.703 interface is bulky and expensive and *as a leased line interface* offers no significant advantage over a traditional single channel interfaces such as X.21 for a router product. More importantly, G.703 is used as the physical interface for many implementations of Primary Rate ISDN and I describe this system later in the Chapter.

6.2.4   Link Level Framing

There are three types of Link Layer protocol used in IP internetworks:

- Proprietary protocols used between routers from the same vendor.

- The Point to Point Protocol (PPP) used over synchronous connections between IP routers (possibly from different vendors) or hosts.

- Serial Line IP (SLIP) used to carry IP over an asynchronous line between IP hosts, or from an IP host to a router or Terminal Server.

These possibilities are summarized in Figure 6.3.

SLIP is defined in RFC 1055. SLIP allows IP datagrams to be transmitted over an asynchronous serial line using dial-up modems, or private line connections. SLIP is an encapsulation protocol; the IP datagram within a SLIP frame is identical to any other IP datagram. In fact the encapsulation is stunningly simple. SLIP defines two hex characters; SLIP END (C0h) and SLIP ESC (DBh). Thereafter, the rules are simple:

- A standard IP datagram is framed with two SLIP END (C0h) characters.

- If a character within the datagram happens to have the value C0h, a 2-character sequence of SLIP ESC (DBh) followed by DCh is sent *instead* of the C0h. The receiving end strips out the 2-character sequence and re-inserts the C0h. In Figure 6.4 the lower frame shows the insertion process.

- If a character has the value of SLIP ESC (DBh), then a 2-character sequence of SLIP ESC (DBh) followed by DDh are sent instead. The receiving end strips out the 2-character sequence and re-inserts the DBh character. In Figure 6.4 the lower frame shows the insertion process.

Since SLIP is sensitive to specific bit patterns in the data, certain flow control procedures (namely XON/XOFF) may cause problems. SLIP requires a serial port configuration that provides all 8 bits for data transmission. For example, 8 data bits, no parity, hardware flow control.

SLIP is a crude, but effective protocol. However, it does suffer from limitations in error detection. NFS, for example, would normally rely on lower layer protocols for error detection. NFS was designed to run in a mythical environment where bandwidth is free and infinite and error rates are zero. The nearest we can come to this ideal in our imperfect world is a LAN and that isn't always good enough! If you want to run NFS over SLIP, you should be prepared for trouble. Finally, SLIP offer no form of error detection or correction. Today, SLIP is being superseded by asynchronous PPP.

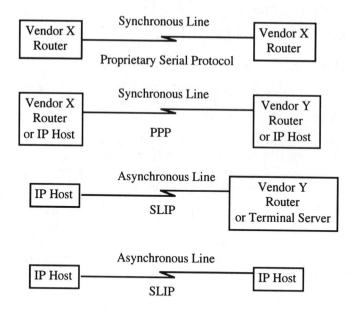

Figure 6.3: Serial Line Protocols for IP

6.2.5   SLIP

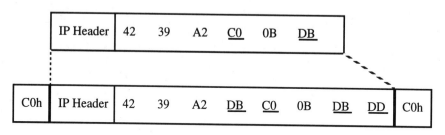

Figure 6.4: SLIP Encapsulation and Character-Stuffing

6.2.6   Proprietary Serial Protocols

Cisco, Wellfleet and Proteon routers are happy to communicate over LAN media, where frame formats are standardized by RFC 894 or 1042. However, over the serial lines they use a proprietary encapsulation format. The lack of a standard frame format was rectified by the introduction of PPP. In all cases I recommend you move your proprietary serial protocols over to PPP as soon as you can. Apart from the interoperability opportunity, PPP is more efficient and functional than any proprietary protocol.

6.2.7   Point to Point Protocol (PPP)

There are three big advantages offered by PPP:

- It is a standards-based protocol, so routers from different vendors are able to be connected over serial lines.

- PPP provides a mechanism so that datagrams from different protocol stacks (e.g., IP, IPX, DECNet) can be multiplexed sequentially over the same physical circuit.

- PPP includes a number of sophisticated features that actually make it superior to proprietary protocols for serial interconnection.

PPP provides a method for transmitting datagrams from various protocol stacks over serial point-to-point links. Originally the serial links were intended to be synchronous links running the High Level Data Link Control (HDLC) protocol. PPP has now been extended to operate over asynchronous connections, offering an alternative to SLIP in this respect. PPP is designed to offer the following functions:

- A *Link Control Protocol* (LCP) to establish, configure and monitor the serial connection.

- An encapsulation format.

- A set of *Network Control Protocols* (NCP) to allow several Network Layer protocols to be multiplexed over the same serial channel.

Table 6.3 summarizes the current PPP RFCs.

PPP Connection Establishment

PPP established a data connection in several stages:

1. LCP packets are exchanged to establish the link and to ensure its quality. *Link Quality Monitoring* (LQM) is used for this purpose.

2. If the link is established, NCP packets for each configured protocol are sent to establish logical connections for this protocol. For example, if the router is running IP and IPX, separate NCP packets are sent for each protocol and successful NCP negotiation will result in an active route being inserted into the Routing Table for the protocol.

3. Datagrams for the protocols are sent over the link using PPP encapsulation. One LAN frame is mapped onto one PPP packet (unless the LAN MTU exceeds the serial line MTU). LAN packets from the same, or different protocols are not combined into the same PPP packet.

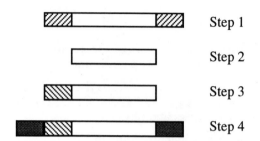

Figure 6.5:   PPP Encapsulation Procedure

Table 6.3:   PPP RFCs

RFC Number	Content
1548	The PPP protocol
1332	PPP IP Control Protocol (IPCP)
1333	PPP Link Quality Monitoring (LQM)
1334	PPP Authentication Protocols
1376	DECnet IV Control Protocol
1377	OSI CLNP Control Protocol
1378	AppleTalk Control Protocol
1552	IPX Control Protocol

PPP Encapsulation Mechanism

Figure 6.5 shows the way that LAN datagrams are encapsulated in PPP. One of the reasons why PPP is so efficient is that, for routed protocols, the MAC Layer information is stripped off the LAN frame to leave a standard IP datagram. The appropriate destination LAN MAC Layer framing is but onto this datagram at the other end of the connection.

Step 1 is the LAN frame being received by a router. The white block represents the IP datagram, with the shaded blocks being the LAN MAC header and trailer. For an Ethernet frame, this adds up to 38 bytes (this includes the equivalent of a 96-bit interframe gap).

Step 2 shows the MAC data stripped off the datagram.

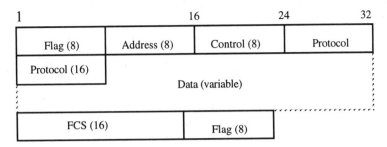

Figure 6.6: PPP Data Link Layer Frame Structure

Step 3 is for the router to add the 2 byte PPP header onto the datagram. One part of this header represents the protocol type for the datagram inside the PPP package.

Step 4 shows the final addition of the HDLC frame header and trailer. For an individual frame this is 4 bytes, but consecutive serial frames "share" the 8-bit interframe flag.

PPP Data Link Frame Structure

The PPP frame structure is shown in Figure 6.6.

Flag Field

This field is a standard HDLC flag of 01111110 binary. In back-to-back traffic, a single flag is used at the end of one frame and the beginning of the next. HDLC bit stuffing is used to preserve the appearance of flags despite the occurrence of "01111110" patterns in the data. Bit stuffing means that the sending station inserts a 0 bit after a sequence of 5 sequential 1s in a non-flag data stream. The receiving station monitors the bit stream. If a pattern of 5 1s is detected, the sixth bit is examined. If it is a 0, the receiver deletes it. If it is a 1, the receiver interprets the character as a flag.

Address Field

The address field is a single byte field and in PPP it always contains the "all stations" address 11111111 binary (FFh). HDLC is also used as a multidrop protocol, where station addresses are significant. PPP is not defined in this context. This field serves no useful purpose and PPP end stations can negotiate to eliminate it.

Control Field

For PPP this field contains the number 00000011 binary (03h). This binary sequence identifies the frame as connectionless Un-numbered Information

(UI)[1]. This field serves no useful purpose and PPP end stations can negotiate to eliminate it.

Protocol Field

Instead, it indicates the PPP Control Protocol type, either LCP or NCP. Values in the "Cxxxh" range are reserved for LCP. Values in the "0xxx" range are reserved for NCP and identify the Network Protocol for the specific datagram contained in the PPP packet. PPP end stations can negotiate to reduce the size of the protocol field to 8 bits.

FCS

The Frame Check Sequence is a 16-bit Cyclic Redundancy Check.

Network Control Protocols

Serial lines must also cope with other behavior patterns of LAN protocols. In particular, the way in which broadcast and multicast traffic is propagated over the connections. For this purpose, a Network Control Protocol (NCP) is defined for each of the Network Layer protocols transmitted by PPP. This is why the list of PPP RFCs is so long.

Useful PPP Features

The Protocol field and the NCP concept in PPP means that it can be used to multiplex protocols from different Network Layer stacks over the same physical link. Even bridged traffic can be sent over PPP, following the RFC1220 recommendations.

However, I think that the three most interesting features of PPP are:

- Its interoperability

- The compact and efficient framing

- The LQM feature

PPP has a good interoperability track record, although initially all the testing was done with IP packet. For IPX, vendors must follow the guidelines in RFC 1362 and its related documents. Initial trials have been very promising and a formal study performed by the RMT Connections Ltd. test lab showed high levels of multiprotocol interoperability between eight different router vendors.

As you can see from Figure 6.6, PPP adds only 2 bytes of overhead onto a normal data frame. This is a big improvement over many proprietary framing protocols. However, PPP does insert LCP and NCP frames into the data stream for control purposes. As you'll see from the RFCs, you can decide the

---

[1]Note the similarity to SNAP encoding. HDLC, and 802.2 can be used in connection oriented and connectionless applications. SNAP and PPP are connectionless.

frequency of insertion by adjusting configuration timers. The more frequent the control information, the more overhead, but the better your control.

One of the most exciting features of PPP is its Link Quality Monitor (LQM) feature. LQM offers a way to detect leased line failure in a rapid and user-definable way. You may think this is a strange advantage; surely we can tell if a leased line is down. However, it's not always that easy. Sometimes a leased line transmission quality drops, until it falls below some critical threshold for reliable data transmission. Router may still see the line as "up" from a physical point of view. LQM allows a Network Administrator to define acceptable quality levels, that they can map to guaranteed levels of service form the PTT. If the Link Quality falls below this threshold, the router can reroute. Using link state routing protocols like OSPF, this rerouting can occur within seconds.

6.2.8   Address Configuration and Resolution

For address configuration, leased lines were initially seen as a 2-station LAN. This simplifies many of the programming issues for leased line treatment, because traditional ARP and RARP mechanisms work just fine. However, as shown in Chapter 11, serial lines can use up valuable IP address space unless we use variable length subnets, or un-numbered serial lines.

Routing protocols that allow the use of variable length subnets (e.g., OSPF, I-ISIS) can help to economize on subnet usage. However, the procedure can be tedious and difficult for humans to understand (unless you are lucky enough to be able to think in binary).

The real answer to the problem lies in the use of *un-numbered serial lines*. I explain this feature in Chapter 11. Whatever the internal representation, un-numbered serial lines allow us to avoid using addresses at all for serial connections.

RFP Question: Does the router support un-numbered serial lines?

6.2.9   Network Level Multiplexing

Using PPP, we can multiplex frames from different IP data streams, or from different protocols. This is shown in Figure 6.7.

Apart form the obvious issue of sharing the bandwidth, the figure implies another issue. PPP multiplexes on a packet by packet basis (as do X.25, ISDN and Frame Relay, by the way). A long packet will occupy more line time than a short packet, in fact I've summarized the line latency for the most common line speeds and packet sizes in Table 6.4.

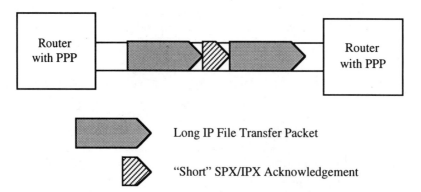

Long IP File Transfer Packet

"Short" SPX/IPX Acknowledgement

Figure 6.7: Protocol Multiplexing with PPP

Table 6.4: Line Latency (in seconds) For Typical Serial Line Rates

Packet Size	2400bps	9600bps	56kbps	64kbps	256kbps	T1	E1
64	2.13E-01	5.33E-02	9.14E-03	8.00E-03	2.00E-03	3.33E-04	2.67E-04
128	4.27E-01	1.07E-01	1.83E-02	1.60E-02	4.00E-03	6.67E-04	5.33E-04
256	8.53E-01	2.13E-01	3.66E-02	3.20E-02	8.00E-03	1.33E-03	1.07E-03
512	1.71E+00	4.27E-01	7.31E-02	6.40E-02	1.60E-02	2.67E-03	2.13E-03
1024	3.41E+00	8.53E-01	1.46E-01	1.28E-01	3.20E-02	5.33E-03	4.27E-03
2048	6.83E+00	1.71E+00	2.93E-01	2.56E-01	6.40E-02	1.07E-02	8.53E-03

There are three major issues with this store-and-forward delay:

- With pure IP systems, higher level protocol such as UDP may time out because longer packets take too long to clock through slow leased lines.

- In multiprotocol systems, bursts of packets from one protocol may cause time-out problems with other protocols.

- We can never multiplex voice and data together in this way.

The solution to the first problem is simple, but tedious. We must change the timeouts for sensitive protocols so that end systems that communicate over the WAN will not suffer timeouts. The classic vulnerable IP protocol in this respect is UDP, which has a standard timeout of 700ms *for the entire UDP message block (8kB).* Since the popular NFS protocol operates over UDP, it is very likely that you'll need to tune the timer to get NFS to operate successfully over low speed lines.

In Chapter 5, I talked about the new LAN switches, some of which use fast packet (or "on-the-fly") switching where only the first few bytes of the frame are clocked in before switching takes place. In the LAN/WAN case, fast packet cannot help us. There is a massive speed difference between a 9600bps WAN line and a 10Mbps Ethernet. If we clock in WAN traffic in 6-byte chunks (i.e., the length of a MAC address required to make a switching decision) it takes 5ms to enter the router and at 10Mbps (assuming we can access the Ethernet immediately) only 5µs are needed to clock the 6 bytes out (we're clocking out around 1000 time faster than we're clocking in). Thus, for every 6 byte transmission we sent onto the LAN, there will be about a 5ms "gap." This just isn't legal on Ethernet. The only valid alternative is to wait for the entire frame to clock into the router before starting to clock the frame out.

Fast packet techniques obviously work better if there is less of a speed differential between the input and output data streams; but then there's no reason to implement them because the clocking in delay is much shorter! In fact, there are very few true fast packet devices on the market today (which is one reason why the term has lost its original meaning).

6.3   N-ISDN

Narrowband ISDN seems to have been arriving for the last couple of hundred years now. I seem to remember hearing about this marvelous new service when I first got involved with routers. ISDN was always described in very vague terms, usually involving high speed WAN connections to the desktop.

There's a reason why the early descriptions of ISDN were vague: it's just not that exciting! ISDN is simply a fast dial, digital telephone system. That was what it was designed to do and that's still what it does best.

In a normal telephone network, digital devices must use modems to convert their digital data streams into analog tones that can be passed over the audio circuits of the telephone system.

In contrast, ISDN allows data devices to connect directly to the digital circuits. The digital connections for ISDN operate at 64kbps, full duplex. ISDN service is delivered in two flavors. The Basic Rate Interface (BRI) offers two 64kbps connections, plus a 16kbps signaling channel. The more expensive Primary Rate Interface (PRI) is delivered as a cluster of 30 data channels at 64kbps and one 64kbps signaling channel.

The 64kbps data channels are known in ISDN terms as *B channels*. The signaling channels are always called *D channels*, regardless of the line rate. ISDN components include multiplexing circuits so that the B and D channels pass along the same channel. I show this principle in Figure 6.8.

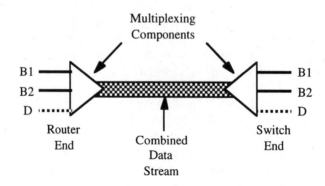

Figure 6.8:   ISDN Channel Multiplexing

For BRI, the Combined Data Stream I show in Figure 6.8 is 144kbps. For PRI, the combined bandwidth is 1.984 Mbps.

I'll need to resort to the correct ISDN jargon to allow you to match up my explanations with those in the references. Unfortunately, ISDN was conceived within the telephony industry so few of these terms make much sense to the typical IP guru.

6.3.1   Logical Representation

Figure 6.9 shows the ISDN Reference Configuration Model. I have reproduced this model exactly as it is described in ISDN reference documentation.

Like the OSI Model, the ISDN Reference Model is an essential tool for technical discussions about ISDN.

The Reference Model contain two types of object, a *functional group* and a *reference point*. In real-world terms, a functional group is a piece of ISDN-related hardware such as a Terminal Adapter or Router. A reference point is a type of cable, such as an X.21 serial link, or a 4-wire, RJ45-terminated UTP cable.

ISDN Functional Groups

Network Terminator Type 1 (NT1) and Network Terminator Type 2 (NT2). These functional groups were originally defined to be implemented as physically separate units within ISDN. The NT2 unit contains multiplexing functionality that allows up to 8 *TE1* units (see below) to share in individual ISDN connection. In most implementations of ISDN, however, the functions of NT1 and NT2 are combined into a single box. In combined implementations, the T interface (which is used to interconnect the NT1 and NT2) is internal to the NT device.

Terminal Equipment (TE). This functional group includes devices such as digital telephones as well as data-oriented DTE equipment such as routers and bridges. *TE1* equipment must be equipped with a true ISDN interface and is capable of signaling over the ISDN D channel. TE2 equipment does not require an ISDN interface and cannot become involved in D channel signaling.

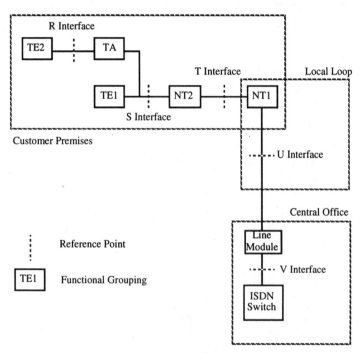

Figure 6.9: ISDN Reference Configuration Model

Terminal Adapter (TA). These devices allow *TE2* equipment (i.e. equipment that does not have a direct ISDN interface) to access an ISDN network. Terminal adapter functions are defined in a series of additional CCITT standards. The information in brackets indicates the relevant countries and the type of conventional serial interface supported by the standard.

- V.120 (USA; V.24, V.35)
- V.110 (Europe, Japan; V.24, V.35)
- DMI-1 (USA/AT&T; V.35)
- DMI-2 (USA/AT&T; V.24)
- T-LINK (USA, Canada/ Northern Telecom; V.24, V.35)
- X.30 (Germany, Scandinavia, Japan, UK; X.21)

ISDN Reference Points

R Interface. This reference point defines a functional interface between a non-ISDN DTE device and the TA. This interface allows the use of RS232, X.21 or V.35 connections. Although the ISDN community regard the R Interface as an interim solution, it is likely to remain with us for a number of years to come.

S Interface and *T Interface.* Originally defined as separate functional interfaces into the NT2 and NT1 functional groups respectively, these reference points can now be regarded as being identical. In essence they are both defined as 4-wire cables terminated in an RJ45 jack plug. In a BRI, the signal passing along the S/T interfaces is clocked at 144kbps, with the B and D channel information multiplexed together.

U Interface. The U interface operates between the NT device on the Customer Premises and the *Line Module* (essentially a repeater) located in the ISDN exchange. This is a 2-wire interface which operates at 192kbps. A Time Domain Multiplexing (TDM) mechanism is used to recover the 2B+D channels. The remaining bandwidth is used for framing and physical layer control information. The typical maximum distance quoted for such an interface is 5km. This is sufficient to drive the signal from urban locations into the local exchange. Longer distances require in-line repeaters.

6.3.2   Basic Rate ISDN

The ISDN Basic Rate Interface (BRI), defined in I.420, consists of 2 B channels (at 64kbps) controlled by a single D channel (at 16kbps). The physical connector is a standard RJ45 (ISO 8877) jack plug. ISDN requires that at least 4 wires (differential TX and RX signals) are connected, but an additional two power in and power sink connections (making a total of 8 wires) may be optionally added. This feature was included to allow telephone equipment to be "powered" from the network. Since modern data equipment exceeds the power limits originally defined by ISDN, the power wires are not normally connected.

6.3.3   Primary Rate ISDN

The ISDN Primary Rate Interface (PRI), defined in I.421, offers 30 B channels controlled by a single D channel (note that in the USA, Canada, Japan and Korea, I.421 defines a 23B+D service). Within the PDH multiplexing hierarchy this corresponds to an E1, 2.048 Mbps data rate. Indeed, the physical connection for Primary Rate ISDN is a G.703 twin coaxial BNC connector, identical to most European E1 services.

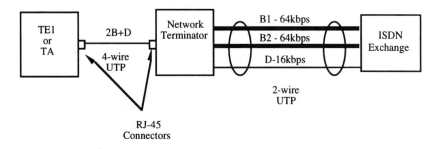

Figure 6.10: ISDN Basic Rate Interface

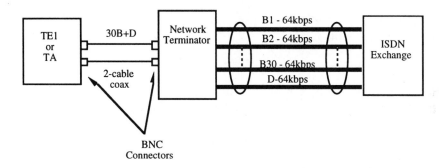

Figure 6.11: ISDN Primary Rate Interface

The G.704 and G.732 standards divide this stream into 32 channels. In a PRI service connection, one of the channels is used by the PTTs' mux management, one channel is used as the D channel, leaving 30 B channels for data transmission.

The signaling protocol which passes over the PRI D Channel is defined in Q.931. However, many early ISDN implementations are based on an existing installed base of Integrated Services PBX switches (ISPBX). These are used to build private voice networks using traditional leased lines.

6.3.4   ISDN Awareness In Routers

There are three levels of ISDN awareness that you can imagine:

- ISDN-ignorant
- ISDN-tolerant
- ISDN-capable

Each of these levels of awareness implies different levels of ISDN functionality. In general, the industry has identified three things we might like to do with ISDN:

- Circuit Backup
- Dial-On-Demand
- Bandwidth-On-Demand

Circuit Backup

As the name suggests, we are using an ISDN dial-up connection to back up a more conventional WAN circuit. The most usual form of primary circuit is a leased line, although I have seen proposals for the backup of X.25 and Frame Relay connections with ISDN.

Dial-On-Demand

In this technique, ISDN represents the primary means of WAN connection. When the router has IP data to send, it dials the ISDN connection, sends the data and then clears the connection. Dial-on-demand is useful in small office sites that can't justify the cost of a permanent WAN connection.

Bandwidth-On-Demand (BoD)

The most exciting, but least understood use of ISDN. BoD is a simple concept. If we have a conventional leased line connection of 64kbps, why not use ISDN to dial up additional bandwidth during time of congestion? This is a very powerful concept because leased line networks are usually dimensioned to allow for peak bandwidth utilization. In LAN applications, peak utilization is often 10 times higher than average. If we analyze the utilization rate for a traditional leased line network, we typically come up with numbers in the 5-10% range. In other words, we are throwing away 90% of our lease payment.

If we can get BoD implementations right (none exist today), then this offers a very exciting range of design options for Wide Area Internetworks.

ISDN-Ignorant Routers

This describes most router equipment that uses conventional serial interfaces. Routers see ISDN as a form of serial line. The problem is that serial lines are "always there," whereas ISDN connection must be established using D Channel signaling. To a normal, healthy IP router, an ISDN circuit should be marked as "down" in the Routing Table.

To overcome this problem, there are products available from several Terminal Adapter manufacturers that spoof the serial connection. These are generically known as *ISDN Backup Adapters*.

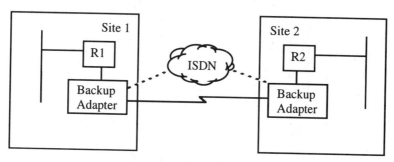

Figure 6.12: ISDN Backup Adapters

Backup adapters are *always* used in conjunction with a permanent leased line. The leased line circuit is connected through the adapter into the router, as shown in Figure 6.12. If the leased line has problems, an ISDN connection will be dialed to the backup adapter at the other site.

The important point to remember with the backup adapter is that the router has only one physical serial port and that port is a conventional V.35, X.21 or RS232 interface. As far as the router is concerned, there is just a serial connection on the router. No special hardware or software is needed so the router can remain blissfully ignorant of "that telephone system." Even better is that the router requires no formal ISDN approval for use with an external backup adapter. Within Europe, the ridiculous formality of approvals is the biggest single reason for the slow adoption of ISDN in the data communications business.

Backup adapters can be a little more expensive than normal ISDN TAs because the more effective versions contain signal quality monitoring circuits. Nevertheless , this form of ISDN backup is currently the most effective and easy to implement. However, it can be very expensive approach because backup adapters must be installed in pairs: one at each end of the specific leased line.

ISDN Tolerant Routers

The next stage in ISDN awareness for routers is what I call ISDN Tolerant. This is where the existing hardware (i.e., a conventional serial interface) is retained and physical connection to the ISDN is made using a Terminal Adapter. The software in the router must be modified to make the Routing Table tolerate the "non-existent" serial connection for ISDN.

As soon as the Routing Table can do this, we can install routers where ISDN is the only WAN connection.

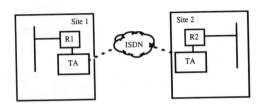

Figure 6.13:   ISDN-Tolerant Routers

Figure 6.13 shows this concept. Within the router, there are two levels of support that we can expect:

- Raise DTR
- V.25*bis*

With a Raise DTR technique, the ISDN telephone number of the destination TA is configured into the local TA during installation. When the router receives traffic that needs to be routed over the ISDN network, it raises a special line on the conventional serial interface called *Data Terminal Ready* (DTR). The TA uses DTR as the signal to dial the pre-programmed ISDN number. When the router drops DTR, the ISDN call can be cleared.

Raise DTR can be used for Backup and Dial-On-Demand. It could also be used as a crude Bandwidth-on-Demand technique.

V.25*bis* is a more elegant version of Raise DTR. Rather than a single ISDN telephone number being entered into the TA, the router is allowed to keep track of a list of ISDN numbers associated with IP destination addresses. So a V.25*bis* router can connect to different ISDN destinations.

V.25*bis* is a CCITT standard and it allows any serial DTE device to send information into a modem. Note that V.25*bis* is an in-band signaling technique. This means that the signaling messages pass in the same channel as the data. In contrast, ISDN uses out-of-band signaling because the D Channel is kept logically separate using the mux circuits within ISDN. The effect of this difference is that in a V.25*bis* device, only one of the ISDN B Channels can be used at any time, because once the connection is made, signaling cannot take place to establish the second channel.

Nevertheless, V.25*bis* is a major improvement in ISDN-awareness and can be used very effectively in pre-ISDN equipment with only software changes. The technique can be used to implement Backup, Dial-on-Demand and Bandwidth-on-Demand.

Note that some TAs also allow the use of Hayes modem commands. The Hayes commands are designed for use by *asynchronous* modems. Most routers operate as *synchronous* devices so the preferred signaling standard is V.25*bis*.

ISDN-Capable Routers

The ultimate ISDN development is to install an ISDN S/T interface *inside* the router. Although this seems logical, products have only been available since 1993 thanks to three main problems:

- Router manufacturers are US-based and must be convinced of the size of the market opportunity. Since the overall growth of companies like Cisco and Wellfleet look like a rocket's trajectory, they could afford to ignore the lure of the ISDN market.

- ISDN is the least standard of any standard I've encountered. There are different versions all across Europe and the Far East. Two or three versions exist in the US. Recently two breakthroughs have helped: Euro-ISDN and US National ISDN. On the other hand, you could think of these as just two *more* standards!

- The time and expense of a single ISDN certification for a single country is frightening. Since each European country requires separate certification, this is multiplied by the number of markets.

Despite the obstacles, native ISDN implementations are available from both Cisco and Wellfleet. In addition, UK-based Spider Systems has been shipping ISDN routers for several years and has captured a significant revenue prize from the ISDN-phobic Americans.

D Channel and Data

The D Channel in all ISDN implementations is used for call signaling. However, the 16kbps channel used in a BRI represents quite a lot of bandwidth. Some ISDN evangelists have promoted the idea of using the D Channel as a "free" pathway for some form of useful data traffic.

One of the most mature services offered on the ISDN D Channel is the joint offering from France Telecom (operating the French ISDN service) and Transpac (operating the French Public X.25 service). The D Channel service can be used to bring a 9 600 bps X.25 connection into the subscriber site and still leave plenty of signaling bandwidth.

Several other ideas are being proposed for the D Channel, but let me just point out a problem that exists with this system. Figure 6.14 shows a detailed view of the ISDN connection from router R1 to routers R2 and R3. I've shown the D Channel as a solid line and the two switched B channels as dotted lines. You can see from this diagram that the D Channel connection only goes as far as the first ISDN exchange. Remember that the D Channel is just a signaling channel and it does not extend point-to-point over the network.

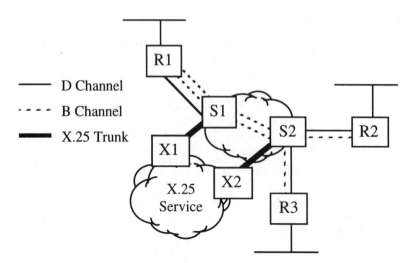

Figure 6.14:   Data Over ISDN D Channel

Here I show the D Channel connection to the X.25 service. The X.25 switch and the ISDN exchange have to be co-located, which is one of the limiting factors on this facility. However, British Telecom recently announced an equivalent D-channel service which hopes to provide X.25 and clear-channel data access. The big benefit of D-channel data may actually be to send overhead traffic such as routing protocol updates and network management polls without actually making an ISDN connection.

6.3.5   ISDN Problems

Despite the usefulness of ISDN in internetworking, there are several basic problems associated with the technology. I'll give a quick rundown of these problems here. Manufacturers of ISDN equipment will address these problems in many different ways and you need to get a clear idea of ISDN functionality using the RFI document.

The problem areas can be summarized as:

- Interoperability
- Line pooling
- Inverse multiplexing
- Address translation
- Network management

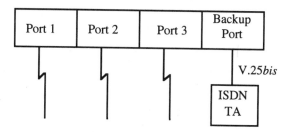

Figure 6.15:   ISDN Line Pooling

Interoperability

The big issue with any serial technology is the definition of the framing structure. Serial lines have PPP, X.25 has RFC 877 and 1356. ISDN has no specific RFC describing its encapsulation format. The early ISDN implementations have been based on PPP encapsulation since ISDN is essentially a serial connection. This generally means good interoperability between vendors. However, you need to take care; there are some proprietary implementations out there and you should avoid these at all costs.

Line Pooling

The concept of ISDN backup is very attractive. However, consider the situation if you have 20 remote sites with 20 leased line connections into them and they all connect back to a central location. The router in the central location requires 20 ports, one for each leased line. However, if we want to back up each of these leased lines, do we have to assign a "backup port" to each of the primary ports on the central router? If this is the case, we'll end up with 40 ports on the central router, which gets pretty expensive.

Figure 6.15 shows the basic principle, but with a smaller number of ports.

This diagram shows the concept of a backup port on the router. If any serial port fails, the router software transfer the configuration of the serial port to the designated backup port. Included in the transfer is the ISDN address for the router at the other end of the link. The backup port then sends V.25*bis* signals down to an external ISDN TA to make the backup connection.

In this implementation, a single backup port can be used to safeguard all of the serial ports on the central site router. Note that the backup port could also be a native ISDN adapter inside the router, but the Raise DTR capability I described above isn't enough to implement this feature because the central router must be able to call any of the remote sites.

Inverse Multiplexing

The concept of inverse multiplexing is not unique to ISDN, but the spread of ISDN technology means that inverse muxes will be in greater demand. The

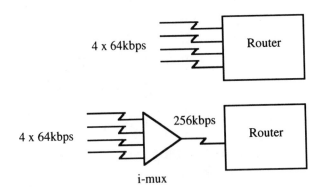

Figure 6.16:   Inverse Multiplexing

concept is simple. In a mux, we take a number of lower speed access connections and multiplex them onto a higher speed trunk. In an inverse mux, we take a high speed access line and use multiple lower speed trunks to carry the signal.

In Figure 6.16 I highlight the essential differences.

In the upper part of this diagram, the router has 4 serial ports, each of which is given a clock of 64kbps. In the lower diagram, the i-mux combines the four 64kbps lines together and presents a clock speed of 256kbps to the router.

With serial lines, the economics of i-muxing are usually not good. In most of Europe, if you lease more than 6 or 7 64kbps lines between the same two points, it's actually the same price to lease a 2Mbps circuit. In the US, studies show a range of break-even points from two lines up to eight [7].

However, with ISDN, we have two 64kbps lines at our disposal and these could be i-muxed with one or more leased lines to give a Bandwidth-on-Demand feature.

> RFP Question: Describe any inverse multiplexing features available in your ISDN implementation.

Address Translation

This is a common problem today with any switch WAN technology. The issues of ISDN Address Translation are virtually identical to X.25, Frame Relay SVC and ATM.

In Figure 6.17 I show three routers with local LAN and ISDN BRI connections.

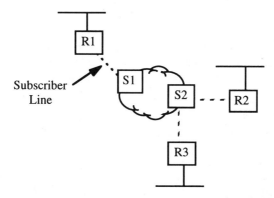

Figure 6.17: Typical ISDN Connection

Each router is on a separate site, with a *subscriber line* connecting it to the nearest ISDN exchange (S1, S2). Remember for BRI, the subscriber line runs at 144kbps and carries both B Channels and the D Channel.

ISDN is a *connection-oriented, circuit switched* network. In other words, when the subscriber signals for a connection, a circuit is established through the network for the duration of the call. The addressing structure used by ISDN is based on the international telephone numbering system defined in CCITT E.164. Since this is rather different from the IP addresses used on our LANs, we need to build an Address Translation Table. Today this is done manually, although there's at least one initiative: the *Next Hop Resolution Protocol* which is currently under development in the IETF.

ISDN Security

ISDN is a public, dial-in network. In France, some lucky telephone users actually have ISDN lines rather than normal telephone connections. For the corporate network user, the prospect of any telephone user simply dialing in to his or her network backbone is a little scary. For this reason, ISDN offers a number of interesting security options.

- *Calling Line ID* (CLID)
- *Password Authentication Protocol* (PAP)
- Challenge Handshake Authentication Protocol (CHAP)

CLID

When an ISDN device requests a connection, the calling telephone number is passed to the destination. This is a very secure ID technique.

PAP

PAP is a PPP technique [8] that passes an authentication password when the PPP connection is established. PPP is not a secure technique, because the password is sent only once and it is inserted in the frame in clear text.

CHAP

CHAP is also a PPP feature. CHAP authentication is sent at PPP connection time and periodically during the connection. The authentication continually changes using an encryption technique.

The Holistic Approach

A true security scheme for ISDN must involve both CLID and CHAP because CLID may not always be transmitted *between* PTTs. CHAP will be transmitted because it operates above the ISDN layers.

6.4   Frame Relay

As I write this book, ATM is enjoying an unprecedented degree of media hype. In 1990, Frame Relay was in the limelight. At that time, many of the existing X.25 public data services in Europe were nearing overload. The switches used were old, steam-driven devices that could just about manage a few hundred packets per second switching rate. Delays over the networks were becoming too much for LAN-style protocols such as IPX/SPX and in general the system was having a hard time.

Frame Relay was touted as the solution to all of these problems and amazingly enough, virtually all of the promise has come true.

Frame Relay sneaked up on the data communications world, because most of the protocol development was done to use Frame Relay as the framing protocol for the ISDN D Channel. Because of the deployment issues with ISDN, someone suggested using Frame Relay as a communication protocol in its own right.

6.4.1   Logical Representation

A Frame Relay service is made up of a number of Frame Relay Switches interconnected by a mesh of conventional leased line circuits. DTE devices such as routers connect to the service, again using a conventional leased line. I show this physical view of the network in Figure 6.18.

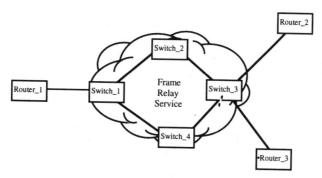

Figure 6.18:   Frame Relay Physical Representation

Logically, Frame Relay looks a little different. Inside the physical connection, there are multiple VCs. In today's Frame Relay, these VCs are actually permanently assigned between two end-points, as I show in Figure 6.19.

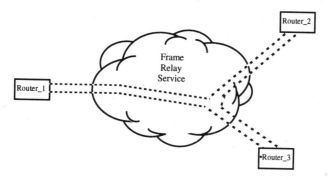

Figure 6.19:   Logical Representation of Frame Relay

When the service provider sets up the Frame Relay network for the customer in Figure 6.19, they will actually configure *Permanent Virtual Circuit* (PVC) connections between the three sites. For example, Router_1 will see PVCs to Router_2 and Router_3. Router_2 will see PVCs to Router_1 and Router_3. Router_3 will see PVCs to Router_1 and Router_2. In fact, this network is *fully meshed* because all of the routers have direct PVCs to all the other locations. If there were no direct PVC between Router_1 and Router_2, for example, it would be possible for Router_1 to send traffic to Router_3 and for Router_3 to forward that traffic using conventional IP routing to Router_2.

Figure 6.20 shows the structure of a Frame Relay frame. There are only 10 addressing bits in this frame (although extended addressing is possible). With 10 bits we can address up to 1024 possible locations. The bits actually represent a VC number, or as Frame Relay describes it, a *Data Link Connection Identifier* (DLCI). DLCI addresses are purely local to the link between the router and the first Frame Relay switch. These numbers can be re-used elsewhere in the network. For this reason, the 1024 limit is not really a problem for most users. In fact, some of these addresses are reserved for link management and other reasons. User channels are allowed to operate on DLCIs 16 to 991 so any router on a Frame Relay service can connect up to 975 possible end-points over a single cable using the default 2-byte addressing.

Frame Relay Addressing

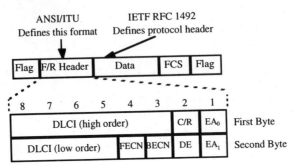

Figure 6.20:   Frame Format for Frame Relay

The other bits in the header are:

C/R: Command/Response

EA_X: Extended addressing. If these bits are set to 1, then the next byte is an address byte

FECN: Forward explicit congestion notification. Sent if the F/R device is experiencing congestion in the direction in which the data is traveling.

BECN: Backward explicit congestion notification. Sent if the F/R device is experiencing congestion in the direction from which data originates.

DE: Discard eligibility. Frames in which this bit is set should be preferentially discarded in the event of congestion.

6.4.2   Physical Interfaces and Speeds

Frame Relay is typically described as a T1/E1 speed service (i.e. 1.544 or 2.048 Mbps). In fact, the protocol is very versatile and will operate quite happily down to 9 600 bps or even lower. To date, the fastest I've seen it operating is 45Mbps T3, but that's only because there are no higher serial interface line speeds generally available. Overall, Frame Relay is an excellent serial protocol and imposes much lower loading on DTE devices than a connection-oriented protocol such as X.25.

An interesting capability for Frame Relay is a form of Bandwidth on Demand. Put yourself in the position of a network designer trying to calculate the line loading for a given site.

Committed Information Rate

Let's say we connect to a Frame Relay service over an E1, 2.048Mbps connection. We may not actually need 2Mbps of bandwidth and we certainly don't want to pay for 2Mbps. Initially we calculate that we need around 100kbps for the site. The PTT offers us the option of a *Committed Information Rate* (CIR) of 128kbps (CIR normally goes up in increments of 64kbps). In effect, we are paying the PTT for a 128kbps line, but the connection into the Frame Relay network is at 2Mbps. It sounds good, doesn't it? What happens is this. While we are transmitting data at less than the CIR, the frames that enter the Frame Relay network will have the DE bit *clear* (i.e. =0). If DE is clear, the network *must* deliver the frame, not congestion excuses.

If we exceed CIR, then the frames that do so will have DE set. If the Frame Relay network has the capacity to pass the traffic we're sending, then all the frame will get through. However, if the network is congested, then frames marked with DE will be discarded to relieve congestion before frames with DE clear. In theory, a Frame Relay provider should dimension the backbone so that CIR can be guaranteed to be congestion-free.

6.4.3   Address Configuration and Resolution

Frame Relay is comparatively simple because it uses PVCs. Since we are not explicitly charged for making connections, we can send short routing queries such as ARP or OSPF over Frame Relay without a cost penalty. For this reason, many of us in the industry strongly favor Frame Relay as a LAN-friendly WAN system.

As you can imagine, setting up a fully meshed Frame Relay network actually involves a lot of configuration. Imagine the situation in Figure 6.21. Each of the routers on this network has at least one IP address, for the LAN or LANs attached to it, plus the "dummy" addresses assigned to the Frame Relay connections.

The DLCIs have a purely local significance, the only rule is that two PVCs on the same physical link cannot have the same DLCI address.

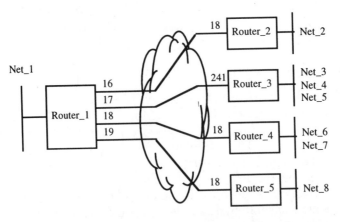

Figure 6.21:   Frame Relay Addressing Issues

Inverse ARP

One option is to manually map the IP addresses of the far-end networks into an address translation table. Another option is to design a simple protocol to do the work for us. In Frame Relay, this protocol is defined in RFC 1293 and is called *Inverse ARP*. Inverse ARP works very well with Frame Relay because ANSI and ITU defined a link management protocol that operates over the cable between the router and the Frame Relay switch. This protocol actually tells the router what DLCIs are active when the cable is plugged in. The router then sends an Inverse ARP query down each active DLCI. If an Inverse ARP router is on the other end, it will answer and the two routers will exchange IP addresses, which are dynamically entered into the address table. Very slick.

RFP Question:	Does your Frame Relay implementation support RFC 1293 Inverse ARP? For which Network Layer protocols?

6.4.4   Routing Protocols and Full Mesh Networks

Frame Relay was originally designed as a Switched Virtual Circuit (SVC) WAN. This means that there is no equivalent to a MAC broadcast capability. In other words, protocols such as RIP (broadcast) and OSPF (multicast) cannot operate in the same way as they would on a LAN. In Figure 6.21 you can see four remote sites connected back to a central site, with one Virtual Circuit operating between each remote site and the central site. If a routing update is sent from the central site, the Frame Relay implementation on the router must be aware that the single *physical* cable connecting it to the Frame Relay network actually represents multiple *logical* connections, and that these connections go to different locations. The routing update has to be copied onto each appropriate outbound VC.

Another issue with routing protocols is the concept of Split Horizon. Unfortunately I talk about Split Horizon in Chapter 14, but the concept is very simple. If a router learns about a route on a given physical interface, it must not re-advertise information about the same route out of the same interface. For LANs this makes a lot of sense and it was for this technology that Split Horizon was devised. For Frame Relay, it doesn't make sense to apply Split Horizon on the basis of a *physical* connection. Instead we have to apply Split Horizon separately for each VC. In Figure 6.21, this means that Router 1 will receive the route to Router 2 on VC number 16. Router 1 can then re-advertise this route out of VCs 17, 18 and 19 even though these are on the same physical cable.

Some router implementations of Frame Relay do not apply Split Horizon on a per-VC basis. These implementations require that the Frame Relay network is designed as a *Full Mesh* if you need any-to-any communication. I spent about half an hour trying to re-draw Figure 6.21 as a fully meshed Frame Relay network, but it was just too complicated. In a Fully Meshed network, each site has at least one VC connected to every other site! This means that if you have five sites, each site will have four VCs, one to each other site. So for n locations, each location would have $(n$-1$)$ VCs so the entire network would contain $n(n$-1$)$ VCs. For a five site network, there would be 20 VCs. For a 100 site network, a fully meshed backbone would require 9900 VCs!

Fully meshed networks are necessary for true peer-to-peer networks. In Figure 6.21, you can imagine that this is a banking network. Each remote site would normally communicate with the central site. Occasionally, a branch site may want to send information to another branch. If the router Frame Relay implementation does not require a fully meshed network, then the traffic can pass to the central site and be forwarded to the other branch.

RFP Question:	How does your router Frame Relay implementation apply Split Horizon?

6.4.5   Frame Relay Interoperability

Assuming we can connect to the Frame Relay network and get our DLCIs and IP addresses sorted out, how do we represent Network Layer information on the PVCs? For example, if I'm running multiple protocols on my router, do I need a separate DLCI for each protocol?

The answer to this question is given in RFC 1490 [9], which describes the encapsulation of multiprotocol traffic over Frame Relay. Figure 6.22 shows the header for the encapsulation scheme.

In this scheme, the SNAP/Type mechanism used by LANs is replaced by a single byte Network Layer Protocol ID (NLPID) field. In Figure 6.22, I show this field containing the value CCh, which indicates IP. The value 80h is defined for SNAP, with a SNAP header containing the OUI and Type fields further into the frame.

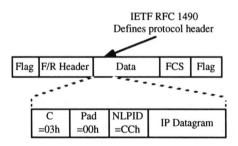

**Figure 6.22:   Multiprotocol Encapsulation on
Frame Relay**

6.5   X.25

In router terms, X.25 is very similar in concept to Frame Relay, although the technology predates Frame Relay by over a decade. X.25 has three major differences:

- •   X.25 was always deployed as a Switch Virtual Circuit (SVC) network, rather than a PVC network.

- •   X.25 was designed to operate over circuits with high bit error rates so includes extensive error checking and retransmission functions.

- •   X.25 networks often limit the MTU size to 128 or 256 bytes, whereas the Frame Relay UNI requires devices to support 4 500 byte MTUs.

In addition to these differences, X.25 has had years of installation and development experience and has penetrated into all market areas. It is also available world-wide, although this availability can be trickier in the USA.

Let's look at the differences in turn. For a fuller description of X.25, I refer you to [4].

SVC Operation

Fortunately for the LAN community, the Frame Relay committees could never get their act together on signaling so the first generation of Frame Relay products hit the streets offering a PVC service. This is ideal for LANs because we can make use of Inverse ARP to simplify configuration. X.25 has always operated on SVCs. In other words, when you plug the X.25 cable into a router, there are no active circuits that Inverse ARP can flow over. This results in a big problem for address translation. In Chapter 4 I described the problem in some detail and discussed a promising new draft proposal: NARP.

Figure 6.23 shows a schematic X.25 network as an IP router would use it.

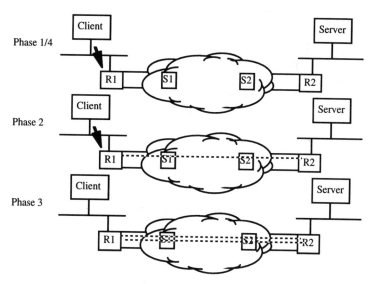

Figure 6.23:   X.25 SVC Operation

In Figure 6.23, Phase 1 shows an IP packet arriving at the router, R1 from the Client. The router makes the next hop decision as I describe in Chapter 4 and sees that there is currently no connection over the X.25 cloud to the required destination. The router makes an X.25 call and establishes a single *Virtual Circuit* (VC).

In Phase 2 I show the VC established over the X.25 cloud. The first IP packet that caused the VC to be established is now in a transmit queue for the X.25 connection. Meanwhile another IP packet arrives at the router. The router will then establish a *second* VC to the same end-point and will queue the second packet for transmission over the second VC. If a third packet arrives, the router will check to see if any of the *existing* VCs have an empty queue. If they have, the packet will be queued for that VC. If all the VC queues are occupied, an additional VC will be established. Most implementations limit the number of simultaneous VCs to 4.

Note that if there are 4 VCs established over the connection between Router 1 and the first X.25 switch, S1, then all 4 VCs will share the bandwidth of the access line. Establishing additional VCs does nothing to increase bandwidth. The motive for the additional VCs is that each VC has its own window size for the transmission of X.25 packets without an acknowledgment from the other end. By increasing the number of VCs, we effectively increase the window size.

This technique was valid in the early 1980s when X.25 only supported up to 7 outstanding packets. Today, more recent implementations of X.25 support extended window sizes, up to 127 frames. In fact the new RFC for multiprotocol operation over X.25 comments that multiple VC connections offer no real performance improvement [9].

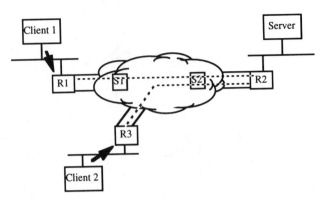

Figure 6.24: Multipoint Connection with X.25

When all the IP packets have been transmitted over the X.25 cloud, the router will clear down all but one of the VCs and will start a timer. If no further packets arrive for the same X.25 destination, then the timer will expire and the final VC will be cleared. If further traffic does arrive, the dynamic making and breaking of VCs will continue.

X.25 To Multiple Locations

Another major benefit to X.25 is that it allows connection to multiple locations using a single cable connection from the router.

In Figure 6.24 I show that R2 is configured with a single X.25 connection, yet can accept connections from Client 1 and Client 2 and many other end-points simultaneously. Moreover, each of these clients can establish multiple VCs as I described above. In fact a single X.25 connection can support inbound connection and outbound connections in any combination. The number of simultaneous *active* VCs is limited by the RAM available to the specific router implementation. Typically we could expect 32 or 64 active VCs on an entry level unit, rising to several hundred for a backbone router.

Error Correction

The big complaint that most people have about X.25 and LANs is the slow response time over the WAN. X.25 was designed at a time when one bit in every million sent was likely to be corrupted. This is a BER of 1 in 10^6. Today, on the best quality fiber circuits you might wait hours or days between bit errors. The X.25 error checking is redundant. Even worse, it causes delays to build up as packets traverse the network. If you're using Telnet over an X.25 network, you may get frustrated. If you're transferring a file, it might not be so bad, because the network will pipeline packets for transmission and the individual hop delays are minimized.

In the last couple of years, X.25 services have been offered at speeds up to 2Mbps in France and Germany. This speed of X.25 shows up the processor-intensive nature of the protocol. To fill a 2Mbps X.25 connection, we require almost the top end routers from Cisco and Wellfleet (the 7010 and BLN respectively). To fill a 2Mbps Frame Relay line needs only the entry level models from these companies (the 2500 and AN respectively).

Fragmentation Algorithms

If the MTU size of an X.25 network is around 128 bytes, it is likely that a significant amount of fragmentation will be needed. As I mentioned earlier, this is never a good thing for performance. Two things apply in X.25's favor here. First, the fragmentation mechanism in X.25 is quite efficient. Second, modern high speed networks are offering MTUs of 2kB or 4kB.

When an IP datagram enters an X.25-equipped router, the datagram is broken down into blocks that are small enough to fit the network MTU. These are sent over the same VC (no load balancing is allowed) as an "m-bit" sequence. The m-bit in X.25 indicates that this particular packet is part of a sequence. The final packet in the sequence has the m-bit clear to indicate the end of sequence.

6.5.1   X.25 Interoperability

Router connections over X.25 are wonderfully interoperable. A "mature" RFC, RFC 877 has been around since 1983! Every X.25-equipped router in the world supports RFC 877 and many host implementations do too (SunLink X.25, Eicon PC card, DEC PathWorks etc.). Interoperability levels should be virtually perfect for this RFC.

In August 1992, a multiprotocol version of RFC 877 was introduced: RFC 1356. This uses the Network Layer Protocol ID (NLPID) mechanism to indicate IP, or SNAP-encoded packets. Note that the IP format is identical to RFC 877, so the two implementations should be mutually interoperable.

6.6   X.32 Asynchronous Packet-Mode Connections

X.32 is a dial-up variant of X.25. If a host computer is equipped with a TCP/IP stack and an X.25 adapter (e.g. Eicon PC card, SunLink X.25) then it can connect directly over an X.25 network to an RFC 877/1356 router, as I show in Figure 6.23.

In Figure 6.25 you can see a number of workers who have decided to work from home. They need occasional access to information on a corporate server. The company chooses X.25 as the connection option because it's available everywhere they have a homeworker and it means only one port on the central router.

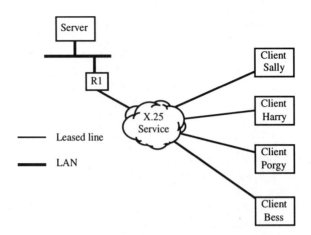

Figure 6.25:   Conventional X.25 Host Access

The problem is this. I don't know too many companies that can justify the cost of a dedicated leased line from every homeworker's house to the office. If the company uses modem technology, then they'll need a big modem pool and hunt group at the central site. This will involve hiring addition MIS people to look after the modems and will be too expensive.

As an alternative, one of their staff who worked in France for a while tells them about X.32. In Figure 6.26, you can now see the homeworkers are dialing in over conventional telephone lines. They still connect to a modem pool, but this time it's run by the service provider and no additional staff is needed. The X.32 PAD converts the incoming async data stream to a packetised, synchronous X.25 data stream and pumps it over to the RFC 877 router, R1.

X.32 has so many advantages, even over ISDN for homeworking, that it makes you wonder why there aren't more X.32 millionaires walking around:

- The router at the central site has just one physical connection.

- The router software is standard X.25 and RFC 877/1356. No special X.32 software is required.

- The homeworker PCs use a standard modem, driven by regular client software like DEC PathWorks.

- If the operator offered a high performance X.32 PAD (they don't, yet), then the homeworkers could use high speed V.34 modems.

- The technique can even be used by mobile workers such as salesfolk or engineers, dialing in from telephone booths, cellular phones or hotel rooms.

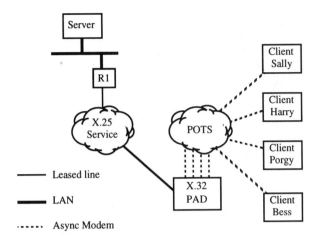

Figure 6.26: X.32 Homeworking

6.7 SMDS

A few years ago, some engineers at Bellcore sat down to design a high speed data service that was suited to LAN communication. The result was eventually the *Switched Multimegabit Data Service* (SMDS). I'm not going to go into details about IEEE 802.6 or Dual Queue Distributed Bus (DQDB). These are the underlying technologies and they have never been (and will never be) implemented directly inside a router. The nuts and bolt of SMDS remain hidden from most users, inside the service provider's equipment.

When I first joined Wellfleet, I heard several colleagues describing SMDS as the "LAN in the Sky." It's a great analogy. SMDS is designed to offer LAN services over a wide area. The WAN service basically means that MAC Layer broadcasts and multicasts can be supported over the WAN without complex additional software in the routers.

RFC 1209 describes the way that IP datagrams are transported over an SMDS network. SMDS datagrams can be up to 9180 bytes long and carry a standard SNAP header (not NLPID). The datagrams are then broken down into IEEE 802.6 cells by a *Segmentation and Reassembly* (SAR) device. This process is identical to ATM attachment, so I'll explain it in more detail in a moment.

6.8 ATM

Asynchronous Transfer Mode (ATM) must definitely take the award for the most media-hyped technology of the century. In terms of IP networks, ATM is just a transport network (ATM = "Another Transport Mechanism"). When we (eventually) move to native ATM protocol (i.e., we're not using IP at all), then we'll see some interesting and exciting applications for this technology. Until then, evaluate ATM just the same way you would X.25, Frame Relay, or ISDN.

Like X.25, ATM networks are connection-oriented, SVC networks. In other words, we can expect some initial hassle sorting out address translation, signaling and call holding. However, ATM is designed to operate much faster than X.25. In ATM networks, the unit of transfer is called the *cell*. Unlike packets or frames, cells are fixed length, short data units; in fact they are only 53 bytes long.

By using shorter transfer units, we achieve several things:

- We can multiplex data streams more evenly.

- We can fill the data units and ship them out more quickly.

- We can build hardware-based switches with non-blocking architectures.

- We take a big hit on the overhead since each cell needs addressing headers.

The final point is an interesting one: each cell in an ATM network is 53 bytes long and has 5 bytes of ATM-level overhead. That's 10% overhead already. In contrast, a 1500 byte Ethernet frame has 1.2% frame overhead. The major benefit of ATM comes because WAN operators can scale their multiplexing equipment up to much higher bandwidth levels.

6.8.1 Physical Representation

At the time of writing, there are no true ATM WAN services available, simply because the standard to offer SVC connection are not fully agreed. Indeed chipsets to build ATM WAN interfaces are not even available as production units!

Nevertheless, we can make a good guess as to the nature of ATM connections when they do become available. I summarize these in Table 6.5.

6.8.2 Logical Representation

Today, ATM products are changing very rapidly. Dozens of manufacturers are scrambling to get product to market before the standards are fully agreed so that they can capture market share. For this reason, you'll often see a phased transition into ATM.

Table 6.5:   Likely 1st Generation ATM Interfaces

I/F Name	LAN/WAN	Speed (Mbps)	Comments
TAXI	LAN	100/140	Based on FDDI components. The original ATM LAN I/F. Losing ground to OC3.
OC3	LAN/WAN	155	SONET/SDH speed rating. The classic ATM speed. Likely to be one of the two popular LAN speeds (IBM is the other). A bit high for 1st generation WAN infrastructure.
OC1	WAN	51.8	SONET speed rating, but very uncommon (i.e., non-existent) as subscriber speed.
T3/E3	WAN	45/34	Obvious choice for high speed integrated WAN services. Still expensive in US and virtually unaffordable in Europe.
T1/E1	WAN	1.5/2	Since T3/E3 is so expensive, these are obvious candidates for 1st generation integrated WANs.
IBM	LAN	25	Proposed by IBM, rejected by ATM Forum, but productised by IBM nevertheless. Now supported by over 20 hub and adapter companies and based on an IBM chipset. Runs on existing STP and UTP cabling and IBM's adapters are cheaper then their Token Ring equivalent! Along with OC3, likely to be the most popular LAN choice.

Phase 1: Frame-Based Connection

Figure 6.27 shows a typical ATM connection today. The routers attaching to the cloud are fitted with conventional HSSI interfaces running at the local service rate. In N. America and Japan this will be 45Mbps T3, while in most of the rest of the world it will be 34Mbps E3. The protocol running over this link can be one of two candidates:

- ATM *Data Exchange Interface* (DXI), as defined by the ATM Forum.

- Frame Relay UNI, as defined jointly by the Frame Relay Forum and the ATM Forum.

The ATM DXI is a frame-based pre-formatting protocol that prepares the LAN traffic for Segmentation and Reassembly by an external *Digital Service Unit* (DSU). The DXI theoretically contains signaling indications for address

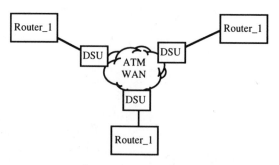

Figure 6.27: Phase 1 ATM Deployment

mapping between IP and ATM addresses. In reality, ATM Switched Virtual Circuits are not widely available because of the lack of standards.

In practice today, the Frame Relay UNI connection is much more attractive since users are already familiar with the interface and it is widely available from DSU vendors. From the router viewpoint, the ATM cloud just looks like a Frame Relay cloud. As I said earlier, Frame Relay is a perfectly good protocol at these speeds.

Phase 2: Integrated ATM Interfaces

The next stage of ATM development involves native ATM integration into the router. Since ATM is a cell-based service and LANs are a frame-based service, the router must contain the hardware to perform Segmentation and Reassembly (SAR) on the LAN traffic. This is normally implemented as an add-in card to the existing, frame-based infrastructure of the router. Products of this type have been announced by Cisco, Proteon, and Wellfleet with either a TAXI or OC3 interface.

Figure 6.28 shows a schematic path of a LAN frame into a router (1), across the internal bus to an ATM card (2), ATM connection setup by the slot CPU (3) conversion to cells, and transmission to the ATM network (4).

ATM will be a real challenge for router performance. Initially only T1/E1, T3/E3 ATM will be readily available over a Wide Area. However, ATM can scale to much higher speeds. The true "minimum" speed for ATM should be the SONET OC3c line rate, running at 155Mbps (note: OC1 is 51.8Mbps). And remember this is a *full duplex* connection, whereas an FDDI is a mere 100Mbps *half duplex*.

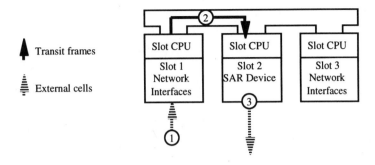

Figure 6.27:   AAL5 Routing

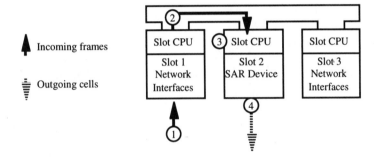

Figure 6.28:   Integrated ATM DTE in Router

ATM is a multiservice transport system and several *ATM Adaptation Layers* (AAL) are defined [3]:

- AAL1 is intended for voice.

- AAL2 is intended for digitized video, but the standard was never completed.

- AAL3/4 is becoming less popular, but it may still survive as the Adaptation Layer for SMDS over ATM

- AAL5 is a simplified form of AAL4, with much less overhead and is intended for LAN traffic. In addition, many video applications are using the raw speed of ATM coupled with the simplicity of AAL5.

Industry analysts are pushing for *high performance* routing to disappear altogether, to be replaced by ATM switching. However, the initial experience with ATM has indicated that this cannot happen for several years yet. Tests by the French Aristote Lab (LARA; L'expérimentation Aristote de Réseau ATM) [1] indicates that the congestion management capabilities of the current generation of ATM hubs make it difficult to integrate ATM at different speeds, or with multiaccess to servers, for example. In simple terms, if an ATM switch experiences congestion, it can throw data away. What does it throw away? Cells, of course. But remember, that if an ATM switch throws away a few cells, they could all be from different LAN frames. At the receiving end, these LAN frames arrive incomplete, leading to long timeout waits and eventually re-transmission. ATM has no way to decide if all the cells are from the same LAN frame, or from different frames.

An alternative approach is to use a high performance router as the buffer device between ATM workgroups and between the ATM LAN and WAN. In Figure 6.27 I show the path of incoming *cells* (1). The cell stream is then reassembled into a complete LAN *frame* (2). This frame is then *routed* in the conventional way to the outbound ATM port, where it is converted back into *cells* for transmission (3). This mechanism has been dubbed *AAL5 Routing*.

If congestion occurs during AAL5 Routing, the router has the ability to buffer the information as frames, or in extreme cases, throw away complete frames. Note that the current generation of ATM LAN hubs cannot buffer cells because of their non-blocking architectures. These devices are designed on the assumption that peer-to-peer traffic (rather than multiple clients to server) is the norm.

6.8.3   ATM Interoperability

ATM is in a very early phase of its development. Standards exist for Physical Layer connections, signaling, and cell formats. The big missing pieces of the jigsaw are in congestion management and ATM call routing. The two current RFCs on ATM are 1483 [10] and 1577 [11]. These describe the encapsulation format over AAL5 and broadcast/multicast emulation procedures respectively.

At the time of writing, only a few trade show demonstrations had been made of these RFCs so it's unclear what level of interoperability we should expect. What is certain is that by the end of 1995 a new generation of ATM architectures will be available in both the LAN and WAN sectors, along with a real ATM Application Programming Interface.

6.9   A Final Word on Security

With the exception of standard dial-up telephones and ISDN, most WAN systems require some form of subscriber access. Leased lines pass only between the end-points, although a determined enemy could try to penetrate the PTT exchange. X.25, Frame Relay, SMDS and ATM are subscriber services in which traffic flows can be monitored by the provider for security breaches. In Chapter 18 I'll be looking at the general topic of Security and offering some advice on how to analyze your networks for possible threats.

6.10 Summary

- WAN communication has its own special problems. These include bandwidth, connectivity, addressing, interoperability, and security.

- Leased lines are the most traditional form of WAN technology. Since 1990, the introduction of PPP has delivered improved performance, features and interoperability.

- ISDN is a dial-up digital telephone system that is gaining ground rapidly in Europe and Japan.

- The major application areas for ISDN are in backup of leased lines, but now a new generation of applications is emerging in which ISDN is the only form of WAN connection.

- Frame Relay is a popular alternative to leased lines. It offers multipoint connection over a single cable and excellent performance even on entry level router platforms.

- Frame Relay interoperability is excellent.

- X.25 is very similar to Frame Relay, but was designed at a time when line qualities were much lower. As a result, the error detection and correction protocols of X.25 do not always allow the system to be used for interactive communication.

- X.25 is still developing, with newer backbone networks offering reduced backbone delay and high access speeds. However, high performance X.25 will always require more CPU power than the equivalent Frame Relay access.

- X.32 is an exciting option for mobile, or homeworking users. Essentially a form of dial-up X.25, X.32 requires no modification to router equipment, or to host software.

- SMDS is a high speed WAN solution, generally cell-based, that was specifically designed for LAN interconnection.

- ATM is also cell-based, but is designed as a general purpose transport network. As such it may one day be capable of integrating voice, video, and data over the same infrastructure.

- ATM is a promising future technology for WANs but is currently only available in tiny pockets. It is unclear how ATM congestion control can be developed to meet the real integration needs of a multiservice network.

6.11 References

[1] J. Lemagnen. R. Mandeville. "Assessing ATM for Enterprise Networks." *Data Communications.* June 1994.

[2] G. Kessler. "*ISDN, Second Edition.*" McGraw-Hill 1993.

[3]   M. De Prycker. *"Asynchronous Transfer Mode, Second Edition.".* Ellis Horwood NY 1993.

[4]   R. J. Deasington. *X.25 Explained.* (Ellis Horwood, 1989).

[5]   Philip Smith. *Frame Relay: Principles and Applications.* Addison-Wesley 1993.

[6]   N. Lippis and J. Herman. "Widening Your Internet Horizons." *Connexions.* October 1991.

[7]   J. Postel. "User Datagram Protocol." *RFC 768.* August 1980.

[8]   B. Lloyd. W. Simpson. "PPP Authentication Protocols," *RFC 1334.* October 1992.

[9]   A. Malis. D. Robinson. R. Ullmann. "Multiprotocol Interconnect on X.25 and ISDN in the Packet Mode," *RFC 1356.* August 1992.

[10]   J. Heinanen. "Multiprotocol Encapsulation over ATM Adaptation Layer 5," *RFC 1483.* July 1993.

[11]   M. Laubach. "Classical IP and ARP over ATM," *RFC 1577.* January 1994.

CHAPTER 7

Bridging Overview

> *Build a system that even a fool can use and only a fool will want to use it.*
>
> *Shaw's Principle*

7.1 Defining Bridging

Earlier in this book I described bridging as a LAN extension technology. In the next three chapters I'll describe three different bridging technologies in some detail:

- Traditional Bridges

- Token Ring Bridges

- Translation Bridges

As an introduction, I'd like to discuss general bridging concepts to allow you to decide where bridging and routing fit into your design requirements.

7.2 Interconnection at the MAC Layer

Bridges generally operate at the MAC Layer, as I show in Figure 7.1. They are used for a variety of reasons, which I will describe in a moment. However, I'd like to suggest a few reasons why I keep on referring to bridges as LAN extension devices and not as true internetworking devices.

What is a LAN? A working definition would be something like:

> *A communication channel, generally operating at high speeds, that is shared amongst host computer systems within a strict geographical area.*

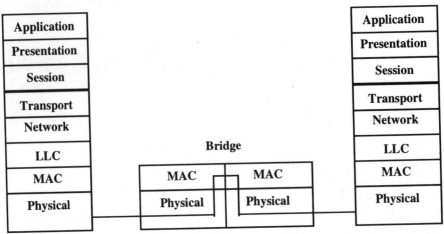

Figure 7.1: Bridges in the OSI Context

A key word in this definition is "shared." When the word is applied to LANs, it is meant in a beneficial sense; implying shared bandwidth. However, when we connect hosts to the same LAN, we end up sharing a few other things as well. One of these is the concept of MAC address space. In Figure 7.2, I show several LANs that have evolved independently. In a real enterprise, they may have been purchased by different department heads without any central consultation. As I described in Chapter 2, the hosts on each LAN will be blessed with a MAC address. These addresses allow the hosts to exchange messages with specific destinations, even though all the hosts are connected on a shared medium. Each of the LANs in this diagram has its own MAC address space, that does not interfere with the other LANs while these LANs remain separate.

Even so, this shouldn't present a problem because MAC addresses are "centrally" administered in the IEEE LAN scheme. Therefore no two hosts in the world should ever have the same MAC address.

The hosts on these LANs could use *locally administered addresses*, which does oblige the network administrator for each LAN to allocate addresses in a systematic way. Obviously, if we connect the LANs together with a MAC device, the administrators on each site will have to co-ordinate their efforts. This becomes a real problem if the LANs are already well established and especially when they have large populations of hosts.

A much more important side effect of address space sharing is the impact of broadcast traffic. In Chapter 3 I explained the way that IP hosts find each other using the ARP protocol. For a single LAN segment, ARP traffic should represent a tiny fraction of overall traffic. However, if we bridge many LANs together, their ARP traffic will be propagated onto all of the bridged segments on the extended network. At some point, the level of broadcast traffic will start to impact the performance of the network hosts.

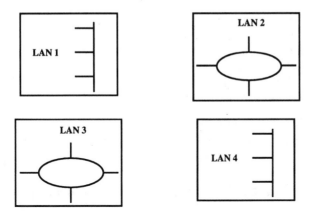

Figure 7.2:   The Birth of an Internetwork

As the separate, departmental LANs began to expand, network administrators used any device they could get their hands on to keep the network running. Bridges for Ethernet seemed to offer a new lease on life for overloaded Ethernets, they allowed LANs to be extended beyond the local site and with Spanning Tree they even offered the opportunity to build resilient networks. However, by using bridges to interconnect LAN segments, we were obliged to verify a few minor details.

First, we needed to verify addressing. A bridged network is one single MAC address space, so address conflicts must be dealt with *before* the LANs can be interconnected.   Second, in Figure 7.2 it seems that LAN1 and LAN 4 are Ethernets, while LAN 2 and LAN3 are Token Rings. Until recently there was no reliable way to bridge these LANs (some might say that there still is no *reliable* way). Finally we face a variety of design compromises and decisions regarding Spanning Tree, broadcast reduction, etc.   In each of the specific bridging chapters, I deal with these issues under the guise of bridge/router interaction.

At the end of the 1980s, bridge users really discovered the advantages of routing technology.   Manufacturers of bridges were slow to recognize the trend. Without exception today, all of the original bridge manufacturers have declined, or have been acquired by other companies, or both.

Many network users that are in a decision-making position for networking equipment are faced with the tricky choice: should I bridge or route?

Even today, there is a vast scope for both networking technologies. Bridges are a mature and highly useful networking technology. They are not and never will be, an internetworking technology.

7.3   Why Do We Use Bridges?

Sometimes we look at a technology from the point of view of the benefits that it will bring to us; for example, we could say that the appearance of an E-mail system on our desktop PC allows us a vast expansion of our communication options. On the other hand we could take the view that we now have to find out how to use this damned E-mail package, because it's the only way we can reliably leave messages for our colleagues.

I'd like to take the same two points of view into account to look at the reasons for the continued popularity of bridges, in a communications world that seems to be dominated by router technology.

7.3.1   Pessimistic Reasons for Bridge Popularity

If everybody had agreed that bridges were a network extension device, then internetworking would have been a lot easier today. Instead, several "real-world" situations combined to create the seeds of future chaos:

Easy to Design and Build

The manufacturers of interconnection devices saw that bridging was essentially a hardware issue: building faster RAM and CPU designs to keep up with higher LAN speeds. In contrast, routing involves large amounts of complex software. Even better was that as bridging devices became limited in functionality, additional value-added features could be introduced into the bridge because RAM and CPU prices were dropping. Therefore, bridging was an "easy" market to get into, whereas routing was "hard." In reality, it's almost as easy to design and build a lousy router as it is to design and build a lousy bridge! Like any other market sector the trick is to produce a quality product at the right price that performs the right functions.

Non-Routable Protocols

Programmers saw LANs as an excellent target system, but there was no agreed *Application Programming Interface* (API) for them to use in their development systems. At least two of the ad hoc APIs that have been developed are based on non-routeable technology (NetBIOS and 3270 Streams). Of course, developers in one technology area did not discuss interaction strategy with developers in other areas.

Bridges don't need to use Network Layer protocols to do their job and the difficulties that bridges cause can be largely ignored until the network scale issue is encountered.   Specific examples of protocols that are unsuited to internetworking are DEC LAT and NetBIOS.

The DEC Local Area Transport (LAT) protocol is a lightweight, high performance terminal protocol developed by the Terminal Server group in DEC. It *was not* intended to be a part of DECnet and was only ever designed to operate within the bounds of a single Ethernet segment. The advent of MAC bridges, both local and remote, allowed LAT to be used in many areas where it just didn't belong. However, when customers have tasted forbidden fruit, they cannot go back! We no longer have the option to tell customers not to use LAT and DEC still haven't come up with a routeable alternative with the same performance. Router manufacturers and Network Designers just have to make the best of it. So, we end up supporting bridged protocols like LAT over a corporate internetwork backbone.

NetBIOS is another non-routeable protocol. IBM dipped its toes into the PC LAN business back in 1983 by rebadging the PC LAN from Sytek. This LAN was essentially obsolete on the day it first shipped, but it introduced a protocol stack called the *Network Basic I/O System* (NetBIOS)[2]. NetBIOS is essentially a network-based extension to the PC BIOS chip. It's very rich and functional at the higher layers, offering programmers an excellent API on which to build distributed applications. At the lower layers (that is, below the Session Layer), NetBIOS is barely capable of existing on a single LAN. Initially all of its traffic was sent as a broadcast! Later versions have improved this situation, but only just. NetBIOS is still notorious as a LAN protocol, but is highly prized amongst programmers. Remember the advice for computer buyers: "Select the Application, then the Computer, then the Network." Since NetBIOS contains no information that routers can work with, the "native" implementations need to be bridged. As an API, NetBIOS can also be implemented over a routeable protocols stack such as IP or Novell's IPX.

IBM also moved its native SNA protocol onto Token Ring LANs in 1986. While SNA can be routed (see Chapter 18, "Dealing With SNA"), the routing doesn't happen in the conventional sense (i.e., at the Network Layer). Thus IBM have promoted the use of bridge technology amongst their mainframe users.

Easy to Install

Bridges can be considerably easier to install than routers. In particular, any form of Transparent Bridge is virtually "configuration-free." Source Route bridges need to be correctly installed and this process is about as difficult as installing a single protocol router. So, a bridging strategy may be retained to simplify installation issues. However, the Network Administrator then spends proportionately more time fire-fighting bridge traffic management issues.

7.3.2   Optimistic Reasons for Bridge Popularity

Bridges are a mature, reliable technology for network connection. They are essential to allow "unroutable" protocols to pass around the network. For many businesses, their core communication software is designed to use "unroutable" protocols.

Bridges are still useful in modern networks, even those that have been designed to use sensible APIs and fully routeable protocol stacks. To be blunt, bridges are easy to install and configure. Using Source Routing and Spanning Tree mechanisms, bridges can be used to construct resilient networks.

A more significant trend for all networks is the emergence of dual-function bridge/routers. Throughout this book I use specific examples of products from Cisco, Proteon and Wellfleet. All three of these manufacturers have developed devices that remove the need for the network administrator to choose between bridging or routing. By careful use of these hybrid devices we can construct departmental networks using bridge or routing technology and interconnect them using routing technology. I discuss the interaction between routers and bridges at the end of each specific bridging chapter.

7.4   Unicast and Promiscuous Mode

Imagine you are a LAN adapter chipset installed in an end system. There are hundreds of frames passing every second on the LAN segment. Some, but not all are intended for you. You've got three choices of how to deal with this traffic stream:

1.   You could receive all of the traffic frames and interrupt your end system's CPU so that it can check if the frame is addressed to this end system.

2.   You could receive all of the traffic frames, but implement a CPU software on the LAN adapter to check if the frame is addressed to this end system.

3.   You could implement simple pattern-matching hardware in the LAN adapter so that only frames addressed to this end system at the MAC Layer will be received. Broadcasts and multicasts would also be received. Only if one of these frame types is received will the LAN adapter interrupt the CPU.

You might not be surprised to learn that all of these methods have been implemented in real products. Option 2 was implemented in the Sytek PC LAN adapter and this technology sent all LAN frames as broadcasts.

Options 1 and 3 are implemented in conventional LAN technology. Option 1 is called *Promiscuous Mode*. It is implemented in LAN analyzers like the Sniffer and in Transparent Bridges. For these systems, LAN data stream analysis is the primary function of the host on which the LAN adapter resides, so the CPU must accept the interrupt frequency. Option 3 is called *Unicast Mode*. It is the normal operating mode for end system LAN adapters and routers. A modified form of unicast mode is used by Source Route Bridges. The implications of these operating modes are illustrated in more detail in the Diskette Tutorial, but let me summarize the implications. If a connection device operates in promiscuous mode, its CPU will be interrupted for every LAN frame transmitted on the network, even if that frame is not supposed to leave the LAN segment.

This can cause a very high load on the CPU, leaving it unable to perform additional functions such as routing, routing updates, network management, etc.

7.5 Bridging Definitions

As users and manufacturers have valiantly tried to extend bridging technology beyond the conventional Ethernet bridge, different techniques have been employed. In very simple terms, we can summarize four generic bridging types, each of which may have some form of variant, plus combinations of two techniques in a single box. The four fundamental bridge types are:

- Transparent

- Source Route

- Encapsulation

- Translation

7.5.1 Transparent Bridge

A Transparent Bridge is used to connect two or more LAN segments. Each LAN segment must use an identical technology, but this technology may operate at different transmission speeds on each port. The Transparent Bridge will not modify forwarded frames in any way and will make its forwarding decision purely on the basis of the LAN MAC Layer information. During the forwarding process, the Transparent Bridge will buffer the frame and will obey the access control protocol for the destination LAN segment. The communication software operating in End Stations on all LAN segments attached to the Transparent Bridge is unaware of the Bridge.

7.5.2   Source Route Bridge

A Source Route Bridge is used to connect two or more LAN segments. Each LAN segment must use an identical technology, but this technology may operate at different transmission speeds on each port. The End Stations on all LAN segments must be capable of transmitting special Explorer frames to discover the best route to the desired destination End Station. End Stations are addressed at the MAC Layer. Each LAN segment and each Source Route Bridge will be designated with an appropriate identification number so that routes through the network can be uniquely identified. The Source Route Bridge will process the Explorers frames and frames that have been marked to travel through a specific Source Route Bridge. The Source Route Bridge is capable of recognizing and modifying, routing information in the frame as the frame is forwarded through the bridge. During the forwarding process, the Source Route Bridge will buffer the frame and will obey the access control protocol for the destination LAN segment.

7.5.3   Encapsulation Bridge

An Encapsulation Bridge is used to connect two or more identical LAN segments (referred to as "workgroup ports") over a non-identical, intermediate communication path (referred to as "the backbone"). The backbone may be a point-to-point serial connection, or a LAN. The Encapsulation Bridge may use either Transparent or Source Route Bridging on the workgroup ports, but an identical technology must be used on all workgroup ports. During the forwarding process, the Source Route Bridge will buffer the frame and will obey the access control protocol for the destination LAN segment. Each workgroup port must use an identical LAN technology, but this technology may operate at different transmission speeds on each port. Frame forwarding information for either Transparent or Source Route operation is distributed over the backbone to other Encapsulation Bridges using a special bridge-to-bridge protocol. End Station software will treat an Encapsulation Bridge as though it were a local Transparent or Source Route Bridge.

7.5.4 Translation Bridge

A Translation Bridge is used to connect two or more LAN segments. Each LAN segment can make use of identical, or different LAN technologies. The Translation Bridge will modify (translate) forwarded frames so that they are appropriate to the destination LAN technology. The Translation Bridge will use appropriate exception-handling software to resolve differences in the source and destination LAN technologies. During the forwarding process, the Translation Bridge will buffer the frame. End Station Software which is operating on a Transparent Bridge LAN technology will see the Translation Bridge as though it were a Transparent Bridge. End Station Software which is operating on a Source Route Bridge LAN technology will see the Translation Bridge as though it were a Source Route Bridge.

These definitions may seem pretty complex. They look that way because they have to be phrased in such general terms. For example, I don't mention Token Ring or FDDI in the definition of a Source Route Bridge, even though these are the only technologies in which Source Routing is used commercially. I mention that bridges can be used to connect LANs running at different speeds. This is obviously true for Token Ring because there are 4Mbps and 16Mbps versions. Surprisingly, it is also true of Ethernet, because there is a 1Mbps version of this technology, called StarLAN, that was designed to operate over telephone grade UTP. You might notice that I've grouped all kinds of Encapsulation Bridges, both local and remote, into one definition. I think that one definition is enough for this technology and I handle the discussion of Encapsulation Bridges in one subsection of Chapter 8. Look at the definitions and see which bridging technologies can be used to link similar or dissimilar LANs. Hopefully, at the end of this chapter you'll come back to these definitions and re-read them. They have been useful to me in the past during discussions with other vendors on their specific bridging architectures.

Each of these bridge definitions shows that way that different types of bridges make forwarding decisions. Remember that a bridge doesn't really know what the network looks like. It cannot use hierarchical addressing to decide if a specific end system really can be found on a specific port. The forwarding criteria for a bridge are the single most important design decision to be made for the unit.

What is a Brouter?

The term "bridge/router" is so clumsy that it inevitably became abbreviated to "brouter." The operation of a bridge/router is relatively simple. The network ports on operate in Promiscuous Mode. Each frame received is examined to determine whether the router portion of the bridge/router recognizes the Network Layer protocol in the frame. If the protocol is recognized, the frame will be routed. If the protocol is not recognized, the frame will be bridged.

Unfortunately, some manufacturers have implemented what I would term "value added bridging," yet are describing these units as brouters. These multiport bridges implement sophisticated caching algorithms, but do not perform any real Network Layer routing. As a reaction the three major router manufacturers, Cisco, Proteon, and Wellfleet, have tended to return to the original term "bridge/router." In a sense, this is a good thing since the words "router" and "brouter" sound too similar and verbal presentations that must differentiate the technologies may be misleading.

7.5.5 Bridges and the IEEE

IEEE committee 802 is involved with many aspects of LAN technology. The subcommittee 802.1 has the responsibility for defining bridging standards, although other committees have been involved in the past (like 802.5D). The 802.1 subcommittee is divided into working groups, each of which specializes in a particular bridge technology. Here is a short summary of the current bridging workgroups in 802:

- IEEE 802.1D MAC Bridges, Spanning Tree.
- IEEE 802.1h Draft recommended practice for the bridging of Ethernet Version 2.0 over IEEE 802 networks.
- IEEE 802.1i MAC bridging in FDDI networks.
- IEEE 802.5D Source Route Bridging in Token Ring networks.
- IEEE 802.5m Unapproved draft for SRT bridging.

7.6 When Do I *Stop* Extending With Bridges?

Bridges are a mature, stable technology. In the next three chapters, you'll discover some of the detailed ways in which this technology has evolved to deal with modern internetworks. However, there'll come a time when bridges can no longer do the job. I'd like to look at just two aspects of this issue:

- Scaleability
- Interoperability

7.6.1 Bridge Scaleability

My assertion about the scaleability problems of bridges may not completely agree with some manufacturer claims. Bridge manufacturers have worked hard to add sophisticated software to make bridges more intelligent.

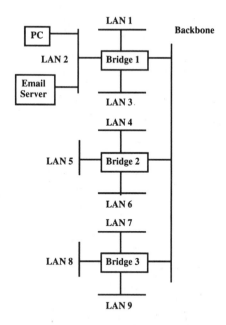

Figure 7.3: Typical Bridge Scale Problem

In Figure 7.3 I show the unavoidable problem with bridges. The diagram shows three multiport bridges linked to a backbone. On LAN2, a PC is switched on and sends out an ARP request for an E-mail server on the same LAN. An ARP request is sent as a MAC broadcast so Bridge 1 must forward the frame onto the backbone and flood it to the locally connected LAN1 and LAN3. This means that this broadcast will take up bandwidth on LAN1, LAN2 .. LAN9 *and* the backbone. Every host on every LAN, regardless of the protocol stack it's running, will have its CPU interrupted. All this happens even when the initial broadcast is to find a local machine!

For the network shown in Figure 7.3, the additional bandwidth lost to uncontrolled broadcasts is annoying, but at least this is a purely local network. Imagine if the backbone is a leased line WAN; first of all the bandwidth is significantly more limited and second it's not "free." Another issues arises if we consider that the bridges are linked by a switched WAN (e.g., ISDN or X.25). Switched WANs require internetworking devices to translate between LAN addresses and WAN addresses. Address translation is significantly easier to implement if we can refer to entire LAN segments, rather than to individual end stations. This requires Network Layer addressing.

In Token Ring bridged networks, the problem arises from the popular use of the All Routes Explorer (ARE). I'll explain the significance of this term in Chapter 9 and I'll look at one innovative solution; *Data Link Switching* (DLSw) in Chapter 15.

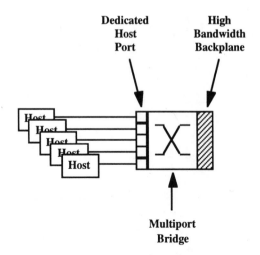

Figure 7.4:   Generic LAN Switch

For IP networks, there is an obvious problem with extended bridge networks. All the hosts on the LANs shown in Figure 7.4 must be configured with the same IP Network ID, because there is no router on this extended network to route traffic *between* Network IDs. Today if you request an IP address from the NIC, you'll be given one or more Class C addresses. This means that the maximum number of hosts on a given extended bridge network is 254. For users of LAN switches today, this is a limiting factor.

7.7   When is a Bridge not a Bridge?

The answer today is "when it's a LAN switch." These are an interesting new development in LAN connectivity. LAN switches are being positioned as a way to increase the LAN bandwidth to the desktop. The principle is as follows. Ethernet is a great LAN technology, but its access control mechanism is inefficient if there are lots of collisions on the network. You get more collisions as the number of hosts on the same LAN segment increases. So, the ideal Ethernet has just two hosts and then we get a full 10Mbps. A generic LAN switch is shown in Figure 7.4.

In a typical LAN switch, each host connection is a dedicated port on a multiport bridge. The bridge functionality ensures that traffic from one port only appears on another port if it's supposed to be there. The high bandwidth backplane (typically over 1Gbps) is able to guarantee that multiple 10Mbps conversations can take place simultaneously. Like a traditional LAN bridge, LAN switches offer a way to extend the lifetime of a conventional Ethernet network, but ultimately do not offer a scaleable solution for internetwork growth. In combination with routers, however, switches may provide a near-ideal solution for scaleable internetworking.

7.8   Bridge Interoperability

Local bridges will typically interoperate quite happily. However, there are some significant exceptions.

The Spanning Tree loop detection protocol has been shipped in many versions. Some are legitimate IEEE 802.1 protocols and a few are based on pre-standard best-guess implementations. Interoperation of these protocols is poor and the consequences of a mistake can be disastrous.

Remote bridges from different vendors will generally not interoperate. The only chance is that the vendors implement the PPP protocol, with the extensions for bridging included (currently defined in RFC 1220).

One of the only occurrences of the IEEE 802.1 management protocols is within bridging products. Fortunately this situation has now been corrected and almost all vendors implement SNMP management. A specific MIB for bridges is defined in RFC 1286.

Multiport Token Ring Bridges have a special interoperability problem, which I describe in detail in Chapter 9, but here's a quick summary. Due to the limitations of current Token Ring bridge chips, a multiport bridge will add 2 hops to the Routing Information Field (RIF) of an explorer frame. Most manufacturers implement special "RIF reduction" algorithms and these are always proprietary. These multiport bridges will work happily with dual-port Token Ring bridges, but may have problems operating correctly with multiport devices from other manufacturers.

7.9   Summary

- Bridging is a mature, high performance method for LAN extension.

- A bridge operates at the MAC Layer.

- Ethernet bridges address four specific issues that limit the initial growth of an Ethernet, namely the 4-repeater limit, segment traffic separation and LAN interconnection over serial lines.

- Token Ring bridges allow traffic separation between LAN segments and interconnection over serial lines.

- Translation Bridges allow different LAN technologies to be interconnected without worrying about Network Layer addressing schemes.

- Although bridges allow LAN segments to be extended, this process cannot continue indefinitely. The way that bridges operate has a direct impact on the scaleability of the internetwork design.

- Bridges interact with routers, typically in a beneficial way. Specific interaction is discussed in the relevant chapter.

- Switches are a new form of multiport bridge. Thanks to their low cost and low transit latency, switches offer an interesting local workgroup expansion capability.

- There is a real and well-defined place for bridges, switches and routers in any network design.

7.10 References

There are no specific books on bridging, although Radia Perlman's *Connections* is an excellent theoretical description. The relevant IEEE standards are:

- IEEE 802.1d for Transparent Spanning Tree Bridges

- IEEE 802.5d for Source Route Bridges

- IEEE 802.5m (unapproved) for SRT Bridges

- IEEE 802.1i and 802.1j for FDDI and Translation Bridges

CHAPTER 8

Traditional Bridging

> *It's difficult to make systems foolproof, because fools are so ingenious.*
>
> **Corollary to Shaw's Rule**

8.1 What is Traditional Bridging?

When I use the term "Traditional Bridging," I'm referring to the Transparent Bridging technology that is used to extend Ethernet LANs. It is this type of bridging that most of us would identify with first. When we make design decisions on bridging, our internal prejudices and opinions were probably formed from experience of, or information about, Transparent Bridging.

Ethernet-to-Ethernet local and remote bridges are probably the simplest and most effective examples of bridges. There are three main reasons why these bridges are installed:

The 4-Repeater Limit

To overcome the "4 repeater" limit of Ethernet systems. An Ethernet repeater adds a certain amount of delay to the signal and excessive delay will interfere with the Ethernet CSMA/CD algorithm. Long delays in an Ethernet network mean that host adapters cannot always guarantee that they will be able to "listen before transmitting" and this can lead to an increased collision rate. In small networks it may not matter, but it gets worse as you add stations, or they become busier on the LAN.

Traffic Separation

To provide traffic separation. As an Ethernet segment become busier, and/or is configured with more hosts, the probability of collisions occurring increases quite dramatically. Collisions on an Ethernet are very bad news, causing stations to "back off" and wait for clear time on the wire. This reduces the efficiency of Ethernet LANs and gives Token Ring fans an argument to use in sales situations. If traffic levels on an individual segment can be reduced, however, the efficiency of Ethernet can be maintained, even as the LAN is extended. The most important use of traffic separation is where two sites are linked by a lower speed connection, as in remote bridging.

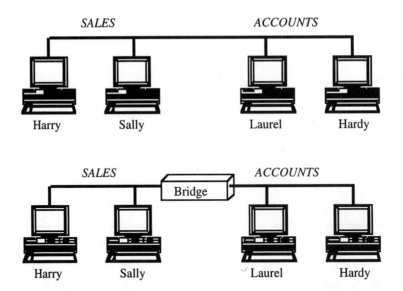

Figure 8.1:   Using a Bridge to Separate Workgroups

Ethernet operates at 10Mbps and it uses a standardized MAC frame format. WAN serial lines typically operate at much lower speeds and use an HDLC frame format. To interconnect two Ethernet LANs over a serial line requires a device to resolve the LAN access control mechanism on each site, to make efficient traffic separation decisions and to act as a store-and-forward buffer to resolve speed differences. The assumption with remote bridges is that they only need to be fitted with enough buffer to cope with bursts of LAN traffic and that only a tiny fraction of the 10Mbps traffic on one site needs to pass over the WAN link.

In Figure 8.1 I have drawn a simple bridged network. There are two groups, named "Sales" and "Accounts." In the upper part of this drawing both groups are connected on the same wire. Hosts in both groups have to compete for the same amount of free time on the wire. At some stage as this LAN grows, we will run into collision problems. Ideally, we need a device which can learn if a given end system is on its left hand side or its right hand side and only forward Ethernet frames if the stations are on different sides.

The Network Administrator inserts a bridge between the groups. When the bridge is operating, it is configured in *Promiscuous Mode*, as I explained above. This means that its Ethernet chipsets are configured to receive every single frame which is transmitted on both sides of the bridge. By listening to the addresses on these frames, the bridge can learn end system positions. As frames are received by the bridge, it operates a simple set of rules and I have presented these in pseudocode form in Appendix C. If you don't like the look of the pseudocode, here is an example of the learning process. The overall objective is for the bridge to build a table of end system addresses, with each address associated with

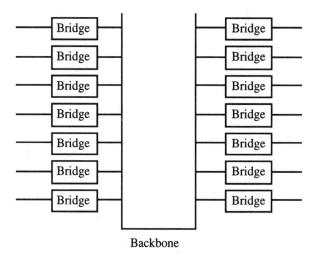

Backbone

Figure 8.2:   Bridged LAN Backbone

one of the bridge's ports. This table is called the *Learning Table*. An empty learning table would look like this for a two-port bridge:

Port 1 Addresses	Port 2 Addresses

The table will grow to have as many rows as are needed to include all of the end systems on the bridged network. Typical Ethernet bridges have a limit of 1024, 2048 or 4096 entries in their learning table. You may think this is a large number of entries, since each of your LAN segments may have a limited number of hosts, but Figure 8.2 shows why even workgroup bridges need large tables.

This bridged LAN has only 14 Ethernet segments on the backbone. If each segment has 100 stations, then each bridge will need space for 1,400 MAC addresses. If we now bridge this site to another similar site, the RAM requirement doubles! For most IP users, the address space of a single Class C Network ID, 254 nodes, will actually limit the growth of the bridged network.

8.2   The Learning Process

The learning process follows a simple set of rules that we can follow for the small internetwork of Sales and Accounts machines shown in the lower part of Figure 8.1.

First let's imagine that we switch this network on and have completely clear configurations in all of the hosts and in the bridge. I cover the details of this IP transaction (i.e., ARP,, etc.) in Chapter 3.

In this example, the first thing that happens is that Harry decides he needs to talk to Hardy. Harry sends out an ARP as a MAC broadcast, with Harry's MAC address in the MAC Source Address field. Normally, bridges must forward broadcasts so the bridge will copy the frame to all of its ports except the port on which the broadcast was received (in this case, Port 1). Although the ARP MAC Destination was a broadcast, its is carrying Harry's MAC Source so the bridge inserts this into its Learning Table for Port 1. The table looks like this. I'll underline the latest entry in the table as I explain the learning process.

Port 1 Addresses	Port 2 Addresses
Harry	

Hardy receives the ARP request and responds. Unlike ARP requests, ARP responses are fully addressed frames, not broadcasts. In this case, the frame will carry Harry's address as its MAC destination and Hardy's address as its MAC source. When the bridge receives this frame on Port 2, it sees that the frame is a unicast. The bridge then consults its Learning Table to see if the MAC Destination is in the same columns as the port on which this frame was received (in this case, Port 2). Harry's address is not in the Port 2 column and so the bridge will forward the frame Meanwhile, the bridge checks to see if the MAC Source on the frame is already in the table for Port 2. As you can see, Hardy's address is not in the Port 2 column so the bridge adds the address. Our table now looks like this:

Port 1 Addresses	Port 2 Addresses
Harry	Hardy

The conversation between Harry and Hardy continues happily. But how is this extending the life of our Ethernet? At this stage the bridge seems to be behaving just like a repeater. OK, let's now say that Harry sends an ARP to Sally. Unfortunately, the bridge has to copy the broadcast and Harry's address is already in the Learning Table so the bridge doesn't need to do anything new. However, when Sally sends back her ARP response, the bridge learns that Sally is on Port 1. This is how the Learning Table looks at this point:

Port 1 Addresses	Port 2 Addresses
Harry	Hardy
Sally	

The destination of the frame, Harry, is also on Port 1. The bridge *doesn't* copy the frame over to Port 2 because it can see that the MAC Source and MAC Destination are on the same Port so there is no point in copying the frame anywhere else. When the bridge Learning Table has obtained a few addresses, it will begin to keep *intrasegment* traffic from "leaking" onto other segments. The more addresses that the bridge learns, the more efficient it becomes at filtering traffic. The full Learning Table for our example network looks like this:

Port 1 Addresses	Port 2 Addresses
Harry	Hardy
Sally	Laurel

Ultimately the bridge can totally separate *unicast* traffic from the Sales and Accounts departments. However, the nature of communication protocols such as ARP means that bridges *must* forward broadcast traffic. Take a look at Figure 8.2 again. Each of these bridges *must* forward an ARP broadcast from one LAN segment to all the other segments. This behavior of bridges has a direct impact on scaleability behavior.

When a bridge learns the location of the station, does it remember forever? In fact, there may be good reasons why a bridge should be forced to "forget" end systems after a certain time, as I shall now explain.

8.3 Moving Hosts Around

When Ethernet was first devised, host machines tended to stay pretty much where they were first installed. The prospect of physically moving a PDP-11 or VAX and still have it working properly, was not something to be undertaken lightly. Today though, we have portable machines that can be operated from batteries and moved all around an office building, connecting to different LAN segments. Many businesses today use the "dynamic team" approach, where a project team is assembled to tackle a specific job, will stay together for the duration and will then be broken up and moved to the next project. Such moves and changes can

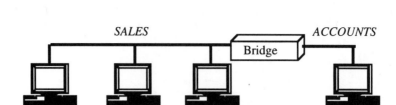

Figure 8.3:   Hardy Moves to Sales

be supported very well with flood-wired office buildings and UTP LAN technology. However, how does our bridge cope?

Let's assume our little workgroups change and that Hardy's accounting expertise is temporarily required in the Sales Department. Physically the LAN now looks like I have drawn it in Figure 8.3.

However, the Learning Table still contains the same addresses as before:

Port 1 Addresses	Port 2 Addresses
Harry	Hardy
Sally	Laurel

During the first morning that Hardy works with Sales, he just connects up his PC and then goes into a meeting to discuss the strategy for the new group. He has asked Laurel to send through a summary of financial data that Hardy urgently requires in the meeting. Laurel already has an ARP cache entry for Hardy, so his traffic is directly addresses to Hardy's MAC address. The bridge picks up the traffic and as far as the Learning Table is concerned these two hosts are on the same segment and the bridge just drops the frame. No matter how many times that Laurel tries to get through, the frame will just be dropped. In fact, in this situation, Laurel will have to wait for Hardy's machine to transmit something on Port 1. The bridge then has the opportunity to discover a "duplicate MAC address" problem. In some way we want the bridge to change its Learning Table to this:

RFP Question:	How does your bridge Learning Algorithm behave in the face of End Stations which move from segment to segment?

Here are some possible strategies for the maintenance of bridge Learning Tables.

Port 1 Addresses	Port 2 Addresses
Harry	~~Hardy~~
Sally	Laurel
Hardy	

8.3.1   Automatic Aging of Table Entries

When MAC address entries are first put in the table, they are given an *age value*. The age value can be configured in the bridge as a certain number of seconds; let's say for example 240 seconds. Every so often, the bridge will check its internal clock and decide if it needs to age the table. If so, it will subtract the time since the last aging from every entry in the table. If any entries are less than or equal to zero, they are removed from the table and the bridge will re-learn the location of this host when the host transmits its next frame. Whenever a station transmits a frame, the bridge will check the source address to see if it needs to be inserted in the Learning Table. If the bridge finds the address is already in the table, the age of this entry will be reset back to 240 seconds. This process is called *cache refresh*. In this way, addresses that are used regularly will be retained in the table. Addresses that move from one segment to another will probably be aged out of the table by the time they have moved.   The implementation of address aging is not a trivial decision for a bridge/router manufacturer to take.

8.3.2   Triggered Address Updates

A second table management strategy is for the bridge to update entries when it learns a new host location, a *Triggered Update*. In our example, when Hardy moves to the Sales Department, the first time his station transmits a frame with its own source address, the bridge will delete the entry for Hardy in the Port 2 column of the Learning Table and re-enter it in the Port 1 column. Automatic updates are an alternative to aging, but in dedicated bridges (as opposed to bridge/routers), aging and updating are used together.   In our example, if Hardy's PC had not transmitted a frame at all before Laurel tries to reach him, the same problem will occur. However, many implementations of TCP/IP send out an *ARP response* frame broadcast[1] as part of their boot procedure. In that case the bridge will be able to keep track of Hardy even when he moves from one segment to another. The performance impact of automatic updates can be significantly less than aging. To implement automatic updates, when the bridge

---

[1]Remember that in normal operation, an ARP response is a fully addressed frame, not a broadcast.

learns a new address, it must look in all other columns to check if this address has already been learned and if so to delete the old entry. This may not be as much work as it sounds because many bridges tend to use a special type of memory called *CAM* (Content Addressable Memory). CAMs are used to perform very fast pattern matching with virtually no involvement of external processors. If CAM is used in the bridge, then Automatic Updates are a trivial exercise.

8.3.3   Manual Address Updates

To complete the picture of update strategies, I need to mention manual updating. In this procedure, the Network Administrator must be notified that Hardy has moved from Accounts to Sales. His address will be manually deleted from the Accounts (Port 2) column and can be manually added in the Sales (Port 1) column. Manual updates mean a lot of extra work for the Network Administrator, as you can imagine. However, there are secure hub products which use a variation of this strategy to achieve some additional control over stations on the network.

8.3.4   The Preferred Strategy?

Bridges really must allow end systems to move around the network. The Automatic Aging and Triggered Update methods will both work, although the former is the "pure" mechanism originally intended for Transparent Bridges. If the aging strategy for the bridge is operating correctly, then you will be able to relocate a host without changing its Network Layer address.

The only unacceptable option is "no updates," in which the bridge process must be restarted in order to learn about the movement of end systems.

8.3.5   Duplicate MAC Addresses

If two stations on the network are using the same MAC address, there will be some very interesting problems. I discussed the concept of MAC address allocation earlier. So, if you find that you have duplicate addresses you are probably trying to use a locally administered, software-assigned address scheme. Please ask yourself right now why you decided to do this. Look back in your meeting minutes and find out whose idea it was. Call them up and get them to explain their reasoning; even better get them to write it down officially. Unless they can come up with a cast-iron reason for this additional workload, forget it. It really isn't worth the extra hassle. If a manufacturer makes a mistake and issues duplicate addresses, you have a good reason to be annoyed, but at least you have the satisfaction of knowing that it's not your fault. On a global basis, the prospect of manual address allocation at the MAC layer may put an unacceptable additional load on the Network Administrator.

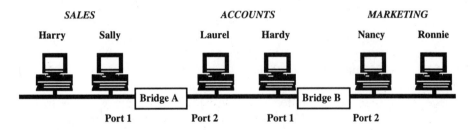

Figure 8.4:   In-line Bridge Topology

8.4   Bridge Topologies

Transparent Bridging is a mature and well-devised piece of technology. However, there is a limit to the way in which the network can be expanded. What happens, for example, if we introduce a third workgroup to our network: Marketing? Nancy and Ronnie work in Marketing and they would like to be able to connect to the Sales and Accounts folks. One option is shown in Figure 8.4: to purchase a second 2-port bridge. The three Ethernet segments are now linked in a line to each other, Sales then Accounts, then Marketing. Each bridge will build its own learning tables.

For this network, the Learning Tables will eventually look something like this:

<table>
<tr><td colspan="2">Bridge A</td><td colspan="2">Bridge B</td></tr>
<tr><td>Port 1</td><td>Port 2</td><td>Port 1</td><td>Port 2</td></tr>
<tr><td>Harry</td><td>Laurel</td><td>Harry</td><td>Nancy</td></tr>
<tr><td>Sally</td><td>Hardy</td><td>Sally</td><td>Ronnie</td></tr>
<tr><td></td><td>Nancy</td><td>Laurel</td><td></td></tr>
<tr><td></td><td>Ronnie</td><td>Hardy</td><td></td></tr>
</table>

So, we can keep on expanding our Ethernet by adding bridge after bridge. In fact, there is no absolute limit to the number of bridges[1]. Even in our simple network, we can see the beginnings of a problem. For two segments linked by a bridge, we can guarantee address separation and quality of service for each segment (actually this depends on how tightly we define quality of service). As soon as we add a third bridge, then the traffic loading on the middle segment, Accounts, is directly affected by the level of traffic flowing between Sales and

---

[1]Technologies such as Spanning Tree and Source Routing impose individual limits on bridge numbers.

Marketing, as well as the impact of traffic which "leaks" out of these two departments. The actual effect on users obviously depends on how busy the individual segments become, but sooner or later, linear bridge topologies run into problems. Are there other topologies we can play with? In Figure 8.5 I show four possible designs for a bridged network. The Conventional Backbone design might be the most familiar to you. This is a very common way for a bridged network to be expanded, especially when the bridges are located in conventional cabling hubs. The Collapsed Backbone is a newer concept arising from the availability of multiport bridges. The Transparent Bridge algorithm is quite applicable for multiport operation, we simply add one column into the learning table for each port on the bridge. There are some issues here. For example, in a two port design, the bridge simply forwards any frames if it is not sure about the end system location. The analogy in a multiport bridge is for the bridge to *flood* copies of the frame in question out of every port, except the one on which the frame was received.

The two other topologies are simple examples of networks that could become quite complex. Parallel bridges would seem to be very useful to boost internetwork forwarding rates beyond that of a single bridge. Meshed bridges allow us to create redundant connections between any two end systems on the network. However, there are significant problems in designing these two topologies with Transparent Bridges.

8.5 Spanning Tree Bridges

A major extension to traditional bridging technology was the adoption of a loop detection mechanism called Spanning Tree. If we extend Ethernet networks using Transparent Bridges, we absolutely must avoid topologies which include <u>active</u> loops. A typical loop topology is shown in Figure 8.6.

In this network we have four Ethernet segments, S1..S4. There are five Transparent Bridges B1..B5 linking these segments together. The issue is that if we sent traffic from S1 to S4, there are actually three possible routes over which traffic can pass. At first you might think that the only issue is that if there are *n* routes between two segments, *n* copies of any message will be generated on the receiving segment. In fact the situation is *much* worse than that and I give a worked example in the Diskette Tutorials. In most cases where active loops are allowed to form, the entire bridged internetwork becomes unusable until the loops are removed. If loops form in bridged networks even for a few seconds, the traffic levels on the network can easily overload an Ethernet and cause a lock-out of real traffic. Indeed, the term *Ethernet Meltdown* was very popular with router salesmen in the mid-80s (right up to the time that bridging was introduced into routers in fact).

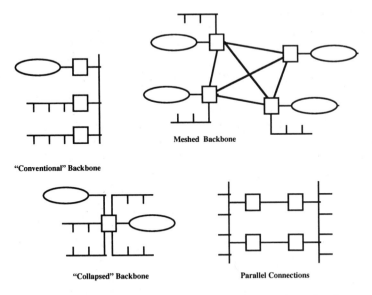

Figure 8.5: **Typical Bridge Topologies**

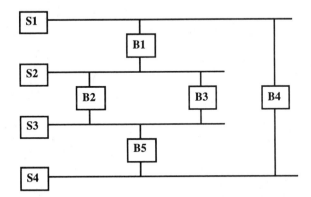

Figure 8.6: **Bridge Topology with Loops**

The problem is that looped topologies are so darned useful for resilience and so we can't simply forbid their use. In fact, we can state a few things right now about the way that the loop detection should operate:

- Because overloads can happen so quickly when loops are formed, it's unrealistic to expect a human operator to detect and remove loops manually. There must be an automated loop detection feature included in bridges.

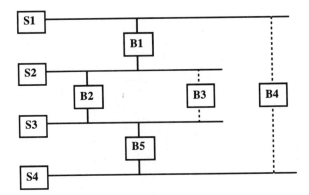

Figure 8.7:   Loop-free Network

- When a bridge is first switched on, it doesn't know if it may be in a redundant loop configuration. Since active loops are so dangerous, the bridge must begin in standby mode, listening for loop detection transmissions.

- If the bridge is not forwarding traffic while it looks for loops, then the loop detection must happen quickly.

- If links go down in the network, the technique must rapidly re-establish the backup routes.

- The protocol used to achieve all of this must be an open standard to allow bridges from different vendors to interoperate on the same bridged network.

The result of these demands was the IEEE 802.1 Spanning Tree Protocol. If we guess at the way that loops would be removed from the network shown in Figure 8.6, we might end up with a logical topology something like this...

The dotted lines in Figure 8.7 indicate that these links have been switched into a "standby" mode. You may be thinking that this doesn't look very much like a tree, but it just depends on the way you draw it. Figure 8.8 is redrawn to show the tree concept. I've also highlighted the difference between bridges and segments by inverting the segment coloring.

This diagram clearly shows two very important concepts. First, bridges that are in standby mode do not appear anywhere in a Spanning Tree. Second, there is just one possible path between two segments in a Spanning Tree network.

In the event of a failure of one of the *active* bridges, Spanning Tree will re-establish one or more of the backup links until full connectivity is restored. In this case, if bridge B1 is powered down, a backup link through bridge B4 will be established. This is shown in Figure 8.9.

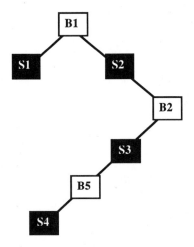

Figure 8.8:   Tree-like Interpretation of Figure 8.7

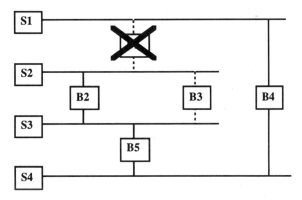

Figure 8.9:   Redundant Connection with Spanning Tree

It should be fairly obvious that Spanning Tree can only re-establish connectivity if redundant links exist to bypass failed connections. For example, if we're having a really bad day and bridge B4 also fails in Figure 8.9, then we can no longer connect to Segment S1.

Spanning Tree works by using a simple inter-bridge protocol and then following a set of rules to ensure than only one active path (the path with the lowest cost) is operating between any two LAN segments. The procedure is as follows:

    1.   Choose one of the bridges on the network and define it as the *root bridge* of the Spanning Tree.

    2.   Calculate the shortest path from any segment on the network to the root bridge.

3.   Close down links on bridges which are not part of this shortest path.

4.   Monitor the network for bridge or link failures. In the event of a failure, recalculate the Spanning Tree.

8.5.1   Spanning Tree Parameters

It looks as though we have to start differentiating one bridge from another. Since these bridges are "transparent," that shouldn't be possible, should it? To implement Spanning Tree, bridges need to be given identity parameters and a bridge-to-bridge protocol must be defined to allow these parameters to be advertised around the network. Since the protocol must only be detected by Spanning Tree bridges, a special multicast address was defined. In canonical form this address is:

Spanning Tree Multicast Address: 01 80 C2 00 00 00

The messages that pass between Spanning Tree bridges are known as *Bridge Protocol Data Units* (BPDU). The parameters that are assigned to a Spanning Tree bridge are:

- Bridge Address (48 bits)
- Bridge Priority (16 bits)
- Port Address (8 bits)
- Port Priority (8 bits)
- Path Cost (16 bits)
- Max Age
- Hello Time
- Forwarding Delay

Some of these terms are combined:

- Port ID (16 bits; combination of Port Priority plus Port Address)
- Bridge ID (64 bits; combination of Bridge Priority plus Bridge Address)

Bridge Address, Bridge Priority and Bridge ID

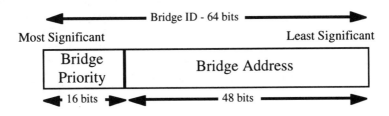

Figure 8.10: The Spanning Tree Bridge ID Field

The *Bridge ID* field, shown in Figure 8.10, is a 64-bit address which must be unique across the bridged network. The field consists of the *Bridge Address* as the least significant 48 bits and the *Bridge Priority* as the most significant 16 bits. The Bridge Address is normally taken as the lowest MAC address of one of the interfaces in the bridge. The Bridge Priority is a generic configuration parameter. By default, this is set to 0. The network designer can adjust this value to customize the behavior of the Spanning Tree. Because adapter MAC addresses must be unique, we know that no two bridges in the network will have the same Bridge ID so there should never be a tie for Root Bridge. If we only based Root Bridge selection on Bridge Address (i.e. MAC address of one port), it would mean that we would have no real design control over the Spanning Tree. This is the reason for the Bridge Priority parameter. The Bridge ID field is the <u>combination</u> of Bridge Priority and Bridge Address, with the Bridge Priority field as the most significant. We can control which bridge is Root using Bridge Priority. This is a 16 bit field so we can afford to start at a reasonable number. If two bridges have the same priority, the one with the lower Bridge Address will become Root.

Port Address, Port Priority and Bridge ID

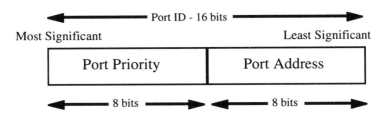

Figure 8.11: Spanning Tree Port ID Field

Port ID is combination of *Port Priority* and *Port Address* (Port Priority is most significant) and is shown in Figure 8.11. Port ID really becomes useful in multiport bridges where loops might be formed within the bridge itself and is described in more detail below.

Path Cost

Path Cost is the parameter which allows Spanning Tree to determine the "shortest path." This value is set on a per-link basis and describes the "cost" of using this link. Path Cost can be set to a different value on for each port on the bridge if necessary. IEEE 802.1 contains an algorithm to determine a default value for Path Cost. Take 10^9 and divide by the link speed in megabits per second. In this scheme Ethernet ends up with a cost of 100 and FDDI a cost of 10^1.

Max Age

The *Max Age* timer should be set to the same value for the whole Spanning Tree. This timer is used to determine how long a bridge will use a particular configuration entry before it is discarded. Setting Max Age to a lower value may allow the bridge to notice changes in the Spanning Tree more quickly, but in a larger network (where the probability of packet loss is higher), values that are too low may cause Spanning Tree to be recalculated without real reason.

Hello Time

The *Hello Time* should also be set to the same value throughout the network. Bridges will send out BPDUs when the Hello Time timer elapses. When a bridge receives a valid BPDU it will use it to reset its Max Age timer. Setting the Hello Time to shorter values will allow the Spanning Tree to converge more quickly, but will mean that more BPDU traffic is generated.

Forwarding Delay

The *Forwarding Delay* timer decides how long a bridge will spend in the "learning" and "listening" states. In simple terms, a bridge will decide that a particular port is to become a part of the Spanning Tree. It will then wait for (*Forwarding Delay*) seconds in the "learning" state and then another (*Forwarding Delay*) seconds in the "listening" state and then it will finally start to forward data (assuming that no change in the Spanning Tree has taken place during the "learning" or "listening" period. Setting the Forwarding Delay to a lower number will minimize the time that a bridge spends in a stand-by state before forwarding data, but in extreme cases, too low a value will result in temporary loops forming in the network.

8.5.2   Spanning Tree In Action

I can summarize the process of Spanning Tree with a simple set of rules.
1. The bridges decide who will be the Root Bridge. The bridge with the lowest Bridge ID wins.

---

[1]In the original DEC Spanning Tree the constant was 10^8. This gave Ethernet a cost of ten and FDDI a cost of one.

2.   Bridges advertise the lowest cost that they know to reach the Root.
        When bridges hear "better" costs to reach the Root they update their
        BPDU transmissions accordingly.

3.   Bridges decide if they are part of the Spanning Tree and shut off
        active ports accordingly.

4.   Once the Spanning Tree forms, the Max Age timer ensures that the
        shape of the tree will be recalculated if bridges are lost. Note that
        the entire Spanning Tree will only need to be recalculated if the
        Root Bridge is lost.

So how do bridges decide which ports are part of the Spanning Tree? There are
two possible situations where a port can be part of the Spanning Tree:

1.   Normally, all ports on the Root Bridge are in the Spanning Tree.
        The one exception to this is for multiport bridges, where two (or
        more) ports are connected on the same LAN segment. I discuss
        multiport tie breaking below.

2.   If a bridge on a LAN segment is advertising the lowest cost path to
        the Root Bridge, then this bridge becomes the *Designated Bridge*
        for that segment. Ports on the Designated Bridge are included in
        the Spanning Tree. Once again, in a multiport bridge if two (or
        more) ports are connected to a segment for which the bridge is the
        Designated Bridge, then a tie breaker process will switch off all but
        one of these ports. The active ports on the Designated Bridge are
        known as *Designated Ports*.

Tie Breaking in Multiport Bridges

In the description of Spanning Tree that I gave above, you can see that the
protocol relies on unique values of various parameters to make tie breaking
decisions. However, some of the parameters are common to the whole bridge.
The example I'd like to consider is shown in Figure 8.12, where I show a 4-port
bridge connecting two Ethernet segments, S1 and S2. Each segment has two
connections to the bridge.

During its Learning and Listening states, the bridge sends out BPDUs advertising
itself as Root Bridge. The BPDU sent by Port 1 will be received by Port 2 (and
vice versa). The BPDU sent by Port 3 will be received by Port 4 (and vice versa).
Both Port 1 and 2 receive a path to the same Root Bridge, with the same cost
(let's assume that the Path Cost of all ports on the bridge are the same). How
does the bridge decide which ports to switch off? Well, remember the Port ID
parameter I described above. This can be used as a final tie breaker. The Port
ID is made up of the Port Address and the Port Priority. The Port Address is
some internal number used by the bridge. In most multiport architectures, Port
Address starts at 1 and increments by 1 each time you add a port to the bridge
configuration. This is quite adequate as a tie breaker, but it might be nice to
have a deterministic way to decide the shape of the Spanning Tree for multiport

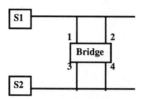

Figure 8.12:   Multiple Connections Between LAN Segments

bridges. This is done using the Port Priority parameter. This is the most significant part of the Port ID so it will take precedence over Port Address. Let's say in this case that we wanted Ports 2 and 4 to be our "primary" ports on the bridge, with 1 and 3 as "backup" links. We could set the Port Priority of Port 2 and Port 4 to 16 and the Port Priority of Port 1 and Port 3 to 128. The lowest Port ID will "win" so Ports 2 and 4 will be chosen in favor of Ports 1 and 3.

8.6   Encapsulation Bridges

The next type of Traditional MAC bridging that I'd like to discuss is Encapsulation. This type of bridge is used to connect two similar MAC layers over a dissimilar connection. Classically the first Encapsulation Bridges were to allow Ethernet LANs to be connected over a serial link. Since then Encapsulation has been used in the following scenarios:

- Ethernet to Ethernet over FDDI

- Ethernet to Ethernet over Token Ring

- Ethernet to Ethernet over an IP cloud

- Token Ring to Token Ring over FDDI

- LAN to LAN (identical LAN types) over X.25, Frame Relay, SMDS or ATM

8.6.1   Remote Ethernet Bridges

The first type of encapsulation bridge that became popular was the Ethernet Remote Bridge. This was used to connect two Ethernet LANs over a serial line and is shown in Figure 8.13. In this diagram I've tried to show that this type of bridge is logically equivalent to a local bridge (shown in the upper diagram). Local bridges connect their respective chipsets using a high speed bus which is internal to the bridge.

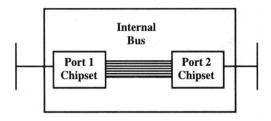

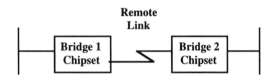

Figure 8.13: Local and Remote Bridges

Remote bridges use the leased line to connect their chipsets. In fact, individual remote bridges are often called *half bridges*. Each half bridge performs the Ethernet collision handling for its local segment so distance limitations are removed. Each half bridge has a Learning Table, which allows traffic over the leased line to be minimized. Note that the Spanning Tree protocol defined by IEEE 802.1D does not currently include remote bridges, but virtually every manufacturer of remote bridges includes remote Spanning Tree support. The major issue for remote operation is the effect of additional store and forward delay caused by low speed remote connections on the Spanning Tree timers. These timers can obviously be adjusted to suit remote operation, but this may involve a compromise of a longer convergence time for the Spanning Tree. Since Spanning Tree parameters such as *Max Age* and *Hello Time* must be identical for all the bridges in a single Spanning Tree, then the remote bridge delays effectively compromise the performance of the entire bridged network.

8.6.2   FDDI Encapsulation Bridges

While the need for FDDI backbone networks was quickly recognized by manufacturers and users, the standards that were needed to build these devices were slow to evolve. Even today, 10 years after FDDI's conception, a complete set of routing and bridging standards for FDDI is still not available. Even as the standards were beginning to take shape, several vendors introduced proprietary schemes for the interconnection of Ethernet and IEEE 802.3 LANs over an FDDI backbone. This type of bridge is also known as an *Encapsulation Bridge*. In Figure 8.14 I show three encapsulation bridges in operation. Each bridge is shown with just a single Ethernet port, but multiport operation is quite normal

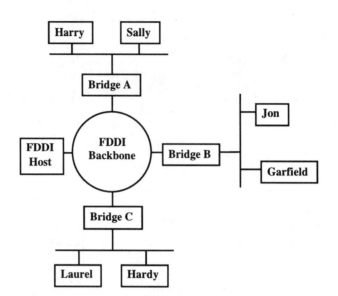

Figure 8.14:   Encapsulation Bridge Internetwork

for modern bridge/router units.   Note all the names (Harry, Garfield,, etc.) actually represent 48-bit Ethernet MAC addresses.

An encapsulation bridge operates its *Ethernet* port (or ports) in promiscuous mode and learns the MAC address of all the active hosts on its own segment in the usual way. The FDDI operates in unicast mode and may use unicast or multicast addresses to communicate with other encapsulation bridges. On a periodic basis, each bridge sends out a copy of the Ethernet Learning Table to all of the other encapsulation bridges on the FDDI ring. When fully developed in this way, Bridge A's Learning Table will appear like this:

Table 8.1:   FDDI Encapsulation Bridge Learning Table

Local Addresses	Non-Local Addresses	
Station Address	Station Address	Via Bridge (FDDI Address)
Harry	Jon	Bridge B
Sally	Garfield	Bridge B
	Laurel	Bridge C
	Hardy	Bridge C

FDDI Encapsulation Bridges work very well and allow a high level of plug-and-play operation. In particular, they operate the FDDI chipset in unicast mode,

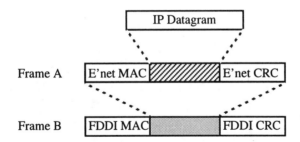

Figure 8.15:   Ethernet-in-FDDI Encapsulation

which means that the performance demand on the bridge CPU is significantly lower than for the Translation Bridges I describe in the next Chapter. However there are two problems. Referring back to Figure 8.14, we can see an FDDI Host on the backbone ring. Since the packets transmitted by the Encapsulation Bridges are not "native FDDI," this host cannot understand the traffic.

You can see why the host has a problem by looking at Figure 8.15. Frame A is a regular Ethernet-encapsulated IP datagram such as I describe in Chapter 3. Frame B is not normal at all. Unlike router operation, an Encapsulation Bridge does not strip off the Ethernet MAC information at all (it needs to retain this because the MAC address is used for frame delivery). So Frame B looks nothing like a true FDDI-encapsulated IP datagram.

The other problem about reaching the host is that the FDDI chipset is operating in unicast mode and will not learn MAC addresses on the FDDI backbone. Other Encapsulation Bridge addresses are learned using a proprietary bridge-to-bridge protocol, usually based on a multicast address. Indeed, you can see that the Learning Table shown in Table 8.1 doesn't even contain the FDDI Host's address.

These problems do not just apply to FDDI hosts. Since the encapsulation format and the bridge-to-bridge protocol are proprietary, all of the bridges in Figure 8.14 must be made by the same manufacturer in order to communicate successfully.

> RFP Question: List the products in your range that support FDDI Encapsulation Bridging. Can all of these products communicate between each other over the same FDDI ring?

This question is necessary because router companies have begun to acquire other router or bridge companies. This means that there may be incompatible products within the same manufacturer's product range. While all manufacturers will strive for compatibility, this process takes time. Users should be aware of the potential problems and timescales involved.

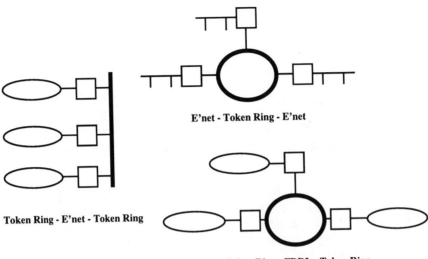

E'net - Token Ring - E'net

Token Ring - E'net - Token Ring

Token Ring - FDDI - Token Ring

Figure 8.16: Other Encapsulation Bridges

Today, Encapsulation Bridging for FDDI is essentially an obsolete technique. CPU power and RAM are cheap enough to make the FDDI Translation Bridge the favored method.

8.6.3   Other Encapsulation Combinations

Figure 8.16 shows a range of other Encapsulation Bridge options. Most of these combinations are available from the major bridge/router manufacturers. Today the trend for Encapsulation Bridging is to use IP as the encapsulating protocol, with a proprietary higher level protocol to handle Learning Table update. This option is actually quite a good one, since it allows the construction of IP Tunnels through which bridged traffic can pass, as I show in Figure 8.17.

IP Tunneling is another proprietary system, but standards are beginning to emerge. The most prominent of these is the *Data Link Switching* (DLSw) standard initially defined in RFC 1434, discussed in detail in Chapter 18.

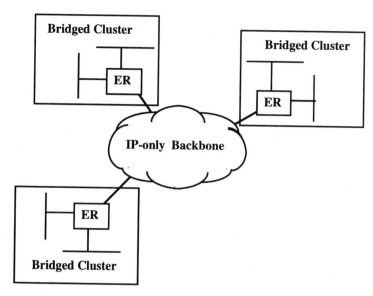

Figure 8.17: IP Tunneling of Bridge Traffic

8.7 Bridge/Router Interaction

I've mentioned that there are specific scaleability issues inherent in Traditional Bridging. The conventional solution to these issues is to separate bridging domains using routers. Let me first look at the issues in a pure IP network. Figure 8.18 shows a simple example.

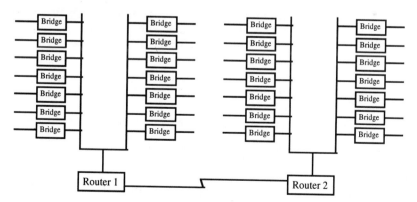

Figure 8.18: Bridged Backbones Connected Through Routers

The bridged backbone network I originally showed in Figure 8.18 is now connected to a similar backbone using two IP routers. This is the way the network looks *physically*. But how do the routers see the network?

Logically, the Ethernet bridges are totally transparent to the router so the network appears as in Figure 8.19.

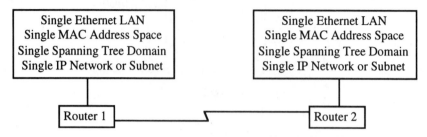

Figure 8.19:   Logical View of Figure 8.18

So each LAN port looks like a single Ethernet to the router. The effect is to enable scaleability in the network. Each Ethernet is now a single, separate MAC address space. This itself has multiple consequences:

- MAC addresses an be duplicated between sites. They have only local significance.

- ARP broadcasts are resolved by the router and they will not pass over the WAN link.

- Most other broadcasts can be stopped by the router. The exceptions today are BOOTP (and related protocols) and NetBIOS-over-IP.

- Multicast traffic is also stopped by the router. This is currently under review and development by the IETF in order to standardize multicast routing.

- The bridge Learning Tables on each site can be sized according to the number of end stations on that site and does not need to take into account the MAC addresses on other sites.

The extended LANs are each operating as their own Spanning Tree domain. Once again, there are multiple consequences:

- The time to recalculate a Spanning Tree is proportional to the number of bridges in the extended network. Each Spanning Tree calculates according to the number of bridges on that site and does not interact with the other site's Spanning Tree.

- A bridge failure on one site causes only that Spanning Tree to recalculate. It does not affect the other site.

- The remote routers do not take part in the Spanning Tree; therefore the parameters on each site can be tuned for local operation only.

- The Spanning Tree parameters on each site can be independently tuned.

Each site must appear as a single IP Network or Subnet ID. The consequence of this is that each site can administer its own IP address space without affecting the other site. The downside is that some routing information must be exchanged by the routers to allow inter-site communication. This information may be in the form of static routing, or dynamic routing protocols.

The router itself doesn't need to be equipped with special hardware or software to allow these beneficial interactions with Transparent Bridges.

There is a problem in using routers to interconnect bridge domains. What happens if the sites are using a non-routeable protocol such as LAT or NetBIOS and this protocol must be used between sites? I could take the easy way out and claim that this book is about IP backbones. However, I'll take a guess at a few alternatives you might like to consider.

First, is it possible to encapsulate the bridged traffic in IP? This should only be done if the non-routeable traffic makes up a minority of inter-site traffic. IP encapsulation adds frame overhead and will reduce leased line efficiency.

Second, can the routers act as hybrid bridge/routers? The answer today is normally "yes," but we have to be careful if we take this option. As soon as we switch on bridging, we lose all of the MAC address and Spanning Tree advantages I outlined above. Addressing isolation is maintained because of the way that bridge/routers operate.

The best solution is to remove the inter-site, non-routeable protocols. This approach is not as draconian as it sounds. Even DEC's own terminal servers are capable of dual LAT/Telnet operation today and third party devices have offered this capability for years. NetBIOS can be operated over a variety of routeable stacks, including IP. Native SNA protocols will benefit from Data Link Switching (DLSw), which has now been defined for Ethernet as well as Token Ring.

8.8 Summary

- The first form of bridges were used to overcome specific Ethernet problems, such as the 4-repeater limit and traffic segregation.

- Bridges are also used for remote connection and act as store-and-forward buffer devices.

- Ethernet bridges act in promiscuous mode and learn the MAC addresses of hosts on their attached LAN ports.

- The learning algorithm must include a way to remove MAC addresses from the Learning Table so that moves and changes of hosts can be supported.

- Transparent bridges can never operate in meshed topologies with active redundant connections.

- To allow redundant connections to be included, a loop detection protocol called Spanning Tree has been developed.

- Spanning Tree is administered by the IEEE 802.1D committee.

- Spanning Tree will switch redundant links into standby mode and ensure that only one active link remains between any two LAN segments. The active link will be the lowest cost path.

- Spanning Tree requires that certain parameters are assigned to the bridges. Most of these can be derived automatically, but there is an option for the Network Administrator to tune these parameters and control the behavior of the Spanning Tree.

- If an active link fails, Spanning Tree will automatically switch to the lowest cost backup link, if one exists.

- The reconvergence process requires a finite time to complete and during this process, bridges are switched into a non-forwarding state to prevent loops forming.

- The time to converge the new Spanning Tree is proportional to the number of bridges in the Spanning Tree.

- IEEE 802.1D does not include support for remote bridges and the default timers are intended to operate at LAN-like speeds and latencies.

- Most manufacturers support remote Spanning Tree, but convergence time will be compromised.

- Encapsulation Bridges are another form of Traditional Bridge.

- Encapsulation Bridges are generally used to interconnect Ethernet LANs over a non-Ethernet intermediate network. The most common example of an Encapsulation Bridge is remote Ethernet connection over serial lines.

- Encapsulation Bridges are also found in Ethernet over FDDI applications. There are no standards describing this type of bridge and individual implementations are proprietary.

- Ethernet/FDDI Encapsulation Bridges allow Ethernet hosts to interchange any type of LAN traffic, but do not allow Ethernet hosts to communicate with hosts that are located directly on the FDDI backbone.

- Routers can be used to control the size and therefore the reconvergence time of a large Spanning Tree LAN.

- Routers generally have a beneficial interaction with bridges and they require no special software.

- In order to transport non-routeable protocols, routers can also operate as bridges.

CHAPTER 9

Token Ring Bridging

> *Murphy was an optimist.*
>
> *O'Toole's Commentary on Murphy's Law*

9.1 Why Are Token Ring Bridges Different?

The main argument for bridging is the ability to extend the scope of a network without imposing addressing or configuration considerations. In other words, bridges should be "plug and play". The Source Routing technique demands that we enter some configuration information to the bridge, so there must be some reason why the industry has deliberately changed the bridging technique from that used by Ethernet and FDDI. In fact there are four main reasons why this has come about. I'll describe these reasons rather briefly to give you a perspective on the subject and then expand on the explanations later in the Chapter.

Chipset Differences

Most 1st and 2nd generation Token Ring chipsets were not designed to operate in promiscuous mode, which is the mode required by Transparent Bridges. Token Ring bridges that were not specifically designed for SRT operation require a hardware modification (i.e., the addition of external circuitry) to operate promiscuously. In Token Ring sales situations, the unicast mode of operation is positioned as a functional advantage since it prevents "wire tapping" by unauthorized users. In practice, LAN analyzers were and are, too valuable to forego, so modified Token Ring chips soon became available.

Support for Meshed Networks

The Spanning Tree standard I described in the previous chapter has allowed us to build Transparent Bridged networks with multiple links. However, all but one of the redundant links in a Spanning Tree network will be operating in standby mode and will not forward data. Source Routing allows multiple *active* routes to be used between any two LANs, although an individual host will always use the same route to another host.

MTU Efficiency

Different LAN technologies may use different MTU sizes. Source Routing allows a host to determine the MTU for any given path in the network, so will use a given heterogeneous path to its optimum efficiently.

The "A and C Bit Problem"

Ring-based LANs such as Token Ring and FDDI utilize a MAC Layer acknowledgment scheme using two special bits on the frame (the A and C bits). When the bits were originally defined, LAN interconnection was never considered, so Transparent Bridging may cause some anomalies. The FDDI bridging standards directly address these anomalies. Unfortunately Token Ring standards did not. To make matters worse, the introduction of SRT bridging highlighted the flaws in the original idea. The matter has still not been settled in a standards document (the SRT standard was never approved).

9.1.1   Why Should I Bridge?

There are several reasons why interconnection and especially interconnection at the MAC Layer, is very important to Token Ring:

Traffic Levels

Despite Token Ring's comparatively high access efficiency, there comes a time when traffic levels exceed the capacity of a single ring. In addition, a department may wish to offer a given "quality of service" to its users and to ensure that this is not affected by users in other departments a separation device is required. Like Ethernet bridges, Token Ring bridges can offer a high level of traffic isolation.

Accumulated Jitter

As LAN traffic passes down a cable, it actually travels at slightly different speeds in different sections of the cable. The effect is known as "jitter". Because of jitter, a single Token Ring has a very specific limit to the number of active hosts that can be supported. For Shielded Twisted Pair or fiber optic connections, this number is 260. For Unshielded Twisted Pair, the "conventional" number is 72, although some vendors are able to support larger ring populations. By passing through a bridge, the jitter effect is zeroed, so each ring in a bridged network is able to support the maximum number of hosts.

Non-Routeable Protocols

Interconnection at the MAC Layer is particularly important because the predominant Token Ring protocols are NetBIOS and "SNA", neither of which contain information which is suitable for routing at the Network Layer. Since Token Ring is still a predominantly SNA connection technology, bridging is currently the only option available to expand the network.

Address Independence (aka "Plug and Play")

The main reason to use Source Route Bridges in an IP environments is simplicity. All of the hosts on an extended SRB network are within the same Broadcast Domain. If you don't need to bother designing addressing schemes, then bridges are an easy alternative. Just like in Ethernet bridging, however, Source Route Bridge networks are not indefinitely scaleable. Sooner or later the network will become overloaded with broadcast traffic from ARP, RARP, BOOTP, RIP and other protocols. In fact, the nature of Source Routing actually makes these networks more vulnerable to scaling issues since active meshed routes will probably exist.

9.2   Token Ring Bridging Methods

There are currently three different types of bridging that can be found on Token Ring LANs today. In order of popularity these are:

1.   Source Route Bridging (SRB, IEEE 802.5D)

2.   Translation Bridging ("8209")

3.   Source Route Transparent (SRT, IEEE 802.1)[1]

I'll be describing the first and last of these techniques in this chapter and looking at general Translation Bridging issues in Chapter 10. Here is a brief summary of the environments in which each technique is used:

SRB Bridges

SRB bridges operate only between two Token Rings. They must use drivers in the adapter cards that are capable of sending out Source Route Explorers [2]. SRBs can operate between 4Mbps or 16Mbps Token Rings and can convert between a 4 and 16 Mbps ring. They can also be used to interconnect Token Rings over WAN links.

8209 Translation Bridges

Translation bridges allow pseudo-MAC Layer operation (i.e., operation that is independent of Network or higher layer addressing) between heterogeneous networks. An IBM product called the 8209 is able to perform proprietary translation between Token Ring and Ethernet. No standard currently exists for translation between FDDI and Token Ring. Instead, most outer vendors who bridge between FDDI and Token Ring use either Encapsulation Bridging, or native Source Route Bridging (i.e., the FDDI is just treated as a Token Ring).

---

[1]SRT bridges may seem to be more popular than true SRBs, but because of the severe side effects of using SRT, many users will configure the bridges to operate in SRB-only mode.

SRT Bridges

The IEEE 802.1m unapproved draft standard describes SRT bridges. SRT bridges operate only between two Token Rings. Hosts can use Source Route drivers or older, non-Source Route drivers. SRT bridges cannot perform translation between Ethernet and Token Ring. While it is true that the scope of the IEEE 802.1D standard was intended to cover this mode of operation, the difficulties of producing a standardized bridge were simply too great for agreement. So, at the time of writing, none of the IEEE standards apply directly to 8209 Translation Bridges, although it is possible to describe subsystems of the 8209 in terms of these standards (e.g. 802.1D, 802.5D, etc.).

9.3   Source Route Bridges

When it comes to LAN expansion, Token Ring has two specific advantages over Ethernet. First, it does not use a CSMA/CD access control algorithm, which means that there is no equivalent "4 repeater" limit to LAN expansion. Second, *Token Passing* is a much more efficient access control technique than CSMA/CD for higher traffic levels [2]. In other words, to steal an old Proteon marketing slogan, "Tokens Don't Collide". The absence of collisions on a Token Ring LAN leaves us more time to send actual data.

9.3.1   The Source Routing Procedure

In an Ethernet bridged network, both the LAN itself and the bridge is "transparent". Ethernet bridges operate in Promiscuous Mode and select frames to be forwarded using the Transparent Bridging Rules and their learning tables. IBM decided that there were some things they would like to change about this situation.

They decided that host, rather than an intermediate system, should be allowed to select the best route across the network. This implies that the host should use some form of routing procedure. This procedure is simple. If a host needs to know how to get to another host, it will send out a broadcast request called an *explorer*. The destination host will respond and both hosts will cache the route that is discovered.

To make this procedure work, we need to fill in a few details.

Intra-Ring Communication

The procedure must include a step to establish if hosts are on the same ring. This can't be done using MAC addresses, since there is no LAN-specific portion of the address. It cannot be done with IP addresses, since the bridges are operating as MAC Layer devices and will ignore higher layer protocols or addresses.

Defining The Route

To define the route between the hosts, rings and bridges must be given addresses. This is the decision that makes SRB more difficult to configure than Transparent Bridging. Bridge and ring addresses are not the same as MAC addresses.

The Explorer

The explorer frame is given a special property. It is allowed to "collect" the route entries as it is broadcasted by bridges along the route. This means that an explorer frame will actually grow in size as it crosses each bridge. The bridge will insert the appropriate routing marker and will recalculate the CRC for the frame.

Adding Value to the Explorer

Since we're now obliged to generate explorers, we may as well make sure we get some extra value from them. Specific explorer behavior can be defined to make the process more efficient for broadcast-intensive protocols. Information on the nature of the route, such as the minimum MTU for the route, can also be carried on the explorer. This allows the SRB technique to avoid fragmentation and reassembly within the SRB domain.

Preventing Infinite Loops

One of the advantages of the SRB technique is that it allows *active* redundant loops in the network. When explorers are sent out they may possibly appear on all the rings in the extended network (it depends on the type of explorer). Bridges take special precautions to ensure that explorer traffic doesn't pass through the same bridge twice. Once a route is established between two hosts, every frame sent between them will be explicitly marked with the route. This ensures that frames will not loop in the extended network.

So let me take these issues one by one.

9.3.2   Intra-Ring and Inter-Ring Communication

In Figure 9.1 you can see two Token Rings joined by an SRB. When Sally talks to Harry, we don't want the traffic "leaking" onto Ring 200. We need to find a way to mark a frame so that SRBs will know whether or not to forward it, i.e., is the frame local or non-local? Secondly, we need to insert a phase into the Source Route procedure to take intra-ring communication into account.

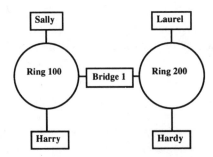

Figure 9.1:   Connecting Rings with a Single Bridge

The Source Route Indicator (SRI)

The marker for a local/non-local frame is called the Source Route Indicator (SRI) bit.   There was no such bit defined in the original Token Ring specification, so IBM had to be creative.   They decided to use a bit that already was defined in the frame, but that could be "recycled" without effecting existing software implementations.   The bit that they chose was the *Group/Individual* (G/I) bit in the MAC *Source* Address field.   If this bit is set in the MAC *Destination* Address, it indicates that the frame is a broadcast or multicast.   In the source address field, the bit has no real meaning since a frame cannot come *from* a multicast address (actually several people have suggested uses for this bit, but it's too late now).   So the SRI bit acquired its new meaning for Token Ring networks.   I show the position of the SRI bit in Figure 9.2.

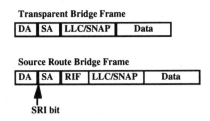

Figure 9.2:   Transparent and Source Route Frames on Token Ring

Pure SRBs use a simple rule:

SRB Rule: *If the SRI is clear, ignore the frame.*

The Local Ring Procedure

Think about the kind of IP addresses that would be used in Figure 9.1.   All of these hosts should be on the same Network or Subnet ID (otherwise they would need a router to route between the respective networks).

In other words, the hosts couldn't make the intra/inter ring decision based on IP address. Neither could they base it on MAC address. This decision requires a specific procedure, which is very simple and is described in RFC 1042 (amongst other places).

> *The first request you make for a specific host is transmitted with the SRI bit clear.*

In Figure 9.1, if Sally knows Harry's IP address and wants to find his MAC address, she sends the very first ARP request as a MAC broadcast with the SRI bit clear. Harry will respond because he's on the same ring. If Sally wants to find Laurel, she still sends the *first* ARP request with SRI clear. Bridge 1 ignores the frame so Laurel never receives it. After a short timeout, Sally sends the second ARP request with SRI set. This time, Bridge 1 forwards the frame and Laurel responds. Note, RFC 1042 states that only one attempt should be made with the SRI bit clear. If we consider the case where Sally is ARPing for Harry, the first frame is sent with SRI clear, but let's assume that Harry's adapter was unable to copy the frame (because of adapter congestion, for example), when Sally sends the second ARP, it will be copied onto the other ring , but it will *also* be received by Harry, who will then respond.

9.3.3   Ring and Bridge Addresses

In order to identify a route, we need to give each Token Ring and Bridge an address. IBM made the decision that a *Bridge ID* would be 4 bits long, with a value of 0 being illegal. A *Ring ID* is 12 bits long, with 0 being illegal.

The combination of a Bridge ID and Ring ID is known as a *Route Descriptor* (RD). However, a single 16 bit Route Descriptor is not enough to allow bridges to detect loops, route frames, etc. A routing (or loop detection) decision is made on the combination of inbound Ring ID, Bridge ID and outbound Ring ID. In Figure 9.1, an explorer frame passing from Sally to Laurel would have [100] [1] [200] appended. Since it is only possible to add complete Route Descriptors to an explorer, a "dummy" Bridge ID of 0 is added to complete the entry. Later in the Chapter I describe the way that a multi-hop routing entry is made (to give you a preview, only the first bridge adds this double RD entry).

The use of this compound RD has an interesting consequence. Since the compound RD consists of two Ring IDs, we only need to insist that the Ring IDs are unique across the network, as I've shown in Figure 9.1. In other words, if we install multiple SRBs around the network, we can re-use the same Bridge ID as long as all the Ring IDs are unique this means that the 4 bit Bridge ID is actually not a restriction. Later I'll describe an exception to this rule where parallel bridges are used between the same LANs.

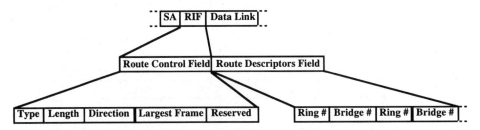

Figure 9.3: The Structure of the RIF

9.3.4   Storing the Routing Information

If the explorer is supposed to pick up routing information in the form of Bridge IDs and Ring IDs, where do we put the information?

The Routing Information Field (RIF)

To store the route which is collected by the explorer, a special field is defined in Token Ring called the *Routing Information Field* (RIF), the structure of which is shown in Figure 9.3. The RIF consists of the *Route Control Field*, (RCF) and the *Route Descriptors Field* (RDF). The RCF contains explicit control information about the explorer, while the RDF is used to hold the Route Descriptors.

The Route Control Field

The Route Control Field contains 5 fields with a total length of 2 bytes:

- Type (3 bits)
- Length (5 bits)
- Direction (1 bit)
- Largest Frame (3 bits)
- Reserved (4 bits)

The RCF Type Field

The Type Field (3 bits) identifies the frame as either being an "Explorer" frame or a *Specifically Routed Frame* (SRF). An SRF is used for data transfer *after* the route between two hosts has been discovered. Table 9.1 summarizes the different types of frame that can be sent. The binary value 110 in the Type field is particularly useful in meshed networks, sine the original request is sent down the Spanning Tree and just one copy of the explorer reaches each ring. However, the response is sent as an ARE, which will find all possible routes back to the requesting host.

The RCF Length Field

The Length Field (5 bits) indicates the total length of the RIF field measured in bytes. Since the RCF field is always fixed at 2 bytes, the length of the Route Descriptors Field can be calculated. If there are no Route Descriptors in the RIF, the Length Field will have a value of 0x00010 (2 bytes). The 5 bit limit of the Length field imposes a limit of 7 Route Descriptors.

Table 9.1: Summary of Token Ring Frame Types

Type Value	Frame Type and Behavior
000	Specifically Routed Frame (SRF). A non-broadcast frame which will contain a specific RIF. This frame will only be routed over specified bridges.
100	All-Routes Explorer (ARE). The type of explorer will be copied by every bridge once only (i.e., no loops will be allowed). In meshed topologies this will result in multiple copies of the explorer (containing different RIFs).
110	Spanning Tree Explorer (STE), All Routes Explorer Return. This frame will be transmitted across bridges that are part of the SRB Spanning Tree, which will result in the explorer request appearing only once on each ring. The explorer response will be sent as an ARE. In meshed topologies, multiple copies of this ARE will appear on each ring.
111	Spanning Tree Explorer (STE), Spanning Tree Return. This frame will be transmitted across bridges that are part of the SRB Spanning Tree, which will result in the explorer request appearing only once on each ring. The explorer response will also be sent as an STE, which will appear only once on each ring.

The RCF Direction Field

The *Direction Field* tells the bridge which direction to "read" the RIF. When the source station transmits the explorer, the direction bit is cleared and the RIF is read from left to right. When the destination station replies, rather than reversing all of the route descriptors, the station simply "flips the bit". The bridges on the return route now read the RIF from right to left.

The RCF Largest Frame Field

The *Largest Frame Field* (3 bits) indicates the largest buffer size that can be supported over a particular path. The largest frame size which can be supported on Token Ring systems is determined by a timer which is started as soon as a station claims a free token (in IBM terminology the "T(any_token)" timer). For hosts which comply with the IEEE 802.5 standard, this timer is a maximum of

10 milliseconds[1]. For stations running at 4Mbps, the maximum possible data field size specified by ISO 8802/5 (IEEE 802.5) is 4472 bytes. At 16 Mbps the maximum frame size is 17,800 bytes. The Largest Frame parameter is particularly important because MAC Layer devices do not perform packet fragmentation or reassembly. During the exchange of explorers, the value in this field changes to reflect the largest buffer size that can be supported for a specific route. The field values and associated frame sizes are listed in Table 9.2.

Table 9.2:   Packet Size Values for Token Ring LANs

Field Value	Packet Size
000	Up to 516 bytes. This represents the smallest maximum frame size that a medium access control implementation must support under ISO 8802/2 LLC (IEEE 802.2) and ISO 8473 Connectionless Mode Network Service.
001	Up to 1500 bytes (maximum size currently accepted on a Wellfleet sync line). This represents the maximum frame size supported on an ISO 8802/3 (IEEE 802.3) LAN.
010	Up to 2052 bytes. In SNA terminal applications, this size of frame is sufficient to transmit a single screen of 80x24 characters plus control information.
011	4472 bytes. This represents the maximum frame size supported on an ISO 8802/5 (IEEE 802.5) LANs operating at 4Mbps and also the maximum frame size supported by the ANSI X3T9.5 FDDI LAN.
100	Up to 8144 bytes. This represents the maximum frame size supported on an ISO 8802/4 (IEEE 802.4) LAN.
101	Up to 11407 bytes. This particular frame size should not normally be generated on an IEEE 802.5 LAN.
110	Up to 17800 bytes. This represents the maximum frame size supported on an ISO 8802/5 (IEEE 802.5) LAN operating at 16Mbps.
111	Used in an All-routes broadcast frame. This field is interpreted by bridges as "largest possible frame size up to 17800 bytes". Often referred to as "Any size".

Most SR Bridges are capable of buffering frames up to 4472 bytes, which is the maximum frame size for a 4Mbps Token Ring. If explorer frames requests larger frame sizes than this, bridges should negotiate the size down to their maximum acceptable value. Unfortunately, the flaky nature of some Token

---

[1]Many documents quote a 9ms timer. 10ms is the maximum defined by the IEEE 802.5 specification.

Ring driver software means that some hosts may not always respond to frame size negotiation. In these cases, if an SR Bridge receives a frame which is larger than it can handle, it is perfectly within its rights to discard the frame. This is one disadvantage of trying to put too much intelligence into host software. It's a lot more difficult to replace the drivers in 2000 PCs that are spread all around a network than to upgrade 50 bridges from a central Network Management System.

> RFP Question: Assume that the SRB receives a frame size which is greater than its internally configured value. If the bridge has the capability to buffer and forward the frame, does it do so?

This question arises from a common trait of bridge/routers. Since many of these devices are designed around Ethernet buffer sizes, they may have an internal MTU of 1500 bytes configured, to ensure that Token Ring frames can be transmitted over Ethernet without fragmentation (see the next Chapter on Translation Bridging). If the bridge receives a frame on a multiport Token Ring interface, then this *slot* may have a local MTU of 4500 bytes. If the frame is to be forwarded out of a Token Ring port on the same slot, then the bridge may be able to handle the frame. Note that a strict adherence by an SRB to the frame size rule may mean that the Network Administrator has some host MTU configuration to do.

> RFP Question: What possible error messages are generated by the SRB if frames are received that exceed the negotiated MTU?

This can be an important consideration in large Source Routed networks. Assuming that some host software chooses to ignore MTU negotiation, you can imagine that many bridges will be impassable to inter-ring traffic from these stations, even though the explorer traffic was able to pass through and collect the route. Ideally, the Network Administrator should be able to track these events, so that when the user of the host complains, there is an existing base of information to start the debugging process. If an SRB receives a frame that is too big to process, this must generate some internal error message in the SRB. This error message could be transmitted by a LAN Network Manager, or SNMP agent process directly as an alert to the NMS. Ideally the error message should contain the source and destination addresses on the LAN frame, as well as the address of the bridge. This allows the Network Administrator to track and solve the problem very quickly. The two possible solutions are to upgrade the driver software to a version which obeys the Frame Size rules, or to set an appropriate MTU in the host.

The RCF Reserved Field

The Reserved Field (4 bits) should be set to 0x0000.

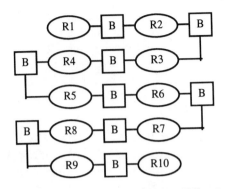

Figure 9.4: The 7-Hop Effect

Route Descriptor Field

I introduced the concept of a Route Descriptor earlier in the Chapter. In Token Ring, there is room for 8 RDs in the RCF, so it's possible to cross up to 7 dual-port SRBs (or 6 multi-port SRBs) to communicate between two hosts. If more bridges are included in the link, then certain hosts will be unable to communicate. I've tried to show this phenomenon in Figure 9.4.

In this example, the extended Token Ring stretches beyond the 7-hop maximum, so what will happen? Consider a host on ring R1. If it sends out an ARP request, this explorer will pass through the bridges, collecting RDs. When it passes through the bridge linking R7 and R8, eight RDs will be in the RIF, which is the maximum allowed. As the explorer attempts to pass through the bridge linking R8 and R9, the bridge will detect that the RIF is full and will discard the explorer. No errors are generated, since IBM never defined an error-reporting protocol[1]. The bridge cannot use ICMP, because it has no TCP/IP "identity". Note that in this network, some hosts will not be able to communicate with all possible rings, whereas some hosts in the "middle" of the network will be able to communicate with all other rings. I've drawn up a simple matrix in Table 9.3. An entry of "Y" indicates that these two rings can exchange traffic.

I'd now like to illustrate the way that SRBs operate with a series of incremental examples.

Source Routing for IP Example 1

I've already used Figure 9.1 to explain the basic operation of Source Routing. Let's take a look in more detail now. In this figure, Harry and Sally are on the same ring and Sally needs to send some kind of information to Harry using IP. On an Ethernet LAN, she would first send out an ARP. Normal IP software knows if Sally and Harry are on the same *IP network*, but there is no way for the software to know if the two hosts are on the same ring. The Token Ring

---

[1]Not entirely true, a managed bridge may report a hop-count exception to the NMS.

convention (documented for IP in RFC 1042) states that Sally should send one "normal" ARP broadcast with no RIF entry and the SRI bit cleared.

Because the frame is explicitly marked as local, Bridge A will ignore the frame and Harry will receive it and respond. The IP conversation proceeds in just the same way as if it were on an Ethernet.

Table 9.3: Communication Matrix for Figure 9.4

Ring #	R1	R2	R3	R4	R5	R6	R7	R8	R9	R10
R1	Y	Y	Y	Y	Y	Y	Y	Y	N	N
R2	Y	Y	Y	Y	Y	Y	Y	Y	Y	N
R3	Y	Y	Y	Y	Y	Y	Y	Y	Y	Y
R4	Y	Y	Y	Y	Y	Y	Y	Y	Y	Y
R5	Y	Y	Y	Y	Y	Y	Y	Y	Y	Y
R6	Y	Y	Y	Y	Y	Y	Y	Y	Y	Y
R7	Y	Y	Y	Y	Y	Y	Y	Y	Y	Y
R8	Y	Y	Y	Y	Y	Y	Y	Y	Y	Y
R9	N	Y	Y	Y	Y	Y	Y	Y	Y	Y
R10	N	N	Y	Y	Y	Y	Y	Y	Y	Y

Source Routing for IP Example 2

Now let's look at the way that inter-ring Source Routing works. Sally wants to transmit to Hardy. Sally's IP software still can't determine if Hardy is on the same ring or not, so the ARP request is transmitted with the source route indicator bit cleared. Bridge 1 ignores the frame just as it should do and Hardy does not receive the ARP request. After a suitable timeout Sally's software decides to try source routing the frame and re-transmits the ARP request with the Source Route Indicator bit set. Bridge 1 recognizes the instruction to source route the frame and performs the following actions:

1.   The bridge recognizes that the frame is an explorer and will copy the frame into its receive buffer. The bridge *will not* set the A and C bits on the Token Ring frame [2] because the destination address on the frame is a broadcast and the MAC Layer acknowledgment scheme is not applicable.

2.   The bridge inserts the appropriate route descriptors ([100] [1] [200] [0]) and forwards the frame onto the outgoing interface.

Hardy receives the frame that is forwarded by Bridge 1 because it appears on Ring 200 as a broadcast, is marked as an ARP request and Hardy is running IP

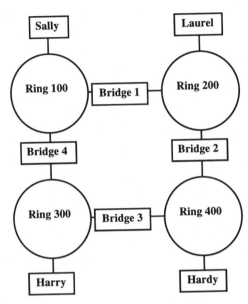

Figure 9.5: **Meshed-Ring Source Routing**

software. His CPU checks the ARP request and realizes that the request is for him. Hardy now constructs an ARP response. He knows Sally's MAC address but he also knows that she is not on the same ring (because the ARP request he received was Source Routed). Instead of sending the ARP Response locally first, Hardy can move directly to the Source Routed transmission. He also has cached Sally's MAC address against the RIF he received on the ARP explorer.

The easiest approach for Hardy is to keep the Route Descriptors in the same order as received, but to set the "direction" bit in the RCF. This will indicate to bridges that they should interpret the RIF from right to left. Some early Token Ring drivers actually reversed the order of the Route Descriptors and kept the "direction" bit clear. Sally and Hardy will maintain their ARP caches and do not need to send out explorer traffic to each other unless the cache entries timeout or a link is broken (in a meshed network). Let's look at a more complex example now.

Source Routing for IP Example 3

I mentioned earlier that one of the great advantages of Source Routing was its ability to maintain multiple, active routes in a meshed network. In Figure 9.5, we see just such a network. How does Source Routing work here? Well first of all we assume that all local communication will take place using the "first try" mechanism stated in RFC 1042.

Now let's assume that Sally wants to send a message to Laurel. She tries first with the SRI-cleared ARP broadcast and gets no reply. Sally now sends out an ARP broadcast with the SRI set. Bridge 1 receives the broadcast and decides to forward it (based on the SRB Rules). Let's follow the path of this frame:

- Bridge 1 inserts the incoming ring number, its own bridge number, the outgoing ring number and then a "null" bridge number (to complete the 2-byte entry) as the first Route Descriptor. In other words: RIF = [100] + [1] + [200] +[0] ; RIF length = 6 (2-byte RCF + two 2-byte Descriptors). The ARP request is transmitted onto Ring 200.

- Bridge 2 receives the ARP request and decides it will forward the frame. Bridge 2 extends the RIF as follows. The outgoing ring number for Bridge 1 now becomes the incoming ring number for Bridge 2. The "null" entry is overwritten by Bridge 2's address and a new outgoing ring number is added; 400. The entry is terminated with another "null" bridge number, 0. So the RIF becomes: RIF = [100]+[1]+200+[2]+[400]+[0]. The RIF length is increased to 8. The frame is transmitted onto Ring 400.

- Bridge 3 receives the frame and extends the RIF to: RIF = [100] + [1] + [200] + [2] + [400] + [3] + [300] + [0]. The frame is transmitted onto Ring 300.

- All stations on Ring 300 receive the frame (it is a MAC broadcast), but Harry's software recognizes that his IP address is being requested. Harry immediately replies to the ARP request. The frame is sent out with Sally's address as the destination MAC address. Harry uses the RIF that he has just learned from the explorer, but he sets the "direction" bit in the RCF so that all bridges will read the RIF from right to left.

Now let's look at the path of the ARP response:

- The ARP response is sent as a Specifically Routed Frame (SRF). Unlike an explorer, an SRF is not "flooded" around the network. Since it contains an explicit route, each bridge will parse the RIF to ensure that the SRF follows the correct route.

- The ARP response is received by Bridge 4. The bridge sees that the SRI is set, but then looks to see if the RD sequence "[300]+[4]+[100]" is in the RIF.[1] This sequence is not in the RIF, so Bridge 4 drops the frame.

- The ARP response is received by Bridge 3. Bridge 3 checks for the RD sequence "[300]+[3]+[400]" in the RIF and finds it. Bridge 3 decides to forward the frame onto Ring 400.

- Bridge 2 and then Bridge 1 make similar checks as the frame passes through them and eventually reaches Ring 100.

- Sally receives the ARP response.

---

[1]Bridges will obviously take the "direction" bit into account when making this decision.

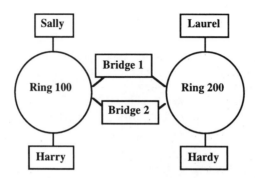

Figure 9.6:   Parallel Source Route Bridge Links

Using Redundant Paths

The scenario I've described in Example 3 is the path of the frame that used Bridge 1 to exit Ring 100. However, Sally's original ARP explorer is also received by Bridge 4. This bridge forwards the frame onto Ring 300, where it's received by Harry. In theory, this path should be "shorter" than the one through Bridges 1, 2 and 3. If the path is shorter, it means that Harry will receive this ARP request first and will send an ARP reply more quickly. The normal convention is that Sally should use the first ARP response she receives and all other responses for the same destination should be ignored.

The pathway with the lowest number of hops may not always turn out to be the shortest route. LAN or WAN speeds may vary for different routes. For routes with a homogeneous LAN type, individual bridges on the path may be congested and delay the forwarding of frames. In Source Routing terms, the "shortest path" means the one where the explorer/response path is the quickest.

Once a host has established a route, all traffic to this specific destination will be sent as an SRF, with the route included in the RIF. So, even if active loops exist, they will not cause problems because bridges will drop frames unless the appropriate RD is present.

Source Routing for IP Example 4

There is one other kind of Source Route topology I'd like to consider and this is the concept of the *parallel link*. Figure 9.6 shows two rings connected by parallel bridges.

Is this a valid topology? The answer is "yes". Explorers which pass from Ring 100 to Ring 200 will have the following RIF entries, depending on which bridge they use:

Bridge 1:   [100]+[1]+[200]+[0]

Bridge 2:   [100]+[2]+[200]+[0]

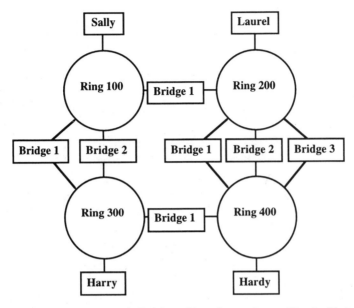

Figure 9.7: Re-use of Bridge Numbers in a Mesh Network

Because the Bridge Numbers are different, the RIFs will be different, so it is possible for parallel bridges to differentiate each other. However, the Bridge Number field is only 4-bits long. Does this mean that a Source Route Bridge network is restricted to only 16 bridges? Here's an example to illustrate the re-use of bridge numbers.

In Figure 9.5, we could actually reconfigure the Bridge Numbers to use the same number, Bridge 1 for example. This is because there are no parallel bridges in the network. In contrast, in Figure 9.7, there are a number of parallel bridges. The two bridges installed between rings 100 and 300, for example. And the three bridges installed between rings 200 and 400. These parallel bridges must be configured with unique bridge numbers.

Remember that the Bridge Number field is only 4-bits long, so we need to be frugal with our use of these numbers. As you can see, Bridge Numbers for parallel bridges can be reused in other bridges in the network.

> *Two or more Source Route Bridges which link the same two rings must be configured with different Bridge Numbers.*

9.3.5 Single and All-Routes Explorers

As Source Route topologies become more meshed and include parallel links, the amount of excess explorer traffic may become an issue. IBM have actually devised two separate ways to control explorer proliferation. One of these, DLSw,

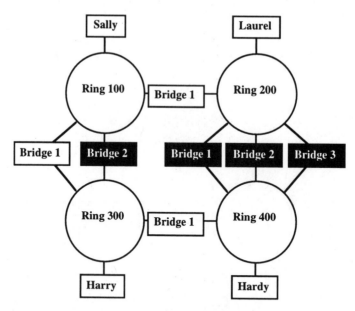

Figure 9.8: Token Ring Spanning Tree

is described in Chapter 15. The other is a more basic mechanism and operates as follows. I have already said that Source Route Bridges are able to operate with active loops, so do not require a Spanning Tree to close off redundant links. However, imagine if you could build a Source Route Spanning Tree that only worked for <u>explorer</u> frames. Only explorer traffic can be effected by loops in the network because of two fundamental advantages of Source Routing:

- Transparently bridged frames (with the SRI bit clear) cannot cause loops because they never leave their originating ring.

- Specifically Routed Frames cannot form loops because bridges can detect if a copy of this frame has already passed through and drop additional copies.

An additional subtlety of the SRB procedure would be to allow a host to indicate that certain types of explorers should follow all possible paths through the network, while other types of explorers should only follow the Spanning Tree. This capability is offered by setting the "type" field in the RCF (see Table 9.1 above). In Figure 9.8, I show just such a principle.

In this diagram, the bridges I have blacked out have been removed from the Token Ring Spanning Tree. If a host sends out an explorer which is marked with a type of "111" or "110", this explorer will only be allowed to pass by bridges which are part of the Spanning Tree. However, if hosts send out explorers marked as AREs (a type of "100"), these will ignore the Spanning Tree and will be forwarded by all bridges.

> *In an extended Token ring network with multiple paths, a host will receive one copy of an ARE for each route that exists in the network. However, a host will receive only one copy of an STE, regardless of the number of routes that exist.*

The Spanning Tree protocol used on IEEE 802.5D (SRB) bridges is distinctly different from IEEE 802.1D Spanning Tree. The Spanning Tree BPDUs sent by Token Ring bridges <u>must not</u> be interpreted by Ethernet or SRT bridges, because the respective Spanning Trees are supposed to carry different types of traffic and should be logically separate. On Token Ring, all bridges remain active at all times to ARE or SRF traffic. Token Ring Spanning Tree can be configured as a dynamic protocol, so that failures in the Spanning Tree will be automatically bypassed, if possible. However, there are several reasons why IBM administrators prefer to use a manual configuration technique. In particular, Token Ring Spanning Tree was not well standardized by IBM, who produced several versions which were not fully interoperable. Most third part router vendors offer three possibilities for the treatment of STE frames.

- A specific version of IBM Spanning Tree is implemented.

- STE frames are treated as AREs.

- A port blocking command is offered to allow the network administrator to configure a manual Spanning Tree.

RFP Question:	How does your Source Route Bridge treat Token Ring STE traffic?

RFP Question:	List the versions of IBM Source Route Spanning Tree to which your Source Route Bridge implementation complies.

In general, most Source Route Traffic uses ARE frames (e.g. IP, IPX, LU6.2). The main user of STEs is NetBIOS.

9.4 Multiport Token Ring Source Route Bridge

All of the examples of Source Route Bridges that I have given so far are shown with just two ports. Even then, you can appreciate that a Source Route Bridge has quite a few decisions to make based on the contents of the RIF. To operate at maximum speeds, Source Route Bridges require an additional hardware accelerator component. In the case of the Texas Instruments TMS380C16 chipset, this is the "Kestrel" Source Route Accelerator (SRA) chip. These SRA chips are dual-ported. In other words, they restrict the bridge/router to just two operational ports. Evidently the multiport devices from Cisco, Proteon and Wellfleet have overcome this problem, but how? Figure 9.9 shows the internal

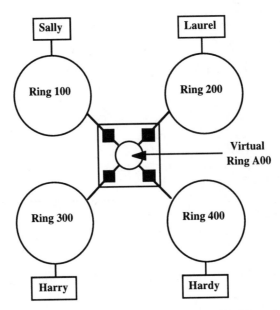

Figure 9.9:   Internal Structure of Multiport SRB

logical structure of a multiport Source Route Bridge. Each SRA (or equivalent) chip is connected to an internal, *Virtual Ring*.

From the outside, the bridge/router appears to be multiport, but internally each SRA, shown as the small black square, is dual-ported. The Virtual Ring is given its own, unique number; in this case A00. You can see that each of the SRA chips is acting as a separate Source Route Bridge, so they should each be given a Bridge Number. However, this architecture does not involve parallel bridge connections between the external rings and the virtual ring. That means that all of the SRAs inside the multiport bridge can use the same Bridge Number.

Hop Count Reduction

There is a problem with this architecture, however. Each multiport bridge/router will appear to add 2 hops to the RIF when an explorer frame traverses the unit. Since there is an overall limit of 7 hops for a Source Route RIF, this means that only 3 multiport devices can be placed between hosts. Initially this did not cause too much of a problem, because users had no alternative. However, as Token Ring networks grew, the pressure for a solution became quite intense and the main bridge/router manufacturers soon came up with solutions The "hop count reduction" solutions from Cisco, Proteon and Wellfleet all work in a similar way.

First of all let's assume that we are building the entire SRB network from a single vendor's equipment, Vendor X. These bridges are all given the same bridge number and *that bridge number must not be used by other vendor's bridges on the same extended network*. Each bridge can now recognize whether another

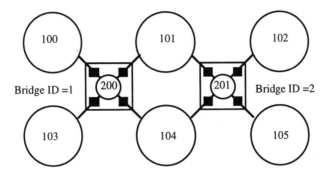

Figure 9.10: Parallel Multiport Token Ring Bridges

Vendor X bridge is present in the network and can "cancel" its position in the RIF. The exact details of how this is done vary from vendor to vendor, so you might assume that these techniques are mutually incompatible. However, they do seem to work well enough together and have the overall effect of reducing the total hop count span of the network to 6 bridges if a single vendor's bridges are employed, 5 bridges if 2 vendors, 4 bridges if 3 vendor's so on. All of the techniques are specifically designed to operate correctly with IBM's dual-port bridges and in fact any dual-port bridge which is included in the route does not reduce the overall hop count below 6 in a multivendor network.

9.4.1   Parallel Multiport Bridges

Just when you thought it was safe to put down your beer glass, there's another situation that needs to be considered. For parallel bridges that link the same two rings, I said that each bridge must have a unique number. However, for multiport bridges, I also said that we need to reserve a bridge number to allow the hop count reduction mechanism to operate correctly. Both statements are true, but what happens if you install parallel multiport bridges, such as shown in Figure 9.10?

As you can see in this diagram, we simply allocate the two bridges different Bridge IDs. However, these Bridge IDs must both be different from any other vendor's bridges in the same extended network. In addition, we must inform Bridge 1 that Bridge 2 exists, so that Bridge 1 will be able to recognize Bridge 2's ID for Hop Count Reduction (and vice versa). This normally has to be done manually.

9.4.2   Duplicate Links

There is one configuration for multiport Token Ring bridges that is currently illegal. I show this configuration in Figure 9.11.

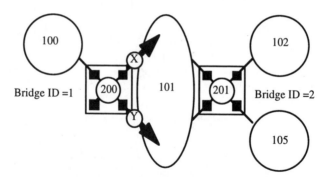

Figure 9.11:   Illegal Multiport Configuration

What am I trying to do in Figure 9.11? I've tried to add some link resilience to this network by connecting two ports on the same bridge to the same LAN. Both bridges are connected in this way. Why is this configuration illegal? Well imagine an explorer generated by a host on Ring 100. When the explorer that I've marked as X passes through Bridge 1, it picks up the following RD:

[100] [1] [101] [0]

The explorer I've marked as Y picks up the following RD:

[100] [1] [101] [0]

In other words, the same RD, which would lead to active loop problems in the network because the bridge is unable to distinguish either the explorers or the resulting SRFs. At the time of writing, the major router vendors do not offer support for this topology. The main reason is that it would significantly increase the configuration required by the bridge and may result in exhaustion of the scarce Bridge numbers (on 15 possible numbers).

9.5   SRB/Router Interaction

I've mentioned that there are specific scaleability issues inherent in Source Route Bridging. The conventional solution to these issues is to separate bridging domains using routers. Let me first look at the issues in a pure IP network. Figure 9.12 shows a simple example.

This is the way the network looks *physically*. But how do the routers see the network? Logically, the Token Ring bridges are totally transparent to the router, because they're MAC Layer devices. But there is a significant problem: the router must act as a Token Ring host and generate explorer frames in order to discover routes over the SRB domain. If this is the case, the internetwork will appear as in Figure 9.13.

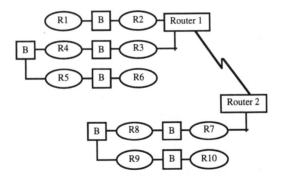

Figure 9.12:   SRB Domains Connected Through Routers

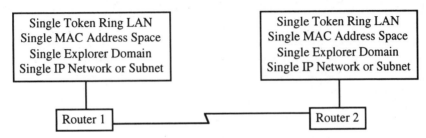

Figure 9.13:   Logical View of Figure 9.12

The capability of a router to generate Source Route explorers is usually known as *Source Route End Station Support*. As with Traditional Bridging, Source Route Bridge interaction produces effects in the MAC address space and the IP address space. However, there is no *equivalent* Spanning Tree issue since SRB uses Spanning Tree in a different way from Ethernet bridges. Instead, we need to consider that the explorer domain is limited to each site.

There are several direct consequences to the separation of the MAC address space:

- MAC addresses can be duplicated between sites. They have only local significance.

- ARP broadcasts are resolved by the router and will not pass over the WAN link.

- Most other broadcasts can be stopped by the router. The exceptions today are BOOTP (and related protocols) and NetBIOS-over-IP.

- Functional address traffic is also stopped by the router. This is currently under review and development by the IETF in order to standardize multicast routing.

- Source Route explorer traffic is limited to a specific bridge domain. Thus, for routeable traffic, routers can be used to extend the hop count limit imposed by Source Routing,

Finally each site must appear as a single IP Network or Subnet ID. The consequence of this is that each site can administer its own IP address space without affecting the other site. The downside is that some routing information must be exchanged by the routers to allow inter-site communication. This information may be in the form of static routing, or dynamic routing protocols.

Like Traditional Bridge/Router interaction, there may be a requirement to allow non-routeable traffic to be bridged simultaneously over the WAN link. In fact, in a Token Ring environment this is a very likely situation because of the popularity of NetBIOS and SNA protocols on Token Ring. Let me look at the same three solutions as I proposed in Chapter 8.

First, is it possible to encapsulate the source routed traffic in IP? For Traditional bridging, this should only be done if the non-routeable traffic makes up a minority of inter-site traffic because of the overhead of IP encapsulation. For Token Ring the encapsulation method is Data Link Switching (DLSw). DLSw does impose a high overhead (around 80 bytes) on each frame, but can offset the WAN efficiency loss because it offers a significant saving on LLC2 session maintenance traffic and a number of caching features. I discuss these mechanisms in Chapter 15. The second option of operating as a hybrid bridge/router is very much more common in the Token Ring world.

The solution to remove non-routeable protocols is not realistic for Token Ring sites today. The majority of Token Ring users are also SNA users (why else would they be using Token Ring?). Until a form of Network Layer SNA is available (APPN), Source Route Bridges will continue with their central role.

9.6   Source Route Transparent Bridging

It's possible to summarize the functionality of an SRT bridge in one sentence:

> *An SRT Bridge will act as an SRB for Token Ring frames which have the Source Routing Indicator (SRI) bit set, but will act as a Transparent Bridge for those frames which do not have the SRI set.*

In other words, if we look back at Figure 9.1, let's now imagine that Bridge 1 is an SRT bridge. The bridge has a "dual life". First of all it keeps watch on the ring for Source Addresses which have the SRI bit set and these frames are source routed as described above. In its other life, source addresses which do not have the SRI bit set are "learned" just like the Ethernet Learning Bridge described above. For non-Source-Routed frames, the SRT bridge has the same set of rules as the Ethernet bridge.

This mode of operation has several interesting implications:

- The Token Ring chipsets of an SRT bridge must operate in Promiscuous Mode. This is not the normal way that most chipsets were designed and may require a hardware modification for the adapter to operate correctly.

- SRT bridges must operate an Ethernet-style Spanning Tree, since SRT bridges may form active loops, whereas pure SRBs do not. This Spanning Tree is logically separate from the Source Route Spanning Tree described above.

- If you use two SRT bridges in parallel between the same pair of rings, Spanning Tree will operate in the same way as for Transparent Ethernet bridges. So all the inter-ring traffic will pass through only one of the bridges and no load balancing will result.

- If you use an SRT bridge and a standard Source Route bridge in parallel, you will be wasting your money. Read through Example 1 of Source Routing IP above and you will see that all hosts transmit at least their first frame with the SRI bit clear. So, if there is an SRT bridge on the ring it will always forward this traffic. The Source Route Bridges will never even see the traffic. However, the SRBs will operate if the SRT bridge fails, assuming that the end stations on the rings are capable of generating Source Route Explorer frames.

- SRT bridges do not perform conversion between transparent source route traffic. By this I mean that if a host transmits a non-source routed frame, it can never pass through a pure SRB. The entire path of the frame must be connected by SRT bridges.

Looking at this list of disadvantages for SRT bridges, you might wonder why on earth they were ever invented. Indeed, SRT bridges seem to remove the few advantages that Source Routing offers over Transparent Bridging. In real networks, SRT bridges are often used in a "Source Route only" mode.

In my experience, SRT bridges have one purpose in life. They allow inter-ring communication between hosts whose driver software cannot generate Source Route Explorer traffic. SRT bridges can be installed without entering Ring or Bridge IDs and they will then operate only as Transparent Token Ring Bridges. This "plug and play" capability of SRT bridges may appear attractive in small networks, but the technology has many limitations. In addition, there is an interesting phenomenon that occurs when Token Rings are transparently bridged, that is generally known as the "A and C bit problem".

9.6.1   The "A and C" Bit Problem

On ring-based LANs, the transmitter of a frame is also responsible for removing (stripping) the frame from the LAN. In Figure 9.1, Sally sends a message to Harry. Harry actually "receives" the frame by copying it into his receive buffer. The frame carries on around the ring and back to Sally. She is responsible for actually stripping the frame from the LAN. The designers of Token Ring and FDDI took the opportunity offered by this mode of operation to build in an acknowledgment mechanism. Two special bits are defined at the end of a Token Ring or FDDI frame. These are known as the A bit and the C bit and you can see their exact locations in the frame in Appendix D. They are used as follows:

• A receiving station will set the A bit if the destination MAC address on the frame is set to the receiving station's address. For this reason, the bit is also referred to as the *address recognized* bit. If the destination address on the frame is a broadcast or multicast address, then the A bit will be left cleared.

• A receiving station will set the C bit if the frame was successfully copied into the station's receive buffer. For this reason the bit is also known as the *copy bit*. If the destination address on the frame is a broadcast or multicast address, then the C bit will be left cleared.

• The A and C bit will not be set by a receiving station if the destination MAC address on the frame is a broadcast or multicast address.

If Sally transmits a frame she will send it with the A and C bits clear. When the frame comes back around the ring, there are four possible states for the two bits:

• A and C are both clear. This indicates that Harry didn't recognize the frame at all. Depending on the driver software in Sally's adapter, this may be enough to trigger a fast retry.

• The A bit is set, but the C bit is clear. Harry recognized that the frame was for him, but didn't have time to copy it into his receive buffer. Maybe his adapter was congested at the time. Again, a fast retry is called for.

• The A bit is clear and the C bit is set. This indicates that somebody on the ring has copied the frame, but apparently did so without recognizing their address. Since this is technically illegal, this combination of bits should never arise.

• The A and C bits are set. Harry recognized that the frame was for him and he managed to copy it into his receive buffer. Apparently a successful transmission.

In theory the A and C bits are an excellent idea. They offer an host the opportunity to resend information with an extremely short timeout. Bus-based LANs such as Ethernet cannot easily emulate the A and C bit acknowledgment concept, so the equivalent timeout might only occur at the TCP level. Since the TCP timer is intended to allow WAN communication with network latencies of several seconds, the overall performance increase for a ring system in a "noisy" LAN environment can be quite impressive.

Given that A and C bits are a "good idea" for hosts, why should they cause such problems for bridges? The simple answer is that A and C bits are designed to be set by the station which should ultimately receive the frame <u>at the MAC level</u> (A and C are MAC layer indicators). If we only have one ring, there's no problem. If we're using routers there's no problem because the MAC destination address on the frame is that of the router and no other station on the ring should try to receive the frame.

If we're using pure Source Route bridges there's no problem with A and C. Using SR bridges, the MAC destination address on the frame is not the address of the bridge, BUT inside the RIF the bridge can see its own bridge number and decide if it's the intended receiver of the frame on this ring. So a Source Route Bridge is quite within its rights to set the A and C bits on behalf of the destination station for an SRF.

However, if we're using an SRT bridge we do have a problem. Like the Source Route bridge, the MAC destination address on the frame is not the MAC address of the bridge. But this time, there's no RIF inside the frame to help us out. We've no way to know if we should set the A and C bits or not. There are only 3 strategies we can adopt and I'd like to present the consequences of each scenario:

SRT Scenario 1: Always leave A and C clear.

Referring back to Figure 3.13, let's first assume that Bridge A will leave A and C clear, even if the bridge decides to forward the frame. If Sally transmits a frame to Harry, the frame passes Bridge A. The bridge is operating in promiscuous mode and has learned that Sally and Harry are on the same ring. It leaves the A and C bits clear and everyone is happy. OK, now Sally transmits to Hardy. Again, Bridge A knows that these machine are on different rings and will forward the frame. Even so, it leaves the A and C bits clear and the "original" frame passes back to Sally. Her adapter software assumes that Hardy didn't receive the frame and sends again. Same thing happens. Meanwhile, since Hardy will have received a few outstanding requests from Sally, he will eventually get round to sending a reply. When Sally's software receives the reply it becomes really confused because, according to its MAC layer "records", Hardy hasn't acknowledged any transmission yet. Many fine examples of Token Ring software usually take an opportunity like this to have a rest for a few minutes (i.e., they crash).

SRT Scenario 2: Always set A and C.

In Figure 9.1, Sally sends a frame to Harry. As the frame passes Bridge A, it sets A and C even though it knows that Sally and Harry are on the same ring. The frame carries on to Harry and he recognizes the address on the frame, but notices that somebody has already set the A and C bits. This situation was once suggested as a means of detecting duplicate MAC addresses, so Harry immediately reports an error to the local Network Management station (in 802.5 this will be the Ring Error Monitor which ironically is often the Bridge!). However, he does copy the frame and proceed with the communication, but the local management system may get a bit tired of hearing all the complaints (and you may find the additional load on the network to be a matter of concern).

Marketing people tend to call this technique *Unconditional SRT*, while techies know it better as *Poor Man's SRT*. Eventually, host driver software will be modified to be SRT-tolerant, but this may take a few years yet to upgrade all the installed drivers.

SRT Scenario 3: Set A and C conditionally.

In Figure 9.1, Sally transmits a frame to Harry. Bridge A has already learned that the two nodes are on the same ring. The bridge ignores the frame. Sally now transmits to Hardy. The bridge knows that the two nodes are on different segments and will set A and C. Everyone's happy. However, the technique is not perfect. The bridge knows where these hosts are located because it learns when they transmit a frame, just like an Ethernet Transparent Bridge. If a given station has not transmitted what should the bridge do? In the case of an Ethernet Transparent Bridge, the rule is "if in doubt, forward the frame". Extending this to the SRT example, one assumes that "if in doubt, forward the frame and set the A and C bits". This is not too bad, but it does result in a number of spurious "duplicate address" errors to the NMS until the bridges have learned all of the station addresses.

A more serious consequence of Conditional SRT is that bridges don't have very long to make this decision. In Figure 9.14, I show a simplified Token Ring or FDDI frame. The bridge can start to make its decision when it receives the Destination Address field. It must complete its decision process by the time it receives the *Frame Status* (FS) field which contains the A and C bits.

For an 18kB Token Ring frame, the "decision period" that I've highlighted amounts to a sedate 9ms. Unfortunately we can't assume that this is always the case. For a 64 byte frame on FDDI, the decision period drops to 5 μs. In other words, the bridge would have to be capable of making 200,000 of these decisions per second. Ethernet bridges use special memory units called CAMs to allow decisions to be made this fast. Standard Source Routing doesn't need this kind of processing, so many Token Ring chipsets were not designed to accept CAM components.

The Standard Solution

IEEE 802.1m is the standard which governs SRT bridges and the committee decided that all SRT bridges should be allowed to SET the A and C bits *unconditionally*. However, as I explained above, if two stations are on the same ring, the destination host may receive the frame with A and C already set by the bridge. In this case, some Token Ring software will report a "Duplicate Address" error to the Ring Parameter Server (RPS)[1], which will then send the error as an alert to a specified management system (usually NetView). You can disable this reporting by the RPS, but this job needs to be done for every ring on the network.

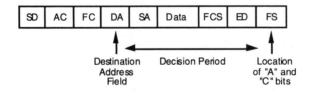

Figure 9.14: The SRT "Decision Period".

9.7 SRT Bridge/Router Interaction

In a very simplistic way, we could say that an SRT bridge will act like an SRB sometimes and a Transparent Bridge at other times, depending on the setting of the SRI bit. The issue here is that SRT is such a poor technique in scaleability terms that it's very unwise to use it at all in router environments! Do Bridge/Routers specifically need to offer SRT support in order to cope with SRT traffic? Maybe not. Take a look at Figure 9.15.

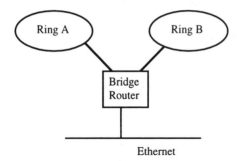

Figure 9.15: SRT/Router Interaction

In this diagram we see two rings connecting into a Bridge/Router. Let's say that we've installed this Bridge/Router as an End Station Support device and all we want it to do is to route IP traffic from the ring domain into the Ethernet LAN. Do we need SRT support? The answer is "no". Traffic that arrives from Ring A that is destined for the Ethernet arrives with the SRI bit clear. as far as the router knows, this traffic *might* have come through an SRT bridge, but it doesn't really care because this traffic looks just like it's arrived from the local ring. Traffic that arrives with the SRI bit set is just Source Routed. We should also be OK for traffic passing from Ring A to Ring B. SRI-clear traffic is indistinguishable from traffic generated on the local ring.

In Figure 9.16 I show an instance where SRT functionality might be required. The hosts on Ring C are configured with obsolete LAN drivers that are incapable of generating Source Route Explorers. The bridge connecting these device with Ring B *must* be capable of operating in SRT mode.

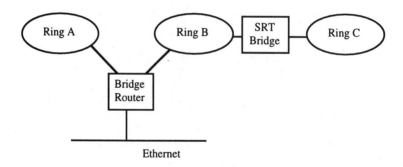

Figure 9.16:   SRT Support Required

9.8   Summary

- Whereas bridging is a convenient option in the Ethernet world, it becomes essential in the Token Ring world due to the importance of non-routeable protocols such as NetBIOS and SNA.

- Three types of bridging are currently used by Token Ring systems: Source Routing, SRT and Translation. This chapter described the first two techniques.

- A procedure and a special bit called the SRI bit are used to decide if a destination host is on the same ring, or a different ring.

- In a Source Route Bridge, the hosts send special frames known as explorers to collect route information if the destination station is on a different ring.

- IP ARP requests are sent as explorer frames (specifically as an ARE). The procedure is currently described in RFC 1042.

- In Source Routing, rings and bridges are allocated numbers to allow routes to be specified. This makes Source Route Bridges more difficult to install than Transparent Bridges.

- Bridge and Ring addresses are totally separate from MAC addresses or IP addresses.

- SRBs should only process frames with the SRI bit set.

- SRBs are able to operate in meshed topologies, with all redundant paths in the active state.

- When two hosts discover a route, they will cache this route and only this route will be used for communication even if additional routes exist.

- If a route fails, the cache entry will be aged out and an explorer will be used to find a new route, if one exists.

- SRT bridges act as Transparent Bridges for frames which do not have the SRI bit set and Source Route Bridges for frame that have SRI set.

- SRT is not currently defined by an approved standard.

- SRT bridges can be installed without using Ring IDs or Bridge IDs.

- SRT bridges allow only one active path through the extended network.

- There are significant interoperability issues between SRT bridges and SRBs.

- SRT bridges cannot operate between a Token Ring and an Ethernet.

- SRT bridges are often configured for SRB operation only.

9.9 References

[1]   IBM. *Local Area Network Technical Reference*. Document number SC30-3383-2, Third Edition, 1988.

[2]   M. Hammer. Claire and Gerald R. Samsen. *Source Route Bridge Implementation*. IEEE Network. January 1988.

[3]   J. Postel. J. Reynolds. "Standard for the transmission of IP datagrams over IEEE 802 networks", *RFC 1042*. February 1988.

Translation Bridging

10.1 What Are Translation Bridges?

Translation Bridges are a superb example of the triumph of programming ingenuity and expertise over common sense. They have the job of resolving the *enormous* difference between different LAN frames at the MAC Layer. As if this wasn't difficult enough, Translation Bridges also have to resolve various difficulties that arise because of the different ways in which we use protocols over Ethernet, Token Ring and FDDI LANs. To make the whole exercise more of a challenge, Translation Bridges are required to perform these miracles at wire speed!

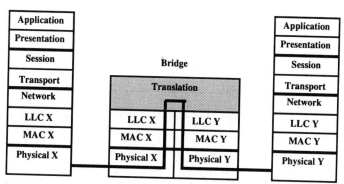

Figure 10.1: Translation Bridge Concept

I'm sure you'll agree that Translation Bridges have the most difficult bridging job of all to perform. Let's face it, if we were really meant to interconnect LANs at the MAC Layer, we wouldn't have such a range of MTU sizes, or bit order reversals, or protocol encapsulation issues to contend with. The conceptual "Translation Bridge" is shown in Figure 10.1. In this case I show the requirement to connect a LAN Type X with a LAN Type Y. In order to perform this function below the Network Layer, the bridge has to convert of the LLC and MAC structures, as well as transmitting the frame over the appropriate physical medium.

10.1.1 Why Should I Use Translation?

There must be a good commercial reason for using Translation Bridges, since they require enormous effort to engineer:

- Plug and Play installation. That's, right, we don't want to bother understanding, designing or configuring this network, so we'll just plug in a bridge and see what happens.

- Non-routeable Ethernet protocols. Unfortunately DEC still hasn't come up with a sensible replacement for LAT, so we now find that this protocol, which was only ever designed to be used within a single Ethernet segment, is being supported over bridged backbones.

- Non-routeable Token Ring protocols. As LAN protocols, NetBIOS and SNA appeared on Token Ring before Ethernet. However, Ethernet continues to be the most popular workgroup LAN technology. The result is Ethernet in the workgroups and Token Ring on the FEPs with non-routeable protocols operating between.

Taken together these are impressive arguments for us to avoid using Network Layer devices such as routers and to cling onto bridging for as long as possible.

10.2 Ethernet-FDDI Translation

In the previous Chapter I discussed Ethernet/FDDI/Ethernet Encapsulation Bridges. These were the first type of FDDI bridge to be used because they placed a comparatively low demand on the Bridge CPU and RAM. The main problem with this bridge technology was that the encapsulation technique was always proprietary, so all bridges had to be bought from one vendor. In addition, the FDDI frame format was not compatible with directly attached FDDI hosts.

Translation Bridging answers both of these issues. When a frame passes from an Ethernet to an FDDI, the resulting FDDI frame looks as though it was generated by an FDDI-attached host or router. This guarantees connectivity to FDDI hosts and interoperability with FDDI routers.

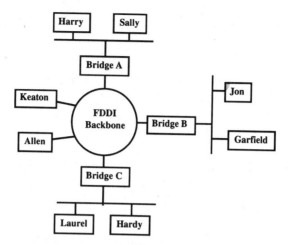

Figure 10.2:   Ethernet/FDDI Translation Bridges

In Figure 10.2 I show a typical Ethernet/FDDI Translation Bridge installation. A number of Ethernet workgroups are connected via bridges onto an FDDI backbone. Unlike in an Encapsulation Bridge network, these Ethernet hosts can communicate directly with the FDDI hosts, Keaton and Allen. From now on, I'll refer to this type of bridge as an *802.1h* bridge, since this is the standard covering Ethernet/FDDI bridging.

10.2.1   How Does it Work?

An 802.1h bridge needs to solve a few problems to operate successfully. I can summarize these as:

- Resolve different methods of on-wire frame forwarding (i.e., transparent or Source Route operation)
- Spanning Tree interaction
- MAC address formats
- Maximum frame sizes
- Frame format conversion
- Protocol Fixes
- LAN speed differences

Frame Forwarding

Both sides of an 802.1h bridge operate in Promiscuous Learning mode. For an FDDI interface, this may require a very high filtering rate from the FDDI chipset. In fact the maximum frame rate for an FDDI ring is 446,000 frames per second (28-byte frame). In real networks, the figure is *much* lower, since FDDI tends to be a backbone network, carrying mainly file transfer and client/server traffic. Typical frame sizes tend to be much larger than 28 bytes. Even so, the FDDI chipset can get very busy, so it's normal for 802.1h bridges to include CAM chips as a standard, or optional component.

A much more significant demand is the size of the Learning Table, which can become rather large for this type of bridge. Imagine an FDDI backbone with 10 bridges. Each bridge connects to 6 Ethernets and each Ethernet has 50 end systems attached, Each bridge Learning Table would contain a total of 3000 end system addresses. This is one example of the "flat address space" principle that characterizes bridged internetworks and is a major scaleability issue. The addresses are stored in fast CAM chips located on the FDDI interface of the bridge and high-end bridge manufacturers allow this CAM address space to be expanded for larger networks. Once again the flat address space issue works against us because we would have to expand even a small FDDI bridge to be able to cope with the *total* number of end system addresses in the bridged network.

Spanning Tree Interaction

802.1h bridges operate the same Spanning Tree for the Ethernet and FDDI domains. Both sides are acting as independent Transparent Bridges, so active loops must be removed from the network. The Spanning Tree is configured and operates just as I described it above for Ethernet bridges. Moreover, if we connect a Translation Bridge network with an Ethernet Transparent Bridge network, there is just one common Spanning Tree. This contrasts with the case for the IBM 8209 (described later) and with the Source Route Spanning Tree (described in the last Chapter).

MAC Address Formats

Ethernet/FDDI Translation includes the conversion of address formats at the MAC Layer. I discussed the bit order problem for different LAN technologies in Chapter 5 and in the Diskette Tutorials.

Maximum Frame Sizes

This is a real issue for 802.1h bridges. FDDI supports frame sizes up to about 4000 bytes, which is considerably longer than Ethernet. Unlike routers, bridges cannot cope with fragmentation and reassembly of frames since they do not understand the Network Layer. To solve the problem, in Figure 10.2, we could set the FDDI hosts Keaton and Allen to use an MTU of 1500 bytes. However, this would impact the performance of communication from Keaton to Allen, or between any other FDDI hosts. For 802.1h bridges there is no solution to this problem, other than to reduce the overall MTU size. The best solution of all is to use routing between the Ethernet and FDDI and let MTU Discovery select the best MTU size. Note also that Source Routing is capable of MTU Discovery, but in a different way.

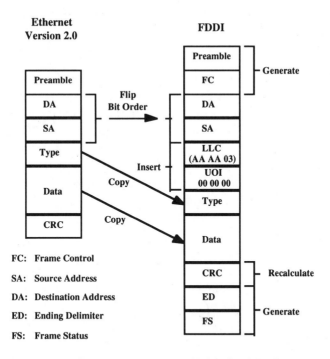

Figure 10.3: Ethernet V2 to FDDI SNAP Conversion

Setting the MTU manually is consistent with the behavior described in IEEE 802.1h. RFC 1042 also has something to say on this subject: "hosts must not send datagrams longer than 576 octets unless they have explicit knowledge that the destination is prepared to accept them." This is not quite applicable to the 802.1h bridge issue since the bridge is not the destination, I would substitute the phrase "transit path" for "destination."

Frame Format Conversion

Frame format conversion is a process that can be performed by brute force in the bridge. I've shown the basic procedure in Figure 10.3 for an Ethernet to FDDI conversion. If you were using IP/SNAP/802.3 encapsulation, the bridge would have a slightly easier job to do.

Don't worry about the extra fields in the FDDI frame; they're native to this LAN technology and are inserted automatically by the FDDI chipset.

Protocol Fixes

There is a danger in Translation Bridging that the bridge may need to be aware of some of the Network Layer functions that are used by the specific protocol. In the case of TCP/IP the main examples are ARP and RARP [3]. Packets of these two protocols carry MAC addresses in the *data* portion of the MAC frame.

Remember that Ethernet and FDDI disagree about the bit order in the data field, but have the same bit order in the MAC address field. This creates a problem because hosts and bridges may get the MAC addresses carried by ARP or RARP packets mixed up. There are two possible strategies. First, allow the bridge to "recognize" ARP and RARP packets and explicitly convert the MAC addresses inside the packet. Second, make each LAN driver responsible for translating MAC addresses that are taken from within the data field. For 802.1h bridges, the second option was chosen, which has resulted in a lot of reduction in hassle (compare this situation with the 8209 described later).

The precedent was set by RFC 1042 for the handling of ARP and RARP messages. In simple terms, the bridge must "know" about the bit order preference of the underlying network.

LAN Speed Differences

802.1h bridges operate between a 10Mbps Ethernet and a 100Mbps FDDI. Bridges do not allow any form of flow control protocol to operate. In this case, for example, ICMP Source Quench will not work because it's designed to apply flow control between IP hosts.

802.1h bridges usually contain a reasonable amount of buffer memory, but when that's full, the bridge will "silently discard" frames that are arriving too fast for it to forward. Obviously the situation applies more to FDDI hosts that are forwarding onto the Ethernet segments.

10.3 Ethernet/Token Ring Bridging: The IBM 8209

To paraphrase the American presidential candidate, Adlai Stevenson, "technology is what happens when impossibility yields to necessity." By this definition, the IBM 8209 Translation Bridge is a fine example of technology. This device allows Token Rings and Ethernets to be connected so that non-routeable protocols such as NetBIOS and LU6.2 can pass across. In effect, the 8209 allows existing SNA users to install Ethernet LANs in their workgroups, but attach to Token Ring FEPs and Cluster Controllers. In this section, I'll be referring to the "8209," even though this functionality is offered by Cisco, Proteon, Wellfleet and other bridge/router manufacturers. The reason is that the 8209 is not covered by any IEEE standard; it is its own standard! To clarify this point further, there are parts of the 8209 which are covered by IEEE 802.1D, other parts that are covered by IEEE 802.5D and the overall concept which bears some relation to IEEE 802.1H. However, none of these standards fully covers the 8209. 8209 functionality is not "Source Route Transparent" and I think you will agree that the 8209 cannot qualify as a "Transparent Bridge."

In the first part of this section, I'll refer to "Ethernet" rather than write "Ethernet/IEEE 802.3." Later in the discussion, differences between these technologies will emerge and I'll differentiate them clearly at that time.

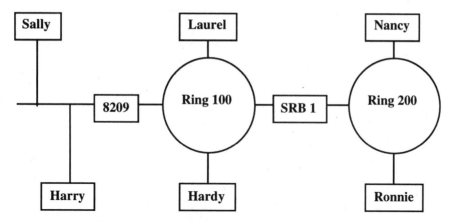

Figure 10.4: An 8209 Translation Bridge Installation

To translate between Ethernet and Token Ring, the 8209 must address 7 areas of incompatibility between the two LAN technologies:

- Frame forwarding (i.e., transparent or Source Route operation)
- Spanning Tree interaction
- MAC address formats
- Maximum frame sizes
- Frame format conversion
- Protocol Fixes
- LAN speed differences

Frame Forwarding

Figure 10.4 shows an 8209 connecting an Ethernet domain with a Token Ring domain. Our friends Harry and Sally are on Ethernet, with Laurel, Hardy, Nancy and Ronnie on Token Ring.

Like any other bridge, the 8209 must decide whether or not to forward frames from one side to the other. However, on the Ethernet side the 8209 must use a Promiscuous Learning technique, while on the Token Ring side it must use Source Routing. How does the 8209 resolve the difference between these techniques? The bridge uses a two-part internal database, one part for Token Ring and one part for Ethernet. I show the structure of the database in Table 10.1.

Table 10.1:   Sample 8209 Database

Token Ring Database			E'net Database		
MAC Addr	RIF	Age	MAC Addr	Encaps	Age
Laurel		8s	Sally	Ev2	24s
Hardy		30s	Harry	Ev2	18s
Nancy	[100]+[1]+[200]	12s			
Ronnie	[100]+[1]+[200]	4s			

On the Ethernet side of the 8209, the chipset operates in promiscuous mode and learns station addresses exactly like a normal Ethernet bridge. An additional feature of the 8209 is that the Ethernet database contains a "type" field which can be either Ethernet V2 (Ev2) or IEEE 802.3 (802.3). This field is determined by examining each station's transmissions, which are by the 8209. On the Token Ring side of the 8209, forwarding is decided by sending Source Route Explorer traffic and caching the RIF responses.

Spanning Tree Interaction

So in effect, the 8209 is schizophrenic. On one side it appears to be a perfectly normal Ethernet bridge, running Spanning Tree to prevent active loops. On the other side it appears to be a perfectly normal Source Route Bridge running Spanning Tree to create a single path for explorer traffic. How do these two Spanning Tree processes interact? In very simple terms, they don't. The respective Spanning Trees are kept logically separate. To external Ethernet devices the series of bridged Token Ring appears as a single Ethernet segment. To external Token Ring devices, the Transparently Bridged Ethernets appear as a single virtual ring segment.

Spanning Tree BPDUs from the Ethernet are sent over the Token Ring Spanning Tree. Spanning Tree BPDUs from the Token Ring are, obviously, sent over the Ethernet Spanning Tree.

MAC Address Formats

In Chapter 2 and in the Diskette Tutorial, I discussed MAC address formats, so you will realize that Ethernet and Token Ring "disagree" on this issue. The task of swapping bit order for the 8209 is trivial because, unlike Transparent Bridges, the 8209 has to do so much other work on the frame.

Maximum Frame Sizes

Ethernet supports a maximum frame size of about 1500 bytes. Token Rings support frame sizes up to 4.5kB at 4Mbps and about 18kB at 16Mbps. What happens if a 4.5kB Token Ring frame tries to be forwarded onto the Ethernet segment? We have four possible options:

1. We implement protocols to allow the fragmentation and reassembly of packets.

2. We configure our end systems so that they do not generate frames larger than 1500 bytes.

3. We use an MTU discovery technique.

Option 1 is possible, but very messy indeed. Most protocol stacks have difficulty in fragmenting packets. TCP/IP is the most flexible in this regard, but remember that the 8209 was specifically designed to forward NetBIOS and LU6.2 traffic. These protocol types are not capable of fragmentation. In addition, the 8209 is already busy converting frames and deciding whether to forward traffic and it doesn't need any more hassle if there's an alternative.

Option 2 is OK and will work with any translation bridge combination (like Ethernet to FDDI). There probably isn't much loss in performance using the smaller packet size, but there may be lots of host systems to set up. Also, most host manufacturers will set the maximum possible packet size in their software without considering the total path over which the packet will travel. They tend to assume that the bridge/router/gateway device should be able to handle the problem.

Option 3 is the winner. The 8209 is a bridge, so it cannot take part in IP MTU Discovery. But remember that when a Token Ring host sends out an explorer, the RCF contains a "maximum length" field. The 8209 will overwrite the value in the "maximum length" field with a binary value of "001. This indicates a maximum frame size of 1500 bytes, which effectively solves the problem without us having to set up lots of end systems.

Frame Format Conversion

The 8209 was designed to be used to allow end systems on Ethernet to run native NetBIOS and LU6.2 applications and connect to a Token Ring Cluster Controller, FEP or AS/400. In this mode of operation, all of the Ethernet traffic will appear as IEEE 802.3 with true LSAP encoding. The bridge needs to perform the following conversion functions:

1. Conversion of Ethernet/Token Ring specific fields in the MAC frame.

2. Insertion or removal of the SNAP header.

The low level differences between Ethernet and Token Ring are fairly easy to incorporate into the conversion process, while the Ethernet Type to SNAP conversion is a little more complex and is conditional on the destination host. Protocols on Token Ring are either represented with their own Link Service

Access Point (LSAP) numbers (e.g. NetBIOS, SNA), or use the IEEE 802.2 SNAP, which I describe in Chapter 1. If a frame has Ethernet encapsulation and is moving to the Token Ring side of the 8209, then a SNAP header must be built.

If the frame is moving from the Token Ring and will be forwarded by the bridge, then the 8209 will consult its internal database to see if the end system is known to be operating as an Ethernet Version 2 or IEEE 802.3 end system. If the 8209 decides to convert the frame, then the SNAP/Type conversion is shown in Figure 10.5

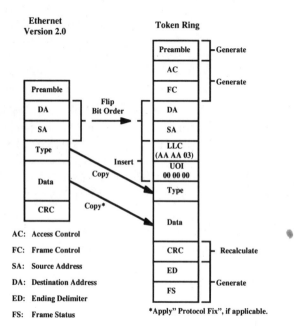

Figure 10.5: Ethernet V2 to Token Ring SNAP Conversion

In Figure 10.5 I show what happens if the 8209 decides it has an incoming Ethernet V2 frame that it must convert to a Token Ring SNAP frame. Note that there are some minor conversion tasks like the generation of the appropriate preamble for Token Ring (a Manchester encoding violation), the insertion of fields like AC, FC, ED and FS and the recalculation of the CRC for the frame. Fortunately all of these processes are taken care of by the Token Ring chipset itself. The reverse translation is handled in the same way, but in this case (i.e., from Token Ring to Ethernet/802.3), the 8209 must decide if the end system is operating as an Ethernet V2 or 802.3 end system. The Ethernet Database has a column for this, as I show in Table 10.1. If the 8209 does not know about a given end station, it is allowed to transmit both kinds of frame. Both frames will be sent to the same MAC address, but of course the end system will simply ignore one of these because it will not be able to understand the encapsulation scheme.

8209 Protocol Fixes

When IBM called the 8209 a "bridge," people took them seriously and they expected the device to be "protocol independent" (even today, some people refer to the 8209 as a "Transparent Bridge"). In the real world, there are special issues relating to protocol conversion for the 8209.

First of all, let's look at IP connectivity. Most IP traffic on Ethernet is represented as Ethernet Version 2 encapsulation, with a Type field of 0800h. To pass this traffic onto a Token Ring LAN, the 8209 must recognize the protocol number, insert a SNAP header and protocol type and recalculate the CRC. Any other Ethernet-style protocol would require the same treatment. In the reverse direction, the 8209 receives a SNAP-encoded IP packet and examines the Ethernet Database to see if this end system is operating as an Ethernet or 802.3 station (see Table 10.1). The bridge can then decide whether or not to discard the SNAP header in favor of a Type field. Tedious perhaps, but not impossible for a device that has already overcome so much. However, there's a problem. Within the IP protocol family, we have two protocols that are a challenge to the 8209: ARP and RARP. These protocols carry MAC addresses within the Information field of the packet. Because of the bit order problem, these MAC addresses will be meaningless (or misleading) when they pass through the bridge. To solve the problem, we have to add a conversion function for IP on the 8209. In Algorithm #2 and #4 above, we would have to insert a conditional routing in the conversion function. For packets with Type numbers of 0806h (ARP) or 8035h (RARP), a special routine will seek out the MAC addresses (which are located at a constant offset within the frame) and change their bit order.

The Novell IPX protocol has a similar problem. An IPX address uses the station's MAC address as the local wire portion of the Network Layer address (IPX avoids the need for ARP by doing this). Unfortunately this means that, once again, MAC addresses appear in the Information field. Unlike ARP and RARP, the IPX address does not always appear in the same place in a Novell packet. This is partly because there are many different encapsulation schemes for Novell, but also because lists of Network Layer addresses appear in a variety of other areas of the packet (for Service Advertising Protocols, etc.). In this case, the solution is quite clever: the operator can optionally switch on "Netware Recognition." Packets which are as IPX do not have their MAC address formats converted by the 8209. This solves the problem, but potentially creates several more. The MAC addresses on one side of the 8209 now appear to be "inverted." In rare cases this can lead to address duplication, but more commonly a unicast address might be interpreted as a multicast and upset the driver software. The use of this feature is optional (if you don't use it, IPX frames are simply dropped by the 8209) and usually means that the Network Administrator must manually verify all MAC addresses for inversion problems. It also means that the burned-in addresses on some end systems must be replaced by a software configured address.

The "Opaque" Bridge

The 8209 may be the first example of an Opaque Bridge device! Most of the popular protocol stacks, IP, IPX, DECnet, OSI, and AppleTalk, carry MAC Layer addresses within the data portion of the LAN frame. IBM has implemented a "fix" for IP and a separate "fix" for IPX. Currently, however, the 8209 does not support the forwarding of DECnet Phase IV, OSI (DECnet Phase V) or AppleTalk protocols. A separate "fix" would have to be implemented for each protocol stack. An attractive solution for bridge/router devices that emulate the 8209 is not to implement any "routeable protocol fix," but simply to route those protocols in the conventional way. This allows each device in the hybrid unit to get on with the job it was designed for.

RFP Question:	How does your bridge/router handle routeable protocols on a Token Ring port that is configured for 8209 Translation Bridge operation? List this behavior by protocol type.

Adding Value to the "Basic 8209"

Remember I said that there was no standard to follow to implement 8209 functionality? This is especially true if we move away from the direct functions offered by the 8209 device, which is a two-port local device. Multiport devices from Cisco, Proteon and Wellfleet should all try to implement multiport 8209 functionality and to offer this functionality over Wide Area connections. Multiport operation is relatively easy to achieve with the existing architectures in these bridge/router devices.

RFP Question:	Does the 8209 function operate in a multiport (>2 ports) configuration?

Wide Area functionality is also offered by at least one of these manufacturers and turns out to be surprisingly popular. Figure 10.6 illustrates why this is the case. The bank in question implements a Token Ring LAN in its central HQ, but a mixture of Ethernet and Token Ring in individual branches. Like many banks, it implements SNA and NetBIOS protocols and needs to provide seamless connectivity for existing applications, in addition to supporting new IP applications. This function requires an interesting design decision to be made. We know that an 8209 need to perform a conversion process on traffic before it can pass between Ethernet and Token Ring. In Figure 10.6, where do you think this conversion process should take place? There are four possibilities:

1.   Conversion is made on the incoming interface, unconditionally.

2.   Conversion is made on the outgoing interface, unconditionally.

3.   Conversion is made on the incoming interface, conditionally.

4.   Conversion is made on the outgoing interface, conditionally.

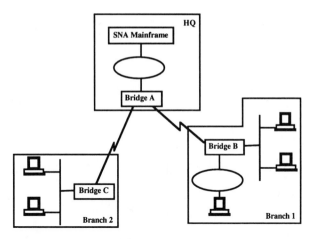

Figure 10.6: Remote 8209 Operation

Options 1 and 2 present a problem. If we always convert on the incoming interface then communication is always assumed to be between opposite types of LAN. That means if we transmit from a Branch on Ethernet, we arrive at the HQ on Token Ring and that's fine. If a Branch has Token Ring, there's a problem because the originating Token Ring interface has already converted the frame into an Ethernet format and the receiving Token Ring interface will not understand it.

Options 3 and 4 are better. In other words, we only convert if we know that the destination LAN is the opposite of what we are. Either of Options 3 or 4 will work, but it would be more elegant to allow the software to realize that the frame originated on either an Ethernet or Token Ring and to allow the receiving end to convert the frame if necessary.

RFP Question:	Does the 8209 functionality allow operation over Wide Area Networks? Which WAN types are supported? How and where does the Ethernet to Token Ring conversion take place in this mode?

10.4 Summary

- Translation Bridging is a brute-force technique that converts the frame format of one LAN into the frame format of another.

- The technique is useful to support legacy protocols that were not intended for large scale internetworking.

- As a bonus, FDDI Translation Bridges do not require complex setup parameters, so are effectively "plug and play."

- Extreme measures are required to perform translation between Ethernet and Token Ring. No standards apply to this technique and all commercial devices are based on the methods pioneered by the IBM 8209.

- In addition to the basic conversion process, the 8209 must implement certain "protocol fixes" to account for bit order problems.

- FDDI Translation Bridges are vulnerable to MTU differences.

- The 8209 can use Token Ring Source Routing to MTUs for a given session.

- FDDI Translation Bridges operate the same Spanning Tree as a pure Transparent Bridge.

- 8209 Bridges operate separate Spanning Trees for the Token Ring and Ethernet portions of the bridge.

10.5 References

[1] A. Latif. E. J. Rowlance, R. H. Adams. *The IBM 8209 LAN Bridge* IEEE Network, May 1992.

CHAPTER 11

Routing Principles

> *If it ain't broke, don't fix it.*
>
> **First Law of Rural Mechanics**

11.1 Introduction

A router is a Network Layer packet switch. The concept of routing and Network Layer addressing are thus irrevocably linked. In short, if we're using routeable Network Layer protocols such as IP, IPX and AppleTalk, we should be using routers as our network interconnection devices.

11.1.1 Single Protocol Routers

As I show in Figure 11.1, routers are simply packet switches. In this figure, a packet entering on Port 1 is examined by the IP routing software and its destination address is recognized as being out of Port 3, so that's where the router sends it.

Single protocol routers are very common. If you take a UNIX computer and install two network interfaces, it will probably act as a router (a potentially expensive one). Novell File Servers with two or more network adapters installed will actually route IPX traffic between the various LAN segments.

11.1.2 The Multiprotocol Router

In the early 1980s, Proteon was working in several areas of networking. Amongst them was router technology. Proteon released the world's first commercial multiprotocol router on a PDP-11 minicomputer around 1982 and

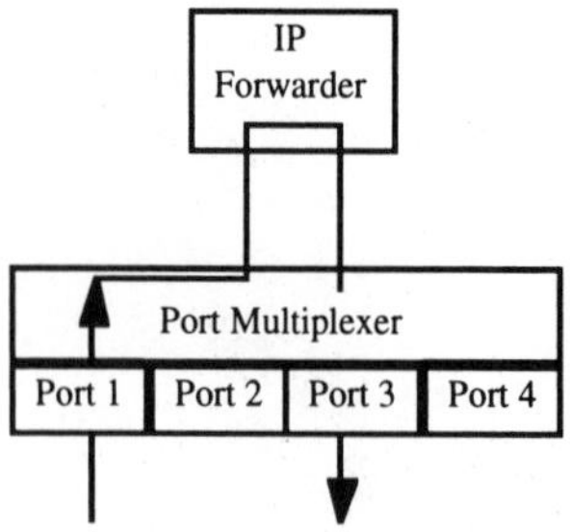

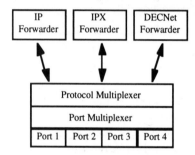

Figure 11.1: A Single Protocol IP Router

**Figure 11.2:   Schematic Multiprotocol
Router**

Multiprotocol routers operate on a very simple principle. They implement a *Protocol Multiplexer* driver that detects the identity of the Network Layer protocol on an incoming packet. Remember from Chapter 3 that this can be done by examining the Type field, or SNAP field of any LAN packet. The number found in this field tells the Protocol Multiplexer which *Protocol Forwarder* it should pass the packet to for further processing.

Some types of packet will terminate *within* the router. Examples of these are:

- PING diagnostics that are addressed to an interface within the router
- Telnet sessions with the router
- TFTP file transfer of configuration files or operating system images
- SNMP management packets
- Routing protocol updates
- RARP or BOOTP requests
- Spanning Tree updates (if Bridging is enabled)
- Source Route Explorers (Source Routing is enabled)

11.1.3   The Internetwork Decision

In Chapter 4 I described the mechanics of IP communication. When IP packets pass through a router, the originating host must already know that the packet is an *inter*network packet (by comparing source/destination addresses), so it deliberately sends the packet to the *default router's* MAC address. This has a *very* important consequence for router operation and leads to the First Rule of Routing:

First Rule of Routing

Pure Routers operate their LAN ports in unicast mode.

This is in contrast to transparent and translation bridges that operate in promiscuous mode. By operating in unicast mode, routers can maintain performance on their CPUs.

11.1.4   Route or Bridge?

Today, many routers operate as hybrid bridge/routers and in this case the router ports that are configured for bridging will be operating in promiscuous mode.

For all the bridge/routers on the market today, a simple set of rules allows the router to decide between bridging and routing on a frame by frame basis. When a frame arrives at a promiscuous port, the router will immediately examine the Type (or SNAP Type) field. If the number in this field matches one of the numbers assigned to an active protocol forwarder, then the *packet* will be *routed*. If the number does not match, then the *frame* will be *bridged*.

Second Rule of Routing

Bridge/routers will route if they can and bridge if they must.

11.1.5   Packet Switching: The Routing Table

Routers make switching decisions by comparing the destination IP address in the packet with entries in an internal table: the *routing table*. In Table 11.1 I show the makeup of a typical routing table for Router_1 shown in Figure 11.3.

Let's say that Harry is sending a datagram to Sally. In Chapter 4 I concentrate on how Harry would form the datagram. Now I'd like to look in detail at what happens when the datagram reaches the router.

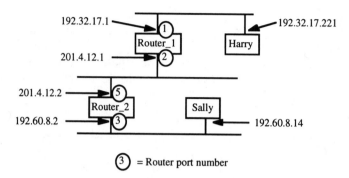

Figure 11.3: Sample Routing Environment

Table 11.1: Routing Table, Router_1, Figure 11.3

Destination	Next Hop	Type	Cost	Age	Status
192.32.17.0	-	Direct	1	-	Up
201.4.12.0	-	Direct	1	-	Up
192.60.8.0	201.4.12.2	OSPF	2	3	Up

Step 1

The LAN frame is addressed to Router_1, Port 1's MAC address. The chipset on the LAN adapter recognizes the frame and copies it to the receive buffer. The CPU that is running the port is interrupted.

Step 2

The CPU checks the Type field (or SNAP Type) on the frame. If the number in this field indicates an IP packet (or ARP, RARP), the CPU strips the LAN-specific Data Link information from the frame.

Step 3

The router looks at the IP destination address on the packet. If the network is directly attached to the router, then the router will also be aware of the explicit subnet mask for the network. If the network is not directly attached to the router (e.g. network 192.60.8.0 in Figure 11.3), then the router may have been informed of the subnet mask by a routing protocol (such as OSPF). However, some routing protocols don't pass subnet information (e.g. RIP, IGRP), so the router will assume the default mask. The router will AND the destination IP address with the explicit, or assumed mask. In this example, the destination address is 192.60.8.14, the default mask is 255.255.255.0, so the result of the AND is 192.60.8.0.

Step 4

The router will take the result of the AND and will search the routing table for a matching entry in the Destination Address column. If a match is found, the router will look up the corresponding entry in the Next Hop column, in this case, 201.4.12.2.

Step 5

The router will then determine which of its physical ports matches the Network or Subnet ID for this next hop. Implementations vary in the way that this is achieved. A generic (and slow) method is to perform an AND between the Next Hop and its corresponding mask and then match this against the entries for each port's IP address. An alternative method is to re-enter the routing table using the Next Hop as a destination. By definition, the Next Hop address *must* be on a directly attached network or subnet. On this second pass through the routing table, the direct route can be linked to a pointer to the physical port.

Step 6

The IP packet is passed to the device driver for the exit port. This device driver will build an appropriate network frame around the packet and transmit it using the appropriate access control mechanism. Note that this stage involves an ARP transaction on a broadcast multi-access network such as Ethernet or FDDI.

Later in this chapter I'll look at the other columns in this table.

11.1.6   Address per Port

Third Rule of Routing

Each port on a IP router must be configured with at least one unique IP address.

An IP router is configured with an explicit IP address for each port on the unit. In Figure 11.4 I show how this looks for a simple case of a Class C network. We could, for example, allocate address 192.32.17.5 to Port 1. If we allocate another port on the router (or indeed any node on the same network) with the identical address 192.32.17.5, we have broken the 3rd Rule.

Note that the concepts of having a unique address per port, and that each address must be in its own Network or Subnetwork, are not the only possibilities in addressing terms. However, they are the assumptions made by IP, IPX, XNS and ISO CLNP. The other option is to send all traffic using a group (multicast) or

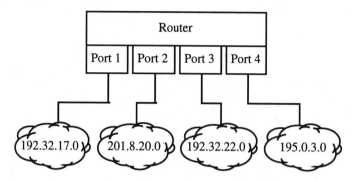

Figure 11.4:   Unique Network Number per Port

broadcast address. In fact this was the approach taken by the original Sytek PC Network system.

DECnet, AppleTalk and Banyan VINES use different address allocation concepts [2, 3].

Un-Numbered Serial Lines

Serial lines between routers normally require an IP address at each end of the link. Since any serial line is effectively an independent network or subnet, serial connections may not be able to use IP address space efficiently. Over the course of router development, several proprietary solutions have been implemented that allow serial lines to operate without any IP addresses at all. These *un-numbered* serial implementations normally suffer from this lack of IP identity. Three simple examples illustrate the problem:

- I am trying to diagnose a reachability problem using PING. I am gradually stepping through the network from one IP address to another. When I get to an un-numbered serial link I find that I can't explicitly PING it.

- I am using ICMP's TRACEROUTE option. Since the serial line has no IP address, then I lose track of the connection at that point.

- I want to Telnet into a router. Without an IP address, I can't use a serial connection as a Telnet destination.

To get around these problems, the router requirements draft suggests the use of one of the IP addresses already assigned within the router and that all un-numbered links will use this IP identity. This address is known as the *router ID*.

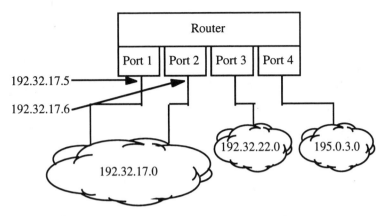

Figure 11.5:   Illegal Multiconnected Router

11.1.7   One Port Per Segment

Fourth Rule of Routing

On a single IP router, only one port may be connected to a given Network ID or Subnet ID.

In IP terms, the situation I show in Figure 11.5 is illegal (in this context, illegal means that unexpected and generally undesirable behavior may result). In this router, I have configured Ports 1 and 2 to be on the same Class C network. While this configuration is very useful for resilience purposes, most router implementations cannot handle this situation. The reason is to do with the routing table. Let's take an example using the router configuration in Figure 11.5. In this case, we have an outbound packet with next hop 192.32.17.147.

Outbound next hop = 192.32.17.147

Outbound mask = 255.255.255.0

The router performs a binary AND between this next hop and the mask.

Result of binary AND = 192.32.17.0

The router will then look in an internal table to see which of its ports matches this Network ID. To do this, the router will take the IP address that you configure for a port and AND this address with the mask you configure for the port. This calculation is pre-computed in the internal table to save time.

Port 1: 192.32.17.5 AND 255.255.255.0 = 192.32.17.0

Port 2: 192.32.17.6 AND 255.255.255.0 = 192.32.17.0

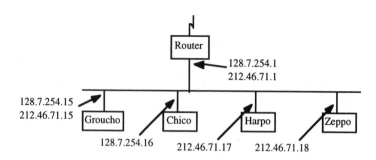

Figure 11.6:   Multinetting

As you can see, the router has no way to distinguish between these outbound ports. In theory, the router implementation could allow traffic to be divided equally between the matching ports on a packet-by-packet basis. In practice, this could lead to packets arriving out of sequence at the receiving hosts, which will have an impact on performance. In Chapter 16 I look at ways around the Fourth Rule to achieve routing resilience.

11.1.8   Multinetting

> *Fifth Rule of Routing*
>
> *A given port on an IP router may be configured with multiple consistent IP addresses and subnet masks. Each address is treated as though it were on a separate port.*

This technique is called *multinetting*. Multinetting was originally introduced to allow an IP user to migrate from one addressing scheme to another. For example, you may have implemented a private Class A network addressing scheme in the past, but now you want to attach to the Internet. This means that you'll probably have to migrate over to a set of Class C addresses.

In this configuration shown in Figure 11.6, the user is migrating from a private Class B scheme over to a registered Class C scheme. During the migration, the "new" hosts that are added to the network are given only registered Class C addresses (Harpo and Zeppo). Existing hosts with Class B addresses are also given Class C addresses, but this process will take a finite time to achieve. This means that some hosts, like Groucho, will have two addresses assigned, while others, Chico, only have the older Class B address. In this network, there are four possible communication modes:

- Communication within an address scheme (e.g. Harpo-Zeppo) operates in exactly the way I described in Chapter 3.

- Communication from a multinetted host to a uninetted host (e.g. Groucho-Harpo, Groucho-Chico, Groucho-Zeppo). In this case the host software is aware of two addresses used by its interface. In the IP Transmission Algorithm that I describe in Chapter 3, Line 8 will be modified to allow multiple IP host addresses. If a local communication option (i.e., a direct ARP for the destination IP address) is possible, this is chosen in preference to non-local options.

- Communication between uninetted hosts in different address schemes (e.g. Chico-Harpo, Chico-Zeppo). Here the hosts will believe that they are located on different IP Networks and will send their packets via the router. The router interface must be configured as a member of both address schemes in order for communication to take place. In these cases, the IP packet will cross the LAN segment twice.

- External communication. Any internetwork communication takes place *through* the router in the way I described in Chapter 3.

11.2 Routing Convergence

All the routers in an IP internetwork will contain routing tables. When a router receives a packet and it cannot match the destination network to an entry in its routing table, the router should send an ICMP NETWORK UNREACHABLE message back to the originating host.

Ideally, all the routers in an internetwork should have corresponding views of the internetwork. The routing tables will be different, but they should be mutually consistent. When all of the routers in the network reach this happy state, we say that the network has *converged*. The period between a change in the network (say a WAN connection going down) and all the routing tables returning to a consistent state is called the *convergence time*. During the convergence time, the behavior of the network is unpredictable. Packets could be sent in *loops*, or simply "disappear" into *black holes*.

Routing loops are a nuisance, but are trivial compared to bridge loops. Each IP packet has a counter called the Time To Live (TTL) field which is decremented by each router the packet traverses. When TTL reaches 0, the next router to process the packet must discard it. So *temporary* routing loops cause no real damage to the network bandwidth. Transparent and Translation Bridges have no equivalent capability. Source Route Bridges have very effective loop-prevention mechanisms (see Chapter 9).

Fast convergence is the single most important design goal for most internetworks. Along with fast convergence comes resilient, reliable networks and happy users. To achieve fast convergence, we need to be able to monitor the state of network connection, get this information into our own routing table and then pass it on to the other routers within our internetwork.

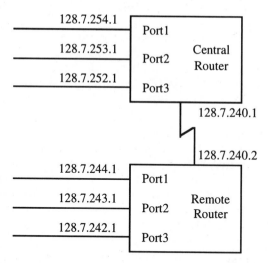

Figure 11.7:   Sample Router Installation

11.3 The Routing Table Revisited

It's a bit emotive, but you can regard the routing table as the heart of an IP router. This table tells the router how to get to any particular IP destination. Let's look at a simple routing table for the Central Router shown in Figure 11.7.

Table 11.2:   Routing Table with Direct Routes

Destination	Mask	Next Hop	Cost	Type	Age	Status
128.7.254.0	255.255.255.0		1	Direct		U
128.7.253.0	255.255.255.0		1	Direct		U
128.7.252.0	255.255.255.0		1	Direct		U

Earlier I looked at the path of a packet through the router, under the guidance of the routing table. Now I'd like to look at the table entries more closely.

Destination

First, the *Destination* column contains the destination *network* or *subnetwork* ID addresses. Routing tables achieve their compactness by only storing the address for an entire network or subnetwork, they don't normally store the individual IP or MAC addresses for end systems. When the packet reaches the router which is directly attached to the destination network, this router directs the packet to the correct end system by using ARP.

It is possible to enter complete IP addresses, such as 128.7.254.4 in a routing table and these entries are normally called *Host Routes*. Host Routes are normally entered into a routing table manually, as I describe below although they can also be inserted by routing protocols. Obviously a number of host routes for the same network take more space in the routing table than a normal Network ID entry, so there must be a pretty good reason to use them. In fact, host routes can be used to ensure that traffic to a specific IP end system uses a specific route and this use must be implemented in conjunction with routing table management schemes that allow multiple routes to the same destination to be given *route priority* values.

Next Hop

The *Next Hop* column must contain an IP address which is a member of one of the networks or subnets that are directly attached to the router. This is logical because if you entered an address that was not on a directly attached network, the router would have to go back into the routing table to find out how to get there! In other words, the Next Hop is a pointer to the router exit port for this packet. A second table is then used to determine the physical exit point, given the IP address. The exact format of this table and its relationship to the routing table depends on the specific vendor implementation, but it is derived from the console entries made by the Network Administrator. In Table 11.2 I have not entered any value for "Next Hop" because all of these entries are Direct. This convention may vary between different manufacturers. For example, a possible entry for the route to 128.7.254.0 would be 128.7.254.1, which is the router's own IP address for the destination subnet.

Once the next hop has been identified, the router can use ARP to derive the hardware address for the frame. Like hosts, routers make use of ARP caches. In Figure 11.8, I show how each physical port on the router will have an associated ARP cache. Routers would not need to make use of ARP for serial links (since no MAC addresses are used on a serial link). In Chapter 6 I explain how address resolution operates for Wide Area switched networks such as X.25 or Frame Relay.

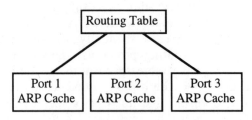

Figure 11.8:   Relationship of Routing Table to ARP Cache

Route Cost

The *Cost* column allows the router to select the best cost for a specific routing decision. It is possible for more than one possible route to a given destination to exist at any time, but the router will normally only use one of these routes, the lowest cost route.

Route Type

The *Type* column allows the router to "remember" how it learned the route. Possible values in this column include:

- Direct; i.e., this network is directly attached to the router.

- Static; the route has been manually entered.

- RIP; the route has been learned through the Routing Information Protocol, described below.

- OSPF; the route has been learned through the Open Shortest Path First protocol, described below.

- External; the route has been learned from another Autonomous System and may have been imported using a different *Interior Gateway Protocol* (IGP), an *Exterior Gateway Protocol* (EGP) or Static Routes.

- Host; the route is marked as a Host Route (see above) and can optionally be given priority over network routes.

Route Age

The Age field in the routing table is designed to allow the router to remove routes that are no longer current and for Bellman-Ford protocols such as RIP and IGRP to use the counting-to-infinity mechanism that I describe later.

In the case of RIP, when a Route is first learned, the age is set to 3 minutes. Every 30 seconds the router will expect a route update and if it doesn't receive one it will decrement the Age value by 30 seconds. When the Age reaches zero, the route is removed from the table. Link State protocols such as OSPF and I-

ISIS don't use Age entries in the same way because they use a reliable route update mechanism. In theory, when updates are sent using a reliable exchange protocol, then timers are not as important for the detection of failed routes. In the case of Direct and Static Routes, the Age entry is not used at all since the route will never be removed from the table.

Other Fields

There are several other possible fields in a routing table. One obvious field that I'll be discussing later is the Status of the route (e.g. "Up" or "Down"). Since Direct and Static routes are never removed from the routing table, the Status field is needed to indicate is the route is valid or not. Another possible field is the Route Priority. I have mentioned this concept a couple of times already. In essence, Route Priority offers us a chance to manage the routing table if information in it is derived from several different sources. For static routes, that are themselves entered manually, we can enter a route priority as we enter the route itself. For dynamic routes, we can't easily enter a route priority on an individual basis, but we can allocate default priorities to different types of route. For example, if we believe that OSPF is a good routing protocol, we may decide that we would prefer to use OSPF routes over RIP routes. We may even decide that OSPF routes are "better" than Static Routes because, in theory, OSPF is designed to find the "best" route to a given end-point in the network, while Static Routes are calculated on the basis of some initial condition of the network.

11.4 Routing Protocols

To converge quickly, routers must be provided with a messaging protocol and routing algorithm to exchange routing information. I look at specific routing protocols later, but first I'd like to discuss some basic issues with inter-router communication.

11.4.1 Broadcast or Multicast?

The information sent by routing protocols is not addressed to specific end systems. Instead, it is designed to reach all of the IP routers on a given LAN segment. In Figure 11.9, Router_1 sends out a routing update onto LAN_A. In theory, this update should be received by Router_2 and Router_3. In practice, the first generation of routing protocols (i.e., RIP, IGRP) were transmitted as MAC broadcasts. This means that the hosts on a segment where these protocols are active will be interrupted every time a routing update is transmitted.

This wasn't really the fault of the routing protocols. Early Ethernet chipsets were incapable of receiving MAC multicasts and the first two generations of Token Ring chipsets were similarly brain-damaged.

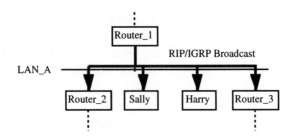

Figure 11.9:   Impact of Routing Broadcasts

Second generation protocols such as OSPF and Integrated ISIS are transmitted as MAC multicast frames. Multicast MAC and IP addresses are reserved for these protocols. Modern Ethernet and FDDI chipsets have operated well with multicast schemes for many years.

11.4.2   Tell Me What You See

Where do we get the information for a routing protocol update? Remember when we install any router, we need to assign IP addresses and subnet masks to each interface in the router. In the routing update, we can just tell the world about the interfaces that are installed in our chassis.

In Figure 11.3, Router_1 knows directly about networks 192.32.17.0 and 201.4.12.0. Its first routing update can tell all other routers that these networks are directly attached to Router_1. When Router_2 receives the update, it already knows about network 201.4.12.0, but the route to 192.32.17.0 is big news.

Any router knows that directly attached networks are bound to be the "best" route to that network. In order to judge between routes, we need to define a cost parameter, or *metric*. When we advertise a route, we include the lowest metric that we know to get to that route. It makes sense *not* to advertise "second best" routes because we're just wasting network bandwidth.

Route Metrics

What kind of metrics can we use? A variety of simple and complex metrics have been developed for use by practical routing protocols. These include:

- *Hop Count*. The hop count is just the number of router you need to traverse to get to the required destination. A directly attached route is defined to have a cost of 1 hop (i.e., instead of zero).

- *Line Speed*. If we just measure hop count, we can't differentiate between a 9.6kbps leased line and a 100Mbps FDDI.

- *Delay*. Some connections may have a longer delay than others. The classic examples are a satellite circuit, which might have a high bandwidth, but has a long end-to-end delay. Long distance leased lines traditionally have shorter delays, but lower bandwidths.

- *Reliability*. Perhaps we have access to a high capacity circuit, but this circuit may be prone to line errors.

- *Monetary Cost*. Public switched networks such as X.25 may be billed on a per-packet basis.

- *Abstract Metric*. OSPF and Integrated ISIS simply define an abstract route cost. Network designers can synthesize any kind of real world criteria they like and apply the resulting value as a route cost. Note that routing protocols that employ formal compound metrics (such as IGRP) must summarize these as a single number anyway for route comparison purposes.

Counting to Infinity

Early routing protocols such as RIP were based entirely on the relative distances of one router from the destination network. These protocols are known as *distance-vector* protocols, or sometimes as Bellman-Ford protocols (after the inventors of the algorithm).

Distance-vector routers send out routing updates on a regular basis. In the case of RIP, the interval is 30 seconds and for IGRP it's 90 seconds. If a route goes away, or an entire router is switched off, routes to the networks attached to the router will no longer be advertised, or propagated through the network. If we *stop* hearing about routes, should we stop using them? The answer is probably "no," because we don't really know if the latest update just went astray. You see, RIP and IGRP updates are not acknowledged, so we don't know if they get through OK. The alternative seems to be that once we hear about a route, we just go on using it forever. This isn't acceptable either.

Instead, RIP and IGRP use two safeguard mechanisms. The first is to define a maximum route cost; which is actually 15 hops. If we *don't* hear about a route at the regular update interval, we increase the cost of the route in our routing table by one hop at each missing update. If the cost reaches 16, then we say that this route has reached *infinity* and we stop using the route. The second mechanism for RIP is that we stop using a route if we don't receive an update for three minutes.

These timers mean that a RIP or IGRP internetwork takes a rather long time to converge if a route disappears.

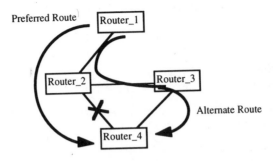

Figure 11.9:   Alternate Routing

Figure 11.9 shows the preferred route between Router_1 and Router_4. If the line between Router_2 and Router_4 goes down, then this route will not be updated.

However, until the route is marked as down (3 minutes), router 2 will just start to "count up" the cost of the route. After the first 30 seconds, the cost of the connection goes up from 1 to 2. This makes the cost equal to the route being advertised by Router_3. After 1 minute, the cost goes up to 3, which is now more expensive than the cost of the route through Router_3. At this point another factor kicks in. If we learn a "better" route, should we start using it right away? Unfortunately the answer is still "no" because of two effects. First of all, the line that went down might not stay that way for very long. If we reconfigure our routing table every time a line goes down, this will cause instability in the network and the tables may never converge. Second, remember that our updates are not acknowledged. How do we know that all the routers in the network have heard about the update?

Hold Down

To overcome this problem, routing protocols use the concept of *hold down*. In the crudest terms, hold down states that you don't believe anything until you hear it three times. For RIP, that means you don't use a "better" route for at least 90 seconds (three update periods). For IGRP, the value is 270 seconds (three update periods).

So, as we are counting the "faulty" route upwards, we may hear about a better route, at which point we apply hold-down. If the new route is still better after three updates, we can start using it.

In this example, the preferred route would be counted up twice before the alternate router is better and then a three-period delay kicks in until we start to use the new route. For RIP that means the convergence time is 150 seconds, for IGRP 450 seconds. So, for up to seven and a half minutes, our network traffic will be disappearing down a black hole!

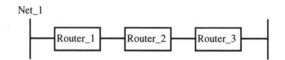

Figure 11.10: Potential Routing Loop

11.4.3 Breaking Routing Loops

As routing protocols discover the internetwork topology, it's possible that temporary loops will form. The classic example is that of the in-line routers shown in Figure 11.10.

Router_1 knows that it can reach Net_1 directly, i.e., a cost of 1. Router_1 uses RIP to advertise the route to Net_1 out to Router_2. Router_2 adds one hop to the cost it receives from Router_1 and then advertises the route to Net_1 out to Router_3. Router_3 knows that Net_1 is 3 hops away and everybody's happy. However, Router_3 is a thorough guy and decides to advertise a route to Net_1 back out to Router_2. Of course, Router_2 now knows that the route to Net_1 via Router_3 costs more than the route to Net_1 via Router_1.

The problem occurs if the direct link between Router_1 and Router_2 goes down. Router_2 is directly attached to this link, so will mark the route down quite quickly (i.e., after a short hold down period). Now the route to Net_1 via Router_3 looks pretty good, doesn't it? The problem is that this route actually loops the packet right back to Router_2 and which point it's sent back to Router_3, etc.

The thing to remember about routers that run Bellman-Ford protocols is that they don't have a global view of the network like we do. They only know what other routers tell them.

To stop this loop happening, RIP implements a very simple heuristic called *split horizon*.

Sixth Rule of Routing

If you are implementing split horizon, *do not advertise information out of the physical connection on which you originally learned the information.*

Look at the simple routing loop in Figure 11.10. If Router_3 were using split horizon, then it would not re-advertise the route to Net_1 back into Router_2.

Poison Reverse

Some of the purists who develop and improve routing protocols took a bit of a dislike to split horizon because it specifically restricts the spread of routing information around the internetwork. The problem is that split horizon solves serious and potentially common topological problems.

To maintain the flow of routing information around the network, a different technique is used. Routers are allowed to *reverse* the routing information (i.e., send back out of the interface on which they learned it), but if they do so, they must *poison* the route cost by setting it to infinity (16 in RIP implementations). The *poison reverse* concept actually improves the convergence time for topologies in which more than two routers share a network segment.

11.5 Filling the Routing Table

So the routing table looks like a useful and exciting tool for directing packets, but it also looks pretty complicated to fill up. I'd like to cover the various ways in which routing entries get into the table.

11.5.1   Direct Attachment

As I explained above, Direct routes are the basis of the routing table and the ultimate source for all routing decisions. Remember that the use of Static Routes or Dynamic Routing Protocols is simply a means to spread the information that a router determines from its own Direct routes.

11.5.2   Static Routes

Figure 11.12 shows a slightly bigger router installation. As you can see, it's already becoming difficult to represent addresses on a single diagram.

Looking at the Central Router we can see that subnets 254, 253, 252 and 240 can all be entered as Direct Routes. But subnets 244, 243 and 242 cannot. Indirect routes are entered into a routing table manually (*Static Routes.*), or by using *Dynamic Routing Protocols*. Static routes are simple enough to understand. At the Central Router console, you'd type something like:

ADD STATIC ROUTE 128.7.244.0 : 128.7.240.2 : 2

There are 3 parameters on this command line that I've chosen to separate with colons. The first parameter is the Destination for the route, in this case 128.7.244.0. The second parameter is the Next Hop address, 128.7.240.2. The third parameter is the cost of this route, in this case 2 (i.e., the number of routers that must be crossed to get to 128.7.244.0). In most implementations, the cost parameter for static routes follows the RIP convention and must be between 1 and 15. The result of the configuration of the Central Route can be seen in Table 11.3.

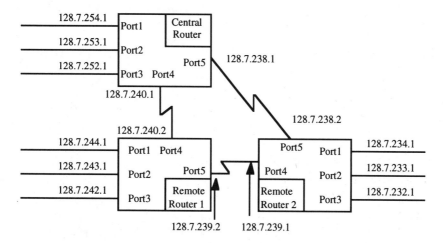

Figure 11.12: Remote Router Connection into Central Router

Table 11.3: Routing Table for Central Router Showing Static Routes

Destination	Mask	Next Hop	Cost	Type
128.7.254.0	255.255.255.0		1	Direct
128.7.253.0	255.255.255.0		1	Direct
128.7.252.0	255.255.255.0		1	Direct
128.7.240.0	255.255.255.0		1	Direct
128.7.244.0	255.255.255.0	128.7.240.1	2	Static
128.7.243.0	255.255.255.0	128.7.240.1	2	Static
128.7.242.0	255.255.255.0	128.7.240.1	2	Static

You can see that the first three rows are identical to the initial routing table I showed in Table 11.2. I've added the WAN link as a "Direct" and three remote destination subnets as "Static." All three remote subnets use 128.7.240.1 as their outbound next hop.

The name "static route" is a little bit unfortunate because it is quite possible to perform dynamic routing using static routes! To illustrate what I mean by this, I'll extend the Central Router routing table entries to include Remote Router 2.

In this configuration we have the possibility of redundant routing between the Central Router and the Remote Routers.

Table 11.4:   Routing Table for Central Router Showing Static Routes

Destination	Mask	Next Hop	Cost	Type	State
128.7.254.0	255.255.255.0		1	Direct	U
128.7.253.0	255.255.255.0		1	Direct	U
128.7.252.0	255.255.255.0		1	Direct	U
128.7.240.0	255.255.255.0		1	Direct	U
128.7.238.0	255.255.255.0		1	Direct	U
128.7.244.0	255.255.255.0	128.7.240.2	2	Static	U
128.7.243.0	255.255.255.0	128.7.240.2	2	Static	U
128.7.242.0	255.255.255.0	128.7.240.2	2	Static	U
128.7.234.0	255.255.255.0	128.7.238.2	2	Static	U
128.7.233.0	255.255.255.0	128.7.238.2	2	Static	U
128.7.232.0	255.255.255.0	128.7.238.2	2	Static	U
128.7.234.0	255.255.255.0	128.7.240.2	3	Static	U
128.7.233.0	255.255.255.0	128.7.240.2	3	Static	U
128.7.232.0	255.255.255.0	128.7.240.2	3	Static	U

To get to network 128.7.234.0, the Central Router has two possible routes (I've highlighted the appropriate rows). The first uses 128.7.238.2 as a next hop and has a cost of 2. The second uses 128.7.240.2 as a next hop and has a cost of 3. Both routes are indicated as "Up," so the router will use the lower cost route. Now if the leased line between the Central Router and Remote Router 2 goes down, then the Central Router can start to use the alternate route immediately. In fact, rerouting of Static Routes can be performed faster than any other routing method; even faster than OSPF!

Static routes have many significant advantages. They can be given priorities, they can be used with Transmission Queue Distribution algorithms, and they do not require router processing or network bandwidth to propagate information. However, they have one simple, but overwhelming disadvantage: they cannot be learned dynamically. Static routes require a lot of careful work to enter without errors. As soon as the network exceeds a certain size, they cease to be a usable option.

Because they do not transmit updates over the WAN connections, static routes are extremely useful in the design of switched service networks such as X.25 and ISDN and this is the most likely environment in which you will meet them in the future.

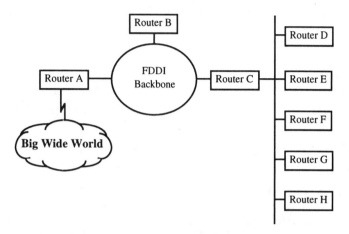

Figure 11.13:   Default Routing In Action

11.5.3   Default Routes

Default Routes are a special case of static routing. I can summarize the way default routing works in one sentence:

> *Seventh Rule of Routing*
>
> *If you don't know how to route this packet, send it to the Default Router assuming one is configured.*

Default routing is easy to set up in a router and works very well in some environments. Figure 11.13 shows a typical application for default routing.

In this installation there is a connection from Router A into the "Big Wide World." Within the local installation, routing information can be distributed using static routing because the installation is rather small. However, if the WAN connection is to the Internet, there could be thousands of routes flooding into the site. One possible solution is to switch on default routing in all routers B..H. Each one would be configured to send any "unknown" traffic to Router A. Router A would only forward the traffic to the "Big Wide World" if it had a specific indication that the route exists. In other words, instead of setting up thousands of static routes in routers B..H, we could just set them up in Router A. More realistically we can use a dynamic routing protocol in Router A (probably an EGP) to avoid the hassle of entering and updating the routes manually.

Problems With Default Routing

Switching on default routing does tend to reduce our control over the routing because under certain circumstances hosts can generate traffic to non-existent addresses. These are known by the whimsical term "Martian Hosts." Martians can occur because of communication software bugs, but today it's more common to find that configuration errors cause packets to be sent to all sorts of unusual addresses. Obviously care should be taken when configuring equipment and routers may be able to help the Network Administrator in this process. For example, the Proteon and Wellfleet routers are capable of generating SNMP Trap messages when a chosen event occurs. SNMP Traps are discussed in Chapter 12, but the message will have the general format:

04 : 0023 : 05/09/94 : 12:22:05:12 : ICMP Network Unreachable. Dest: 192.224.19.12. Source 128.7.254.12.

Again, I've used a colon to separate the parameters, although different implementations used different separators. In this example, the first field represents a "subsystem ID" that allows a Network Management system to quickly decide which part of the router generated the message. In this case the code is "04" which is used by this manufacturer to denote "ICMP." The next filed is the "message ID" which uniquely defines this message; an "ICMP Network Unreachable." The next two fields are the date and time, followed by the ASCII text of the error message. In Figure 11.13, this message would be generated by Router A if it was sent a packet by a local host, or routers B..H, and the destination IP network ID does not appear in Router A's routing table. To summarize:

> *TIP: In the Default Router, set up the SNMP Trap facility to alert the NMS when an ICMP "Network Unreachable" is generated. This is a big clue to the presence of "Martian Hosts."*

11.6 The Routing Hierarchy

Routers have a simple job to do. They receive packets that end systems think should be going somewhere that the router knows about and they have to forward these packets over an appropriate route.

The original IP routers that were used to form the Internet were designed to operate in extended internetworks, with clearly defined addressing structures.

Even in the early days of the Internet, the designer appreciated that only a loose control over local network design was practical. They introduced the concept of "routing frontiers" that would prevent the routing mistakes of one organization from affecting the entire internetwork. These frontiers are called *Autonomous System Boundaries*. and the routing domain within the boundary is the *Autonomous System* (AS). Figure 11.14 shows the concept of Autonomous Systems, with several universities and research organizations connecting to a common backbone network: the NSFnet.

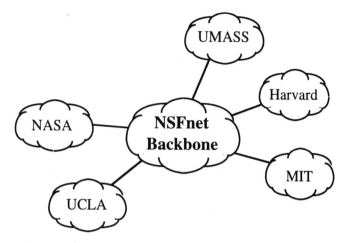

Figure 11.14: Sample of Autonomous Systems

My description of the AS function assumes that IP addresses will be registered with the NIC. The AS has certain properties that can be described as:

- The networks within the AS are fully connected
- Routers within the AS use a single IGP
- Information derived from within the AS is assumed to be reliable
- Reachability information into the AS is advertised using an EGP
- The AS can be identified using a unique number (also assigned by the NIC) called an *Autonomous System Number*.

Fully Connected Networks

The first property is relatively clear: all networks within the AS must be able to reach other networks in the AS using routes that lie within the AS.

In Figure 11.15, this rule has been broken. If the lines represent physical links between the routers, then R1 and R2 are fully connected and R3, R4 and R5 are fully connected. However, the two groups of routers are not connected, so the cloud drawn around the groups does not represent a valid AS boundary.

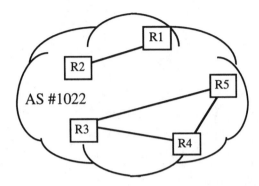

Figure 11.15:   Invalid AS Topology

Single IGP

Each AS is responsible for administering its own routing structure. Internally it may use whatever routing protocol (or static routing) that is appropriate to its equipment. It's normal for a single AS to use a single IGP. The only exception to this rule should be for host-router routing, which I describe later. In addition, the early routing protocols like RIP and IGRP were designed on the assumption that IGP routing information would be transmitted through the AS using LANs; in other words, at high speeds and without cost. Connections over WANs would carry EGP routing protocols, which could be more economical on bandwidth, but less functional.

As time passed, the pressure to improve the efficiency and performance of IGPs led to the development of link state routing protocols such as OSPF and Integrated ISIS.

Interior Gateway Protocols

The routing protocol used within the Autonomous System is known as an *Interior Gateway Protocol* (IGP). Currently two of these are approved for use within the Internet: the Routing Information Protocol (RIP, defined in RFC 1058, but widely deployed before this definition document was written) and the Open Shortest Path First protocol (OSPF, defined in RFC 1247). Other IGPs include HELLO, IGRP and Integrated ISIS.

London and Rome are separate Autonomous Systems. The "European Backbone" is configured to run BGP to allow exchange of routing information between sites. This backbone could consist of a single router, in which case no EGP would be needed.

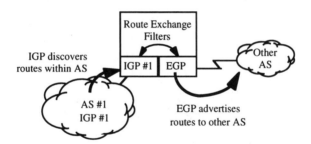

Figure 11.16: Route Exchange Filters

Exterior Gateway Protocols

When we attach a router to the Internet, the IP addresses we use must lie within the assigned address block, or blocks issued by the NIC.[1] The attachment to the NSFnet backbone is made using static routing, or an authorized *External Gateway Protocol* (EGP). The original EGP approved for use in the Internet is actually called EGP (defined by RFCs 904 and 827). Today, EGP is essentially obsolete and the Internet is migrating to a new EGP called the *Border Gateway Protocol* (BGP). This protocol was first defined in RFC 1163, but is now in its fourth version, BGP4

EGPs are not really routing protocols. They are usually described as *reachability protocols*. In simple terms, a reachability protocol simply advertises that a given IP network is reachable through this line and specifies a cost. Routers that sit on AS boundaries draw routing information from *within* the AS using an IGP. Extracts from this information are advertised out of the AS using BGP4. The criteria used to decide what information is advertised are determined by *route exchange filters*.

Other Uses for AS Boundaries

The Internet isn't the only place you'll find the Autonomous System concept. Building a private IP internetwork will use the same techniques, but with different names attached to the clouds. Take a look at Figure 11.17.

---

[1]An alternative is to use a Private IP addressing scheme, as described in Chapter 13.

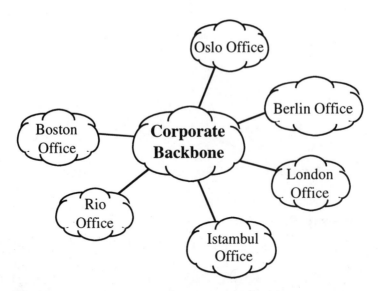

Figure 11.17: AS Concept in Private Internetwork

In this case the AS concept is used to protect one office from the routing errors of another. In addition, there are routing traffic economies to be made over the Corporate Backbone by designing the network in this way thanks to the opportunities offered by these protocols for the summarization of routing information. Another advantage of this approach is the ability to migrate to a multivendor routing solution. A major problem facing many users today is that Cisco's primary IGP, IGRP, is proprietary and doesn't scale well to large networks. Figure 11.18 shows the same private internetwork as in Figure 11.17 with IGPs and EGPs filled in.

By using the AS boundary to allow mixed IGPs, this user can migrate from an obsolete routing protocol such as RIP, or a proprietary protocol such as IGRP to a high performance, standards based protocol such as OSPF or Integrated ISIS.

11.7 Routing Override Procedures

We expect routers to make packet switching decisions based on the rules of IP. However, there are occasions when we may want to exert a manual override on the routing process. I'll describe two possible mechanisms; Routing Precedence and Source Routing.

11.7.1 Routing Precedence

Routing Precedence is only a slight deviation from the normal routing table procedure. If the routing table is receiving its information from many sources (e.g., Direct Routes, Static Routes and Routing Protocols), there must be some way for the Network Administrator to assign a priority to which routing

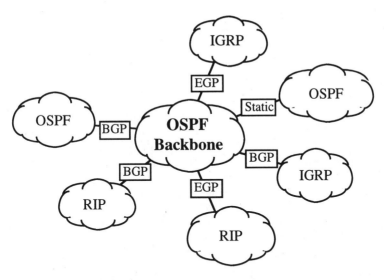

Figure 11.18: Hierarchy of EGPs and IGPs

information will be used. For example, Direct Routes will always be highest priority, the manually designed and entered Static Routes may be next, followed by any Routing Protocol routes.

What happens if we're running multiple routing protocols? This is the usual procedure for a router on the boundary of an Autonomous System. The router must be given some way to systematically choose the preferred type of route and to be capable of exporting routing information discovered by one routing protocol into the data structure of another routing protocol.

11.7.2 Source Routing

In conventional IP routing, the router decides the best route for the packet. If the source routing option is used, the originating host can specify a route (using IP addresses in intermediate routers) that the packet must follow. In contrast to Token Ring source routing, the IP version is not the normal mode of operating and has no automatic route discovery protocol.

The route information is contained within the IP packet header as part of the Options Field (see Chapter 3). Two types of source routing are defined: Strict and Loose.

Strict Source Routing

Strict Source Routing allows a host to specify a list of router IP addresses that the datagram *must* pass through to reach a given destination. If the datagram cannot be forwarded to the appropriate next hop router, then an ICMP Network Unreachable or ICMP Host Unreachable error message must be sent back to the source host. Strict Source Routing is selected as Option Type 9 in the IP header. The main use of Strict Source Routing is to allow Network Management Systems or diagnostic packages to force traffic along a specified route for debugging purposes.

Loose Source Routing

Loose Source Routing allows a host to specify Landmark Routers in an address list. The packet must visit the Landmark Routers, but may be routed by any appropriate (multihop) route between Landmark Routers. An ICMP error message is generated if the packet cannot pass through a Landmark Router. Loose Source Routing is Option Type 3 in the IP header. Apparently Loose Source Routing has been used to gain access to host systems in remote portions of the Internet, possibly over large RIP or EGP domains. With the improvements in routing convergence offered by OSPF and BGP, this use may decline.

11.8 Message Sizes and Fragmentation

Different LAN technologies support different message sizes, or MTUs, which I describe in Chapter 5. If a host system on a Token Ring generates a packet size of 4,500 bytes, but one of the intermediate LAN segments is FDDI (which only supports an MTU of 4,000 bytes), what happens? For IP, the answer is *fragmentation*.

11.8.1   Fragmentation and Reassembly

All IP routers must be capable of fragmenting and reassembling IP datagrams according to the MTU values for the directly attached LAN segments. In Figure 11.19 I show the example of the Token Ring workstations and the FDDI backbone. In this example, Harry sends a 4,500 byte packet to Sally. Router_1 receives the datagram and decides that it must be routed over the FDDI backbone. Realizing that FDDI has an MTU of only 4,000 bytes, Router_1 will split the packet into two datagrams. Each fragment will have its own IP header containing the Source and Destination IP addresses (see Chapter 3 for the structure of the IP header). If additional routers were installed between Harry and Sally, the fragments of the original IP datagram theoretically could be routed over different paths because they are full IP datagrams in their own right.

According to RFC 815, reassembly of a series of fragments can occur at intermediate routers as well as the receiving host.

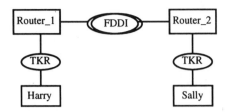

**Figure 11.19:   A Fragmentation and Reassembly
Opportunity**

Who Is Right?

Supporters of host implementations will push for the biggest MTU they can get because it will increase performance and reduce overhead on the network. Router supporters will be more careful and will try their best to avoid fragmentation and reassembly in the network. So let's get a few things straight:

- Big packets *will* improve the performance of network communication in many cases.

- Packet sizes over 1500 bytes *will* result in fragmentation if you have Ethernet in your traffic path.

- Fragmentation *will* reduce the performance of your router.

- Fragmentation is *not* the fault of the host software.

- Fragmentation is *not* the fault of the router manufacturers.

- Fragmentation is a consequence of the proliferation of different LAN technologies coupled with an ongoing lack of co-ordination in our standards committees. If we all used Ethernet (or Token Ring or FDDI), we wouldn't see the phenomenon.

- Given that it's "not our fault," I suggest we approach the problem with an open mind and do the best we can.

To avoid fragmentation in the past it was necessary to configure non-Ethernet hosts to use an MTU size that could be handled by transit Ethernets. This is a pain because you may have a lot of hosts to configure. In addition, you may have shelled out good money for high performance FDDI cards and then find their performance is compromised by a low MTU size. I show such a situation in Figure 11.20.

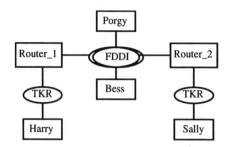

Figure 11.20:   MTU and Performance Issues

Porgy and Bess are equipped with FDDI cards. To get the best performance out of these cards, we should be able to use an MTU of 4,000 bytes. However, if we transmit from Porgy to Harry with this MTU size, then Router_1 is going to be kept busy fragmenting datagrams.

Today we can benefit from a new protocol called *MTU Discovery*.

MTU Discovery

MTU Discovery is a wonderfully simple technique that can have major benefits in terms of the performance and reliability of the internetwork. If this option is supported by a given router, it will monitor the IP Options portion of the IP header (see Chapter 3). In this field, MTU Discovery inserts the minimum MTU for the path traversed by the datagram. In Figure 11.20, Harry would transmit a datagram onto the Token Ring with the MTU Discovery field set to 18kB (this is the MTU for a 16Mbps Token Ring). When the datagram passes into Router_1, the router will see that the outbound interface for this datagram is an FDDI and will adjust the MTU Discovery field down to 4kB (the MTU for FDDI). Returning datagrams from Porgy will have the MTU size set to the minimum value encountered *for that route*. So, the first few packets might suffer fragmentation, but subsequent traffic will have the MTU size automatically adjusted. Note that each host computer has to go through this process to discover the optimum MTU for a given route.

11.9 Host to Router Routing

So far in this chapter I concentrate on the ways that IP packets move from router to router. I'd like to touch on the subject of Host-Router communication now. In Chapters 3 and 4 I describe how the first part of the routing decision is actually made by the host (i.e., the decision that the source and destination are on the same, or different LAN segments). Internetwork traffic is sent to the Default Router.

11.9.1   Default Router

Default Routers can be configured in several ways. Each method has its own advantages and drawbacks.

Manual Configuration

When I first used TCP/IP on a PC, the setup of the Default Router was part of the installation procedure for the software. A single IP address was entered for the PC to use as its default router. If the Default Router was unavailable, the PC could not send internetwork traffic. This situation was fixed by allowing a second IP address to be entered for a backup Default Router. Some kind of timeout facility was used by the application software to decide if the Default Router was unavailable. The technique is quite workable in a small network, but it's rather static and implies continual maintenance for networks in which hosts are moved. Most other aspects of TCP/IP are moving to a more friendly, dynamic approach to network configuration. Two possible approaches have been used to make the task of finding the Default Router more dynamic: wiretapping and router discovery.

11.9.2   Wiretapping (aka "Eavesdropping," aka "RIP Listen")

Routers run routing protocols to allow them to discover routes from one network to another. Why not install routing protocols in the host systems to allow them to find the routers? In fact, RIP is available as a standard part of most UNIX code (the *routed* demon). One slight variation is required to prevent chaos on the network: host systems do not generate RIP traffic, they just listen, or "eavesdrop" on RIP messages sent by routers. If hosts were allowed to transmit RIP, we'd end up with dozens of broadcasts transmitted onto every network segment every 30 seconds. The listen-only technique is actually known as *wiretapping* and is virtually the de facto way of configuring a UNIX host. The problem with wiretapping using RIP is that the hold-down timer is around 90 seconds. This means that the loss of the Primary Default Router will not be discovered quickly. In addition, there's no way to prioritize which router is chosen as the Default Router for a given host. If multiple routers are attached to a LAN segment for resilience or load balancing, the hosts will not be able to use the routers efficiently. Until recently, wiretapping was a good technique for UNIX machines, but it was unusual to find it on PCs.

11.9.3   ICMP Router Discovery

The solution to the problems of gleaning is to implement ICMP Router Discovery according to RFC 1256 in all your hosts and routers. Router Discovery is a simple addition to the range of ICMP messages.

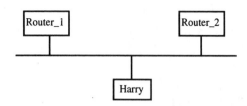

Figure 11.21:   ICMP Router Discovery

In Figure 11.21, Harry would normally be statically configured with the IP address of Router_1 as his Default Router. If the routers and Harry support router discovery, then Harry can dynamically discover either of these routers as needed. Router discovery has two mechanisms to make this work:

- Routers can send *advertisements* to let the hosts know that they're around.

- Hosts can send *solicitations* to see if there are any IP routers on the same segment.

Typically, we would set a fairly long advertisement timer on the routers to prevent excessive traffic on the LAN. Hosts would trigger a solicitation the first time they need to transmit an internetwork packet. Having received a default router address, they simply cache this until it becomes invalid.

If Router_1 goes down, then internetwork traffic will not get through, so hosts will send out another solicitation. Router_2 would then respond and the hosts are back in business.

Priorities can be set to allow half of the hosts on your segment to use Router_1 as their primary with Router_2 as their backup, with the other half using Router_2 as the primary and Router_1 as the backup. Router discovery will scale to more than two routers.

11.10   Router Architectures

Router architecture has a direct impact on performance and scaleability of the internetwork so an understanding of architectural factors will be a major benefit for internetwork designers.

In Figure 11.2 I show a schematic of a multiprotocol router. I'd now like to concentrate on a single protocol device, but also look at the path of packets through the system.

11.10.1   The Central CPU Architecture

The very first routers from Proteon in the early 80's were based on conventional host computers (PDP-11s at first). Around 1984, Proteon started developing a lower cost, dedicated platform based on existing technology. At that time this technology was based on Multibus-1, with a single CPU card based on the Motorola 68000. The layout is shown in Figure 11.22.

The advantage of this design was that Proteon could use off-the-shelf CPU cards, serial cards and even Ethernet cards. They were obliged to develop their own versions of the proprietary ProNET-10 and ProNET-80 LANs.

Below is a description of the path of a packet that is received on Port 1 and is supposed to be transmitted out of Port 2.

Step 1

Shows the packet arriving at the receiving interface. This interface contains a typical LAN chipset, but has no other intelligence associated with it. In order to make any kind of routing decision, the packet must be sent to the Central CPU.

Step 2

The packet being sent over the shared bus to the CPU. Since the bus is shared, the interface on Port 1 may have to buffer the packet until the bus is free. Once the packet reaches the CPU card, the CPU itself is interrupted to indicate the arrival of a data packet. A routing decision is then made on the basis of the destination IP address and the entries in the routing table. In this case the CPU decides that the packet has to be routed out of Port 3.

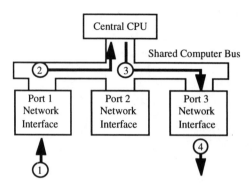

Figure 11.22:   Central CPU Router

Step 3

The packet being transmitted for the second time over the bus to Port 3. Once again, if the bus is congested, the packet may have to be buffered at the CPU card until it can be transmitted to Port 3.

Step 4

The packet being transmitted out of Port 3. If this port is connected to a conventional LAN, then the packet may have to be buffered to await access control "permission."

The single CPU architecture is a very logical first step in router development, since it economizes on CPU and RAM costs by centralizing these resources and sharing them between different LAN ports. However, the architecture has a number of weaknesses that may become severe in a modern, high demand internetwork.

First, the overall performance of the router is dependent on the processing power of the central CPU. For example, the original 68000 based router of the mid-80's could move around 2,000 IP packets per second. However, very few caching or optimization algorithms were used in those days. If a higher performance is required, we need to increase the CPU power. If we want to re-use our source code, we could wait for Motorola's latest chip developments. Indeed, the overall compatibility levels of the 680X0 CPU are excellent and at the time of writing, Motorola 68040 based routers from Cisco and Wellfleet still offer the highest switching performance in a multiprotocol environment. However, towards the end of the 80s, Proteon were the first router company to move to RISC technology, choosing the AMD 29000. Unfortunately, RISC-based routers have never yet delivered the performance levels one would expect when comparing their performance in the workstation world. In Figure 11.23, I've tried to represent the performance curves for a range of single-CPU routers, with a variety of CPUs. As you can see, performance rises in a linear fashion

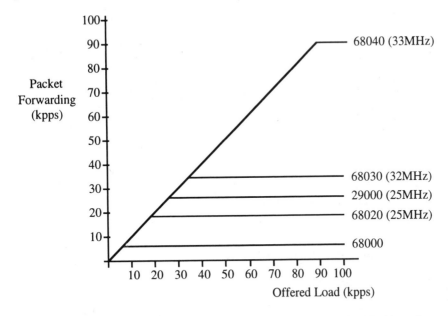

Figure 11.23: **Comparative CPU Performance in IP Routing**

until we reach the saturation level for the specific CPU. In my diagram, I've indicated that performance then levels off. In real life however, performance will often *drop* after the saturation point because of buffer congestion effects. The test of a good quality implementation is that the drop-off effect will be small. The performance numbers I'm quoting are derived from independent benchmarks from Scott Bradner and the Tolly Group.

The limitations of the single CPU architecture have also been encountered in the general workstation world (where they are known as the "von Neuman Bottleneck"). In the router world, a number of strategies have been adopted to overcome the problem:

- Limit the number of ports on the router
- Offload the main CPU with auxiliary CPUs
- Build a multiple CPU architecture
- Build a Router Cluster
- Create a "Stack-able" router

11.10.2 Limiting The Load

This is an obvious way to solve the Central CPU problem and continues to be a valid option even as router technology advances. Today, the cost of an entry level router has dropped dramatically from the levels of only a couple of years ago. Then an entry level device, such as the Cisco IGS, might cost around $5,000 and have limited future expansion (in terms of RAM) and be PROM-based (which meant very messy upgrade procedures). Today, the Cisco 2500 and Wellfleet AN products cost between $2,000 and $3,000, with PC-style SIMM chips for easy upgrade and built-in Flash EPROM to allow centralized software upgrades.

These units are highly integrated and are typically sold in fixed configurations with one or two LAN ports and one or two WAN ports. A single 680X0 CPU is more than adequate to meet these performance demands.

Proteon's CNX 500, with a RISC architecture and slotted configuration, limited the number of access ports by offering only three slots, with each slot supporting only one or two ports.

11.10.3 Asymmetric Architectures

Having invested thousands of man-hours in architectural development, companies like Cisco and Proteon were faced with the problem of boosting their higher end products to meet the demands of higher port counts. Cisco's AGS was first shipped as a Central CPU device. A major problem was discovered when Transparent Bridging was introduced to router product lines. Looking back at Figure 11.22, imagine now that each of the LAN ports is operating in promiscuous mode. Instead of only receiving frames that are *explicitly* addressed to one of the router's MAC addresses, these ports will now receive every frame that passes on all of the LAN segments. Since the individual interfaces have no on-board intelligence, every frame must be passed to the Central CPU to compare its MAC address with entries in the Learning Table. The result is that the router bus becomes totally swamped with traffic.

Offloading at the Network Ports

To solve the problem, Cisco introduced a new card called the Multiport Communications Interface (MCI). The MCI card was equipped with a special chip which was a member of the AMD 29XX family. These chips are generally referred to as bit slice processors because their main job involves moving bits very rapidly from one place to another in an intelligent way. The AMD 29XX can be used to pre-filter Transparently Bridged traffic and prevent it from swamping the CPU. However, the 29XX is not a general purpose CPU. There is no high level language for this CPU and it must be programmed in low level assembler.

To boost the bus bandwidth, Cisco added a secondary bus onto four of the AGS slots. This bus, the c-Bus operates at 533 Mbps and was originally designed to support high speed FDDI connections. The c-Bus versions of the AGS were known as the AGS+. At the time of writing, Cisco have introduced cleaned up versions of this architecture which extends the c-BUS to all slots in the AGS+

chassis.   Five slot versions of this router are called the Cisco 7000, while a smaller three slot version is called the 7010.

The boosted versions of the Central CPU architecture allow router vendors to extend the lift of existing products without massive redesign.   However, by using the 29XX as the auxiliary processor, the result is an asymmetric performance across different protocols.   At the time of writing, Cisco support 29XX offload for IP and IPX only.   All other protocols are still subject to the von Neuman Bottleneck.   Figure 11.24 shows the final AGS+ architecture for IP.

As you can see, the asymmetric architecture of the Cisco AGS+ and 7000 produces a more complex data path.   I'll describe the switching process in more detail.

Step 1

Shows an IP packet arriving on one of the ports associated with Slot 3.   In the AGS+, two pure Multibus slots remain, while in the 7000 the Multibus is now used only for route query purposes.

Step 2

The AMD BSP on Slot 3 is programmed to handle IP packets.   However, it does not have the capacity to route the packet independently and for routing information it must consult the cache at the c-Bus controller.   Step 2 shows the query.

Step 2a

If an IP packet for this destination has already been routed, a cache entry will be present at the c-Bus controller.   However, if this is the first time that traffic has been sent to this destination, the c-Bus controller will send a query over the Multibus to the central CPU.   Since the central CPU is the only general purpose CPU in the router, all routing decisions must be made at this point.

Step 2b

The central CPU responds to the c-Bus controller route cache query.   This routing information will now be cached at the c-Bus controller and subsequent packets to this destination can be routed without a Multibus query.

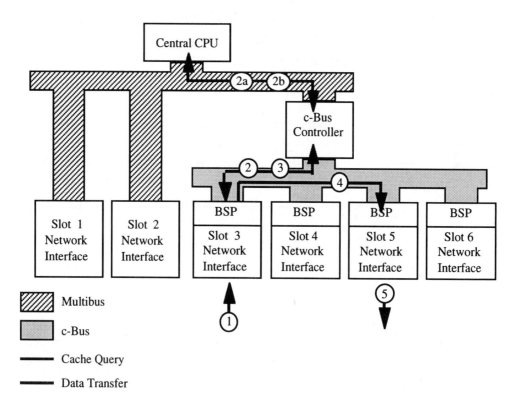

Figure 11.24:   Cisco AGS+ and 7000 Architecture

Step 3

The c-Bus controller sends the query response to the BSP in Slot 3.

Step 4

For the first time, the entire packet is now moved over the c-Bus to the exit slot. Until this point, only abbreviated queries actually cross the bus.

The asymmetric architecture of the AGS+ allowed Cisco to continue to load the AGS design with additional interfaces and higher port densities. During the period from 1986 to the present day, the number of interface ports on each slot increased from one to eight Ethernets. High performance interfaces such as FDDI, HSSI and the various Fast Ethernet derivatives place much higher demands on a single slot. For IP and IPX traffic (with their Version 9.2 software), Cisco moved support of these protocols onto the BSP. Other protocols such as AppleTalk, DECNet, etc., continue to be switched by the central CPU.

Limitations of Asymmetric Architectures

The asymmetric architecture has three fundamental limitations:

1. The central CPU still has a finite switching capability, in addition to the many centralized "housekeeping" tasks such as routing protocol updates and Network Management.

2. The central CPU is a single point of failure. This is obviously inherent in all central and asymmetric designs, however, as port density increases, the number of LAN ports that will simultaneously fail with the CPU becomes unacceptable.

3. The use of a non-general CPU on the interface cards means that comparatively crude software development tools must be used. CASE tools and debugging aids are simply not available "off the shelf."

11.10.4 Auxiliary CPUs

An obvious improvement over the single CPU design is to use multiple CPUs. In fact in the PC world, we are used to such an idea with floating point, graphics or disc I/O coprocessors. These devices are successful because the designers identify specific tasks that can be off-loaded to another processor. In the case of a router, we can identify several centralized tasks of this nature:

- Network Management
- Routing Protocols
- User interface
- Encapsulation protocols (e.g. X.25, DLSw, etc.)
- Data compression
- Data encryption

If we include a dedicated coprocessor for these tasks, we can obviously extend the life of our central CPU. This was the approach taken by Proteon with their CNX600 design. The CNX600 was developed from the RISC-based CNX500, but was equipped with dual AMD 29000 CPUs. The design is shown in Figure 11.25.

For steps 1..4, the procedure is identical to the Central CPU design described above.

Step 5

Shows the arrival of a routing update packet onto Slot 1.

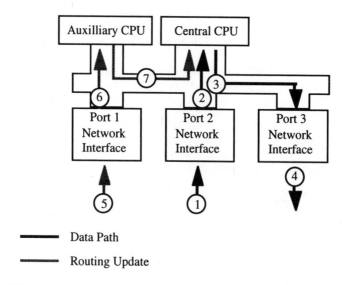

Figure 11.25:   **Auxiliary Processor Architecture**

Step 6

This packet is passed directly to the Auxiliary CPU. Processing of this packet is then performed (for OSPF this may involve re-running the Dijkstra algorithms, for example).

Step 7

The result is passed to the routing table stored on the Central CPU. The routing table must be stored in this location since it is the only way that the Central CPU is able to make a routing decisions.

Multi-Processor Problems

Multi-processor designs are notoriously difficult to get working properly and at the time of writing, Proteon had only shipped single-CPU versions of the CNX600. In contrast, Cisco produced a streamlined version of the AGS+ known as the Cisco 7000. This router is equipped with dual 68040 CPUs and is almost 50% faster on average than the older AGS+. Cisco have also announced a customized CPU that they call the "Silicon Switch." This CPU has so far only been demonstrated with the IP and Transparent Bridge protocols, but has achieved switching of up to 200,000 IP packets per second (measured by Scott Bradner).

For the Cisco 7000, the problem of multiple CPUs seems to have been solved, but with a definite compromise. Each CPU in the unit is dedicated either to switching, or to "housekeeping." If one CPU is congested and the other is idle,

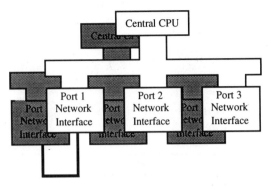

Figure 11.26:   Multiprocessor Architecture Using LAN

there is no load sharing possible. Let's now take a look at the solution to this problem.

11.10.5 Symmetric Multiprocessing

In the minicomputer industry, there is a definition of Symmetric Multiprocessing. This is intended to describe fault-tolerant systems such as Stratus or Tandem minicomputers. In effect, symmetric multiprocessors should have some central task allocation that is responsible for delegating system tasks evenly amongst the available processors. No router on the market today operates in this fashion (fortunately). However, the marketing departments of several router companies have latched onto the term and used it extensively in advertising material. Multiprocessing really is a valid architecture for routers, but not if this constrains the router architecture to the minicomputer model.

Figure 11.26 shows a simple extension of the single CPU router. Each CPU has a limited number of ports allocated to it (e.g. up to eight Ethernets, or four Token Rings, or one FDDI). However, to achieve higher port densities, several boxes are "stacked." In this example, the "gray" router and the "white" router are stacked by connecting two of their ports using a conventional LAN.

In this configuration, each CPU is only loaded to its own capabilities. This is the exact design used by Crosscom in their ILAN XL product. Token Ring LAN ports are used as the connection between router modules because, at the time of writing, the Crosscom backplane is "dormant."

This type of symmetric architecture is the ultimate in scaleable performance but has two major disadvantages. First, the interconnection between "slots" is limited to LAN speeds. Second, the user of the unit does not see the router as one single entity, but as several discrete boxes. The same thing is true for the Network Management system. Setting up such a "router cluster" is actually more difficult than setting up multiple routers because of the loading and congestion that can occur on the LAN "backplane."

Integrated Symmetric Multiprocessing

The logical limit to the architecture is to interconnect the separate router units using a high speed backplane. Two companies (Ascom-Timeplex and Wellfleet) currently offer this architecture. Figure 11.27 shows the basic principle.

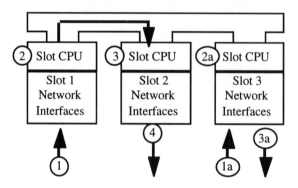

Figure 11.27: Symmetric Multiprocessor Architecture

For this architecture, there are two possible packet paths. First, let's look at a packet that must be switched *between* slots.

Step 1

The packet is received on Slot 1.

Step 2

Since the dedicated CPU on this slot has a full routing table at its disposal, it knows that the packet must be sent directly to Slot 2.

Step 3

The packet is received on Slot 2 and transmitted on the outgoing interface.

Inter-slot traffic only has to cross the bus once in this scenario. However, to achieve this, each slot must be given a full routing table.

The alternative packet path is for traffic that enters and leaves on the same slot. Obviously this requires multiport interfaces (which are now common in all router product lines). In the symmetric multiprocessor architecture, these packets can be totally dealt with on the same slot. In addition, routing protocol packets that arrive on any slot can be processed by the CPU in this slot and the processed results are distributed to the other slots.

Step 1a

This shows the packet being received on Slot 3.

Step 2a

The dedicated CPU on this slot has a full copy of the routing table, so is able to decide that the packet does not need to be transferred to another slot. For a routing protocol packet, the CPU on this slot will process the update. Most routing protocol packets will stop at this slot and processed results (in the form of routing table updates) will be sent to other slots.

Step 3a

This shows the packet being transmitted out of one of the other interfaces on Slot 3. At no time did the packet cross the bus. For routing protocols, a modified update may be sent out, but in many cases this will not be the case.

This architecture has some obvious advantages.

1. It seems to be totally scaleable. The only limit is the speed of the bus.

2. Each slot acts in an autonomous fashion. A crash of one slot may not affect any of the other slots. More usefully, each slot could be "hot swapped" without affecting the operation of the overall system.

3. The CPU on each slot could be matched to the demand of the LAN or WAN interfaces on that slot. So Slot 1 could be equipped with a 68040, Slot 2 with a RISC Power PC chip and Slot 3 with a 68060.

However, there are three fundamental disadvantages to the Symmetric Multiprocessor architecture:

1. It is an expensive architecture. Each Slot has its own copy of the operating system and routing tables. It's likely that each slot will need the same amount of RAM as an individual router of the other architectures.

2. It's difficult to build. For newcomers into the routing marketplace, the multiprocessor architecture is simply not realistic. Hence, most newcomers are focusing on low-cost, single-board products and leaving the backbone routing market to Cisco and Wellfleet.

3. For some tasks, such as OSPF updates or TCP session processes, it makes no sense to run multiple copies of the same process. Multiprocessor architectures may *logically* fall back on a central architecture for some tasks, while fully distributing the packet forwarding. To ensure reliability in these circumstances, there must be a strategy to restart a "solo" task on another CPU in a fully dynamic fashion.

The second two disadvantages can be solved in a good quality implementation. The cost of this architecture, however, must be judged by the power requirements of the individual application. There is no doubt that the symmetric architecture offer the highest switching rates demonstrated to date. It's interesting to note that virtually all of the new generation of ATM LAN hubs implement a form of multiprocessor architecture. ATM hubs today contain very little software (simply because the standards are not finished), so the barrier to market entry for newcomers is significantly lower than for the router marketplace.

11.10.6 Router Clusters

In Figure 11.26, I show the basic Router Cluster concept. In simple terms, if we run out of ports on the basic router platform, we just add another box. This sounds like a great idea, but there are some significant problems.

First, the interconnection of routers in the cluster is made using conventional routing protocols. This is not a problem if we're using a high performance protocol such as OSPF, but using RIP or IGRP, the rerouting performance will be "disappointing."

Second, if we treat each component in the cluster as a separate router, this will just complicate the design of the network. Instead of a 50-router internetwork with larger boxes, we might need to consider a 150-router internetwork of "clusters."

Third, if we cluster boxes together, how do we make the connection? Normally the answer will be to use LAN or WAN connections from the router. These connections will limit the number of ports on each unit in the cluster and will limit the speed of the connection to a much lower bandwidth than a conventional router bus.

Fourth, we need to consider the management problems. If we build a cluster of two or three routers, we find that these routers appear as two or three icons on the Network Management System screen. While this can sometimes be hidden by clever NMS configuration, the reality is that the Cluster is just a collection of routers that share the same cable rack.

11.10.7 Router Stacks

The logical solution to the Router Cluster problems is the "Stack-able" Router. During 1993 and especially in 1994, the Cable Hub market was swamped with a new breed of product called a "Stack-able" Hub. Basically these device are fixed-configuration, low cost hubs that can be clipped together to form a larger unit. The stack concept solves many of the basic problems of device expansion.

For routers, the problem of stacking is a bit more extreme. In effect, to create a router stack we need to be able to extend the backplane of a router outside of the box.

Although several routers have been introduced that are capable of stacking with hubs (e.g. routers from HP and FiberMux), Wellfleet seems to be the first company to announce a router that can stack with other routers. The Wellfleet ASN is a single processor unit (using a Motorola 68040) with four expansion slots. One of the slots can be fitted with a bus extender interface allowing up to four ASNs to be stacked together. When connected with the bus extender, these units appear as a single router.

11.11   Summary

- Routers are designed to switch packets from one network to another using the information contained in the Network Layer portion of the packet.

- Packets are stripped of all network-specific character prior to switching.

- Routers must be configured manually with address information as part of the setup procedure.

- The routing table contains the information the router needs for making the packet switching decisions.

- Routing information is entered into the routing table in several possible ways.

- Direct routes are taken from the addresses of interfaces installed directly in the router.

- Static routes are entered manually and must be removed from the routing table manually.

- Default routes are a useful way to indicate the exit point to a network for all the routers in that network.

- Dynamic routes are passed from router to router using routing protocols. The best route to a given network is used.

- Route "quality" is determined by specific metrics. These include hop count, line speed, delay, reliability and monetary cost.

- The scope of a single routing protocol is called the Autonomous System. AS boundaries protect one AS from routing mistakes made in other AS but still allow connectivity.

- Protocols used to determine network reachability between AS boundaries are called External Gateway Protocols. The routing protocols used within the AS are called Interior Gateway Protocols.

- Several mechanisms exist to override the conventional decision process in a router. These include routing precedence source routing. Routing precedence is a useful tool in the design and control of the network. Source routing is more commonly used as a debugging aid.

- Routers are capable of breaking down IP packets into smaller pieces for transmission over heterogeneous network technologies. This process is known as Fragmentation and Reassembly.

- Several mechanisms are available to allow hosts to discover router addresses. These include static default routers, RIP eavesdropping and ICMP router discovery. The best general purpose technique is router discovery.

- Router architecture has a direct impact on performance, especially when routers are required to perform additional tasks such as compression, or to perform complex routing calculations.

11.12   References

[1]   R. Braden. J. Postel. "Requirements for Internet gateways," *RFC 1009*. June 1987.

[2]   R. Braden, J. Postel, "Requirements for Internet gateways." *RFC 1009*. June 1987.

[3]   R. Braden. "Requirements for Internet hosts - application and support," *RFC 1123*. October 1989.

[4]   R. Braudes, S. Zabele. "Requirements for Multicast Protocols." *RFC 1458*. May 1993.

[5]   Douglas E. Comer. *Internetworking with TCP/IP*. (Prentice Hall, NJ 1991).

[6]   J. Moy. "Multicast Extensions to OSPF." *RFC 1584*. March 1994.

[7]   J. Postel. "Internet Protocol." *RFC 791*. September 1981.

[8]   J. Postel. "Internet Control Message Protocol." *RFC 792*. September 1981.

CHAPTER 12

Network Management

> *"Would you like a cookie, Charlie Brown?"*
>
> *"No thank you, I'd rather manage."*
>
> *Charles M. Shultz*

12.1 Introduction

The world of internetworking is moving away from centralized, mainframe computing towards distributed peer and client/server networks. One of the main consequences of such a move is that management becomes significantly more difficult. The two classic single vendor network architectures, SNA and DECNet, have always had a strong emphasis on management. TCP/IP has also had a strong management story, in the form of SNMP, since 1988, but because no single vendor controls the TCP/IP market, the focus of management products has never been as tight as in the single vendor world.

In this Chapter I'll be looking at the basics of SNMP management and offering some advice on how to get the best from this powerful standards-based system.

Figure 12.1 shows a simplified view of Network Management. Around the network are intelligent communication devices; switches, routers, bridges, hubs and host computers. These are *managed devices*. Somewhere on the network is another host running as a *Network Management System* (NMS). The object of Network Management is to allow managed devices to be *configured, monitored* and (if necessary) *reconfigured* from an authorized NMS somewhere in the network. All of the subtleties of various NMS architectures are simply an attempt to make this process more efficient, effective and, ultimately, scaleable.

The ISO Management Framework

The standards body, ISO, breaks down the task of Network Management:

Configuration Management. Most intelligent devices require some form of configuration information. Configuration management functions would allow a user to enter configuration information at the NMS using some form of friendly interface and to transfer this information into the managed device. Enhancements include the ability to administer and audit configuration information centrally for a large number of remote devices. This allows tight software version control. This is an area of Network Management that suffers in a multivendor environment because, for example, the configuration structure of Vendor X's cable hub is totally different from the structure of Vendor Y's bridge and Vendor Z's router.

12.1.1   The Objectives of Management

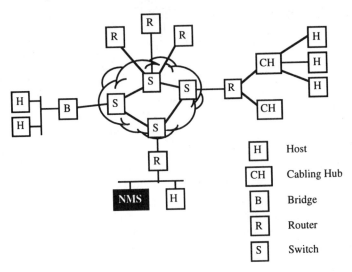

Figure 12.1:   Many Devices, Different Types, Widely Distributed

Performance Management. The NMS is a good place to collect performance data on the network. In theory this data could be fed into the same modeling packages that were used to design the network in the first place. This would allow models to be refined and customized for specific installations. While performance data collection is a reality today, the processing of information and its incorporation into design models has yet to be realized. All of the demonstrations I've seen tend to highlight the weaknesses in current modeling algorithms in peer networks.

Fault Management. This is one of the most successful aspects of Network Management. The object being for the Network Administrator to find out about network problems before the users complain about them.

Security Management. As internetworks become larger and are beginning to interconnect with each other, security is becoming a major concern. Security barriers or traps can be configured around the network and Security Management features in the managed device or the NMS would be responsible for triggering alerts if these were challenged or breached. A wider aspect of Security Management is to ensure that security policy is consistent over the entire network. In effect, if we imagine the internetwork as an extended computer system, Security Management acts in place of the Operating System security function.

Accounting Management. Internetworks cost money. The justification for their existence is that they make the company more efficient. The ultimate cost justification comes in the form of usage-based billing for internetwork services. For TCP/IP internetworks, Accounting Management is the least developed of all the management functions.

Over the last five years or so, these five management concepts have been adopted, with varying levels of success, as core functions by a range of management systems. In the TCP/IP world, the only commercially important management architecture is SNMP. For this reason, most of this Chapter will be devoted to SNMP, with an overview of SNMP2 and a brief mention of CMIS and NetView.

Table 12.1 contains a summary of the current RFCs for all of the management standards that apply to the TCP/IP world. Later in the Chapter I show a similar table for the new SNMP2 RFCs.

12.2 An Overview of SNMP

The five OSI management functions cannot exist without an underlying structure. If you imagine that Network Management is just another network function, then there must be an application protocol that allows it to work. For SNMP, the architecture is built up from several components:

- The Client / Server architecture

- The Structure of Management Information (SMI)

- The Management Information Base (MIB)

- The Simple Network Management Protocol (SNMP)

12.2.1 SNMP Clients and Servers

In a large internetwork, there are many different types of intelligent device that we might want to manage. I'll take two contrasting examples: a router and a host. I've already suggested that the concept of management is really about monitoring devices, or controlling them, or both.

I can "monitor" the contents of a router's Routing Table by asking the router to send me the table.

I can "control" the access rights of an individual user on a UNIX machine by appropriate use of the *user* command.

Table 12.1: Selection of Current TCP/IP Management RFCs

RFC #	Title
1052	IAB Recommendations for the Development of Internet Network Management
1155	Structure and Identification of Management Information for TCP/IP-based Internets
1156	Management Information Base for Network Management of TCP/IP-based Internets
1157	Simple Network Management Protocol (SNMP)
1187	Bulk Table Retrieval with SNMP
1189	Common Management Information Services and Protocols for the Internet (CMOT and CMIP)
1212	Concise MIB Definitions
1213	Management Information Base for Network Management of TCP/IP-based Internets: MIB II
1215	Convention for defining traps for use with the SNMP
1227	SNMP Mux Protocol and MIB
1228	SNMP DPI: Simple Network Management Protocol Distributed Programming Interface
1231	IEEE 802.5 Token Ring MIB
1239	Reassignment of Experimental MIBs to Standard MIBs
1243	AppleTalk Management Information Base
1253	OSPF Version 2: Management Information Base
1269	Definitions of Managed Objects for the Border Gateway Protocol Version 3
1270	SNMP Communications Services
1271	Remote Network Monitoring Management Information Base
1284	Definitions of managed objects for the Ethernet-like interface types
1285	FDDI Management Information Base

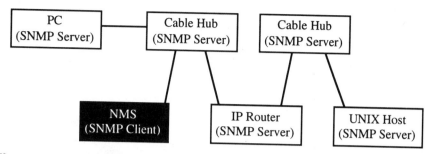

Figure 12.2: SNMP Client and SNMP Server (Agent) Functions

Both monitoring and control functions require intelligent processes in the managed device and the NMS. In the SNMP architecture, an SNMP *server* function (usually known as an *agent*) is implemented in the *managed* device. The *NMS* then uses one or more SNMP *client* processes to *monitor* and *control* the managed devices. Both client and server components require a CPU and RAM-based software to operate, so when SNMP was devised, economy of CPU power and RAM was a major criterion. In fact, back in 1988 I used to give presentations on SNMP and compare its architecture to the ISO management system CMIS/CMIP. At that time, the 80386 had just been introduced and 640kB of RAM on a PC was all you could possibly use. From early studies, it seemed that SNMP agents could be implemented in around 64kB of RAM, whereas a minimal CMIS/CMIP implementation would require over half a megabyte. I've never seen a CPU load comparison between the two architectures, but since CMIS/CMIP is connection-oriented, then loading will be higher.

12.2.2 Structure of Management Information

So a managed device maintains a set of managed objects that can be read and sent to an NMS (this represents the monitoring function), or can be set to a new value by the NMS (this represents the control function).

The actual format of any managed object is defined by the *Basic Encoding Rules* (BER) contained in the *Structure of Management Information* (SMI).

The SMI was developed from a subset of an existing ISO Presentation Layer protocol called Abstract Syntax Notation 1 (ASN.1). In very simple terms, SMI uses the ASN.1 coding rules to define four simple variable types:

- Integer (32-bit, unsigned)
- Octet String
- Object Identifier
- Null

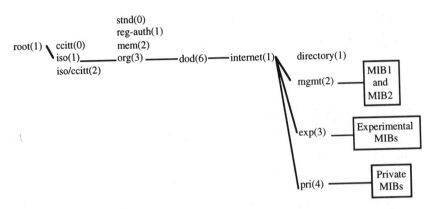

Figure 12.3:   Locations of Important MIB Sub-Trees

Managed objects are identified (i.e., named) using the Object Identifier data type. The values of the managed objects are stored as integers or strings. The Null data type exists to allow programmers to bypass the encoding rules and produce custom data types. Obviously these must be bilaterally agreed between the NMS and the managed device.

12.2.3   Management Information Base (MIB)

If the SMI tells us *how* to represent the managed objects, then we need an additional piece of information to tell us *what* the object represents. This is the job of the *Management Information Base* (MIB).

SNMP MIBs are object-oriented databases and are tree-structured. Each node in the tree can be referenced by tracing the *numbers* of nodes passed through to reach the node we're describing. Alternatively, we can use name references for the nodes. The SNMP MIB is actually a sub tree of "The MIB"; a global data structure that is designed to be used by all possible management systems in the world. In Figure 12.3 I've traced the top of "The MIB." From the root, there are three possible branche, and each is allocated to a separate authority. CCITT (now known as ITU-TSS) is allocated node 0, while ISO is allocated branch 1. These allocations will never change. One of the fundamental concepts in this type of database is that managed objects (nodes) may be made obsolete, but their node numbers will never, ever, be re-used.

The Internet MIBs MIB and MIB2 are shown in Figure 12.3, but I've also pointed out the positions of two other important subtrees. These are the Experimental MIBs and the Private MIBs. Experimental MIBs are written about specific, generic topics like Token Ring or FDDI (see Table 12.1). In contrast, Private MIBs are written by individual companies like Cisco, Proteon and Wellfleet to describe their own devices in detail. This means that there are three ways that the MIB can evolve.

A Note on Naming Conventions

When we refer to MIB objects, we use a combination of names and numbers. Take a look at Figure 12.3.

- If I wanted to refer to MIB2 in its entirety, I would use the reference 1.1.3.6.1.2.1

- I could also describe it using object descriptions as iso.org.dod.internet.mgmt.mib2.

- Notice that the "root" node has a number (1), but does not have an explicit name.

- I can use shorthand to refer to nodes. MIB2 can be described as mgmt 2. i.e., "node 1 under mgmt."

- In the tree, we *know* that MIB2 is the second node because its node number is written in brackets after the name, e.g., mib2 (2).

For management to work, both the managed device and the NMS must agree on the MIB contents. If the MIBs are changing, how can we ensure that an NMS from Sun or HP is able to manage hubs from Cabletron, ATM switches from Fore and routers from Wellfleet? When the MIB is extended, the new structure is described in an ASCII text document using ASN.1 BER. This file is then read by an ASN.1 Compiler (the compiler is usually a part of the NMS package). When the MIB has been compiled, the NMS is able to "see" the new managed objects. MIB2 and Experimental MIBs are available on the Internet and are usually pre-compiled into a good quality NMS. Private MIBs are available from the appropriate manufacturer and must be compiled into the NMS by the user. However, the better-known MIBs are often pre-compiled into the major NMS packages, especially where formal agreements are in place.

12.2.4 Simple Network Management Protocol (SNMP)

The managed device and the NMS are connected by a network. This means that the management commands have to be transported using an appropriate communication protocol; in this case, IP. The original SNMP was designed to operate over a UDP stack (see Figure 12.4).

As an Application Programming Interface (API), SNMP defines four primitive functions to allow message exchange between the managed device and the NMS.

- get {variable name}
- get next
- set {variable name}, {value}
- trap

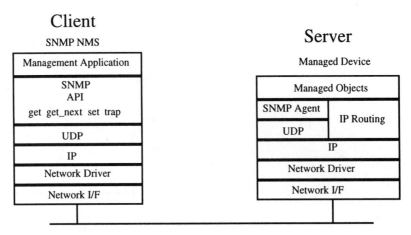

Figure 12.4:   SNMP within the IP Stack

The first three of these primitives are designed to operate from the NMS to the managed device. For example, an NMS could use the get primitive to request information, but there are no mechanisms defined for the router to request information from the NMS.

Get

The get primitive is used to retrieve the value of a specific MIB variable. For example, to retrieve the current status of port #12 of a router, SNMP would use the command:

get <MIB reference>

The get command can only retrieve one MIB variable at a time, which has turned out to be a limiting factor for SNMP. To retrieve multiple MIB variables, the NMS must send multiple SNMP get requests.

The get request is not acknowledged in any way. If the managed device is too busy to respond, or it simply doesn't know how to interpret the management request, no response format has been defined. This can lead to some traffic load problems because the NMS will repeat its get request several times if the managed device doesn't respond. Once again, the lack of an error-reporting message structure has been cited as a problem with SNMP.

Get Next

A powerful feature of SNMP is the *get next* primitive. Let's say that we ask a managed device for the value of a specific MIB variable and the managed device responds. Within the device, a pointer is set to the MIB position of the last variable that was retrieved. The NMS can now issue a get next request without any MIB reference. When the managed device receives the request, it will simply move the pointer to the next variable in the tree and will send the value of this variable to the NMS. The syntax of the get next primitive is very simple:

get_next

No arguments are required because the get next primitive assumes that the MIB pointer in the managed device is at the appropriate position. This can lead to "anomalies" when multiple SNMP management systems are concurrently using get next on the same device. There *should* be no problem here because a get next response contains the full MIB reference of the variable for which the managed device is responding, but the actual behavior of the NMS depends on the implementation. Get next was intended to allow the user of a *MIB Browser* to navigate unknown MIB structures. A MIB Browser is a simple SNMP application that represents MIB variables on managed devices in their original tree structure. The Browser can be used to navigate up and down a MIB tree examining data structures. Browsers are usually provided in a good quality SNMP application.

Set

If the NMS needs to change the current state of a managed device, it uses the set primitive. This has the form:

set <MIB reference> <value>

Like the get primitive, set can only operate on a single MIB variable in one transaction. The set primitive is the subject of concern for network administrators because of the lack of security features in the original SNMP. I discuss the subject of security in detail below.

Trap

The trap primitive was defined to allow the managed device to communicate directly with the NMS and without a prior request for information by the NMS. Trap was devised to allow the managed device to report an error condition to the NMS immediately. The original SNMP (first defined in RFC 1067) defined 6 mandatory traps:

- Warm start
- Cold start
- Link up
- Link down
- EGP neighbor loss
- Authentication failure

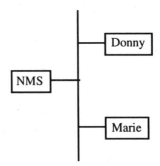

Figure 12.5:   SNMP Client Bottlenecks

I think all but the last are fairly self-explanatory. An authentication failure trap is generated if an unauthorized SNMP Client attempts to send commands to an SNMP Server.

Most SNMP devices today do not implement all of these traps. For example, the EGP neighbor loss is hardly relevant to a repeater, host or hub. However, all SNMP devices should implement an additional trap type; the *enterprise trap*. The enterprise trap, described in detail in [1], is the way that a manufacturer can represent alert information that is specific to the device. For example, in a router we might want to indicate if an unauthorized use has tried to log onto the user interface. The authentication failure trap is not appropriate in this case so an enterprise trap message would be sent out. I give further examples of the use of traps below.

> RFP Question: Describe the way in which the SNMP Enterprise Trap feature is implemented in your device.

Where's The Session?

Since I describe Client/Server concepts, there must be some sessions around here someplace. If an NMS is required to manage a thousand network devices, does it need to hold open a thousand sessions? For SNMP the answer is no. All SNMP transactions are totally connectionless and unacknowledged. In theory, an NMS only needs to run a single SNMP Client process to manage a large network. However, in practice the NMS will spawn multiple Clients to increase performance. To illustrate why, take a look at Figure 12.5.

Donny and Marie are hosts with SNMP agents running. The NMS is running a single SNMP Client. Every 30 seconds, the NMS asks each host if everything's OK. If the host doesn't respond, the NMS has a 10 second timeout and will try three times. At 12 noon, the NMS sends out a poll to Donny. As luck would have it, Donny went off line 10 seconds earlier, so he doesn't respond. The single Client process is now stuck in a timeout loop waiting for Donny. Meanwhile, Marie goes off line too. At 12:00:10 and 12:00:20, the Client will re-transmit the poll. At 12:00:30, Donny is reported as down and finally the NMS is freed up to transmit a poll to Marie. No response and after two more attempts, Marie is reported as down at 12:01:00. With a single, blocking[1] Client process, the management response times are double the expected value for this simple network. For many managed devices, the results could be very bad. For this reason, most NMS systems allow multiple Clients to be spawned. William Stallings goes into a lot more detail on queuing theory if you would like to understand this concept in more detail [5]

Error Reporting

One of the problems highlighted during the use of SNMP is that there is no error-reporting protocol operating between the Client and Server. If the NMS asks the managed device for a variable that does not exist in the managed device, then the convention is that the managed device ignores the request. This typically leads the NMS to repeat the request a given number of times, leading to excessive load on the network. This shortcoming is addressed in SNMP2, which I describe later in this Chapter.

SNMP Communities

SNMP is designed as a system-wide management architecture so there must be a mechanism to control the flow of management traffic between the managed device and the NMS. This can be achieved in two ways:

- The use of Community Names
- Configure the managed device to accept management requests only from specific IP addresses

Community names are a default part of any SNMP implementation. Every managed device must belong to at least one community; the default name is "public." I show the way this can work in Figure 12.6.

In this network, there are two departments; Sales and Research. The managed devices in Sales are configured to belong to the community name "sales." The managed devices in Research are configured to belong to the community name "research." There is a backbone network and the managed devices on the backbone are configured to belong to the community name "backbone." The "backbone" NMS also is configured to manage devices in the "sales" and "research" communities. However, the NMS' in Sales and Research cannot manage each other's managed devices, nor can they manage devices on the Backbone.

---

[1]A blocking process is one that cannot do more than one thing at a time. Timeout loops cause blocking processes to loop until the timer expires.

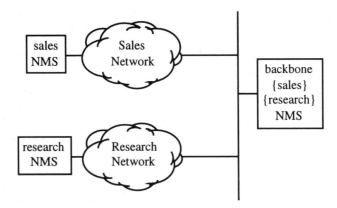

Figure 12.6: SNMP Community Concepts

12.2.5 SNMP In Detail

To understand the design issues involved with SNMP, I now need to go into a little more detail. In particular I'll be looking at the way that information is represented (the SMI syntax) and the ability to work with MIBs.

12.2.6 SMI Defined Syntax

SNMP was designed to be very generic and extendible. This is a great strength for the SNMP fans, who understand the terms and concepts involved. For us humans, on the other hand, it is a weakness. This is because the terminology and concepts used are so abstract, separated from the everyday world. To understand the SNMP concept, keep a firm grip on the idea that each managed device will have a bunch of managed objects inside it. The objects are "serviced" by the SNMP agent. The agent talks to an SNMP server somewhere else in the network. The server runs on a Network Management System.

Now let me apply some SNMP jargon to that simple picture. The managed objects inside the managed device must be represented in a standard way. The construction of the managed object is known as its *object syntax*[1]. In order to get to the managed object, we need to know its name. Each managed object must therefore be given an *object identity*. In Figure 12.7 I've tried to show an analogy to these abstract concepts. The managed object is sitting in a shopping bag. The logo on the bag is the object syntax and it tells us what type of information is in the bag. The handle on the bag is the object identifier and is the only way we can retrieve the bag from the trunk of our car. The syntax of

---

[1]The word *syntax* is used in all forms of language; human or computer-based. Syntax is the branch of grammar dealing with sentence construction.

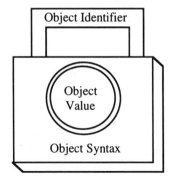

Figure 12.7:   An SMI Analogy

object identifiers and values is defined by the *Structure of Management Information* (SMI).

SMI is actually a subset of a much more complex ISO standard called *Abstract Syntax Notation 1* (ASN.1). Within ASN.1, the syntax of a managed object is chosen from a list. Currently there are three kinds of CHOICE:

- Simple. This refers to the four primitive ASN.1 types I list below.

- Application-wide. This allows SMI to define additional data types.

- Simply Constructed. These define ways of grouping the simple data types.

Simple Data Types

SMI defines four simple data types:

- INTEGER
- OCTET STRING
- OBJECT IDENTIFIER
- NULL

Surprisingly, most numbers in managed devices can be represented by integers (I know some former Z80 programmers who still get nervous when they see a decimal point). Integers are also used to represent enumerated lists of managed objects. For example, if we wanted to describe the type of interface on a particular port of a router, then this could be taken from a list of possible pre-defined interface types (Ethernet, FDDI, E1, T1, etc.). Later I'll describe the concept of MIB objects, but for the moment, let's assume that somewhere in the managed device is a managed object called *ifType*. This object is a single INTEGER variable, but its values are taken from a pre-defined list. For example, if the interface was an Ethernet, the value of ifType would be 6. If the interface was 802.3 the value would be 7, etc. I show the first 17 items of the ifType list according to MIB2 in Figure 12.8.

This Figure illustrates two conventions about the syntax of SMI enumerated lists. The first is that items on the list should never take a value of zero, i.e., the list starts at Item 1. The second is that items must use a number that is on the list and if not they must use the "other" item number. For most SMI lists the "other" category is the first on the list, i.e., Item 1.

Application-Wide Data Types

Internet applications make use of six special data types with SMI definitions. These are:

- **IP Address**. As the name suggests, this data type is designed to represent 32 bit IP addresses.

- **Network Address**. In theory, this type will be used to represent several address families (e.g., ISO NSAPs, E.164, X.25 DTEs, etc.). Only one type of address has currently been defined; IP.

- **Counter**. A 32-bit, unsigned integer. The counter *must* increase in steps of one until it reaches its maximum value and then wrap back to zero.

- **Gauge**. A 32-bit unsigned integer. This data type may increase or decrease, but will "peg" at a maximum value (2^{32}-1), i.e., the Gauge will not wrap back to 0 after reaching the maximum. If the gauge reaches its maximum, it will remain at this value until it is reset.

- **TimeTicks**. A 32-bit unsigned integer. This data type is automatically incremented at 1/100 second intervals and will wrap back to zero after reaching 2^{32}-1.

- **Opaque**. A catch-all data type that allows any data to be passed as an octet string. The devices at each end must agree on the "wrapping" of the data (e.g., the NMS must know how the string is delimited). However, it is quite valid to allow data to be passed, for example, to the NMS, without this device being able to interpret the data.

Note that other MIBs can use SMI coding to define their own application-wide data types. However, the handling of these data types must be agreed also by the NMS.

1:	other
2:	regular1822
3:	hdh1822
4:	ddn-X.25
5:	rfc877-X.25
6:	ethernet-csmacd
7:	iso88023-csmacd
8:	iso88024-tokenBus
9:	iso88025-tokenRing
10:	iso88026-man
11:	starLan
12:	proteon-10Mbit
13:	proteon-80Mbit
14:	hyperchannel
15:	fddi
16:	lapb
17:	sdlc
etc.	

Figure 12.8: The Enumerated List of ifType

Simply Constructed Data Types

Two composite data types are also defined:

- **list**. This data type consists of a defined SEQUENCE of similar, or dissimilar data types.

- **table**. The table data type allows SEQUENCE OF a previously defined list to be repeated.

The Syntax Hierarchy

So the range of possible SMI syntax is quite large, even though each individual definition is so simple. I try to summarize the inter-relationship of the data types in Figure 12.9.

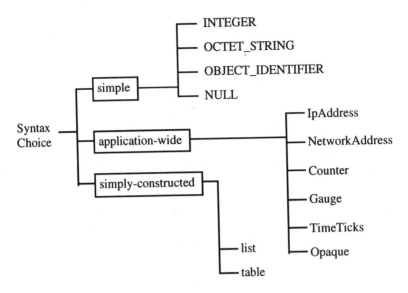

Figure 12.9: Syntax Hierarchy in the SMI

Defining Objects

Objects are defined using the SMI encoding rules to write a macro for the object. The macro has a strict format, like any other type of program. The exact formats are quite complex and are presented in full in [1, 2, 5].

Three important points to note about object macros. They include:

- The syntax definition of the object.
- The object reference to other parts of the MIB. Here the convention is to reference the next node up and give the relative number of the object being defined. For example, MIB2 would be described as "internet 1" because it's the first node on the internet sub-tree.
- The access method for the object (read-only, read-write, write-only, not-accessible).
- The status of the object (mandatory, optional, obsolete, deprecated).

This last point is very important. Remember that a key point about MIB subtrees is that they can never be re-used. The object status parameter gives us a way to prune the trees of "dead wood."

Object macros must be written to describe each part of a MIB.

12.2.7 More about MIBs

So the SMI describes the way that data will be written, but how do we interpret the information? If a router sends us the integer value "42," what is it referring to? 42 packets, 42% CPU load, or 42 Routing Table entries? SNMP deals with this issue in a relatively straightforward way. The NMS asks for a specific management object. The answer received from the managed device is the value of that object. Since the NMS knew what it was asking for, it knows how to assign the answer.

Let me get straight to the point about MIBs for routers. Earlier I mentioned that we could formulate a specific MIB for each different model of router. Maybe the same vendor could define a MIB for their entry level routers and their high end routers. This is quite wasteful since the NMS would have to know about each different router in the world. The original MIB structure was designed to allow three different methods to be used for extending the MIB structure:

- First of all, core data structures were defined. The original one was defined in RFC 1066 and is now known as MIB1. A new version is defined in RFC 1213 and is called MIB2.

- Experimental MIBs were defined for specific network technologies. These include Ethernet, Token Ring and FDDI. There are also MIBs for Bridges, Hosts, Network Analyzers and X.25 switches. The best way to keep up with these MIBs is to download the latest RFC Index and search on "MIB."

- Enterprise MIBs. These MIBs are the way that individual companies can include their specific management variables, but represent them in an SNMP format. Vendors must register their MIBs with IANA and the MIB references are published in the "Assigned Numbers RFC."

The MIB is represented as a tree-structured database and in Figure 12.9 I've traced the top part of it to allow you to see where these different sub-structures fit in.

Don't be put off by the complexity of these references. Remember that even humans can work with tree-structured data bases. Look at your DOS or UNIX file structure and see how long some of your path names can get! Machines find this stuff pretty easy to parse. Let me show you how we can make practical use of this information.

Example 1: Determining Global Parameters in the MIB

There are parameters within any system that are applicable to the entire system, as opposed to subassemblies of the system. For example, in a router, there will be many ports and each port will have a set of management variables. In contrast, there will be variables that apply to the entire router, such as the system name and how long since it last rebooted. In MIB2 these variables are mostly stored in the System Group. Figure 12.9 shows the location of the System Group and other groups within MIB2.

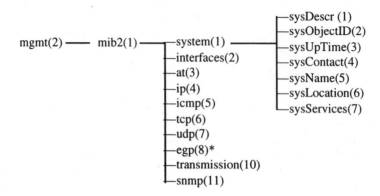

Figure 12.9:   Major MIB2 Groups

The sysDescr object is an octet string describing the managed device. In the case of a router it will contain the manufacturer name and some model description. The sysUpTime object is a counter that stores the time since the management entity was restarted. The assumption is that the entire system was also restarted at that time. Using a simplistic syntax of the SNMP get primitive, we can retrieve the uptime instance using the command:

get 1.1.3.6.1.2.1.1.3

...using object names, the same command would be written:

get {root.}iso.org.dod.internet.mgmt.mib2.system.sysUpTime

The 32 bit integer returned gives the uptime in 1/100ths of a second. Note that in the numeric reference scheme, the root of the tree is given the value "1," whereas in the name reference scheme, it is assumed (I've typed it in curly brackets).

Example 2: Tables in the MIB

In Chapter 11 I described the concept of a Routing Table and I'd now like to show how we can build up this data structure using MIB2 objects. Figure 12.10 provides a sample internetwork for us to work with and in Table 12.2 is the Routing Table for this network. If they look familiar, it's because I used the same example in Chapter 11. The Class B network 128.7.0.0 is subnetted with a mask of 255.255.255.0 throughout.

It's sometimes difficult to imagine how tabular data structures can be represented by tree-structured databases. However, MIB2 contains just such a data structure. As you'd expect, it has a lot more in it than just the simple variables that I discuss. However, I've trimmed down the tree a little bit, as shown in Figure 12.11.

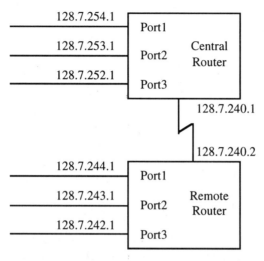

Figure 12.10: Sample Internetwork

Table 12.2: Routing Table for Central Router in Figure 12.10

Destination	Mask	Next Hop	Cost	Type
128.7.254.0	255.255.255.0		1	Direct
128.7.253.0	255.255.255.0		1	Direct
128.7.252.0	255.255.255.0		1	Direct
128.7.240.0	255.255.255.0		1	Direct
128.7.244.0	255.255.255.0	128.7.240.1	2	Static
128.7.243.0	255.255.255.0	128.7.240.1	2	Static
128.7.242.0	255.255.255.0	128.7.240.1	2	Static

I actually leave out a few variables from this table. An asterisk after a variable name means that I've taken one or more variables out for clarity. Another simplification is the use of .".." in the "ipNetToMediaTable" subtree. This name is ridiculously long so the three dots replaces these characters. Finally you'll see the upper case word "INDEX" appear three times in this diagram. I explain my use of this symbol in a moment. For a full description of this sub-tree, you can take a look in the MIB2 RFC [3].

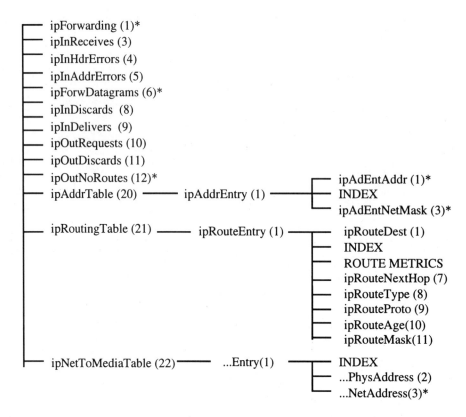

Figure 12.11:   Simplified IP Forwarding Sub-Tree

Looking at the diagram, we can see lots of useful information. First of all, we can get some good error statistics. I'm not going to define all of these variables, but here is a sample of the kind of information we can use in a diagnostic program:

- ipForwarding (1). Integer. This variable indicates if the managed device is a router (i.e., if it's forwarding packets between networks or subnetworks).

- ipInReceives (3). Counter. The total number of datagrams received from lower layers. The count includes error datagrams.

- ipInHdrErrors (4). Counter. The number of datagrams received with an error in the IP header. These datagrams are discarded by the device.

- ipInAddrErrors (5). Counter. Number of datagrams discarded because of IP address errors.

- ipForwDatagrams (6). Counter. Number of datagrams forwarded to another network, or subnetwork. Note of a multinetted host, these datagrams may be transmitted out of the same interface on which they were received.

- ipInDiscards (8). Counter. Number of *valid* datagrams discarded. This is normally due to resource problems (i.e., lack buffers or CPU power).

Obviously by processing these numbers we can get a good idea of the status of the device. Later, you'll see how we can configure the managed device to immediately notify the NMS of a change in one of these variables.

Lower down the tree, we start to see the tables appearing. We can see the interface definition in the ipAddrTable. This table consists of multiple instances of ipAddrEntry(*n*). Each entry has the IP address, subnet mask and most importantly this INDEX variable I spoke about earlier. In this table, the actual name of the index variable is ipAdEntIfIindex(2). The value it contain is a logical pointer to the physical interface inside the managed device. For example, Port 32 on a router might have an index value of 32. You can see that the index appears in the ipRouteEntry and the ipNetToMedia tables. These tables represent the Routing Table and ARP Cache respectively. Each table will have multiple instances of ipRouteEntry(*n*) and ipNetToMediaEntry(*n*) respectively.

12.3 SNMP in Action

The original SNMP standards were proposed back in 1988 and internetworking has changed radically since that time. In this section I'd like to discuss some of the issues of SNMP when it's used in real world situations.

12.3.1 The Trap-Poll Paradigm

Imagine you're sitting at an NMS, looking at your network. How do you know if something changes in the network? There are two possible strategies, or *paradigms*, that you might implement:

1 Every so often the NMS asks the managed device if everything's OK. This is normally known as *poll-based management*.

2 If something goes wrong, the managed device tells the NMS immediately. This technique is normally known as *asynchronous alert management*.

Poll-Based Management

Poll-based management is easier to implement. At regular intervals, the NMS polls the managed device to check that it's still running. This scheme doesn't require any decision-making capability in the *managed* device. The NMS decides if something is wrong based on the information it receives from the managed device.

Asynchronous Alert Management

Asynchronous alert management is more complex. SNMP systems can generate asynchronous alerts using the trap primitive I described earlier. The way that trap is designed in SNMP allows the manufacturer to customize the alert mechanism to the specific device. However, it is the *managed* device that must make the decision that something is wrong. Let me give a few examples to illustrate the problem.

- In a Token Ring hub, each station sends its MAC address as part of the Join Ring process. The hub has a list of allowed MAC addresses stored inside it. As a security mechanism, if a station address that is not on the list tries to join the ring, the hub can reject the station. The hub could be configured to send a specific SNMP trap to the NMS if this happens.

- In a bridge, the network administrator has configured the Learning Table to contain a maximum number of entries, let's say 1,000 addresses. If the table is full, then further frame addresses are not "learned" and traffic will be flooded to all ports on the bridge. Ideally the network administrator would like to know if the table is more than 80% filled. She would like the ability to set this *threshold* value into the bridge to allow it to send an SNMP trap to the NMS.

In the first example, we have a simple yes/no decision and a trap system can be designed and configured very easily. Moreover, the trap generation process can be inserted into the same code path as the security violation code. The second example is more complex. First, how do we detect that we have crossed the threshold? The only practical way is to allow the bridge CPU to poll the table on a regular basis. How often should we poll? The more often we poll, the faster we detect a problem, but the more CPU power we use. Second, where should we set the threshold? Is 80% realistic? Should it be 60% or 90%? In very complex devices like multiprotocol routers, thresholds are an essential aid to the SNMP trap process. The router should be shipped with appropriate default values for the thresholds, but they should be capable of being reset by the network administrator.

Today, the decision on which management strategy to use is being made on our behalf. As the size of networks increases, poll-based management is simply impractical. More and more SNMP-capable devices are being equipped with trap capabilities and some are beginning to use thresholds.

The Trap/Poll Paradigm

The true SNMP management paradigm suggests that managed devices generate a trap if they think something has gone wrong, but that the trap should just be a simple "help" message to the NMS. The NMS can then poll the managed device at its leisure and obtain the additional information it needs on the status of the device.

Trap/poll is widely implemented in SNMP systems today. Good quality managed devices will allow a wide range of configuration for the trap generation, with access to all MIB variable and the possibility to set thresholds.

12.3.2   What Kind of MIB?

MIB and MIB2

I've already described the MIB concept, with its extensible tree structure. I've also mentioned that the SNMP standards define a MIB structure for a generic TCP/IP device in the form of MIB2. In fact there are two ways that MIB or MIB2 can be extended to allow specific devices to be managed: Standard MIBs and Enterprise-Specific MIBs.

The Standard MIBs

Regardless of what you might read elsewhere, SNMP was originally designed to manage routers. Bridges, hosts, X.25 switches, Frame Relay devices, etc. These are all devices with special requirements. Each device can be thought to have certain common management functions and variables, just like a router. So, over the past four years or so, many standard MIBs have been published as RFCs. At the time of writing the list of these MIBs include:

- RFC 1271, Remote monitoring MIB (RMON)
- RFC 1253, OSPF 2 MIB
- RFC 1231, IEEE 802.5 Token Ring MIB
- RFC 1243, AppleTalk MIB

Although these MIBs have been defined, internetworking devices may already be using internal data representations of the same information. The situation in the market today is that commercially available devices such as routers and hubs are migrating towards these MIBs, but may have significant information stored in private MIB format.

12.3.3   The Security Question

Part of the SNMP hierarchy is the concept of a *community*. A community is the set of managed devices and NMSs that are controlled by a single organization. It's a little like the Autonomous System concept in IP routing. The community is an ASCII text string, case sensitive. The default name used by devices is "public."

If I attach an NMS to the network, I need to know the SNMP *community name* in order to manage any of the network devices. We could use community name as a kind of password, choosing something more obscure than "public," "Sales" or "Marketing." Community name is case-sensitive so the password alphabet is quite large (see Chapter 18). unfortunately there are a couple of drawbacks to this strategy. First, we need to enter the community name in each of the managed devices in the network. Since these devices can be out in the open and vulnerable to possible hostile network users, how can we be sure that the community names have not been compromised? If the managed device was a UNIX system, we can rely on the operating system security, but what if it's a DOS PC? Second, even if the community names were secure in the managed devices, they must be sent over the network on each transaction. SNMP does not define any form of encryption and even if it did, some governments (such as France) may prohibit the transmission of encrypted data over the network. Today the only authentication mechanism for SNMP is known as *trivial*. This means unencrypted community names and no authentication password. Even worse is that the community name is sent in clear text for every single SNMP transaction so extracting the name from the data stream is very easy.

The SNMP market chose a very simple approach to this issue: managed devices do not respond to SNMP set primitives. The usual phrase used is "look, but don't touch." Until recently, monitoring of SNMP devices was performed by popular packages like HP OpenView or NetView/6000. When the administrator wanted to reconfigure those units, they would invoke a Telnet process. Telnet is a little more secure than SNMP, at least there is a password protection. However, the Telnet password is sent in clear text so can be extracted from the data stream. It takes a little bit more work than SNMP since the Telnet password is only sent at logging time, so you have to be "listening" at the right moment (not a problem for the average hacker).

12.4 SNMP Shortcomings

SNMP is the de facto management protocol in use today. It is difficult to overstate its success over the past few years. However, the protocol has several obvious shortcomings. As an Internetwork Designer, you'll need to understand the relative importance of these issues, that can be summarized as:

- Security
- Bulk Information Transfer
- Hierarchical Management
- Performance and Error Reporting

Security

Without doubt, the "big problem" with SNMP is security. When it was defined in RFC 1067 and then updated in RFC 1157, the only security mechanism used by SNMP was the community name concept explained above. If we separate an internetwork into "sales" and "research" communities, the NMS in Sales could not manage the devices in Research because the Sales NMS does not belong to the community name "research." But what if we wanted to bypass this mechanism? How hard would it be? The answer is "not very." Community names are sent as clear text in every SNMP packet so if you have a network analyzer (or an Ethernet card equipped with certain public domain utilities) you can see the name directly. If you have access to a router console, you can read the community names on SNMP packets that are switched by the router rather easily.

If the authentication mechanism is so weak, how has SNMP become so popular? The reason is that manufacturers and users were willing to accept a limitation in the functionality of their SNMP management systems; they allowed SNMP **set** to be switched off in their managed devices. This meant that an entire generation of SNMP devices was implemented as "read-only" SNMP.

Until some form of Secure SNMP is available, users simply will not allow their systems to implement the SNMP set primitive. The risks of malicious, or even accidental reconfiguration are too great.

As an alternative, since it is possible to filter SNMP traffic using pattern matching, a Firewall Router (see Chapter 18) can be used to block management attempts from outside the corporate internetwork.

Bulk Information Transfer

Earlier in this Chapter I described the formation of tabular data structures within SNMP using the SEQUENCE and SEQUENCE OF defined data types. However, if we need to retrieve an entire Routing Table, we can only do this one row at a time with each SNMP get request. This is quite wasteful because a separate UDP-encapsulated get is required for each row and a UDP-encapsulated response will come back. The actual overhead is difficult to generalize because the SNMP community name and the Object ID for the requested managed object are variable in length, but we're looking at over 100 bytes for the two packets in wasted bandwidth.

Hierarchical Management

SNMP really succeeded at being simple. Originally, SNMP was deployed in routers and bridges. Now the list of network devices that support SNMP includes hubs, UNIX hosts, PCs and remote monitoring devices. This means that instead of managing tens of devices in a large network, we must manage hundreds, or even thousands. If all of this management information is coming back to a single NMS, then the NMS or the line connecting the NMS to the

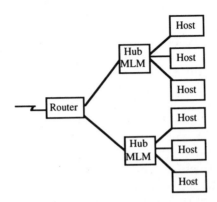

Figure 12.12: The Mid-Level Manager Concept

network will come under heavy load. It seems a good idea to develop some form of hierarchical management capability for SNMP.

In Figure 12.12, I show a simple corporate internetwork on a single site. Each department uses cable hubs to connect PCs into the network. A router is used to group the hubs and connect them to the WAN. The NMS is somewhere off-site, connected to the Corporate Backbone.

In Chapter 1 I discussed the concepts of Service Level Agreements as a tool to help us to define network requirements. In this case, we can think about the service levels we need for management. Ideally, we should install SNMP in every device that's capable of taking it. In this case, that means all the routers, hubs and hosts. We could end up with a lot of management traffic "leaking" onto the WAN, even using the economical benefits of the trap/poll paradigm. A better approach is to install a local *Mid-Level Manager* (MLM) to collect management information, summarize it and transmit the summaries to the central NMS. The local manager could be a smaller version of the Central NMS, or it could be a collection agent installed in the routers or hubs. Current SNMP doesn't describe the communication between an MLM and an NMS.

Performance and Error Reporting

I don't know too many networks that are currently concerned about SNMP performance, but the potential is growing as internetwork sizes increase. The performance issue for SNMP1 is tied up with so many individual problems. The Bulk Transfer problem means that we have excess overhead, and the lack of an error reporting protocol means that the NMS will re transmit invalid requests to the managed device because it doesn't know what else to do. The lack of SNMP security means that the much more bulky Telnet protocol is used to transfer configuration commands.

12.5 SNMP2

SNMP was designed to be an *interim* management architecture to be deployed in a limited fashion while committees were debating the intricacies of CMIS/CMIP. As it turned out, SNMP was *too* successful. So many manufacturers have implemented the protocol today that the momentum behind it seems to be unstoppable. Nevertheless, there are several fundamental limitations to the original SNMP that are becoming more critical as the deployment of the Internet and the ubiquity of SNMP increases.

I describe some of the limitations of SNMP above, so specific targets are set for the development of a replacement:

- Security
- Enhanced performance
- Agent-to-Manager error reporting
- Bulk information transfer
- Multiprotocol Operation (i.e., Independence from the IP stack)
- Manager-to-Manager communication

Secure SNMP

Not all of these deficiencies became clear when SNMP was first deployed. In fact, the first of these, security, was the dominating theme initially for reasons I explain below. The first set of standards to "fix" SNMP were known as *Secure SNMP* and I list the relevant RFCs in Table 12.3. These were published in July 1992.

Table 12.3: RFCs Relating to Secure SNMP

RFC #	Title
1321	The MD5 Message-Digest Algorithms
1351	SNMP Administration Model
1352	SNMP Security Protocols
1353	Definition of Managed Objects for SNMP Parties

While Secure SNMP was a useful prototype, it will not become an important protocol for management for three reasons:

- It only addresses one of several deficiencies in SNMP.

- The method of security implementation has resulted in an increase in message transactions. Since this was becoming a concern for SNMP, Secure SNMP would appear to be worse.

- Secure SNMP uses the DES Algorithm (see Chapter 17) for authentication and encryption. This algorithm is subject to US Dept. of Commerce export restrictions.

The Simple Management Protocol (SMP)

The *Simple Management Protocol* (SMP) is a holistic approach to the problems of SNMP. SMP drafts were published by Jeff Case, Keith McCloghrie, Marshall Rose and Steve Waldbusser in July 1992 (the same time as the Secure SNMP RFCs). The authors represent some of the early SNMP pioneers and this is reflected in the practical approach and scope of the project. There were four stated goals for SMP:

- Scope. SMP was deigned as a *management* protocol, not just a *network management* protocol. In theory it can be used to manage any form of system.

- Simplicity, Performance, Efficiency. These are related properties that are common in the TCP/IP world and extinct in the ISO universe.

- Security. This was the perceived "big problem" with SNMP.

- Compatibility. SNMP has an enormous installed base so a comprehensive coexistence and migration capability must be built in.

Like all the best draft proposals, SMP was the subject of great debate and discussion. Finally, the formula for the new generation SNMP, SNMP2, was devised as a synthesis between Secure SNMP and SMP. In the interim period, deployment of pure Secure SNMP products was discouraged within the Internet so that users would only be faced with a single migration (SNMP-SNMP2), rather than two (SNMP-Secure SNMP-SNMP2).

12.5.1   SNMP2

Security

Early implementation experience and comments from the SNMP2 working group indicated that Secure SNMP as I described above would produce additional traffic on the network due to multi-stage authentication procedures. Since the loading caused by management traffic was already a common concern amongst users, the SNMP2 working group decided to adopt the general outline of Secure SNMP, but to modify the operational procedures to improve performance. The other big problem with Secure SNMP is that its encryption mechanism is based on the *Data Encryption Standard* (DES) Algorithm. DES is a well known and mature algorithm, but is still subject to strict export controls by the US Department of Commerce. For this reason, Secure SNMP can never be implemented in an international network.

Table 12.4:   RFCs Relating to SNMP2

RFC #	Title
1441	Introduction to SNMPv2
1442	Structure of Management Information for SNMPv2
1443	Textual Conventions for SNMPv2
1444	Conformance Statements for SNMPv2
1445	SNMPv2 Administrative Model
1446	SNMPv2 Security Protocols
1447	SNMPv2 Party MIB
1448	Protocol Operations for SNMPv2
1449	Transport Mappings for SNMPv2
1450	Management Information Base for SNMPv2
1451	Manager-to-Manager MIB
1452	SNMPv1/SNMPv2 Coexistence

SNMP2 uses DES as its authentication and encryption mechanism, but its use is optional. While this means a return to insecure SNMP, it does mean that the overall network can be based on a single management protocol.

Enhanced Performance

In management terms, performance is measured in the number of management transactions that can be processed per second. Such a benchmark is only ever useful in a comparative sense. However, a good indication of the relative complexity of SNMP2 was shown in a test made at the Carnegie Mellon University. The results are summarized in Figure 12.13.

Agent to Manager Error Reporting

SNMP2 adds a significantly richer set of messages that can be used between the NMS and the managed device. This allows for acknowledgment of set primitives, as well as allowing the managed device to signal that it has a problem answering the NMS poll. In SNMP, if an agent can't answer an NMS poll, the NMS will probably just keep trying and make the situation worse. For example, let's say an NMS polls a router for some variables in the X.25 MIB. If the router

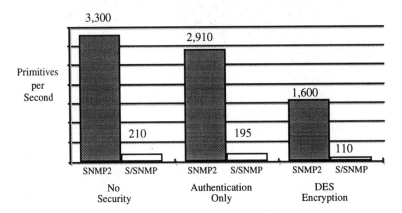

Figure 12.13: SNMP and SNMP2 Relative Performance

doesn't have X.25 installed, how should it answer? The only approach that makes sense is to ignore the request. The NMS will assume that the router didn't hear the first request and will re transmit several times. SNMP2 adds the simple feature of a messaging protocol so that the router can send back the equivalent of "I don't have that information."

Bulk Information Transfer

Bulk information transfer is required in many data communications activities today. Common examples are the transfer of tabular data structures such as ARP caches, Learning Tables or Routing Tables.

The original SNMP required multiple get primitives, each in its own IP packet to complete a table transfer. SNMP2 simplifies the process by defining a new primitive: *getbulk*.

Multiprotocol Operation

SNMP operates over UDP, which operates over IP. This tends to upset the OSI and Novell community so SNMP2 was designed from the beginning as a multiprotocol management system. The programming interface is now defined so that the application developer does not need to administer UDP ports directly. This feature goes beyond the earlier efforts to define SNMP over other transport types.

Manager to Manager Communication

I described the MLM function earlier and said that it allows us to develop hierarchical managed networks. SNMP2 defines a new set of Manager-to-Manager communication functions that basically standardize the role of the

MLM.   Previously, MLMs were restricts to proprietary communication mechanisms.

12.6 CMIS/CMIP

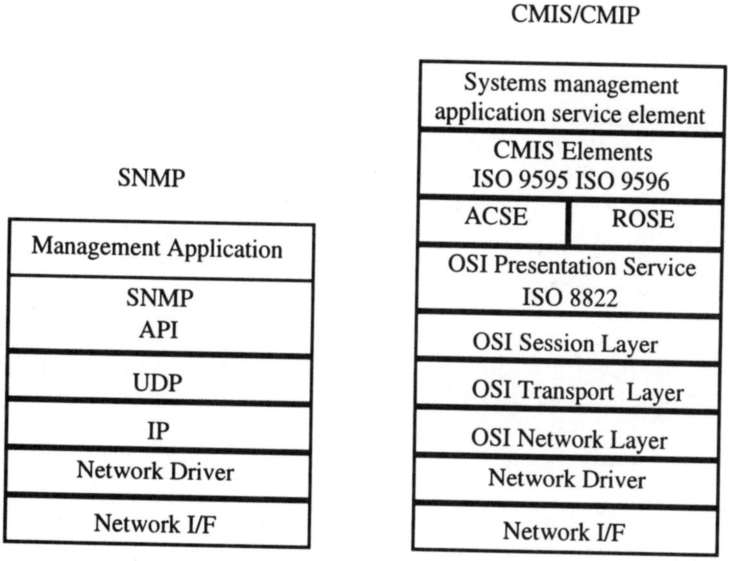

CMIS/CMIP

Systems management application service element	
CMIS Elements ISO 9595 ISO 9596	
ACSE	ROSE
OSI Presentation Service ISO 8822	
OSI Session Layer	
OSI Transport Layer	
OSI Network Layer	
Network Driver	
Network I/F	

SNMP

Management Application
SNMP API
UDP
IP
Network Driver
Network I/F

Figure 12.14:   SNMP and CMIS/CMIP Compared

I've been a little bit cynical about the *Common Management Information Service/Common Management Information Protocol* (CMIS/CMIP) issue in my description so far and I don't intend to repent now. However, I'd like to put the CMIS/CMIP issue into context with a few facts and opinions:

- CMIS/CMIP is the ISO management system. I compare it to SNMP in Figure 12.14.

- CMIS had some good ideas, but was handicapped by its dependence on the ISO Transport and Network Layers and by the heavy overhead imposed by these layers.

- A small consortium of vendors developed CMOT (Common Management over TCP/IP). This went down like a sausage at a Bar Mitzvah. As far as I can remember, vendors hated CMOT because it took a long time for their programmers to figure out how to use the protocol. Users hated it because it took lots of CPU power and RAM and that meant that their 1988-vintage networking devices couldn't support it.

- SNMP killed off CMOT within one year. TCP/IP continues to fight off any challenge from ISO. Therefore, SNMP continues to dominate the market.

- CMIS is actually becoming more relevant today because it includes many of the features that people say are lacking in SNMP. However, most people think that the installed base of SNMP and the overlap between SNMP and SNMP2 will prevent CMIS/CMIP from taking hold. There's still that problem with the ISO stack dependency too.

- CMIS/CMIP is used extensively in carrier networks (like PTTs, RBOCs, Inter-LATA Carriers, etc.). In these networks, the expense of CMIS/CMIP is justified by the cost of the managed devices (hundreds of thousands of dollars each) and the NMS (up to a million dollars for a redundant system). However, most observers would agree that the carrier model simply cannot be ported to the end user market.

- The compromise being considered by many carriers today is to use CMIS/CMIP within the carrier network, but SNMP (or SNMP2) within the user network.

This final point is probably a good description of the future for CMIS/CMIP.

12.7 Living With NetView

Most proprietary management schemes are now dying out in favor of SNMP. One notable exception is IBM's NetView management architecture. NetView is designed to manage an IBM Mainframe network and most of the associated devices. NetView runs on an IBM mainframe, with intelligent terminal access through an application known as NetView/PC. In addition, IBM manage LAN equipment (SR Bridges, 8209s and intelligent cabling hubs) using the LAN Manager agent (not to be confused with Microsoft's LAN Manager which is a Network Operating System). Finally, IBM's 6611 router is managed using SNMP. Quite a confusing range of management strategies.

IBM users who are serious about management will be quite accustomed to multiple terminals and non-integrated management architectures. For that reason, there should be no problem in agreeing to an SNMP NMS in addition to the existing management systems.

NetView/6000

The light at the end of the tunnel may come in the form of NetView/6000. This management application runs on an IBM RS/6000 UNIX machine and was developed from HP's OpenView (IBM claim to have created 60% of the code for NetView/6000 from scratch). This means that full SNMP management capabilities are offered in an IBM-badged device. In addition, NetView/6000 offers gateway capabilities into the old NetView equipment and the LAN Manager platform. The hope is that at least one of these two management architectures will become fully integrated in the next few years.

12.8 Summary

- Management is a critical issue in the Internetwork.

- The current standard management system for TCP/IP is SNMP.

- SNMP offers excellent monitoring capabilities today, but its lack of security means that it is rarely used for configuration purposes.

- SNMP utilizes a tree-structured database called the MIB to store management information.

- MIBs are written as ASCII text files, in a format defined by the SMI BER. The BER is a subset of an ISO standard, ASN.1.

- A core MIB, currently MIB2, describes most of the generic functions in the TCP/IP world.

- Experimental MIBs have been written and described in RFCs for various generic network technologies. At least one of these MIBs (the RMON MIB) has been integrated directly as an extension of MIB2. Most Experimental MIBs are allocated a separate portion of the MIB tree.

- Private MIBs are written by individual manufacturers to describe specific features of their products. These Private MIBs can be obtained (usually free of charge) from the appropriate manufacturer and can be compiled into the NMS using an ASN.1 Compiler.

- SNMP has four major drawbacks: no security; no hierarchy; no error reporting; tied to a UDP API.

- Secure SNMP was written to address the security concerns of SNMP.

- As a long term successor to SNMP, SNMP2 was designed to address all of the major concerns about SNMP.

- CMIS/CMIP is the ISO management framework. Due to its complexity and the lack of enthusiasm in the market for ISO networking systems, CMIS/CMIP is largely irrelevant for internetwork management.

- CMIS/CMIP is used by telecommunications carriers.

- NetView is the IBM management architecture and uses SNA protocols for management communication. Gateway products exist to link NetView to SNMP.

12.9 References

[1]   Marshall T. Rose. *The Simple Book.* Prentice-Hall (Englewood Cliffs, NJ), 1994.

[2]   K. McCloghrie. M. Rose. "Structure and Identification of Management Information for TCP/IP-based Internets." *RFC 1155.* May 1990.

[3]   K. McCloghrie. M. Rose. "Management Information Base for Network Management of TCP/IP-based internets." *RFC 1156.* May 1990.

[4]   M. Schoffstall. M. Fedor. J. Davin. J. Case. "A Simple Network Management Protocol (SNMP)." *RFC 1155.* May 1990.

[5]   William Stallings. *SNMP, SNMPv2 and CMIP: The Practical Guide to Network-Management Standards.* Addison-Wesley (Reading , MA), 1993.

Section 3

DESIGN SPECIFICS

CHAPTER 13

Designing for IP

> *Completion of any task within the allocated time and budget does not bring credit upon the performing personnel, it merely proves the task was easier than expected. (IEEE Spectrum)*
>
> **Pratt's Second Law, First Interpretation**

13.1 Introduction

Every communication protocol has its own characteristic features that will have a major impact on the way that a network is designed. IP is no exception. In this chapter, you should find a structured description of these characteristics to allow you to design a scaleable internetwork system from the very beginning.

The approach I'll take is to:

- Remind you of the hierarchical behavior of IP addressing and look at ways that the IP hierarchy can be matched to a business hierarchy.

- Discuss the question of centralized address registration and describe the favored alternative to registration.

- Look at the Domain Name System, a very powerful tool for centralized resource naming.

- Offer a mechanism for specific address allocation for Network and Subnet ID *within* your organization.

- Finish off with a look at the protocol that already exist within IP to actually distribute these addresses to the host systems in your internetwork.

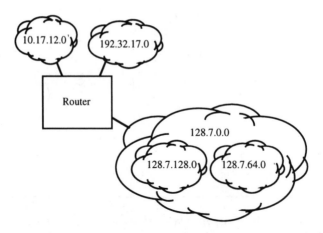

Figure 13.1: Logical View of IP Network from a Router

13.2 Understanding the IP Hierarchy

IP was developed as a hierarchical addressing scheme. The concept of Network ID, Subnet ID and Host ID offers an excellent level of control over the network design.

However, IP is a mature protocol. On the one hand it means that many of the initial teething problems have been removed by natural selection. On the other hand, we live in a rapidly changing world and statements like this tends to imply that the protocol may be nearing the end of its useful life!

I don't think IP is quite ready to retire just yet, but in the area of hierarchical addressing and configuration, it tends to show its age. In this chapter I'll offer some advice to help you extract the maximum amount of useful life from this protocol and to design scaleable IP internetworks.

13.2.1   Match IP Hierarchy to Organization Structure

Figure 13.1 shows the logical view from an example IP Router. In this case, the Class A network 10.0.0.0 appears as a single amorphous address space because no subnetting information is passed into the router. The Class C network 192.32.17.0 is not subnetted. The Class B network 128.7.0.0 is subnetted and the subnet information about networks 128.7.128.0 and 128.7.64.0 is passed into the Router by the appropriate Routing Protocol.

As I described in Chapter 11, this router is able to make intelligent switching decisions once this address structure is defined and configured in the Routing Table.

The problem is that the limited hierarchical model offered by IP addressing doesn't always fit with the structure of our organizations. An obvious example is that of subnetting. Wouldn't it be nice if all our workgroups were made up of about 250 hosts? Then we could make all of our subnets eight bits long.

In most real network designs, we have to answer questions such as:

- Should we use a registered or private IP addressing scheme?

- What subnet structure should we implement?

- How should we assign addresses?

- How should we implement hierarchical naming?

- How does the physical topology of our network relate to our addressing structure?

- How can we limit our Broadcast Domains?

- How do we establish Routing Firewalls?

- How do we configure routers?

- How do we configure hosts?

- Can we devise a Management Hierarchy?

13.3 Designing Naming Systems

Most of the examples I've given so far in this book have used numerical IP addresses. In production networks, IP addresses are rather clumsy for humans to remember and use so the normal method of operating is with *names*.

In the TCP/IP naming system, IP addresses are associated with a clear text, ASCII name such as "fred," or "university." The association between the name and the address is made using a lookup table. For example, let's say that I want to log onto a UNIX machine. Normally I'd type:

telnet 192.32.17.5

...and that will get me to the machine, assuming that IP is working OK. But wouldn't it be more friendly if I could just type in:

telnet SERVER

Within the host that I'm using, the IP software has to find out the IP address represented by the name "SERVER[1]." The first place that the software will look is in the *hosts file*. This is a standard ASCII text file that you would store on your host. In a UNIX system, the file is normally installed in the "/etc" directory. On PCs, the location will vary with the manufacturer of the TCP/IP software.

---

[1]Note, DNS names are not case sensitive, so "SERVER" and "server" are equivalent.

```
;                      use semicolons for comment lines
;
; IP address          name                alias
;
192.32.17.0           loopback
192.32.17.1           def_router          router          gateway
192.32.17.25          Harry               h
192.32.17.88          Sally               s
192.32.17.5           server_sales        server          srv
128.7.254.9           server_corp_sales   main_sales      ms
```

Figure 13.2:   Sample Hosts File

The hosts file has a very simple format and I show an example in Figure 13.2.

As you can see from the above structure, the IP address is resolved against a name. Names can become quite long in a Domain Naming environment so users are allowed to adopt one or more *alias* names. In the case of the server in sales, its formal name is "server_sales," but its alias is "server." Note that each user of a hosts file may have a different "server" entry. The entry that is in the machine you are using is the one that will take effect.

Most IP implementations will search the hosts file for name resolutions before resorting to other means. The problem with the hosts file system is that as the network increases in size, then manual setup and maintenance of distributed tables can be very hard work indeed. Even so, most hosts will be configured with a small hosts file entry for "permanent," frequently-used resources such as default routers.

To go beyond the hosts file, we use the Domain Name System.

13.3.1   Domain Name System

Centralized control of names becomes critical as the internetwork increases in size. The *Domain Name System* (DNS) is the Internet standard mechanism for name registration and resolution. In fact, when you attach to the Internet, your organization must undertake to configure and maintain a primary and backup DNS server.

DNS allows any IP address to be replaced by an alphanumeric name and these names are somewhat easier for us to remember and to apply an organizational structure.

DNS is hierarchical, with each level separated by a dot. While DNS specifies this format, it doesn't say what each level should represent. For some users, the hierarchy of a name could be:

{host} . {department} . {site name} . {company name}

While for an academic user, the structure might appear as:

{host} . {room#} . {building} . {campus} . {university}

In the Internet, IANA has defined a simple structure for names that should be quite familiar to you. At the top level are addressing types. These include "edu" (educational organization), "com" (commercial organization), "mil" (the military). They also include standard 2-letter country codes.

DNS is a client/server protocol. Any IP host can operate as a DNS client. The DNS server is set up somewhere on the internetwork. It makes sense to set up a DNS server on the same site as clients. In this way, client requests are answered quickly and without wasting WAN bandwidth.

Names can be registered by the NIC in exactly the same way as IP addresses and such registration should be done at the same time. For registered names, the NIC defines specific top level names that broadly represent the nature of the user site. Universities have a ."edu" identifier, for example. Below this, we'd expect the name of the university, for example "cmu.edu" for Carnegie-Mellon. The Network Administration at CMU would be responsible for assigning names for lower level entities, like departments.

There are two basic scaleability advantages that DNS enjoys. First, any DNS server is allowed to pass on a name request that it does not recognize to a "higher authority." Second, when we state a name that we're trying to reach, then we only need to give as much of the name as is necessary to "leave" our domain and "enter" the destination domain.

For example, let's say there are two hosts at CMU. One is called *zinfandel.chem.cmu.edu*. The other is called *cadillac.physed.cmu.edu*. In fact the hosts are in two different departments: Chemistry and Physical Education. If I'm sitting at *zinfandel* and I want to telnet into the host *cadillac*, I would only need to type:

telnet cadillac.physed

...and not the whole DNS name for *cadillac*. However, if I was in another organization entirely, e.g. sitting at a host called *sophia.valbonne.wellfleet.com* I would need to type:

telnet.cadillac.physed.cmu.edu

Note that users are not normally assigned individual domain names. Instead, each user attached to a given mail server would be denoted by a user name and the "@" separator.

13.4 Registered or Private Addressing?

This is certainly one of the more important questions you should ask during the design phase. Even a couple of years ago (1992), it wasn't clear that Internet attachment was a good thing for most commercial organizations. Today there is no doubt. Internet attachment offers positive benefits for most types of business.

However, just because a few engineers in your design department want to attach to the Internet, does this mean that your entire organization must be constrained by Internet addressing? Remember that if you request address space from the NIC today, you'll almost certainly receive Class C addresses. Using conventional subnetting doesn't give you much flexibility with a Class C address. If you decide to subnet a Class C address, you *must* subnet within a byte boundary and your subnets can't be very big. Going beyond the simple problems of address design, Routing Table size puts a fundamental limit on the scale of Class C address proliferation. To put it simply, there are around 2,000,000 possible Class C addresses. If all of these addresses were allocated, then every IP AS Boundary router in the Internet would need to be able to store *all* of these networks as *individual* entries in its Routing Table.

For most commercial networks, there is a very simple alternative and that is to implement private addressing schemes. In the past, private addressing was an easy option in the short term, but sooner or later, we would have to pay the price if we ever needed Internet connection.

In reality, Internet connection *does not* imply an Internet addressing scheme for the entire organization. However, to take advantage of this design method, we need to assume a few things about our Internet connection:

- There is a high requirement for access security.
- We can define specific applications that require Internet access.
- The performance limitation to our Internet access is the WAN connection line speed.

If these conditions are true, or largely true, then we can implement a very powerful design method called the *Application Host* (actual names for this method vary).

Let's look at some arguments you can use to satisfy the conditions for an Application Host system.

13.4.1 Security

This is a complex issue to which I've devoted an entire chapter. The Internet was developed as an open communication channel and is used by some of the most intelligent and innovative folks around. So the security threat from an Internet attachment is *very* real. If you're seriously considering attaching your corporate network to the Internet, then you must consider a security policy. Take a look at Chapter 17 for some detailed suggestions.

In a normal network, most of our applications can be classified as one of the following:

- Terminal Emulation
- File Transfer
- Remote Job Execution
- Electronic Mail
- Network Management

However, if we attach to the Internet, it's unlikely that we'll have to transfer Network Management traffic. Our SNMP traffic will probably pass exclusively over our intra-company network.

For RJE traffic, such as client/server, the Internet may not be the best pathway. Client/server is a greedy architecture when it comes to bandwidth. Whereas bandwidth is given away with cornflakes in the USA, it is a very expensive commodity in the rest of the world and will continue to be so for the foreseeable future. So Client/Server over the Internet may be restricted to areas with high bandwidth local service.

So we can limit our Internet connectivity requirements to Terminal Emulation, File Transfer and Mail. This is a vital consideration for the addressing requirements, as well as for a structured security strategy. I discuss this in more detail in Chapter 17.

In this limited connectivity scheme, we can make use of Application Hosts to allow us to build our Corporate Internetwork on a private addressing scheme, while still offering Internet access to the entire organization. I show the schematic of an Application Host network in Figure 13.3.

First of all let me explain this scenario without explicit addresses. Hosts within the Corporate Network are assigned private addresses, i.e., addresses that are not explicitly registered with the NIC.

Communication between hosts *within* the Corporate Network operates just as in any IP network.

To access the Internet, a host in the Corporate Network would log onto the appropriate Application Host. For Terminal Emulation to an internet host for example, the top machine in Figure 13.3 would be chosen. This login could be automated by the System Administrator to hide the process from an inexperienced user. Once logged onto the Application Host, the Telnet Client program is configured to use an Internet-registered address for outbound communication.

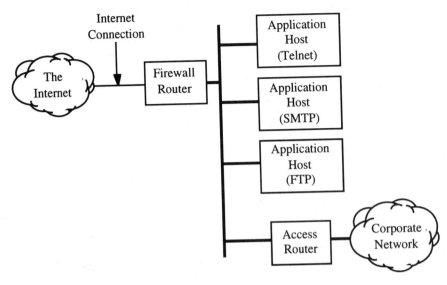

Figure 13.3:   Application Hosts

The beauty of this system is that a 10,000-user Corporate Network can be "hidden" behind a single IP address in the Application Host.

13.4.2   Performance

There are a few more things to say about this technique. First, the bandwidth issue. When I explain the technique, most designers object to the bottleneck that the Application Host represents. In fact, this probably isn't true. In Figure 13.3 I've highlighted the Internet Connection line. For most organizations in Europe, the speed of this line is limited to 64kbps. Even in the USA, it's unlikely that you would use much more than a T1 connection (1.54Mbps). To make sure that the connection is the bottleneck, we just throw a few more MIPS at the Application Host. In Figure 13.3, I've separated the load over three separate Application Hosts, one for each application. There's no reason why two or even three applications couldn't be configured on a single Application Host.

The second objection is usually the reliability aspect. What happens if the Application Host goes down? There are several solutions to this problem. The first is to perform a risk analysis of the network to see if the Application Host really is the most likely point of failure. If it is, we could choose a more reliable system such as a Tandem or Stratus non-stop computer. While these can be expensive compared to low cost, high performance workstations, they do offer the last word in reliability. Another alternative I have seen is for an enterprising Network Administrator to write a simple UNIX application to allow a backup, low cost workstation to be installed on the same LAN. If the primary workstation failed, the backup workstation assumes all of the address identity of

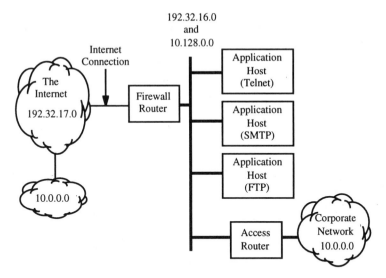

Figure 13.4:   The Route Advertisement Problem

the primary (including Ethernet MAC address) and takes over the job. All active sessions are lost in this scenario, however.

In Figure 13.4 I've shown an Internet Firewall Router. Firewalls are discussed below and in Chapter 17 and their primary job is to allow access filters to be installed for security purposes. But there is one other reason for us to go to the expense of a Firewall Router these days. An Internet connection will involve thousands of routes being sent into the access point. Although it's possible to directly attach an Access Host to the Internet feed, this isn't wise because host IP implementations just aren't designed for it.

The final point of elegance is the inclusion of an Access Router into the Corporate Network. This router mainly provides connectivity into the private address space, but can also be used as an additional filtering location.

13.4.3   Private Address Space

I've said that the address space that we use *within* the Corporate Network doesn't have to be Internet-registered, but there is still a risk of address collision, and to explain why I need to assign some addresses.

In Figure 13.4 I've added a few addresses into the Access Host model. For our Corporate Network, we've decided to use a Class A address: 10.0.0.0. We have a couple of Internet-registered Class C addresses: 192.32.16.0 and 192.32.17.0.

The small LAN segment for our Access Hosts has a "dual identity" because it needs to have addresses in the Internet-registered space of 192.32.16.0 and in

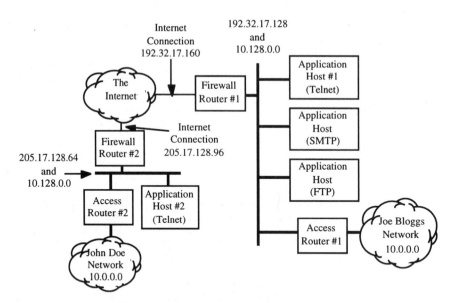

Figure 13.5:   Private Internetworking Using RFC 1597 Guidelines

the Corporate address space, in this case a subnet 10.128.0.0 (I've used a mask of 255.255.255.0).

Everything is just fine, except for one small problem. Somewhere in the Internet, there is a valid, registered address of 10.0.0.0. Routers in this network will advertise its presence using EGP or BGP. Similarly, routers in the Corporate Network will advertise their presence to the Firewall Router using an appropriate IGP. How can the Firewall Router tell the difference?

In the past, it required careful design and lists of exception handlers in the router software. Today, the Route Advertisement problems have been solved by RFC 1597 [3]. This document simply describes a set of address blocks that have been reserved by the IETF for Private Network use. Class A, B, and C addresses are available.

Figure 13.5 shows the effect of implementing an internetwork using the RFC 1597 guidelines.

In this design, we have two organizations: Joe Bloggs Ltd. and John Doe Inc. Both companies have been allocated a single Class C address by the NIC. Joe Bloggs received 192.32.17.0 and John Doe 206.17.128.0. Both companies have decided to use three bits of subnet on these addresses; in other words a mask of 255.255.224.0. Three bits would normally give us eight possible subnets, but remember that an "all-1's" and "all-0's" subnet is illegal. Table 13.1 shows the list of possible subnets for John Doe in decimal, with a binary representation of the final byte.

Table 13.1: Possible 3-bit Subnets for 206.17.128.0

Subnet	Final Byte (binary)	Comment
206.17.128.0	00000000	Illegal
206.17.128.128	100000000	Valid
206.17.128.192	11000000	Valid
206.17.128.224	11100000	Valid
206.17.128.64	01000000	Valid
206.17.128.96	01100000	Valid
206.17.128.160	10100000	Valid
206.17.128.224	11100000	Illegal*

*   Note: An "all-1's" subnet is illegal, but some router implementations may allow it to be used.

Both companies have chosen to use address 10.0.0.0 as their private IP address. Hopefully you are happy with the way that hosts *within* either of these organizations can communicate with each other. Now let's consider how a host in Joe Bloggs can log on as a terminal using Telnet to a host in John Doe.

Step 1

The host within Joe Bloggs will have an IP address within the private 10.0.0.0 address space. The user on this machine is aware that the host they are connecting to is external to the organization, and so logs onto the Telnet Application Host #1. Remember that this host has two addresses; incoming Telnet clients will attach to a private 10.0.0.0 address, and will then invoke an outbound Telnet Client session using an Internet-registered address on the Application Host. Potentially, all the machines in Joe Bloggs could use a single IP address to perform outbound Telnet sessions.

Step 2

The session is now from the Application Host #1 and is Internet-registered with an address on subnet 192.32.17.128. The Firewall Router #1 is able to route the new Telnet session over to the John Doe Firewall Router #2, where a further login is required.

Step 3

The login to Application Host #2 is made to an incoming Internet-registered address. Once the login is complete, a third Telnet session is started which now has an address in the private space 10.0.0.0.

Step 4

The Application Host #2 Telnet session passes into the John Doe network though Access Router #2 and onward to the required destination.

This procedure may seem a little tedious, but it certainly works. The two major concerns are the aspect of security and performance. Because multiple Telnet sessions are acting "back to back," does the user see a poorer response time? The answer is probably yes, although Telnet response over the Internet is a bit patchy even with a direct connection. The additional response delay caused by the multiple sessions may not be too noticeable. The good news is that for file transfers, the delay imposed by additional FTP sessions is "smoothed out" of the system because of the pipelining effect of the FTP protocol. Electronic mail is always a store-and-forward system, so response time is basically unaffected.

The security question is more important. Because of the complex nature of this transaction, some Network Administrators are tempted to automate the process with scripts. Some of these scripts store passwords in clear text, or use system-wide passwords. I discuss the issue of security in more detail in Chapter 17, but to put it briefly, please avoid the temptations to *completely* automate these logins.

13.4.4   Routing Advertisements

In the RFC 1597 scheme, we can vastly simplify the job of filtering routing information. In simple terms, we want the Firewall Routers in each of these organizations *not* to advertise the reachability of network 10.0.0.0 out of their Internet-attached port. Thanks to the RFC, we can be sure that no Internet-registered network will *ever* have the address 10.0.0.0, so we can be safe in applying this filter.

13.5 Address and Subnet Allocation

Whether we use private, or Internet-registered addresses, a major part of our design work is in the allocation of IP addresses within the corporation.

13.5.1   Addressing at Joe Bloggs

Here is one possible design strategy that Joe Bloggs Ltd. might adopt if they decide to use a Class B address; 128.7.0.0. Now the designer of the network has carefully read the appropriate RFC on subnetting; currently RFC 950 [2].

This RFC specifies a procedure for subnetting using the bit-mask technique I described in Chapters 3 and 4. The problem is that RFC 950 leaves far too many loopholes and options to be interpreted by different vendors and even by follow-on RFCs. I can summarize these loopholes as:

- RFC 950 *recommends* that the subnet mask be contiguous, but doesn't make it obligatory. I've not yet heard a good reason for non-contiguous subnet masks when you consider the havoc that this practice causes for diagnostic purposes.

- RFC 950 *recommends* that the subnet bits occupy the *most significant* part of the Host ID field, but a mask of 255.255.0.255 is actually quite valid for a Class B address.

- RFC 950 *implies* that different subnets of the same network could have different length masks, but doesn't state it as a requirement for routing protocols. Hence RIP and IGRP are within their rights to require equal length masks throughout the same Network ID.

If an intelligent and resourceful designer proceeds to design an addressing scheme based on this interpretation of subnetting, we might expect something like this.

Step 1 Subnet Structure

Decide to use 8 bit subnet masks throughout the network. This allows up to 254 hosts to be supported on each LAN segment.

Step 2 Subnet Allocation

As each department comes on stream to the backbone, allocate the next subnet number from the list. In Figure 1, we see that Sales in London was first on line so was given address 128.7.1.0, Sales in Paris and Rome were next with 128.7.2.0 and 128.7.3.0 respectively. The Support departments on each site followed as I show in Figure 13.6.

Step 3 Host Address Allocation

The network administrator at Joe Bloggs realized that hosts on the network perform different functions. Most were workstations, PCs, Macs,, etc., the *clients* of the network. The remainder of the network hosts were *servers* or *service providers*. These include conventional file and print servers, but also access servers such as routers or gateways. The client machines were allocated addresses starting at 1 and working up. The server machines were allocated addresses starting at 254 and working down, with address 254 *always* assigned to the default router for this segment.

Step 4 Routing Protocol

For simplicity and because it provided all the functions Joe Bloggs needed, RIP was chosen as the routing protocol within the Joe Bloggs Autonomous System.

This allocation plan is perfectly logical and each of these steps can be argued as sensible in isolation. The problems with this plan arise because of the interaction between the IP address structure and other external factors.

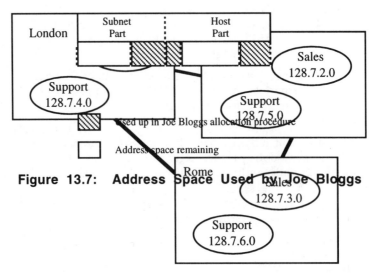

Figure 13.7:   Address Space Used by Joe Bloggs

Figure 13.6:   Joe Bloggs Initial Address Allocation

Subnet Allocation Problems

First of all, is a static 8-bit subnet structure really such a good idea? In Chapters 3 and 4 I discussed how serial lines in an IP network generally need to assigned addresses for routing purposes. The two end nodes on a serial line take only 2 out of a possible 254 addresses; hardly an efficient use of address space.

While it may be possible to configure un-numbered serial links between routers from the same vendor, this feature is not currently interoperable (we have to wait for the new Router Requirements draft to reach formal RFC status).

The real problem with this subnet allocation procedure is that it leaves the designer no leeway to increase the maximum number of hosts supported on a segment above 254. Now I personally would not recommend such a large number of machines on a single segment, but I've always worked for router manufacturers or resellers and the smaller the number of machines per segment, the more router ports we sell. But if the Joe Bloggs designer *wanted* to put 300 nodes on a single segment, he wouldn't be able to do so because if he tries to extend the Host ID field by reducing the subnet mask for certain segments to 7 bits, he has already used the *least* significant bit subnet number 1. You can see this quite clearly in Figure 13.7. If we decrease the subnet mask from 255.255.255.0, we "collide" with the shaded part at the bottom of the Subnet ID space. This is a nuisance because we've actually got space in reserve at the *top* of the Subnet ID field.

If the designer is really determined to extend his host field, he'll have to reallocate the host addresses on subnet 128.7.1.0, modify all the host tables and DNS entries, and so on. If he wants to go further and steal 2 bits of the subnet mask, he's got a real job ahead of him because he'll have to reallocate addresses on 128.7.1.0, 128.7.2.0 and 128.7.3.0.

A similar problem occurs if he wants to increase the number of subnets. By *increasing* the size of the subnet field, we "collide" with the "special" host addresses we thought were a good idea.

Problems With Routing Protocols

The second problem is with Step 2. This method of allocating subnets will actually cause Joe Bloggs to miss out on an important OSPF feature called summarisation. In Figure 13.6, you can see the initial deployment of Joe Bloggs subnets. Consecutive subnets are scattered into different parts of the internetwork. When we come to design the OSPF area structure, then the routing updates for each subnet will be sent as a specific Link State Update. If consecutive subnets of the same IP Network ID are contained within the same OSPF area, then their routing updates are summarized into a *range* of addresses. Note that these subnets must fall within one or more *nibble* (4 bits) boundaries. So subnets 1..15, 16..31, etc. can be summarized. In this case I suppose you could argue that he's chosen RIP anyway, which can't summarize subnets.

13.5.2 Addressing at Jane Doe

An alternative method is used at Jane Doe Inc., where the network designer has been fortunate enough to glance through RFC 1219 [4].

This RFC describes a rather different method for subnet allocation based on a couple of simple assumptions:

- When a network is designed, we don't always know how big our subnets will need to be in the future.

- We need to be able to allocate variable length subnets to cope with different physical network requirements and growth rates.

The method used in RFC 1219 is so obvious that you feel embarrassed that you thought of allocating addresses any other way. To summarize the rules in two sentences:

- Start numbering subnets from the *most significant* bit of the Host ID field.

- Start numbering hosts from the *least significant* bit of the Host ID field.

In Figure 13.8 you can see the logic of this technique. Having decided on the basic subnet mask, say 255.255.255.0, the designer now has the freedom to change her mind in the future. If the mask is *decreased* to allow more hosts on a segment, then there is no risk of "collision" with low numbered subnets. If the

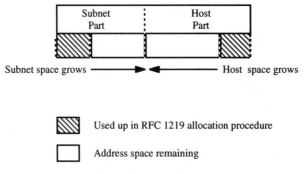

**Figure 13.8:   RFC 1219 Subnet/Host Address
Allocation**

mask is *increased* in size to allow more subnets, then there is no risk of
"collision" with high numbered hosts.

There is one psychological problem with RFC 1219: the so-called *Mirror Image
Counting*. This kind of counting is required for the Subnet ID field. As you
can see, converting from the "mirrored" binary to decimal produces some
strange progressions for subnets!

Table 13.2:   RFC 1219 Host and Subnet Allocation Order

Host ID (binary)	Host ID (decimal)	Subnet ID (binary)	Subnet ID (decimal)
00000001	1	10000000	128
00000010	2	01000000	64
00000011	3	11000000	192
:	:	:	:
11111100	252	00111111	63
11111101	253	10111111	191
11111110	254	01111111	127

But don't panic! Remember that with RFC 1219, the order of subnet allocation
may be bizarre, but the Host IDs are allocated in simple numerical sequence.
Once you've decided on the format of address allocation, you have to get those
addresses into the hosts and routers on the internetwork.

13.6 Host Configuration

IP has been a remarkably adaptable and long-lived networking technology in terms of its addressing scheme and the various routing protocols that have been developed during its history. For host configuration, however, IP definitely shows its age. While the protocol family contains many features and functions for assisting the network administrator, these are spread over a range of different protocols. These include:

• Reverse Address Resolution Protocol (RARP)

• Boot Protocol (BOOTP)

• ICMP Get Subnet Mask

• Router Discovery

• Dynamic Host Configuration Protocol

I summarize the functions of these protocols in Table 13.3. In general these protocols were developed to allow diskless workstations to boot over a network, but they are becoming very useful in general IP networks to provide a means for centralized administration. As you can see from this table, we can't just use one of these protocols; we must select two or more to provide a complete diskless boot capability.

Note: In addition to these standard protocols, some of the early IP pioneers such as Sun Microsystems, developed their own procedures for booting diskless workstations.

13.6.1   An Outline of the Problem

Let's review the problems for a system administrator trying to set up an individual IP workstation. In Figure 13.8 I show a typical installation.

Imagine that you're the administrator that has to install this host onto an IP network. What parameters do you need to set up to make it work? Even in the minimum installation, you'll need to type in:

• The host IP address

• The subnet mask

• The IP address of the Default Router

• (Possibly) the IP address of an Alternate Router

• The IP address of the Domain Name Server (or equivalent)

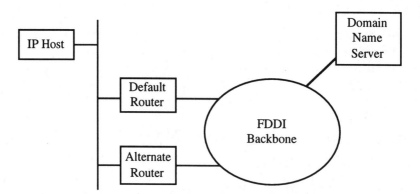

Figure 13.8:   Typical IP Host Installation

Table 13.3:   Review of IP Boot Protocols

	ICMP (get mask)	ICMP (router discovery)	RARP	BOOTP	DHCP	TFTP
Subnet Determination	Yes	No	No	No	No	No
Locate Default Router	No	Yes	No	Maybe	Maybe	No
Static Address Allocation	No	No	Yes	Yes	Yes	No
Dynamic Address Allocation	No	No	No	No	Yes	No
Config & O/S Transfer	No	No	No	No	No	Yes
Operation through router	No	N/A	No	Yes	Yes	Yes

All of these parameters are decided by the Network Administrator; this is one of the design benefits of IP. However, it does make it difficult for us to automate the configuration process. While it might only take a couple of minutes to enter this information into an individual host, imagine the scaleability problem in a network of hundreds or thousands of hosts. Like other networking issues such as cabling, address allocation is also under pressure because of "Moves and Changes" within the organization and especially due to the widespread use of mobile computers.

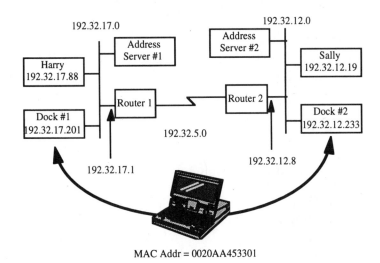

MAC Addr = 0020AA453301

Figure 13.9:   Address Allocation for Mobile Computers

13.6.2   Mobile Computers

Mobile computers pose a special problem from the IP address point of view. I show the problem in Figure 13.9.

Harry and Sally are using desktop computers and as a designer you can decide whether to use manual address allocation, or to use some form of automated system. However, the sales and service teams are issued with portable computers. Some of these are equipped with internal Ethernet adapters, some use "docking stations," as shown in Figure 13.9. A portable user has two problems when he or she attaches to Dock #1. First of all, they need to determine the IP address that's been assigned to the dock. Secondly, they need to know that at Dock#1, their default router address is 192.32.17.1. However, if they attach to Dock#2, their IP address and default router address change. How can we take care of this?

In this case, I've shown two "Boot Servers." I won't be more specific at the moment, since I discuss the capabilities of different protocols below. On Boot Server #1, there is a table entry as shown in Figure 13.10. As you can see, I've decided to allocate Harry's IP address from this server, rather than from his boot disk. In addition, I've chosen to recognize the MAC address from the portable and allocate it an address at Dock #1. Again, it's up to you if you want to tie MAC addresses to specific IP addresses and also to tie specific IP addresses to specific physical locations. The protocols *are* capable of more dynamic operation. It depends on what you're trying to achieve.

Host MAC Address	Host IP Address	Default Router IP Address
0020AA453301	192.32.17.201	192.32.17.1
002014870007	192.32.17.54	192.32.17.1
00101D720101	192.32.17.88	192.32.17.1

Harry →

Figure 13.10:   Sample Boot Table Entries

When Tom the Traveling Salesman plugs in his portable to Dock #1, then Boot Server #1 receives a protocol request for an address and default router from MAC address 0020AA453301h. In Boot Server #1, this is matched with an IP address of 192.32.17.201 and a Default Router address of 102.32.17.1.

The next day, Tom is at the other office and connects into Dock #2. In this case it is Boot Server #2 that receives the request. Inside this boot server, a request from MAC address 0020AA453301h results in an IP address of 192.32.12.233 and a Default Router address of 192.32.12.8 being allocated.

To prevent boot requests being answered by the wrong server, there are two approaches we can use. First, we can prevent boot requests passing between the sites using the appropriate router configuration. Second, if we allow inter-site boot requests, then the router will normally wait for several boot request repeats before forwarding the request. This gives the local boot server a chance to respond.

Given that the boot server concept is alive and well in IP, which particular protocol should we be using?

13.6.3   RARP

Most of the computer systems we're familiar with in the PC and Apple world are fitted with internal disk drives that store the operating system for the computer. When we switch the computer on, it boots the operating system. In the UNIX world this isn't always the case. Diskless workstations boot from a file server on the LAN to which the workstation is attached. Normally the operating system is transferred using standard TFTP packets, so the diskless workstation needs to be provided with an IP address. RARP, defined in RFC 903, performs this task.

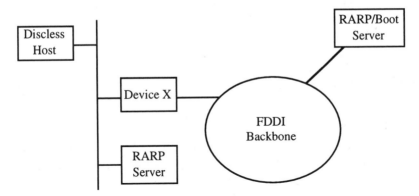

Figure 13.11:   Diskless Workstation Installation

In Figure 13.11 I show a possible layout for diskless workstations. In a RARP environment, the diskless workstation was intended to be attached to the *same segment* as the RARP server. RARP is sent as a MAC Layer broadcast, with a reserved Type number of 8035h so if Device X is a router, the RARP request will not pass through.   If Device X is a bridge, of course, the request will be forwarded.

Assuming the RARP request reaches the RARP Server, it will contain a simple request...

"THIS MESSAGE IS BROADCASTED. I am a RARP request. I am looking for my IP address.   I was sent by a station with a MAC address of 002233445566h."

The only thing the diskless workstation can know is its own MAC address, because this is stored on its LAN card at the time it is manufactured. Within the RARP server, the Network Administrator configures a table of MAC addresses and IP addresses. When the RARP server recognizes the calling MAC address as a table entry, it will respond with the appropriate IP address. The diskless workstation can then take part in normal IP operations.

The problem with RARP is its simplicity. Once the workstation has its IP address, the RARP protocol doesn't say anything more about the boot process. For this reason, RARP implementations are often built on proprietary follow-up mechanisms. In Sun's diskless boot system, there is a combination of standard RARP, standard TFTP (to transfer the operating system and configuration information), but a proprietary *Remote Procedure Call* (RPC) process actually drives the sequence. In addition, the address matching in RARP is totally table-driven and does not allow any form of dynamic allocation and re-use of addresses.

For most cases you can also assume that generic RARP will not provide hosts with a default gateway setting and therefore should never be used over a router.

13.6.4   BOOTP

The Bootstrap Protocol, BOOTP is defined in RFC 951, with suggestions for the use of extension fields in RFC 1084. BOOTP is a more sophisticated version of RARP, with much more information being provided in the transaction. In addition to boot-specific information such as operating system type and the vendor-specific extensions, BOOTP provides several parameters that allow the transaction to be passed over conventional IP routers, as I mentioned above in the section on Broadcast Domains.

When a diskless BOOTP workstation is switched on or rebooted, the assumption is that it has no idea about the IP address of the BOOTP server or of its own IP address and mask. To overcome this problem, the IP broadcast address 255.255.255.255 is used as the destination IP address in the initial BOOTP request and 0.0.0.0 is used as the source address.

Note: If we interpret the IP broadcast address in the same way as a MAC broadcast, then the address 255.255.255.255 would mean "send this datagram to every IP network that is connected." If we were connected to the Internet, this could generate quite a bit of traffic! In fact this address is assumed to mean "send this to every host on this segment, because I don't know enough about my own addressing to be able to send a more explicit broadcast."

Like RARP, the BOOTP is sent as a MAC broadcast, so the nature of intermediate device such as Device X in Figure 13.11 is quite important. For true internetwork operation, you must make sure that your routers support BOOTP helper features that I described earlier under "Broadcast Domains."

If BOOTP is correctly implemented, it's possible to create a very powerful structure for host installation. For example, let's assume that in Joe Bloggs Ltd. we have three different kinds of machines:

- Portable PCs used by the sales force and field service organization. Each machine has a built-in Ethernet interface.

- Desktop PCs used by the office-based work force.

- Technical UNIX workstations used by the engineers.

The Network Administrator at Joe Bloggs makes a policy decision during the design of the network:

- All portable machines will be allocated special IP addresses using BOOTP when they attach to the corporate network to assist in security controls.

- Desktop machines will also be assigned IP address using BOOTP to provide a fast mechanism for moving employees from one office to another.

- UNIX machines will be allocated addresses by the engineering MIS person from a controlled block of addresses.

As portable machines are purchased by the appropriate departments, the Ethernet MAC addresses are registered with MIS. These addresses are entered into the appropriate BOOTP server, as I suggested above. The same thing happens for the desktop machines.

Note that the BOOTP method still allows these computers to boot from their internal disk drives, but IP information can be configured centrally.

So BOOTP can be used to deliver IP addresses, default routers and many other system configuration information. It is also suited to internetwork operation since routers have a mechanism to prevent BOOTP loops. However, BOOTP address allocation is performed manually.

13.6.5 Dynamic Host Configuration Protocol

The latest refinement to the RARP/BOOTP initiatives is the *Dynamic Host Configuration Protocol* (DHCP) defined in RFC 1541. DHCP is based on BOOTP so that it can take advantage of existing router support for BOOTP. In addition, a DHCP client can boot from a BOOTP server and a BOOTP client can boot from a DHCP server. However, DHCP introduces the concept of *dynamic* address allocation from the server and formalizes a range of additional configuration options.

Since DHCP is so similar to BOOTP, I'll just concentrate on the address allocation options, the most interesting part from the design point of view. The address allocation is driven by a message protocol defined in RFC 1541 and summarized in Table 13.4.

DHCP offers a flexible address allocation mechanism. Individual DHCP servers can be configured to allocate addresses dynamically, statically, or to have some combination of static and dynamic addresses.

The dynamic allocation scheme has to solve the problem of duplicate allocation. DHCP defines the concept of an *address lease*. The lease is the amount of time for which a station may use an assigned address and be sure that it is unique. If the lease time is "running out," the DHCP client can request an extension period. The lease parameter can even be set for "permanent" IP addresses as a means to detect hosts that have been removed from the network. This feature is particularly useful in a large network, where individual machines, or LAN interfaces may be removed and scrapped without any formal notification to the network administrator. Note that the minimum lease period is one hour and the 32-bit hex value of FFFFFFFFh represents "infinity." Values below this, expressed in seconds, define the lease time.

Table 13.4:   DHCP Primitives

Message	Meaning
DHCPDISCOVER	Client broadcast to locate servers.
DHCPOFFER	Server to client. Response to DHCP DISCOVER, offering configuration parameters.
DHCPREQUEST	Client to server. A broadcast acceptance of parameters from a specified server. This implicitly declines offers from unnamed servers.
DHCPACK	Server to client. Transfer of requested network parameters, including committed network address.
DHCPNACK	Server to client. Refusing request for configuration parameters.
DHCPDECLINE	Client to server. Explicit message indicating offered configuration parameters are invalid.
DHCPRELEASE	Client to sever. Client relinquishes network address.

If the client is finished with the address, DHCP defines the *DHCPRELEASE* mechanism to allow it to notify the server. However, the client may not be able to gracefully relinquish its IP address   It may be powered off without time for the software to issue a DHCPRELEASE, for example. In this case, DHCP allows the lease to continue to run. If the client re-establishes the lease during this time, it will be allocated the same address. If not, the address become available for reuse.

Network administrators who are close to the limit on address numbers for a given segment may consider a short lease time so that the server can efficiently time out hosts who leave the network and reuse their addresses.

DHCP offers many useful features for centralized address allocation and retains compatibility with existing relay techniques for BOOTP.

13.7 Summary

- IP uses a very structured addressing framework. In its current generation, this framework is relatively static, but can be matched to most business hierarchies.

- In the past, Internet users were obliged to register with the NIC and receive one or more IP addresses. Today the majority of users applying will receive a block of Class C addresses. These offer the least flexibility of all the IP address classes.

- An alternative approach to registered addresses is described in RFC 1597 using the reserved IP addresses for Private Networks.

- Private IP addresses can still be connected to the Internet using a small number of registered addresses combined with the Application Host method.

- Application Hosts allow most forms of Internet-style connections to continue, with little or no impact on performance, but with a major increase in security.

- The Domain Naming System is an integral part of any network design scheme and is an essential component in an Internet-registered address space. DNS can operate quite readily with an Application Host system.

- Guidelines for allocating specific IP addresses to hosts are described in RFC 1219. In short these state that subnets will be numbered from the most significant bits of the Host ID field of the IP address. Host IDs will be numbered from the least significant bits of the Host ID field.

- Once IP addresses have been decided by the designer, a variety of protocols exist in current IP implementations to distribute these addresses automatically to the host systems.

- The combination of address hierarchy, Application Host access, DNS and centralized host configuration allows a network designer to retain centralized control over the corporate internetwork.

13.8 References

[1]   Mark Dickie. *Routing in Today's Internetworks*. 1993. Van Nostrand Reinhold. New York, NY.

[2]   J. Mogul. J. Postel. "Internet standard subnetting procedure," *RFC 950*. August 1985.

[3]   Y. Rekhter. R. Moskowitz. D. Karrenberg. G. de Groot. "Address Allocation for Private Internets," *RFC 1597*. March 1994.

[4]   P. Tsuchiya. "On the Assignment of Subnet Numbers," *RFC 1219*. April 1991.

CHAPTER 14

Designing for Routing Protocols

> *Nothing is impossible for the man who doesn't have to do it himself.*
>
> *Weiler's Law*

14.1 What Are Routing Protocols?

Routing protocols are the map making routines by which routers discover the shape of the network. So we can be pretty sure that understanding the way these protocols work should be a major design advantage.

In this chapter I'll be looking at:

• The concept of a routing hierarchy

• The basic operation behind routing protocols

• Some specific characteristics of the major IGPs

• A brief overview of the major EGP used today: BGP4

14.2 IGPs and EGPs

In Chapter 11 I discuss the concept of Autonomous Systems as routing firewalls. In the rest of this chapter I'll be looking at ways that we can distribute routing information around the network. This must be done with the AS hierarchy in mind. Figure 14.1 shows the concept very simply. Within the AS, we use Interior Gateway Protocols (IGP). Between ASs, we use Exterior Gateway Protocols (EGP). Within the router that represents the AS boundary, a route exchange policy is configured to pass selected routing information outside the AS.

I'll look at EGPs later in the chapter. First I'd like to discuss the requirement for routing protocols in general.

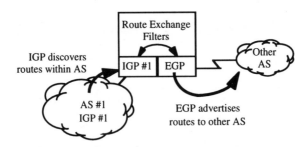

Figure 14.1:   Route Exchange Between IGP and EGP

14.2.1   Direct and Static Routes

In Chapter 11 I show how routers automatically establish routes to directly connected networks. In Figure 14.2, Router 1 will always know how to reach LAN1, LAN2 and LAN3. Router 2 will always know how to reach LAN3, LAN4 and LAN5. However, Router 1 doesn't necessarily know how to reach LANs 4 and 5 unless we tell it in some way.

We can use Static Routes to tell Router 1 about LAN5, but each static route must be entered manually. If we want some form of "best route" decision making, then we must calculate route costs for the total packet path through the network. If the network topology changes, then some, or all, of the static routes must be changed.

Building large networks using static routing is quite possible. SNA and X.25 networks offer resilient, meshed routing capabilities and they operate on a static route system. However, the maintenance of large static routing tables is tedious and is prone to errors. Typically you will find the administrators of these networks to be very resistant to changes in topology because of the work and potential disruption involved.

14.2.2   Default Routes

Default routing is a simple concept. Rather than tell routers *explicitly* how to get to a destination, we can say some thing like "Here is a list of networks and the routes to them. Any other destinations should be sent to FRED." FRED would be the IP address of the *Default Router* for the network.

In Figure 14.3, Router 1 knows how to get to LAN1, LAN2 and LAN3 thanks to Direct Routes. To get to the unspecified "Other Networks," Router 1 just needs to know how to get to Router 2. Ideally, it would be nice if Router 2 knew some more details about the cloud of networks, so that we don't send traffic into the cloud unless it's necessary.

Default routing is an excellent solution to describe routes outside of a campus LAN, or Corporate internetwork. Inside an Autonomous System, however, the

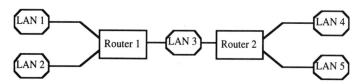

Figure 14.2:   The Need for Routing Protocols

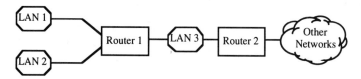

Figure 14.3:   Default Router Topology

concept is less useful because, by definition, there can be only one Default Route. One of the most useful features of the IGRP protocol described below is its ability to automatically advertise alternative default routes (Gateway of Last Resort) if the primary default fails.

14.2.3   Boundary Routing

The Boundary Routing technique is a proprietary combination of Transparent Bridging and Default Routing. Currently it is proprietary to its inventor, 3Com. Boundary Routing allows a router installation to be virtually "plug and play"; in other words, the router configures itself. Unfortunately, Boundary Routing can only operate for a router with one LAN port and one WAN port. Any internetwork traffic on the LAN is passed over the WAN by default and since the Boundary Router does not have any internal intelligence, it is not possible to connect more than one WAN output for resilience of load sharing. Dial backup of the single WAN connection is possible.

Boundary Routing was a noble attempt to reduce the setup time for remote routers. However, it has two fundamental drawbacks. First, the setup times for Boundary Routers are usually made in comparison to a full function router. If the comparison is made against a router using a Default Route, then the time saved is marginal. Second, the time saving is achieved by compromising the functionality of the router. This will mean that more WAN bandwidth is consumed by overhead traffic. Since leased line costs represent over 80% of the cost of ownership for a remote router, perhaps it's worth spending some extra configuration time, aclassic example of "buy now, pay later." For the user, the sad thing about the current Boundary Routing *platforms* is that they cannot be upgraded to full routing should the need arise.

14.2.4   Dynamic Routing Protocols

If an individual router knows about its directly attached interfaces, why don't we just allow each router to advertise all of its directly connected interfaces using a router-to-router communication protocol? In fact this is just what a traditional routing protocol does.

When humans look at a drawing of an internetwork, they can easily establish two very important quantities:

- Connectivity. In other words, are two network segments actually connected to each other, either directly, or by traversing several other network segments?

- Least Cost Route. Given that two segments are connected, what is the least cost path between them?

Unfortunately, routers don't have access to a nice neat drawing of the network. All they know is the address of directly attached networks. They can advertise these connections to other routers, but this does not directly solve the problem.

To process routing information updates, there are two general algorithms that have become popular. The *Distance Vector* algorithm and the *Link State* algorithm.

14.3 Distance Vector Routing Protocols

Distance vector routing protocols offered the first dynamic routing capability in IP internetworks. They are based on variations of the Bellman-Ford algorithm. Using this algorithm, each router maintains a table of *relative* distances from itself to the destination Network ID. The "distance" can be measured using a variety of *metrics*. These include:

- Hop count (i.e., how many routers between this router and the destination network).

- Link speed (summation for the entire path).

- Reliability.

- Monetary cost.

- Delay.

The most common distance-vector protocol, RIP, uses only hop count as its metric. On a regular basis, the router advertises the table of *distance vectors* out of all the active ports on the router. Routers that receive the update will modify their routing tables accordingly.

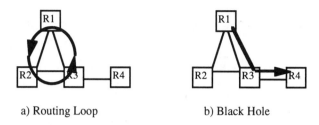

a) Routing Loop   b) Black Hole

Figure 14.4: Typical Convergence Problems

14.3.1 Convergence

When all the routers in the network have agreed on the cost of routes, we say that the network has *converged*. In a converged network, IP datagrams should arrive correctly at their destinations. During *convergence* (i.e., while the routing tables are still changing), IP datagrams may be routed incorrectly and be sent to *black holes*, or simply continue to circulate in *routing loops* until their TTL field expires (see Chapter 3).

In Figure 14.4a I show the path of a packet that is trying to reach a LAN connected to R4. Unfortunately the routing tables in routers R1..R3 have not converged and are routing traffic in a circle. Each time the packet passes through a router, its TTL field will be decremented and when it reaches zero, the packet is discarded. This will produce an ICMP "TTL exceeded" error message. For this reason, routing loops are not as serious as bridging loops, but the traffic still doesn't get to the required destination.

In Figure 14.4b, the packet is trying to reach a LAN connected to R2, but for some reason it is sent to R4. R4 doesn't yet know where R2 is so the packet will be discarded. This will produce ICMP "Network unreachable" error message.

Obviously an unconverged network is undesirable. In a Distance-Vector network, just how long can we expect to wait for convergence? In general, the minimum possible convergence time is slightly more than three times the update interval. For RIP, the update interval is 30 seconds so minimum convergence is over 90 seconds. For IGRP, the update interval is 90 seconds, with a minimum convergence time of over 270 seconds (see the note below on load balancing for IGRP).

Hold Down

The reason we wait for three update intervals is pretty arbitrary really. In an extended internetwork, we need to be reasonably sure that routing updates have reached the farthest limit of the network before we start using new routes. Experience has show that by waiting for three updates, we can be pretty certain that everyone has heard the news. This waiting period is known as *hold down* and you'll see it used in other aspects of the network that are subject to change.

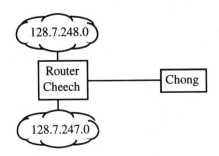

Figure 14.5: The Split Horizon Problem

14.3.2   Speeding Up Convergence

The original Xerox and BSD implementations simply copied the entire Routing Table out of every port. This was too simple an approach for even simple networks I illustrate the problem with the network shown in Figure 14.5.

In this diagram, Router Cheech knows that Network 128.7.248.0 and 128.7.247.0 are directly attached (because the operator <u>must</u> type this information into the router during configuration). Router Chong is told by Cheech that Networks 128.7.248.0 and 128.7.247.0 are one hop away. Chong knows that Cheech is itself one hop away, so Chong will assume that Networks 128.7.248.0 and 128.7.247.0 are 2 hops away and are reachable through Cheech. The Routing Tables for the two routers are shown in Tables 14.1 and 14.2.

Table 14.1:   Routing Table for Router Cheech in Figure 14.5

Destination	Next Hop	Cost	Age
128.7.248.0	128.7.248.1	1	30
128.7.247.0	128.7.247..1	1	30

Table 14.2:   Routing Table for Router Chong in Figure 14.5

Destination	Next Hop	Cost	Age
128.7.248.0	128.7.248.1	2	180
128.7.247.0	128.7.247..1	2	180

In the next update, Chong will advertise that he can reach 128.7.248.0 and 128.7.247.0 at a cost of 2. If Chong sends this information back towards

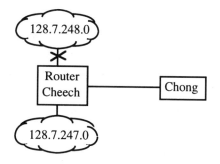

Figure 14.6: Link Failure and Split Horizon

Cheech, then of course Cheech will ignore it because he has better routes to these networks. However, let's assume now that Cheech's direct route to 128.7.248.0 fails, as I show in Figure 14.6. Because this is a direct route, the router will remove the route from the Routing Table very quickly (depending on the link failure detection time for this network type).

Just after the link fails, Chong sends his usual update saying that he can reach 128.7.248.0 at a cost of 2 hops. Cheech will now insert this route into his Routing Table with a cost of 3. Since his direct route to 128.7.248.0 has just gone away, Cheech will now start sending datagrams to Chong, even though Chong will just send them straight back. In fact these datagrams will pass back and forth between Cheech and Chong with their TTL field being decremented on each hop. After 15 hops, the packets will be thrown away, but in the meantime they have wasted network bandwidth. The problem is, of course, that neither Cheech nor Chong has a full view of the network, they only have relative views. This is an example of a very small routing loop.

Split Horizon and Poison Reverse

The solution to this type of routing loop is called *Split Horizon*, which I can summarize as:

Do not advertise a route to a network from the same interface on which you learned the route.

Split Horizon makes so much sense that it's used in many other communication protocols. The main exceptions are the SPF-based protocols like OSPF and I-ISIS.

Poison Reverse is an alternative algorithm available to *simple* distance-vector protocols and can be summarized as:

When you re-advertise routing information in the direction from which you learned the information, "poison" this route by setting its metric to infinity.

As you can see, you can either do Split Horizon or Poison Reverse, but not both because Poison Reverse explicitly allows you to ignore Split Horizon. By sending out poisoned routes, more complex loop topologies will converge more reliably (note: in my experience they don't seem to converge more quickly, but convergence becomes less dependent on time of update).

Poison Reverse is available to distance-vector protocols that use a single metric; like RIP. Protocols like IGRP that use complex metrics have difficulty in expressing a clear idea of infinity, whereas in RIP it's actually *defined* as 16 hops.

14.3.3   The Routing Information Protocol (RIP)

If you've never played with a routing protocol before, it's good fun to practice with RIP. First of all because it is so simple to understand, but mostly because it's such a dreadful routing protocol in a modern internetwork that it makes the effort to understand OSPF really worthwhile.

RIP is a distance-vector protocol. It measures the cost of a route by the number of routers that must be crossed to reach the destination. The starting router counts as one hop so a direct route has a cost of 1 hop in RIP (in the pure Bellman-Ford algorithm, direct routes would have a cost of 0).

RIP sends out routing updates every 30 seconds, even if no changes have taken place in the network.

All modern RIP implementations implement Split Horizon and the better quality router versions offer the choice of pure Split Horizon, or Poison Reverse.

Most router manufacturers today decline to implement triggered updates because in a large internetwork these can cause a synchronized "RIP Storm."

RIP is transmitted as a UDP packet (Port 520 decimal, 208h), with an IP broadcast address of 255.255.255.255 and a MAC broadcast address of FFFFFFFFFFFFh.

When a router receives a RIP update, it will enter the destination and next hop in its routing table if the advertised value is better than the current entry.

The router will apply a hold down of 90 seconds before using the new route and will continue to use the old route, if available.

When the route is re-advertised, the router adds one hop to the cost it was told and sends the update out of all ports (after applying Split Horizon).

RIP routers "age out" entries in their routing tables by incrementing the cost of the route by one unit if they do not receive a route update. If the route cost reaches 16, the destination network is considered to be unreachable. The value of 16 was chosen to limit the convergence time of the RIP network, but it does impose a size limitation in a modern internetwork.

There is an additional aging timer applied to each route entry. If no update is received for three minutes (6 update periods), then the route is removed from the table.

These aging processes are required because RIP updates are not acknowledged and they are sent over UDP, which is an unreliable delivery system. In congested networks, or if rerouting is occurring RIP updates can be dropped or corrupted so the aging timers are important defenses against dropping routes too soon.

14.3.4   RIP Configuration

The original versions of RIP were either off or on, with virtually no other configuration required. Here are a few configurable parameters that you may find on a modern implementation.

RIP Listen-Only

RIP routers would normally transmit RIP updates every 30 seconds while listening for other updates. In *listen-only* mode, a RIP device will listen for updates from active RIP transmitters, but will not rebroadcast these updates. While this is uncommon in routers, it was a common configuration for UNIX hosts running *routed* to discover their default routers (see Chapter 13). Today this option is less efficient since the advent of ICMP "Host Discovery," which will converge on a new default router much more quickly than RIP eavesdropping.

Advertise Default Route

Earlier in the chapter I discussed the Default Router. RIP can be used to advertise the default router in two different ways. First, there is a generic default route, for which the IP address 0.0.0.0 is reserved. Second, a default Network router can be advertised by sending the Network ID with the Host ID bits set to 0. For example, we could advertise 128.7.0.0, or 192.32.17.0, or 10.0.0.0. Router with interfaces belonging to the subnet can use this default route to exit the subnet if they do not have an explicit next hop.

Send Only To...

The broadcast nature of RIP is a severe limitation in a modern network, where every host on every LAN segment is interrupted by every RIP update, even if they're not running IP! In some implementations it's possible to statically define the IP addresses of "adjacent" routers, instead of sending the updates as a broadcast. However, this feature takes so much manual configuration that you should really consider changing to OSPF instead, where you'll gain a number of other benefits at the same time.

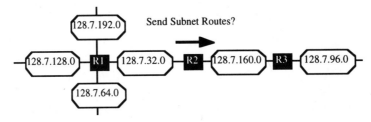

Figure 14.7:   Subnet Routes *Within* Network ID

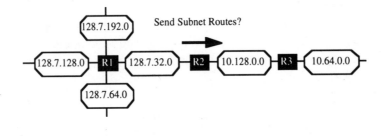

Figure 14.8:   Subnet Routes *Between* Network IDs

Accept Only From...

Some RIP implementations offer a security feature whereby RIP updates will only be accepted from routers with specified IP addresses. This can also be useful when commissioning a router network into an existing extended bridged network, where undocumented loop connections may exist.

Send Subnet Routes

In a subnetted internetwork, RIP does not include the subnet mask in its routing updates. For this reason, you must apply the same subnet mask over the whole Network ID. However, you may be able to specify if RIP will advertise individual subnet reachability. In Figure 14.7 you can see that all these routers are within the same Network ID and are configured with addresses that are subnets of this Network ID. In this case, we should configure router R2 to advertise the reachability of specific subnets in the direction of the arrow.

However, if we are at the "edge" of the Network ID (in other words we're crossing from this router into a different Network ID) we don't need to advertise subnets.

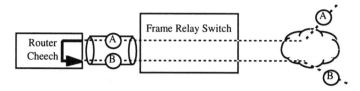

Figure 14.9:   Switching off Split Horizon/Poison Reverse

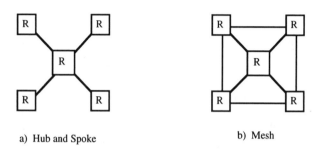

a) Hub and Spoke   b) Mesh

Figure 14.10:   Triggered Updates: Good or Bad?

In Figure 14.7, we would configure router R2 to advertise only network-level routes in the direction of the arrow. In this case, network 128.7.0.0 would appear as a single "cloud." Anything addressed to 128.7.X.Y would be sent to R2.

If we advertise only network-level routes, we can economize on the size of our RIP updates since each subnet route we advertise takes up an entire route entry. The update in Figure 14.7 is four times larger than in Figure 14.8. This is a particularly valuable economy to be made on leased lines that have a limited bandwidth.

Split Horizon / Poison Reverse Switches

Some RIP implementations may allow you to select either Split Horizon, or Poison Reverse, or neither (remember you can't have both). This is normally offered on a per-link basis. The most useful application where the mechanisms are off is for a Frame Relay connection as shown in Figure 14.9.

In this configuration, if we receive a routing update on Virtual Circuit A, we need to be able to advertise the update out of Virtual Circuit B. Both VCs are active on the same *physical* interface. Most first generation Frame Relay implementations would prevent routing updates being passed from A to B, as shown by the arrow if Split Horizon was enabled. If Poison Reverse were enabled, these updates would carry an infinite cost. Disabling both mechanisms on *just this link* allows us to build a non-meshed Frame Relay network (see Chapter 6).

Triggered Update Switch

With this feature enabled, if one of the interfaces on a router changes state, RIP will send out a routing update on all remaining ports. With the feature disabled, RIP will wait for the next update period (on average, 15 seconds but a maximum of 30). Triggered updates are a good idea, but they lead to a "RIP Storm" effect in large RIP Autonomous Systems. Every time a router receives an update, this triggers an update. In meshed networks, this can create a real problem, especially as RIP updates are sent as MAC broadcasts that interrupt every host on the network.

In Figure 14.10a I show an example topology where Triggered Updates are OK and in Figure 14.10b, I show a topology in which they should be disabled.

14.3.5   Interior Gateway Routing Protocol (IGRP)

Around 1986, Cisco Systems began working on a replacement for RIP which came to be known as the Interior Gateway Routing Protocol (IGRP). The details of IGRP have always been kept secret by Cisco, but the routing protocol uses five metrics: Hops, Delay, Bandwidth, Reliability and Cost (monetary). Like RIP, IGRP is a distance-vector protocol that sends out its entire Routing Table on a regular basis. The default update interval for IGRP is 90 seconds which means that the typical convergence time for a small internetwork is around 270 seconds. IGRP does have a major advantage over RIP in that it can operate with multiple active routes and load-balance traffic even when the cost of the routes is not equal. IGRP's load balancing algorithm is such that if there are two possible routes between two networks and one route has double the bandwidth of the other, then one third of the traffic should pass down the slower route and two thirds down the faster route. In practice, this form of algorithm is less important than the fact that a load balanced network has a very low convergence time in the event of a link failure. This property counterbalances IGRP's long convergence time.

IGRP has a number of advantages over RIP that have made it the first choice for Cisco-only internetworks.

Composite Route Metric

While RIP can only express route cost as a function of hop count, IGRP uses a composite metric which is a combination of:

- End to end delay.
- Minimum bandwidth link for total path.
- Path congestion.
- Minimum reliability for any link in total path.

In addition to these basic metrics, IGRP store two "tie breaker" metrics: Hop Count and Minimum Path MTU.

The primary metrics are combined to form a single numerical value, the composite metric, using the formula:

$$[\ (K1 / B_e) + (K2 * D_c) \ ] \ r$$

Where:

B_e = (unloaded channel bandwidth) * (1 - channel occupancy)

D_c = Minimum bandwidth for total path

r = reliability

K1 and K2 are constants that represent the weighting assigned to bandwidth and delay respectively. If the traffic to a given destination network was predominantly real-time interactive traffic such as Telnet, then high delay routes could be assigned a high K2 value to force up their composite metric.

Automatic Metric Assignment

The choice of metrics for IGRP means that, in many cases, the router can assign a value dynamically. For example, the composite delay parameter, D_c could be calculated by periodically sending test frames down each link in the path and then totaling the delays for the specific route. In practice, however, IGRP simply chooses a standard delay for the specific link technology. So all Ethernets, all 64kbps lines, all T1 lines, etc., are allocated the same delay and this delay is static (i.e., it is not recalculated as the network load varies).

Load Balancing

In a RIP network, traffic will flow along the route with the lowest number of hops. If a second path to the same destination exists with an equal, or higher cost, then no traffic will flow along this path unless rerouting occurs.

In contrast, IGRP can be configured to balance traffic over equal, or near-equal cost paths. The closer the cost of the paths, the better this feature works. Ideally the paths should be of equal cost. In complex topologies, it may not always be possible to judge the combination of near-equal routes so IGRP contains a *variance* parameter, V. All routes with the minimum cost composite metric M will be included in the path and all routes whose composite metric is less than (M * V) will be included also. The default value for variance is 1, which means that only equal cost routes will take part in load balancing.

In Figure 14.11, Paths A and B are 256kbps connection, whereas Path C is a 64kbps connection. With Variance set to 1 as in the left hand picture, all traffic

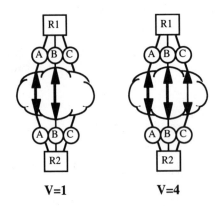

Figure 14.11:   IGRP Variance Factor

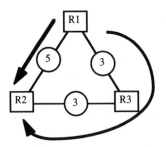

Figure 14.12:   Caveat Emptor

will be load-balanced between Paths A and B, with no traffic passing over Path C. By raising the variance to 4, then Path C will be included in the load balancing group and some proportion of traffic will flow down this link.

In practice, Cisco recommend that variance is kept at 1, or very close to it. For most leased line connections, the jump from one bandwidth to the next is quite big, 64kbps to 2Mbps for example, is about a factor of 30. Setting variance at 30 for IGRP is a recipe for disaster because traffic will be routed in all sorts of directions; even "the wrong way."

In IGRP demonstrations, we would always enable load balancing because the typical convergence time even for a simple topology was so long. In real networks, however, you can't always rely on this technique. In Figure 14.12, I show one of the simplest topologies: a triangle.

The demonstration would be to put traffic between R1 and R2, then to fail the direct link and measure rerouting time. The trick is simple. Configure the metrics so that the direct link has about the same cost as the indirect link. The variance value can be set close to 1 so load balancing can happen between the two routes. If we now fail the direct link, then reconvergence is "instant."

The problem in real networks is that the three connections are probably *the same*. Their true metric should be equal. If we set variance as high as 2, we will probably see a good deal of routing instability. In real networks, we can't usually play around with link metrics as blatantly as this because the design combinations become too complex and things begin to go horribly wrong.

In addition, the benchmark test usually involved non-session traffic from an analyzer. This traffic didn't care about sequencing, it just counted packets. We need to be careful in using load balancing techniques because of sequencing effects in real protocols. I discuss this in more detail in Chapter 18.

By the way, if you think this is a shameful act of trickery, you're right! However, in every case the tests were done with the understanding and co-operation of the customer's technical gurus. They'd decided on the type of router they wanted to buy and just needed the evidence to back up their choice. If you decide to play tricks like this, remember that sooner or later someone will ask why the network is taking five minutes to reconverge instead of the five seconds it took in the benchmark.

Dynamic Defaults "Gateway of Last Resort"

A great title for one of the most useful basic features of IGRP. In RIP, we select a Default Route to advertise and this is propagated through the network with the reserved tag of 0.0.0.0. IGRP actually adds a flag entry to the IP address of a default route, to indicate that it's the current "Gateway of Last Resort." In Figure 14.13 I show a typical application for Default Routes, except this network has two possible exit networks; N1 and N2. Even with IGRP, we can only advertise one of these as the Default Route at any one time, but the selection as to the "best" Default Route can be made on the basis of the composite metric.

In this case, if N1 were a 64kbps leased line and N2 was a Frame Relay connection with a CIR of 256kbps, then the Frame Relay connection would be selected in favor of the Leased Line and then advertised as the "Gateway of Last Resort."

If the connection to N2 fails, then after the hold-down period (about 270 seconds), then N1 would be advertised automatically as the new "Gateway of Last Resort."

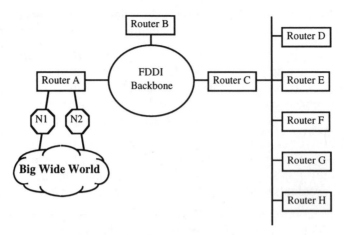

Figure 14.13:   Gateway of Last Resort

Fundamental IGRP Problems

IGRP was a vast improvement on RIP and contains a number of interesting features. However, when you strip off the gloss, there's still a basic distance-vector protocol underneath. The problems with IGRP tend to occur in larger networks.

First, IGRP uses triggered updates. When a route changes state, you can imagine a "wave" of updates passing through the internetwork, where each triggered update itself causes a triggered update. Since the IGRP updates are unacknowledged and are passing over an unreliable network, we still can't be sure that updates are reaching the routers. This means that IGRP must implement hold-down and the update timer in IGRP is three time longer than RIP. In networks where near-equal routes are not available, this means that IGRP will take a *very* long time to reconverge.

Second, IGRP sends the entire routing table at each update. With the added-value information, this can lead to quite bulky updates. The good news is that they happen less frequently, but this results in slower convergence.

Third, IGRP uses a MAC broadcast. This means that all devices on the network are interrupted. Combined with triggered update storms, this can be bad news for densely populated segments with multiple routers attached.

Fourth, IGRP cannot implement poison reverse "cleanly." With RIP, we can "poison" a route by setting the advertised cost to infinity. IGRP's composite metric does not have a true infinity value and the incremental factor is impossible to predict. The most recently published heuristic [3] is that a route will be "poisoned" if its composite metric is increasing at a rate of 1.1 or greater per update.

Finally, the implementation is proprietary. Fortunately Cisco have a stable OSPF implementation available on all of their routers today so this second generation routing protocol is likely to become the preferred choice for true open system internetworking.

14.4 Link State Protocols, OSPF

OSPF was developed to overcome the deficiencies in RIP and IGRP. It was released in 1988 for experimental use in the Internet and then commercially released by Proteon in 1989.

One of the first things you realize about OSPF is that it's a lot more complex than RIP. The complexity arises for three main reasons. First, rerouting performance is drastically improved over RIP or IGRP. This means that the fundamental route determination and update must be different (otherwise we could have just modified RIP).

Second, OSPF was designed to be scaleable and that means that some additional hierarchy concepts must be introduced. Third, since a new protocol was being designed, a few additional features could be thrown in.

I'd like to give you a high level overview of OSPF before touching a little on the specific issues you need to be concerned with when designing an OSPF network.

Performance

OSPF is an IP routing protocol and all of these protocols have basically the same job to do: to distribute direct address configurations around the Autonomous System. When RIP and IGRP were designed, CPU power was expensive and RAM was limited. OSPF was designed with the assumption that RAM is cheap and that reasonable amounts of CPU power can be "claimed" by the routing update process for short periods of time. Given these assumptions, an OSPF router is allowed to calculate *absolute* routes from itself to a given destination. When the calculations are complete, the OSPF router has a complete map of the network. In contrast, RIP relies on *relative* routing information being carried from one hop to another. If routes change, then the RIP router must wait for new information to arrive. RIP is also *connectionless* in nature, with no acknowledgment of routing updates. This means that if a route goes down, then the RIP router must wait for three updates (or a route cost reaching infinity) before it stops using the route. OSPF defines special messages that can be *reliably flooded* across the network, so no counting to infinity. These messages can alert OSPF routers that links have changed state. Since each OSPF router has a complete map of the network, it can select and use a "next best" route immediately, without waiting to be told about a new route. In summary this means that OSPF networks can reroute in just a few seconds, compared with minutes (or never) for RIP. Such a short rerouting time has the direct benefit that higher level protocols such as TCP will not time-out so users may even be unaware that routing has occurred.

The *Shortest Path First* (SPF) algorithm that OSPF routers use is very similar to Spanning Tree; the router calculates the *shortest path* from itself to every other OSPF router. This calculation uses the Dijkstra Algorithm, which I explain in some detail in the diskette tutorials. Dijkstra is an iterative algorithm (i.e., it runs through a loop) that can have many repetitions. This means that it can take up quite a bit of CPU power.

Scaleability

OSPF includes three important scaleability features. First, OSPF is sent, where possible, as a MAC Layer Multicast. This means that only OSPF routers will actually receive the updates and other stations will not be interrupted at all. Second, once an OSPF network has stabilized, updates are only sent if something changes and the update only contains information on routes that have changed. In contrast, RIP sends out updates every 30 seconds even when the network is stable and these updates contain the entire routing table. Finally, OSPF includes a hierarchy concept called the *Area*. An OSPF network can be divided into many areas. OSPF routers that operate exclusively within an area don't need to receive updates from routers in other areas. In addition, the Dijkstra algorithm is only calculated for routers in the same area. This means we can control the number of routers in a given area and the fewer the routers, the less memory and CPU power is required. In fact, in a well designed OSPF network the average CPU utilization is much less than for a RIP or IGRP network.

Additional Features

As a response to the incredible growth rate of the Internet, OSPF was designed to include a number of innovative features. In no particular order, these include:

- Type of Service routing
- Load balancing
- Update authentication
- Route source identification
- Route summarization

In Chapter 3 I briefly mentioned that an IP packet contains a *Type of Service* field. This is a crude indication, allowing a host to request high bandwidth, low delay, or high reliability for a given packet. Unfortunately, very few host systems even set these bits and even fewer routers bother to interpret them. The OSPF specification [4] states that OSPF router can calculate a separate SPF tree (i.e., run a separate Dijkstra calculation) for each service. This implies three time the CPU power and RAM is required over a "vanilla" OSPF that treats all packets as equal. In a multiprotocol internetwork, IP Type of Service is a problem simply because it applies only to IP.

Load Balancing is a great idea in theory, but another big problem in practice. In the earlier section on IGRP I described the fundamental problems caused by Load Balancing and these apply just as much to OSPF.

Update authentication is becoming increasingly critical as the scope of the Internet is extended. When routers receive a routing update, they are happy to accept and process it. But what happens if it was sent "by mistake," or was sent by a malicious hacker trying to disrupt the network? As a first pass solution, OSPF allows authentication passwords to be included in routing updates. Unfortunately, thanks to the US Government's paranoia concerning encryption, the passwords are sent as clear text so they only protect us against accidental misconfiguration.

OSPF was designed to operate in an IP environment where routing information can be derived from many possible sources: RIP, Static Routes, OSPF or EGP/BGP. Some of these systems are more reliable than others. A field was defined in OSPF updates to allow routers to "name their source" and this allows the network administrator to define a trust hierarchy for the internetwork.

Route Summarization is an obvious feature for IP addressing. For example, if we're using a subnetted Network ID, why bother advertising each subnet in detail *outside* of the scope of the Network ID? OSPF allows for this by summarizing IP addresses that lie within a contiguous 4-bit boundary.

14.4.1   The Basic OSPF Network

Figure 14.15 shows the kind of internetwork that we might think of configuring as a single area system. The numbers in circles on each link represent *link costs*. OSPF uses an abstract 16-bit metric to represent costs. The link cost is one of the parameters we need to set on an OSPF router. RFC 1583 includes a simple bandwidth-related cost algorithm [4].

OSPF Autonomous Systems can be divided up into several *areas* in order to make routing more scaleable. Each area is given an address that looks just like an IP address. However, we don't need to register these addresses with the NIC because they remain within the OSPF Autonomous System. The areas are arranged around the *backbone area*. The backbone is given the special address 0.0.0.0.

All of the areas must be connected *directly* to the backbone. If this isn't possible, OSPF allows us to "tunnel" a link through another area to reach the backbone. This is called a *virtual link*. I've tried to illustrate these concepts in Figure 14.14. Each cloud represents a collection of OSPF routers connected by LANs or WANs.

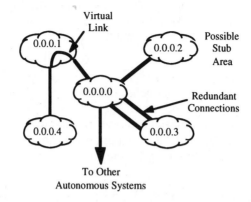

Figure 14.14: Some OSPF Concepts

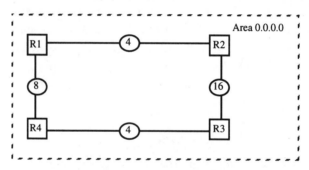

Figure 14.15: Simple OSPF Network

In this network, Area 0.0.0.4 could not be connected directly to the backbone. Instead, a virtual link has been configured through Area 0.0.0.1. Area 0.0.0.3 has two possible routes to the backbone. Area 0.0.0.2 may be configured as a *Stub Area*. A Stub Area has only one link to another area, but the processing load on the routers is much reduced

When we first switch the routers on, they decide a few things amongst themselves. One of these things is the election of the *Designated Router* (DR) for each network segment in the area. The DR performs a few housekeeping functions and for LANs with multiple routers, is a way to offload certain OSPF chores from as many boxes as possible. In this diagram, we can assume that each of these routers will be the DR for at least one attached LAN or WAN segment. If the DR goes off line, OSPF would need some time to elect a replacement, which would slow down convergence. To prevent this, OSPF elects a Designated Router *and a Backup Designated Router* (BDR)at the same time. The DR and BDR operate a keep-alive mechanism using the OSPF hello updates and the BDR will immediately take over if the DR goes off-line. Note that you can control the selection of the DR and BDR using the Router Priority parameter that I describe below. The OSPF protocol is connectionless, but there is an implicit acknowledgment mechanism. The DR maintains a state called an *adjacency* with all the other routers on its network segment. Adjacencies also form between DRs within the same area.

The SPF Algorithm

As humans, we can look at the diagram and see that, for example, the "shortest" path between R1 and R3 is via R4 (cost 12). An alternative route exists via R2 (cost 20). OSPF will be aware of *both* of these routes, but will use the lowest cost route until rerouting is necessary. In the Diskette Tutorials I discuss the way that the routers first determine connectivity and then decide the shortest path between any two routers. The algorithm is the Shortest Path First (SPF) algorithm and is based on the Dijkstra Algorithm.

To determine the Shortest Path, OSPF must have some idea of a cost value. Unlike RIP and IGRP (these protocols use a metric that is directly associated with a real world parameter like Hop Count), OSPF uses a 16-bit metric that is totally abstract. The network designer can associate any combination of speed, reliability, monetary cost and other possible metrics, as long as they can be combined into a single 16-bit number.

The OSPF RFC [4] offers a simple guideline to assign cost based on bandwidth (the lower the number, the better the route).

$$OSPF\ Link\ Cost = 100{,}000{,}000\ /\ Link\ Bandwidth$$

This guideline says that the fastest LAN available, FDDI, is assigned a cost of 1. If we divide bandwidth by 10 to get to Ethernet, the cost rises to 10. 16 Mbps Token Ring has a cost of 6. This is a simple scheme to calculate, but obviously we've got a problem in trying to represent link speeds higher than FDDI because the cost metric must be an unsigned integer.

The problem is that designers are looking at the metric as a geometric description of bandwidth. The difference between FDDI and Token Ring is very small (5), even though the bandwidth difference is large (84,000,000 bps). At the other end of the scale, the cost difference between a 19.2kbps line (cost 5,209) and a 64kbps (cost 1,562) is very large at 3,647, whereas the bandwidth difference is small (44,800 bps).

The good news is that the cost parameter is significant only within the OSPF AS. Different metric schemes can be used in different ASs without interference effects.

Once OSPF has decided the Shortest Path, it is immediately inserted into the Routing Table and traffic flows along it. There's no hold-down period for reasons I can now discuss.

How Can OSPF Converge so Quickly?

Because an OSPF router has several alternate routes in its Link State Database, then a next-best alternative can be inserted into the Routing Table as soon as the router realizes that the best route has "gone away." When a link that is part of this best route changes state, then the change is flooded over the entire OSPF network. This is very similar to the Triggered Update mechanisms used by some RIP implementations and by IGRP. For these older protocols, the Triggered Update reduces the convergence time on average by one half of an update period (i.e., 15 seconds for RIP and 45 seconds for IGRP), but this means that reconverge still takes a *minimum* of 90 seconds for Triggered-Update-RIP and 270 seconds for IGRP (three update intervals). OSPF networks can be tuned to reconverge in five or six seconds, although a ten to fifteen second reconvergence is often more realistic over WAN links.

Unlike Bellman-Ford algorithms, a protocol like OSPF is able to use the Link State change information immediately, without waiting for a hold-down period, because the OSPF updates are implicitly acknowledged.

OSPF uses both MAC and IP multicast addresses so the Triggered Update doesn't bother non-IP hosts or routers, IP hosts or non-OSPF routers. The IP multicast addresses used are 224.0.0.5 for "All OSPF Routers" and 224.0.0.6 for "All OSPF Designated Routers and Backup Designated Routers."

Using OSPF Areas

The SPF Algorithm is calculated by all routers in an area. In Figure 14.15 I showed a single area network containing only an OSPF backbone area 0.0.0.0. As the number of routers in the area increases, then the processing required for the SPF Algorithm increases. Dickie [1] indicates that the CPU load approximates to:

CPU/Router/Area α [(L+N)*logN] +S +E

Where:

L= number of links (i.e., LAN or WAN connections)

N= number of routers + number of transit networks

S= number of summaries

E= number of external routes

The proportionality is based on a number of factors, mainly the quality of the OSPF implementation. If the code has been performance-optimized then this router will be able to support a larger number of routers in the same OSPF area. The OSPF Interoperability Group (OIG) are involved in benchmark tests for OSPF routers to more fully characterize the scaleability of the protocol.

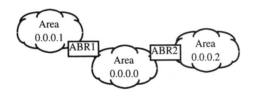

Figure 14.16:   A Multi-Area OSPF Internetwork

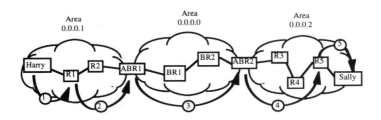

Figure 14.17:   Stages in OSPF Routing

We can reduce the processing load on a given router by reducing the number of routers within the OSPF area. In addition, we can reduce the size and frequency of router updates by using areas. This is particularly important for low speed WAN connections.

Figure 14.16 shows a very simple OSPF network with multiple areas. Area 0.0.0.0 is the backbone, as always. The router marked "ABR1" is the *Area Border Router* (ABR) connecting area 0.0.0.1 to the backbone. Router "ABR2" is the ABR connecting area 0.0.0.2 to the backbone. Area Border Routers have interfaces that belong to more than one area.

For most configurations, ABRs will belong to the backbone and one or more other areas. ABRs are the key to OSPF inter-area routing. In Figure 14.17 I show the steps in inter-area routing. Harry sends a datagram to Sally. Stage 1 shows Harry sending the datagram to his Default Router, R1. R1 has a list of all the Network IDs that are in Area 0.0.0.1 and the destination in this datagram isn't a member of the list. R1 knows the Shortest Path for the datagram to be sent to ABR1, shown as Stage 2.

When the datagram reaches ABR1, this router has a list of the Network IDs in all other areas and can select the Shortest Path over the backbone to reach the ABR for the appropriate area, in this case 0.0.0.2. Step 3 shows the datagram passing through a number of *Backbone Routers* (BR). An OSPF BR is a router that has at least one of its interfaces in the backbone area.

When the datagram reaches ABR2, this router has a list of Network IDs in its area and can select the Shortest Path to get the datagram to R5, which is the router closest to Sally (Step 4). Finally, R5 will send the datagram to Sally by using an ARP cache entry, or sending out an ARP request (Step 5).

Communicating with Other ASs

OSPF areas operate within a single AS. To communicate with another AS, we need to define a logical external connection. In OSPF this job is done by the *Autonomous System Boundary Router* (ASBR).

At the ASBR, we can configure route filters to allow external routes to be imported into the OSPF Link State Database.

The ASBR is also a Backbone Router and may be an Area Border Router. In most OSPF network, the ASBR has the hardest job to do per link. However, even a simple Internal Router that has a large number of physical links may use up more CPU power than a small ASBR.

14.4.2   OSPF Link State Advertisements

Link State Advertisements (LSA) are used to calculate and recalculate Link State Database information. Currently there are five types of LSA defined for OSPF.

- Router Links Advertisement. A Type 1 LSA sent by all OSPF routers and used to summarize the state of all interfaces links in this OSPF area.

- Network Links Advertisement. A Type 2 LSA sent only by Designated Routers. Used to list the attached OSPF routers.

- Summary Links Advertisement. A Type 3 or 4 LSA sent by ABRs into attached areas to summarize the destination networks inside the OSPF AS, but outside the area into which the LSA is sent. The Type 3 LSA describes routes to specified IP Networks, whereas the Type 4 LSA describes routes to ASBRs.

- AS External Link Advertisement. A Type 5 LSA sent by ASBRs to describe routes that are external to the OSPF AS. This LSA is also used to advertise the Default Route into a Stub Area.

LSAs are initially sent by routers to give other routers the information they need to run the SPF Algorithm and thus build the Link State Database. Once this database is established, there are two reasons why routers will continue to send LSAs. First, something changes state (e.g., a Link State, or a change of DR, etc.). Second, a timer expires. The timer in OSPF is set to 25 minutes by default and this ensures that Link State databases don't become desynchronized.

14.4.3   OSPF Configuration Parameters

OSPF is designed for large IP internetworks so there are several configurable parameters in the typical implementation. As the size of the OSPF network increases, we need to take additional care about these parameters, but for a small network, we can just default the parameters, or set them to a sensible value and then tune the parameters after installation.

Router ID

Every OSPF router in a given AS must have a unique, 32-bit identification value. By definition, an IP router must have at least two IP addresses so the OSPF recommendation is to use the lowest IP address in the box.

Area Number

Each router interface can be a member of an area. In OSPF, area numbers look like IP addresses (a source of some confusion), i.e., they are 32-bit dotted decimal values.

Router Priority

This value is used to determine the DR for the network segment. This is an 8-bit unsigned integer. The higher the Router Priority number, the more likely this router will be the Designated Router. A value of 0 indicates that this router should not be allowed to become the DR.

Link Cost

The cost of sending a packet on this interface. In OSPF this is expressed as a 16-bit metric that can be related in whatever way you like to the link parameters.

Hello Interval

The hello protocol is used to establish and maintain adjacencies. The hello interval is the interval between hello protocol messages. This value should be the same for all routers attached to the same multiaccess network.

Advertisement Interval

This is the interval between OSPF Link State Advertisements. The shorter the interval, the quicker adjacencies will form, but at the expense of additional traffic.

Transfer Delay

The time required for an LSA to be transmitted over the link.

Router Dead Interval

If an OSPF router R1 does not see a hello message from another OSPF router R2 for this number of seconds, then R1 will declare R2 as down. This value should be the same for all routers attached to the same multiaccess network.

Authentication Password

This password can be used to ensure that OSPF updates really are originating from authorized routers. However, passwords are currently sent as clear text because of the sensitive nature of Public Key encryption techniques.

14.4.4   OSPF Performance Tips

OSPF is continually criticized as a routing protocol that is demanding of CPU resources. In my experience, a correctly configured OSPF router actually uses less CPU power than a RIP or IGRP router in an equivalent network environment. At the same time, OSPF uses less network bandwidth and offers much better routing performance and features. The two penalties are RAM usage and the willingness to understand the protocol on the part of the network administrator. While every OSPF internetwork will have its own special opportunities for performance enhancement, there are some general tips I can give you that will work in any OSPF network.

- The Designated Router does more work. If you have several routers on a LAN segment, configure the least loaded (or most powerful) router to be Designated Router.

- DON'T run OSPF on hosts as a host-router protocol. ICMP Router Discovery will give you better routing performance and will not kill your OSPF routers.

- Use Stub Areas. For remote sites with only one access to the backbone (typical in the Branch Office environment), configure these as Stub Areas. This is still possible if you're backing up the connection with an ISDN link.

- Control the size of areas. The number of iterations of the SPF algorithm is directly related to the number of routers within an area and the number of physical connections on each router. Reduce these numbers by creating more areas.

- Separate OSPF domains. The ultimate solution for OSPF performance is to create separate routing domains that are linked with another routing protocol. The obvious choices are Static Routes or BGP, but we could even use RIP. However, if you're OSPF network is big enough to worry about performance, then it's probably too big to allow RIP as an inter-domain protocol.

14.5 Exterior Gateway Protocols

In Figure 14.18 you can see a simple representation of the Autonomous System concept. Originally devised to protect one university from the routing mistakes made by another, the AS is a major aid to IP scaleability.

Autonomous System Number

One of the additional values you can request from the NIC is a registered Autonomous System number. This is a 16-bit value so there is a very definite limit to the scale of AS growth. Currently there's no additional level of hierarchy to add on top of the AS.

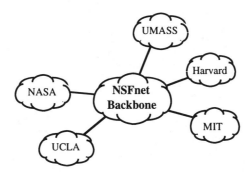

Figure 14.18: The AS Concept Revisited

In the modern Internet, address allocation and AS number control is devolved to local address allocation organizations. As I discuss in Chapter 19, these Internet Providers are changing the way that IP addresses are organized.

The AS defines the scope of the information that is passed around using RIP, OSPF or any other IGP. Within the AS, we expect full control of routing to be handled by a single organization. This means, for example, that routing protocol parameters can be closely co-ordinated and mistakes can be rectified without excessive bureaucratic delay. This is the reason why IGPs can be designed to converge so quickly.

For Exterior Gateway Protocols, the situation is rather different. These protocols are designed primarily as *reachability* protocols. Using the information derived from IGPs, EGPs allow selected routes to be spread into other Autonomous Systems. This is known as *Policy Routing*. Policy routing is becoming virtually essential as the Internet expands. At one time, we simply allowed traffic from any source AS to transit our AS to get to where it needed to go. Today that is becoming less of an option, as well as being commercially unattractive for the Internet Providers.

14.6 BGP and CIDR

To recap, the AS is the ultimate object of scaleability in the Internet because it acts as a point at which routing information can be summarized and, if necessary, terminated.

To pass reachability information, we could use Static Routes, or Default Routes in the routers that act as the border for the AS. However, for larger collections of ASs, a dynamic routing protocol would seem to be preferable. In the past, the IETF defined the Exterior Gateway Protocol (EGP) [5] to pass reachability information. EGP was successful for a while, but suffered from significant scaleability problems.

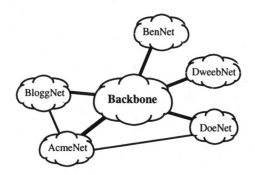

Figure 14.19: Transit AS Configuration

14.6.1 EGP Shortcomings

We can summarize the problems with EGP quite simply. First, EGP was not able to tolerate loop topologies. To clarify what I mean here, take a look at Figure 14.20. In an EGP-connected internet, it would not be possible for the redundant connections of loops to exist between ASs, unless these were constructed "manually" using Static Routes or Default Routes. While loops can exist *within* any of the ASs, EGP cannot tolerate loops *between* the ASs. In other words, redundant connections between ASs that pass through other ASs are forbidden.

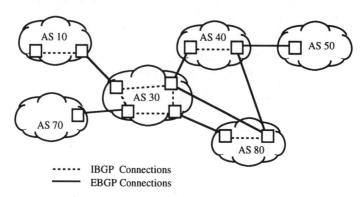

Figure 14.20: Sample BGP Internetwork

As the Internet began to grow, it became clear that AS topologies would become rather complex. EGP has no capability for the Network Administrator to determine the *policy* that applies to traffic entering or exiting the AS. I describe the concept of policy routing in more detail below.

Like RIP, EGP tends to transmit entire routing tables and to keep sending updates even if the network topology is stable. This behavior is not scaleable.

14.6.2   BGP Evolution

BGP was first proposed in RFC 1105 in 1989 [6]. Since then it has gone through several updates to include more features for scaleability and the support of address economy. The current version is BGP-4, defined in RFC 1654. This version has introduced a major address aggregation feature known as *Classless InterDomain Routing* (CIDR).

Different revisions of BGP are interoperable through a *negotiation* feature. In short, when two BGP routers connect to each other, they negotiate the highest version of BGP supported by both devices. For example, if a router running BGP-3 connects to a router running BGP-4, then they will agree to use BGP-3. I'll now give a summary of the major features of BGP-4.

14.6.3   BGP Operation

BGP is configured in the routers that border the AS.

BGP routers form neighbor relationships with the BGP routers at the other end of the connection and these connections (between Autonomous Systems) use External BGP (EBGP). When connections must *cross* the AS, an Internal BGP (IBGP) connection is used. In Figure 14.20 I've indicated the links on which EBGP and IBGP would be used.

BGP connections actually operate over TCP, which means that the routing updates are reliably transferred from router to router. For EBGP router neighbors, the TCP connection normally operates over a single-hop link directly between the routers. For IBGP routers, the connection may operate inside the AS, over several routers. The intermediate routers do not need to be running BGP.

BGP also allows operation over switched networks such as X.25, ISDN or SVC Frame Relay. In these cases, the TCP connections are disabled until routing updates (or actual data traffic) is sent.

14.6.4   Policy Routing

In BGP-connected Autonomous Systems it is possible to define three distinct types of behavior:

- Stub AS
- Multi-Homed AS
- Transit AS

In Figure 14.20 there are several ASs configured. AS 10 is a *Stub AS* because there is only one route into and out of this AS. It is perfectly acceptable to configure BGP in this AS, even though Static Routes, or a Default Route might seem to be the logical alternative.

AS80 is a *Multi-Homed AS* because there are multiple connection to other ASs.

Consider AS40. In this network, there is a connection to AS30, which we could imagine to be a local backbone internetwork. For AS50 however, there is no direct connection to AS30. Instead, AS50 must use AS40 as a *Transit AS*. In the past, Transit AS status was often the unintended "default" condition. For BGP systems, network administrators can select this status by explicit route policy configuration. BGP refers to routing information derived from within the AS as *Network Level Routing Information* (NLRI). By default, NLRI routes are *not added* to the BGP routing table. Network administrators must explicitly select the information they want to add and advertise via BGP. For example, it would be possible for the Network Administrator of AS 40 to define the following policy:

AS40 will act as a Transit AS for traffic originating in AS50 to reach AS30. AS40 will accept traffic directly from AS80 that is destined for AS50. However, AS40 *will not* act as a backup path for traffic originating in AS80 to reach AS30.

In simple terms, this policy says that AS40 is providing access service for its own networks and those networks in AS50, but AS40 is not intended to act as a backup connection for AS80.

14.6.5   CIDR

One of the biggest sources of paranoia in the past couple of years has been the fear of IP address exhaustion. Address agglomeration using CIDR has been instrumental in preserving and extending the useful life of Class C address space, allowing the IETF to make a considered decision on the next generation of IP. I discuss this in more detail in Chapter 19.

Using BGP-4, route updates and routing tables are able to *agglomerate* (group together) IP address ranges using a class-independent *prefix*.

As I explained in Chapters 2 and 3, IP addresses were designed to include a *natural class*. The natural class for an address that begins with 174.X.X.X is Class B and the first 16 bits of this address will be interpreted as the Network ID.

With CIDR, we can override the natural Class C address mask of 255.255.255.0 using an explicit *address prefix*. The address prefix for Joe Bloggs can be expressed as 192.32.0.0, 255.255.0.0. The technique works for any contiguous address block that falls inside a binary-significant boundary. Typically these blocks are 16 or 64 Class C addresses long.

14.7 Summary

- There are four types of route. **Directly Attached**, **Static Routes**, **Default Routes** and routes derived from **Routing Protocols**.

- Within the Internet, individual subscribers can protect themselves with a Routing Frontier and can become an Autonomous System.

- The routing protocols that are used within an Autonomous System are called IGPs. All routers in a given AS will use the same IGP.

- Routing protocols used between Autonomous Systems are called EGPs.

- Static routing can be used as an IGP or an EGP.

- If all networks in an internetwork could be attached to a single router, all routing could be made using **Direct Routes**. This is the case for the classic Collapsed Backbone.

- Ironically, Static Routes can be used to achieve dynamic, resilient routing and have a zero convergence time. However, as the size of the network increases, the hassle of entering and maintaining static routes becomes unacceptable.

- Default Routes are very useful, but can lead to problems if Martian Hosts are active on the network. There are well-proven ways that Martians can be removed from a network.

- Two breeds of routing protocol are available for IP today: **Distance Vector** protocols and **Link State** protocols.

- **Distance Vector** protocols such as RIP, HELLO and IGRP are simple to configure, easy on CPU power, but are slow to converge and can take up a lot of network bandwidth.

- **Link State** protocols such as OSPF and I-ISIS can be more complex to configure, can take up more CPU power during topology changes, but are much more scaleable for large networks. Also, these more modern protocols contain additional features such as variable length subnet support.

- EGPs are designed differently from IGPs. They are not as dynamic as IGPs, but are designed to maintain the integrity of the AS. In addition, BGP contains the capability for **Policy Based Routing**, which is essential for the future growth of the Internet.

- OSPF is a Link State IGP and is designed to offer fast convergence and low overhead even in very large IP internetworks.

- OSPF is an open standard, with demonstrated interoperability for more than 20 different vendors' implementations.

- OSPF floods its routing updates using multicast addresses to avoid bothering non-OSPF hosts.

- On non-broadcast networks, OSPF has special procedures.

- OSPF Hello packets are flooded to all routers in the OSPF area.

- OSPF LSAs are sent only to adjacent routers.

- OSPF routing information flows from one area to another over the backbone.

- IP data packets that are routed using OSPF travel over the shortest path between two areas and do not necessarily travel over the backbone.

- OSPF can be installed in a fairly "plug and play" manner, but the best results will be obtained by a systematic and co-ordinated design of IP addressing schemes and OSPF areas.

- The recommended routing protocol to be used between Autonomous Systems is BGP.

- BGP offers several major advantages over Static Routing or EGP. These are route summarization, reliable connections, triggered updates, change-only updates and policy routing.

14.8 References

[1] Mark Dickie. "Routing in Today's Internetworks," VNR, New York, 1993.

[2] C. Hedrick. "Routing Information Protocol," *RFC 1058*. June 1988.

[3] C. Hedrick. "An Introduction to IGRP." Unpublished Document, Charles Hedrick, Rutgers University, NJ, October 1989. This may be available from your local Cisco representative.

[4] J. Moy. "OSPF Version 2," *RFC 1583*. March 1994.

[5] E. Rosen. "Exterior Gateway Protocol EGP," *RFC 827*. October 1982.

[6] K. Lougheed. Y. Rekhter. "Border Gateway Protocol BGP," *RFC 1105*. June 1989.

CHAPTER 15

Designing for SNA

> *"The only reason God was able to create the world in six days was that he didn't have to worry about the installed base."*
>
> *Enzo Torresi*

15.1 A Brief Overview

What I'm about to present is a drastic simplification of SNA. Unfortunately, many of the complications of this architecture are a result of users' migrations from one SNA paradigm to another. The overall goal of this chapter is to give you an understanding of the issues you'll face in integrating SNA into your corporate backbone.

I've approached the problem of integration of three SNA device types:

- "Legacy" serial devices using SDLC as their attachment protocol

- LAN-attached devices using non-routeable SNA (Dependent Logical Unit devices)

- LAN-attached devices using a routeable form of SNA (APPC/APPN devices)

15.1.1 Understanding The Goals

Systems Network Architecture (SNA) is IBM's ongoing blueprint for corporate mainframe connectivity. Twenty years ago, all corporate computing was performed on a mainframe computer. From then until now, we've seen a gradual migration from mainframes, to distributed minicomputers, stand-alone PCs and now networked systems. In addition, where mainframes still dominate the corporate DP strategy, networked PCs offer a cost-effective alternative to traditional, terminal-based access schemes.

Prior to SNA's introduction (in 1974), user terminals in mainframe or minicomputer systems were connected directly to specific application programs on the central computer. In most cases this meant that the System Administrator logically associated a particular physical port on the computer with an application session when the computer operating system was "booted." Obviously this approach was a bit limiting for the users, but was also very limiting for the mainframe since dedicated I/O capability was assigned to the port and at that time I/O capability typically equated to CPU time.

One of the overriding factors in mainframe connectivity is the cost of CPU cycles on the mainframe computer. If the mainframe is the only source of computing "intelligence" in the network, it's surprising how soon it becomes bogged down with menial tasks.

So, SNA became hierarchical networking architecture that was centered on a mainframe computer (MF), passing down a "chain of command" consisting of *Front End Processors* (FEP), External Communications Adapters (XCA)[1], Cluster Controllers (CC) and Terminals (3270). These devices are shown in Figure 15.1 and are explained in more detail below. Note that the "?" device in Figure 15.1 represents some access to a non-SNA device through a Gateway (G/W), typically using XCA connection.

If you're considering running SNA over your IP backbone, you'll need to understand two things about this hierarchy.

- How do each of these devices make the physical connection?
- How does the device participate in SNA routing?

The goal of your integration effort should be to allow SNA and non-SNA protocols to use the same carrier infrastructure whilst maintaining the connectivity, reliability and response time for the legacy SNA applications.

A additional goal might be to implement a system today that can expand to make use of the newer forms of SNA being offered by IBM, specifically APPN.

---

[1]The XCA is a newer SNA device that I'll discuss later, but the diagram indicates it's relative position.

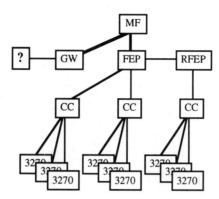

Figure 15.1:   The SNA Device Hierarchy

15.2 SNA Physical Connections

I'll now give a brief rundown on the physical connection of the main SNA devices. Since SNA has been around for quite a while, there are many variations on these devices, some of which are built by third parties. A common example would be the range of banking controllers (such as Teller Machines) built by companies like IBM and NCR.

15.2.1   Terminals and Cluster Controllers

In terms of Figure 15.1, all access to the corporate resources is made through the venerable 3270 terminal. 3270 terminals are actually very efficient at data representation. Data is generally sent to and from the mainframe in blocks. The good news is that the user sees a lively response from the terminal and information can be transferred over a network with a fairly low overhead[1]. The bad news is that a 3270 terminal needs a moderately intelligent "terminal server" to keep the screen updated correctly. SNA terminal servers are called *Cluster Controllers*.

Physically, the original 3270 terminal was just a VDU and keyboard that was connected back to a dedicated port on the Cluster Controller using coaxial cable (and later, UTP). When PCs became popular in the mid 80's, several companies produced cards that would allow the PC to emulate a 3270, while still using the same coax or UTP cable.

---

[1]For example, a poorly tuned Telnet application may send out an entire TCP/IP packet for every character typed at the terminal.

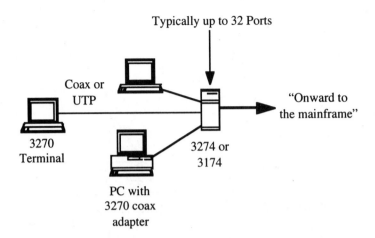

Figure 15.2(a): The Original 3270 Connection Style

When IBM introduced the Token Ring network in 1985, they offered a Token Ring connection method for the *newer models* of Cluster Controller. In general, 3274 Cluster Controllers cannot be fitted with Token Ring (or Ethernet), while 3174 devices can.

The Token Ring PCs run a simple 3270 emulation program and usually make use of NetBIOS protocols to communicate with the 3174. The 3174 can also support native coax or UTP 3270s.

I've shown the progression of 3270 connectivity in Figures 15.2(a) , 15.2(b) and 15.2(c).

In Figure 15.2(a), the connection from the Cluster Controller to the mainframe is undefined. We'll look at the options for these connection a little later.

In Figure 15.2(b), the PCs needed to be equipped with a suitable 3270 emulator. These are available from IBM, and also from third parties such as Novell. All of these emulators communicate with the 3174 using NetBIOS over LLC2 over Token Ring. Multiple rings would need to be connected using Source Route Bridges to allow this protocol to operate correctly. Due to limitations in NetBIOS, early versions of the 3174 software were limited to 32 devices per ring, but were still able to support a population of coax-connected 3270s.

Figure 15.2(c) shows a common implementation of 3270 connectivity used today. The expensive, dedicated 3174 controller is replaced by a PC with "Gateway" software. Many variation of the software and the gateway functionality exist. The big advantage of this approach is the ability to upgrade the gateway, or even to "retire" it if the communication strategy changes and convert it to normal PC operation.

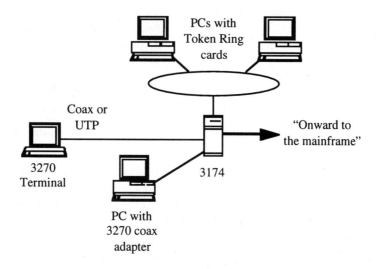

Figure 15.2(b):   Migration from Coax 3270 to Token Ring

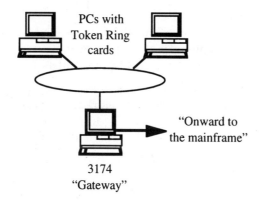

Figure 15.2(c):   Full Token Ring 3270 Environment

Note that the latest versions of SNA offer Ethernet support in addition to Token Ring. The same LAN protocols are used in each case, with IEEE 802.2 Class 2 (LLC2) operating over IEEE 802.3.

15.2.2   The Cluster Controller and FEP

Since the Cluster Controller only contains enough intelligence to refresh the terminal screen, there must be a higher level of controller to take care of more sophisticated session control. For this purpose, Cluster Controllers connect to a *Front End Processor* (FEP). It's the FEP itself that will connect to the mainframe using a high speed *local* connection called a *channel*. Channel connections are high speed (e.g. 32Mbps) parallel connections. There are special "challenges" to running a parallel connection over an extended distance, so the channel was always intended as a connection operating within a single DP facility.

FEP functionality is often required at remote sites from the mainframe. For this purpose, *Remote FEPs* are used, as shown in Figure 15.3(a) .

The original SNA concept for the connection of Cluster Controllers and FEPs was to use the *Synchronous Data Link Control* (SDLC) protocol. SDLC is basically identical at the framing level to HDLC. Like HDLC, SDLC is designed to operate on a dedicated serial cable, although multidrop operation is common.

As SNA has evolved, other connection technologies have been offered for the link between Cluster Controllers and FEPs. Let's look at the evolution: whereas in Figures 15.2(a)...(c) I showed the physical connections from the 3270 to the upstream controller. In this sequence I'll look at the options for the connections from the controller to the FEP.

In Figure 15.3(a) I show the traditional SDLC-connected use of Cluster Controllers and FEPs. Each Cluster Controller is directly connected over a dedicated leased line into a port on the FEP. Also shown in the diagram is a channel-attached Cluster Controller.

This approach for a distributed SNA network is very common and extremely predictable, since dedicated bandwidth is allocated to every session on the mainframe. In some ways, this is the most challenging form of SNA connection we can attempt to emulate over an IP backbone.

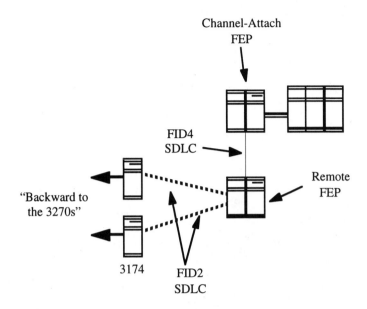

Figure 15.3(a) :   Conventional SDLC-Connected Devices

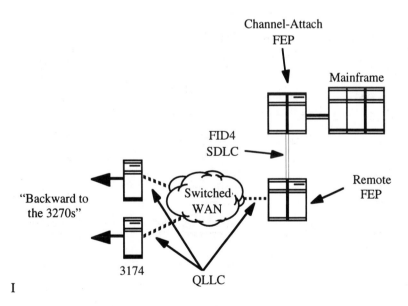

I

Figure 15.3(b) :   X.25 or Frame Relay Connections

In Figure 15.3(b) I show an alternative approach. Here, the remote Cluster Controllers and FEPs can be connected back to the local FEP using a multipoint WAN. At this time, IBM offers direct support for a switched X.25 service, or Frame Relay. Frame Relay is particularly attractive from an SNA point of view since a guaranteed level of service could be offered to specific SNA sessions using the Committed Information Rate feature I discuss in Chapter 6.

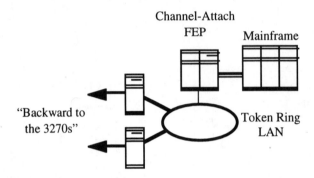

Figure 15.3(c) :   Local LAN Connections

Finally, Cluster Controllers and FEPs can be attached over local distances using Token Ring, Ethernet or FDDI LANs. Realistically however, most local connections will be made using Token Ring, as shown in Figure 15.3(c) .

Each of these physical attachment types poses a different challenge for integration. In addition, we need to consider the role of a given SNA device in the hierarchy to understand the effect of converting or encapsulating its protocol traffic.

15.3 What Do SNA Devices Do?

Back in Chapter 2, I presented the OSI model and described the way that a connectionless protocol such as IP operates. SNA is rather different. Although it's still possible to discuss SNA functionality in terms of the same model, the nature of the protocols at each layer is very different.

SNA is Connection-Oriented and the mainframe is the boss.

In English, "boss" is derived from the word for the metal disc at the center of a shield. For mainframes this description is very appropriate, since it is the device at the center of the SNA universe.

If you say this quickly, it hardly even sounds like an issue does it? In fact, this is a cornerstone of SNA. The connection-oriented nature of the protocol *at all layers* makes SNA communication efficient and highly reliable. It also means additional CPU power at all layers in the communication process and is in direct disagreement with the way in which IP internetworks are designed.

The connection-oriented nature of SNA means that it's very predictable. In fact there are design tools for SNA networks that allow all types of network behavior to be modeled almost completely. If we try to combine this predictable, connection-oriented traffic pattern with the bursty, connectionless traffic of an IP backbone, there is an obvious incompatibility. The trick is to make it work and continue to work when the network is temporarily congested.

Before I explain the challenges, I need to present a quick overview of the way that SNA devices operate and their role within SNA routing.

15.3.1   The Logical Structure of SNA

In this section I'll deal with the job that different SNA devices do. I'll cover the following concepts:

- End Users
- Network Addressable Units
- System Services Control Point
- Subareas and Domains
- Physical and Logical Units
- SNA Sessions

End Users

In SNA terms, an *End User* is one end of a session. The application program that's running the session and the human operator entering data are *both* End Users.

Network Addressable Units

A *Network Addressable Unit* (NAU) is the software that represents a physical device, or a program running on a device, to the network. There are three general types of NAU in SNA:

- System Services Control Point (SSCP)
- Physical Unit (PU)
- Logical Unit (LU)

NAUs use network addresses to identify their routing locations to other NAUs. Since SNA is connection-oriented, addresses are identified at the start of a session and a virtual route is maintained between NAUs so that data can pass.

System Services Control Point

An SSCP is implemented in the communications access software of an IBM mainframe. Typically this is a program called the *Virtual Telecommunications Access Method* (VTAM). In smaller IBM computers, like the AS/400, the SSCP is implemented in the system control program. The SSCP contains the network address tables, name-to-address translation tables, routing tables and pre-defined instructions (or macros) for the various tables. Macros can be used, for example, to offer resilient routing in the event of a line failure. The SSCP is responsible for establishing sessions, routing and session flow control.

SNA networks may have one or more SSCPs. Multiple SSCPs would be configured for several possible reasons. First, in networks with just one mainframe, several copies of VTAM may be running, with each controlling a different logical SNA network. You might run several copies of VTAM if you needed to divide up the network into more manageable chunks. Each copy of VTAM can route connections to the other copy.

Second, in networks with multiple mainframes, each mainframe may have one or more copies of VTAM running and controlling its own logical SNA network.

In both cases, the SSCPs act as peers and the scope of the SSCP defines a *domain*.

Subareas and Domains

As I mentioned above, a domain consists of a single SSCP per access method, plus all of the NAUs within the domain. Each NAU within the domain is assigned a *subarea address*. Like IP addresses, SNA addresses are hierarchical. Each NAU's address consists of the subarea number, plus the *element address*. This is loosely analogous to IP's Network ID and Host ID. In the SNA model, each domain can contain multiple subareas. The mainframe itself will be allocated its own subarea address. This is shown in Figure 15.4.

Subarea addresses are chosen by the Network Administrators and System Programmers within a given SNA installation. Today, an SNA address is a 32-bit value of which 16 bits represent the subarea and the remaining 16 bits the element address. However, earlier addressing schemes may still be prevalent. SNA users may sometimes partition their networks in a variety of ways to prevent address exhaustion. The use of domains, for example, allows extension of address space along with other benefits such as disaster recovery (redundant mainframes), resource sharing and multihost connections.

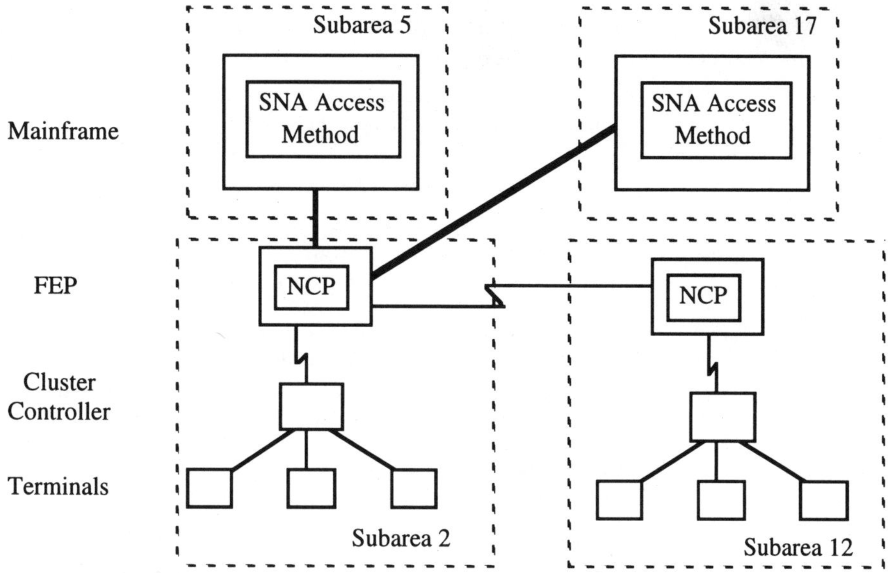

Figure 15.4:   SNA Subareas

Physical and Logical Units

Any technical description of SNA will contain reference to *Physical Units* (PU) and *Logical Units* (LU).

The PU is the lowest level entity in the SNA network that can be controlled by the SSCP. In most devices, PUs are implemented in software and perform session multiplexing functions. Different PU types are used for different devices and functions. Any device that participates in an SNA network should have a PU, so most definitions of PU involve the concept that the PU is a physical device.

The LU is the termination point for the session. Multiple LUs can be supported by a PU. Here are two tables that summarize the range of PU and LU types in today's SNA.

Table 15.1: PU Types and SNA Devices

PU Type	Device
5	Mainframe computer containing an SSCP plus VTAM or TCAM
4	FEP, 37XX
3	Not defined
2	End nodes with limited routing capability. Specifically a Cluster Controller 3274, 3276 or a remote batch terminal that supports SDLC.
2.1	Workstations, controller or minicomputers that have enough intelligence to establish peer-to-peer communications without intervention from the SSCP.
1	This PU is actually located in the FEP for the support of pre-SNA terminals. These nodes are now obsolete.

Table 15.2: LU Types and SNA Software Functions

LU Type	S/W Function
0	Program to Program functions
1	Session used from a host to a remote (batch) printer
2	Session between a host and a 3270 style terminal
3	Session between a host and a printer associated with the 3270 terminal
4	Session between a host application and an SNA wordprocessing device, or between two terminal devices
5	Currently undefined
6	A special session defined as Intersystem Communication (ISC). Essentially a session between two application programs located on the same or different hosts. The two derivatives are LU6.1 and LU6.2
LU7	Session between a host and a 5250 style terminal

15.4 Understanding SNA Routing

When an IP guru talks about SNA, he or she will normally describe it as being a "non-routeable protocol." In fact, SNA has always been capable of routing. It's just that traditional Network Layer routers, including IBM's 6611, are not able to route SNA. SNA is *connection-oriented* and, like X.25, its routing takes place at the time that the session is established. SNA routing is based on *subareas*, *subarea-relative Network Addresses* and *Virtual Routes* (VR) between subareas.

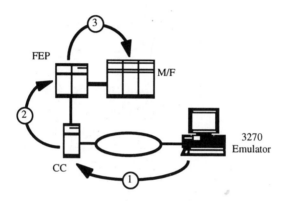

Figure 15.5:   SNA Session Establishment

When a session is initiated from a terminal device such as a PC, the session request (1) is passed right up through the Cluster Controller, into the FEP (2) and then to the host's VTAM program (3). The path of this call request is statically mapped for this terminal into a specific PU2. The PU2 is called a *peripheral node* in IBM terminology and is implemented in 3270 Cluster Controllers, gateways, and some protocol converters. A PU2 is logically mapped to a PU4 (FEP) or PU5 (host VTAM). The PU4 or PU5 that a PU2 connects into is called its *boundary function* and the traffic passing between them is called *peripheral traffic*. The boundary function in the PU4 or PU5 converts the local, non-routeable SNA traffic into *subarea SNA traffic*.

Each terminal device, such as a 3270 terminal, a PC/3270 or a printer, exists within a *domain* and is statically mapped for its initial call to a specific copy of VTAM running on a specific host. When the session is requested by the terminal, routing is set up by VTAM. In other words SNA routing is performed by a PU5. The PU5 establishes a *Virtual Route* (VR) which is assigned to the session and this VR can exist within the same SNA domain, or can pass into another domain and allow the terminal to log onto another SNA host. Once a VR has been established for a given session by a PU5, *rerouting* can be made by a PU4 (a Cluster Controller or

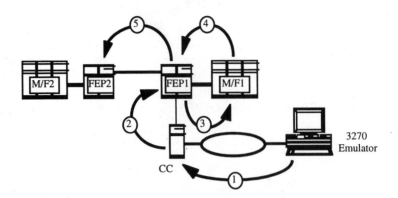

Figure 15.6:   Cross-Domain Routing

equivalent). The PU5 device is responsible for establishing the VR, but a PU4 device is able to re-establish the VR (and thus the session). The software running in the PU4 is called the *Network Control Program* (NCP).

Looking at Figure 15.5 you might think that there isn't that much routing going on here. If you think of routing in the same way as IP, or any other connectionless protocol, then you'd be right. In SNA the entire route establishment is statically defined in VTAM. However, the PU4 (FEP) functionality is very useful in SNA installations and it's this functionality that we need to understand if we attempt to replace any part of the SNA routing path.

In Figure 15.6 I show a cross-domain routing example. In this case, the 3270 End User is still statically defined to be controlled by M/F1 (1, 2, 3). However, the VTAM routing table in this host redirects the session path to M/F2 in a different domain using the rerouting capability between the FEP in each domain (4, 5). Note that a Cluster Controller or Gateway device is *not* capable of such rerouting. Once the session is established, the path of the data no longer passes through M/F1.

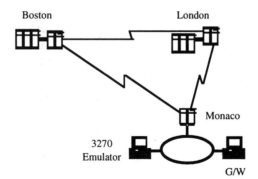

Figure 15.7: SNA Rerouting

When you consider SNA integration options, you need to be confident that SNA traffic will continue to be routed correctly. Let me illustrate the problem with a simple example. A US-based bank has its HQ in Boston. Several years ago it set up a European HQ in London and then opened a Southern European Office in Monaco. Boston and London are equipped with mainframe hosts, but the Monaco office is too small to justify its own mainframe. Instead it has a 3725 *Remote Communications Processor* (RCP). Leased line connections are installed in a triangular configuration between all three sites, as I have shown in Figure 15.7. The MIS staff in London don't have the resources to look after the RCP in Monaco, so it's configured to be in the same domain as the Boston host. 3270 devices in Monaco usually open sessions to applications on the London mainframe, but occasionally connect to the Boston mainframe too.

In this case, the Cluster Controller function is being provided by a Gateway device on the Token Ring in Monaco. The PC-base 3270 Emulator is logically associated with the RCP in Monaco, which forwards the session request directly over the transatlantic leased line to the Boston mainframe. The mainframe makes a routing decision based on "the best route" by looking at its VTAM routing table. In this case, we can assume that VTAM will select the direct Monaco-London connection as the best route and set up the Virtual Route for the session. All subsequent traffic flow now occurs directly between Monaco and London and not via Boston, even though the Monaco PC is logically controlled by the mainframe in Boston.

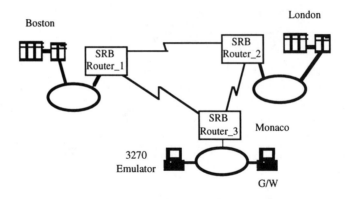

Figure 15.8:   SRBs Replace FEPs

One fine day, a keen router salesman visits the bank with promises of "total integration" for the emerging TCP/IP traffic that is starting to be used in the bank. The salesman bases his pitch on Source Route Bridging and presents an excellent case to throw out the aging 3725, which is costing the bank more each year in software support costs than the entry level bridge/routers that will replace it. The salesman gets the order and I've drawn the new network configuration in Figure 15.8. All goes well, and the PC in Monaco happily logs onto the London host as before. However, an alert Network Administrator in Boston notices an increased leased line usage when the Monaco terminals are connected. Having performed a traffic trace, she realizes what's happening. The Monaco PC is still logically controlled by the Boston mainframe. Routing is still performed by the VTAM in Boston, but now there is no PU4 device in Monaco to provide subarea rerouting. Traffic from the PCs is passing over the Monaco-Boston link, through the FEP in Boston and back down the Boston-London link. Source Route Bridges cannot act as SNA subarea devices; in fact, they are completely transparent to SNA routing.

Is there anything we can do about this? Well, the first thing the poor salesman did was to yell "DLS !!!" (he'd read the brochure on the new feature while he was waiting to see the MIS manager). DLS *does* offer rerouting capabilities for SNA sessions, as I describe below, but it doesn't act as a PU5 device, or even a PU4.

Because the design team failed to understand the implications of SNA routing, they actually reduced the quality of service after installing routers. In fact, with current SNA technology, the only option for the administrators of this network was to map the RCP to the London mainframe. In the near future, APPN should be able to offer some additional functionality for the network, and I describe its main features below.

15.5 Integrating SNA Traffic Types

The overall goal of our efforts is to integrate SNA onto an IP backbone. Assuming we can do this with regard to SNA routing, we now need to consider the nature of the SNA traffic itself. Unfortunately, it's at this point that non-SNA communications people tend to get bogged down with the arcane and seemingly endless variety of SNA connections.

To simplify the issue of SNA traffic, I'm going to divide it into two main types:

- SDLC
- LLC2

SDLC may seem like the simpler option; after all it's just a serial protocol. However, in the SNA world, SDLC causes more problems than any other protocol because of the different operating modes for PU4 devices and PU2, PU2.1 devices.

15.6 Supporting SDLC Traffic

SDLC has three big disadvantages from the point of view of an IP designer. First, it is present in virtually all SNA networks. Second, it's extremely efficient, a "hard act to follow." Third and most important, its demands are very different from IP.

SNA networks will contain large numbers of SDLC devices that cannot be physically upgraded to support Token Ring or Ethernet. Even when devices can be upgraded, such as the FEP, users may not want to bother changing the configuration of the device to provide a short term fix. Many SNA users have their hopes pinned on APPN as the long term solution to their integration requirements. Others will probably regard the SDLC-based Cluster Controllers and Gateways as legacy devices. Ideally they don't want to spend any money on upgrades for the devices since they're long term goal is to get rid of them.

There are three basic methods that we can use for SDLC support:

- SDLC Passthrough
- SDLC Tunneling (basically Passthrough, but with local spoofing)
- SDLC-LLC2 Conversion

Since the first two techniques are so similar, I'll deal with them in one section.

15.6.1   SDLC Passthrough and Tunneling

The SDLC protocol can be used for CC to FEP, FEP to FEP and AS/400 remote communications. SDLC is a serial protocol and cannot exist on a LAN without modification. More importantly, SDLC guarantees connection status using rather sensitive timers that can be an issue for any encapsulation method. To allow SDLC to pass over a multiprotocol backbone, the big three router manufacturers have come up with a variety of schemes. These can be summarized by two titles: *passthrough* and *tunnelling*.

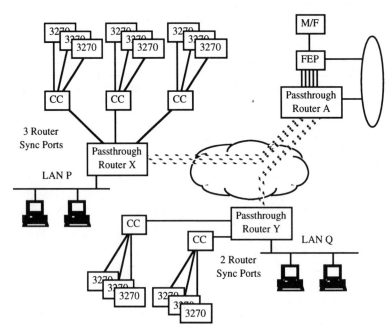

Figure 15.9:   SDLC Passthrough or Tunnelling

SDLC Passthrough

In this technique, the SDLC data stream is received on a normal synchronous port of a router, encapsulated in a LAN frame and transmitted over the multiprotocol backbone. The encapsulation can be IP in the case of Cisco and Proteon, or Ethernet MAC in the case of Wellfleet. Overall SDLC passthrough techniques have some useful advantages:

- The technique is normally "plug and play."
- It works!

There are a few disadvantages to the passthrough technique:

- Passthrough is transparent to SDLC keepalive traffic, which is very wasteful of WAN bandwidth.

- If the backbone becomes congested by non-SDLC traffic, keepalives may not be able to get through the network in time. SDLC timers can be modified, but this requires regeneration of NCP or VTAM and adjustments to individual Cluster Controllers.

- Passthrough requires a dedicated router port for each remote Cluster Controller. This dedicated port must be logically mapped through the backbone to a dedicated port on the FEP. Large number of ports on the FEP can be a processing overhead for the device and will cost more in IBM maintenance charges. This principle is shown in Figure 15.9.

- The "dumb multiplexing" effect of passthrough can lead to session timeouts even if the backbone link is dedicated to SNA. The reason for this is that multiple Cluster Controller sessions are now sharing a single channel without any form of intelligent acknowledgment of their session keepalives. In a traditional SNA environment this is prevented by a remote FEP or passthrough gateway combining SDLC data streams to use a single acknowledgment.

- Passthrough (and tunneling) devices should be capable of operating in either NRZ or NRZI mode. Most routers are not designed to operate in NRZI mode, which is the default for IBM Cluster Controllers and FEPs.

This last point may need a bit more clarification. IBM uses two encodings for SDLC at the Physical Layer; NRZ (Non-Return to Zero) and NRZI (Non-Return to Zero Inverted). NRZI is the default for Cluster Controllers and FEPs, whereas NRZ is the default for most router products, so me products may not be capable of NRZI configuration. Using a passthrough technique, a synchronous port on the router is attached to an SDLC port on the FEP. This means that the FEP must be modified, which means that the Network Administrator has to modify his NCP settings. This is a tedious business and means that the FEP must be shut down, something that always makes SNA-types nervous.

Protocol Priority

One of the ways that passthrough can be improved is to allow the routers to prioritize SDLC traffic in favor of LAN traffic. In Figure 15.9, Routers X and Y also have LANs attached which may be running IP traffic streams. Since LAN data patterns are typically erratic and bursty, these LANs may congest the WAN backbone for a transient period. However, the SDLC passthrough connections are running sensitive "keepalive" connections which may easily timeout. By operating a

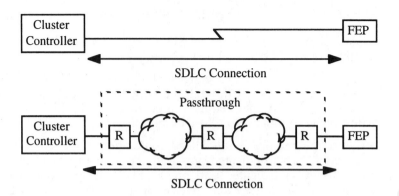

Figure 15.10: Before (above) and After (below) Passthrough

protocol priority scheme, SDLC traffic can be guaranteed to get through and maintain the SDLC connections.

I show the problem in Figure 15.10. The upper diagram shows the Cluster Controller connected over a dedicated SDLC leased line to the FEP. Keepalive traffic is used to maintain the SDLC connection. Since the line is dedicated to this Cluster Controller, then we can't accuse the keepalives of stealing bandwidth from other sessions. Moreover, since the connection is dedicated and since SDLC acks can be "piggybacked" onto data frames, then there is no chance of the connections being lost even if the link approaches congestion. In theory, the sophisticated SNA flow control techniques will ensure that higher level protocols do not timeout.

In the "After" picture, we show the dedicated link being replaced by a multi-hop IP router internetwork. The internetwork emulates the serial connection, and keepalive traffic still passes between the Cluster Controller and the FEP. Since the internetwork is also used by other traffic, the keepalives are stealing from the useful bandwidth. Keepalives still flow when the session is idle, which is doubly annoying and gives connection-oriented paradigms a bad name! If the internetwork becomes congested, some of the keepalives may not make it through in time and if that happens connections will be dropped.

Dropping SDLC connections will cause great consternation to SNA users. A single Cluster Controller may be running tens of sessions. A FEP could be running hundreds. Losing a link between such devices will generate a lot of user complaints, especially since these connections will normally need to be re-established manually.

Even worse is the concept of a FEP-to-FEP connection. Depending on the SSCP configuration of the host, the loss of such a link may invoke SNA rerouting. If the primary link returns, traffic will not flow back onto this connection dynamically.

Some form of restart operation is required. Typically SNA administrators get very nervous about restarts.

I discuss Protocol Priority in more detail in Chapter 18 since it is a mechanism whereby performance levels can be guaranteed with higher levels of confidence.

SDLC Tunnelling

SDLC TUNnelling is a little different from simple passthrough. Currently Cisco is the only one of the major manufacturers to offer this capability. Their STUN (SDLC TUNnelling) protocol includes an SDLC spoofing capability so that SDLC devices attached to the Cisco will receive a consistent stream of acknowledgment frames, even when temporary congestion occurs on the backbone. In Figure 5.11, the effect of STUN is that Routers A, X and Y will terminate the SDLC connections from the Cluster Controllers and FEP. SDLC keep-alive frames do not pass over the WAN.

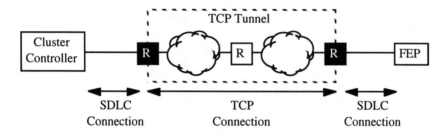

Figure 15.11:   SDLC TUNnelling

STUN must be run over TCP to ensure that the session being spoofed by the Cisco hasn't "gone away." Until recently, IP purists tended to be resistant to the idea of TCP encapsulation, for the following reasons:

- TCP is a "heavy" protocol in terms of CPU load on the router. STUN requires multiple sessions to other SDLC peers.

- TCP is also heavy from a bandwidth viewpoint, adding tens of bytes of overhead onto every packet.

- The technique is proprietary.

In Figure 15.11, the blacked-out routers *must* be bought from the same manufacturer since it is these routers that perform the encapsulation function. Intermediate routers in the network can be configured just as normal IP routers and have no additional routing load.

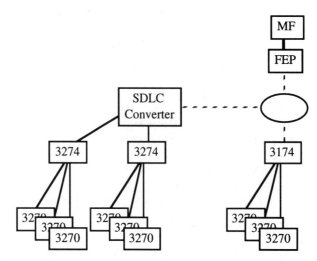

Figure 15.12:   The Role of the SDLC Converter

One event has begin to change our minds about these types of encapsulation scheme, IBM's endorsement of DLSw. I explain this technique in more detail below.

In the meantime, the STUN technique does offer solutions to the worst problems of SDLC Passthrough. The local spoofing prevents session loss during congestion periods and stops the keepalive traffic from using up WAN bandwidth.

However, an even better technique emerged during 1993: SDLC-LLC2 Conversion.

15.6.2   SDLC Conversion

SDLC passthrough and TUNnelling were developed to support 3274 devices that cannot be upgraded to direct LAN attachment. 3174 Cluster Controllers *can* be upgraded to Token Ring or Ethernet, so IBM must offer some form of conversion function between SDLC and LANs. What does SDLC traffic look like when it emerges from these devices? In fact the Token Ring or Ethernet data stream is formatted as IEEE 802.2 Class 2 (LLC2 in the IBM jargon). Is there a way we could *convert* the SDLC data stream from an old Cluster Controller to look as though the Cluster Controller had been upgraded? The answer is SDLC Conversion, shown in Figure 15.12.

In the Figure, you can see a more modern 3174 device which has been upgraded to Token Ring. However, the older 3274s use their existing SDLC connections to link to the SDLC Converter. The dotted lines in the diagram show the location of the LLC2 traffic. There are a couple of things to notice about these connections: First,

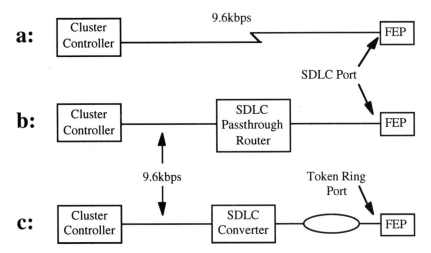

Figure 15.13:   SDLC Transport Techniques Compared

the FEP now only needs one port, a Token Ring connection, to support many Cluster Controllers. In some SNA networks this is enough to justify the purchase of an SDLC Converter. You see, while it's true that a single Token Ring port is more demanding than a *single* SDLC port, it's *less* demanding than multiple SDLC ports. This means that by replacing multiple SDLCs by a single Token Ring, the FEP will be less loaded for the same number of sessions. This may prevent the need to upgrade the FEP, which is always an expensive proposition.

In Figure 15.13, I show the physical layout of SDLC Conversion (c), compared to "native" SDLC (a) and SDLC Passthrough (b). Figure 15.14 is a graph taken from an InterLAB benchmark [4] comparing the throughput of the different techniques.

The technique has a number of additional advantages:

- It requires no modifications to the Cluster Controller.

- Modifications to the FEP can be performed using standard IBM hardware and software and remain under IBM Support.

- The SDLC Converter will spoof the Cluster Controller, resulting in faster apparent response times for the user, less WAN bandwidth wasted on SDLC keepalives and less chance of session timeouts.

- NRZI support becomes a non-issue because all SDLC-LLC2 converters should support NRZI.

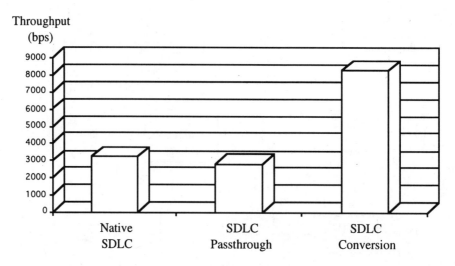

Figure 15.14:   SDLC Transport Throughput over a 9600bps Link

The disadvantages of SDLC conversion are minimal compared to the other solutions, but they are an issue if you're comparing the technique to a true Cluster Controller LAN attachment.

- Individual SDLC sessions lose their identity in the combined LLC2 data stream. This can make problem determination more difficult. This issue is made more difficult because NetVIEW does not see the individual remote links, nor does it see the intermediate Source Route bridge connections for the LLC2 traffic.

- Alerts that are sent by the converter to NetVIEW can contain paradoxical information. NetVIEW may be told by the converter that the Cluster Controllers are LAN-attached, while the Cluster Controllers claim that they are SDLC-attached.

- Different PU types like PU2 and PU2.1 require explicit support in the converter. Not all units support PU2.1 today. AS/400 support may be difficult and/or unreliable.

The most significant long term limitation to conversion is that the SNA traffic is still not routed outside of VTAM. This is not the fault of the Cluster Controller, or of the converter. This limitation is fundamental to the current implementation of SNA.

Internal or External Conversion?

SDLC Conversion may be universally approved, but the question remains: should this function be integrated into the router, or performed in an external dedicated unit? At the time of writing, Cisco was the only router company offering integrated conversion. Wellfleet and Proteon have both signed OEM deals with Netlink Inc. for their SDLC Server product. There are arguments on both sides. If the conversion function is integrated, then only one box is needed for conversion and for routing. Management becomes more integrated and the cost for a small remote site with one Cluster Controller must be lower. However, integrated conversion on the Cisco architecture "steals" power from the single CPU that these units have. In addition, router synchronous ports are significantly more expensive than SDLC converter ports. My personal feeling is that integrated conversion is essential for smaller remote sites. Larger sites may see some advantage to a dedicated conversion capability.

15.7 Supporting LLC2 Traffic

LLC2 traffic can appear from many sources. Native LLC2 data streams are produced by 3174s, 3745s and PC-based SNA protocols such as NetBIOS. LLC2 streams are also created by SDLC converters.

LLC2 is simply a Data Link Layer protocol. Unfortunately, the higher level protocols carried in the LLC2 are not easily routed by conventional IP devices. Since much of the LLC2 traffic in the world today tends to be associated with Token Ring, Source Route Bridging is the preferred method for LAN interconnection.

In Chapter 9 and in the diskette tutorials, I touch on some of the problems we might encounter as we scale up a Source Route Bridge network in size. Most of these problems are due to the way that Source Route Explorer traffic will propagate in a highly meshed network topology. However, there is an independent problem caused by the connection-oriented nature of SNA.

Like SDLC, LLC2 is a connection-oriented protocol, with timers associated with every LLC2 connection. In a modern LAN-oriented SNA network, many devices are capable of forming LLC2 connections. In older networks, 3174 controllers will form one LLC2 connection for each PU they have active. SDLC to LLC2 converters may form several LLC2 connections, especially if they connect to different FEPs.

Each LLC2 connection will generate keepalive traffic. The timers associated with LLC2 are very sensitive and connections will be lost if the network becomes congested. In Figure 15.15 I show some of the possible LLC2 connections that can be made over a Source Route Bridge network.

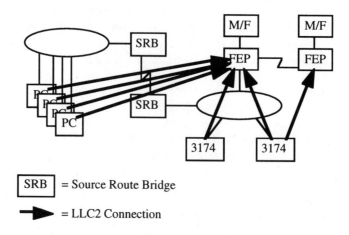

SRB = Source Route Bridge

➡ = LLC2 Connection

Figure 15.15:   Example LLC2 Connections

In this Figure I've only shown a few possible connections. In a real SNA network, there would be thousands of LLC2 connections, with keepalive traffic operating continuously *in both directions* for the session.

Evidently we need to look at a spoofing mechanism for LLC2, just like the one that Cisco provide for SDLC in their STUN feature.

I think it's true to say that the world was pleasantly surprised when IBM announced the Data Link Switching (DLSw) standard in 1993. There were two aspects to the surprise. First, DLSw was designed to enable LLC2 traffic to pass over an IP backbone. Secondly, IBM were prepared to publish the standard as an informational RFC [6] and would not charge royalties on any part of DLSw technology.

15.8 The Scope of DLSw

DLSw is a significant protocol in more ways than one. It attempts to address a number of issues for the transport of SNA traffic over an internetwork:

- Offers a reliable connection over the IP backbone using TCP.

- Defines a set of higher level messages, the Switch-to-Switch Protocol (SSP).

- Defines a mechanism to allow Source Route Explorer traffic to be distributed to DLSw peers over the IP backbone.

- Provides a standardized caching algorithm for MAC addresses to allow SNA All Routes Explorers to be reduced in number.

- Provides a standardized caching algorithm for NetBIOS Names to allow NetBIOS Spanning Tree Explorer traffic to be reduced.

- Offers a per-connection spoofing mechanism to prevent LLC2 keepalive traffic from taking up WAN bandwidth.

Quite an impressive set of goals for any protocol. The big difference with DLSw is that it has the backing of IBM and is the subject of tremendous industry interest.

15.8.1   How Does DLSw Work?

In Figure 15.16 I show a simple DLSw internetwork.

Establishing TCP Connections

In this Figure, the blacked-out routers represent the DLSw encapsulation switches. The routers are just standard IP routers. Each DLSw peer in the internetwork must be configured to know about the other peers. For each peer, a specific IP address is chosen as the "hook" for DLSw sessions. When the DLSw routers are powered on, they will attempt to establish TCP connections with the other peers. When the connections are up, *Switch to Switch Protocol* (SSP) messages can flow between the DLSw routers.

Emulating SRB

I'll now describe the procedures used to make the DLSw backbone look like a bridged network. My description is based on Source Routed Token Rings, but DLSw is also implemented for Ethernet LANs using Transparent Bridging.

Let's say that, in Figure 15.16, Sally wants to establish an SNA session with Harry. This could be done using IBM's APPC protocols (Harry doesn't have to be a mainframe computer). In Chapter 9 I mentioned that SNA over Token Ring typically uses All Routes Explorers (ARE). The idea of an ARE is that the explorer will be copied *at least once* to all rings in the extended Token Ring network. If multiple routes exist between rings, multiple AREs will be copied to the rings.

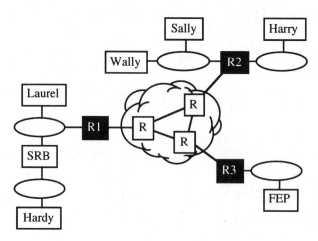

Figure 15.16:   DLSw Internetwork

In this case, the ARE will be received by R1. R1 will act as a regular SRB and copy the ARE onto Harry's ring, but it is also acting as a Data Link Switch, so will perform a specific set of actions.

- First, R1 will check the explorer to see if it is "looking" for a specific MAC address, or a NetBIOS name.

- In this case, the explorer is looking for Harry's MAC address, so R1 will look into its MAC address cache to see if anyone else has found a route to Harry.

- In this case, there's no cache entry, so R1 needs to find out if Harry is somewhere out on the IP backbone, connected to another DLSw peer.

- Using the TCP connection paths already established, R1 sends a special SSP message known as a *CANUREACH* to R2 and R3. CANUREACH is essentially a representation of an explorer that can be transmitted over the IP backbone. Like other SRB explorers, CANUREACH carries explorer type and minimum MTU size information.

- R2 and R3 receive the CANUREACH and each router checks its own SRB cache to see if Harry's MAC address has already been found.

- Neither of the routers has a cache entry for Harry, so R2 and R3 send out explorers onto all attached Token Ring LANs. Since the explorer type was carried in the CANUREACH, each router knows what type of explorer to generate.

- The explorers on the remote rings do not reach Harry, so no response comes back.

From this description, you might be feeling a little bit uneasy about DLSw. It seems to allow explorer traffic to pass over the IP WAN even when the destination station is "local." However, let's now consider what happens if Wally now sends out an explorer for Harry. R1 now has a cache entry showing that Harry is "local." Different implementations of DLSw may allow "local" entries to be cached, but it's more likely that an ARE will be generated on the local rings. This is to preserve the assumption that AREs always find the "best" route. If R1 was not a DLSw switch, then AREs would be passed over the WAN for any subsequent Source Routing requests.

> *Source Routing route discovery benefits only the requesting host. None of the hosts within the same extended network benefit from a given host's discoveries.*

This behavior causes a fundamental restriction in the scaleability of Source Routing. DLSw caching is currently the most attractive answer to the problem.

Let's now look at the situation if Sally sends an ARE looking for the FEP.

- R1 receives the ARE and, having no cache entry for the FEP MAC address, sends the explorer out of all SRB interfaces.

- In addition, R1 sends a CANUREACH to all DLSw peers looking for the FEP MAC address.

- R3 receives the CANUREACH. It has no cache entry for the FEP, so it generates AREs on all SRB interfaces.[1]

- The FEP receives the .ARE and responds directly to R1 using an SSP message known as an ICANREACH.

- The pending query in R1 is answered and Sally receives the ARE response.

This describes the way that cache entries are built up in the DLSw switches. Once a number of cache entries are established, then DLSw can be very effective in reducing broadcast propagation. This is particularly true in the IBM mainframe environment, where many hosts (3270s or emulators) request the same MAC address (i.e., the FEP for the associated mainframe). The first host to request the FEP location "blazes a trail" for its colleagues and prevents the spread of their ARE traffic.

---

[1]Note that there is a "Split Horizon" effect here. AREs are not sent back out along the DLSw peer pathways.

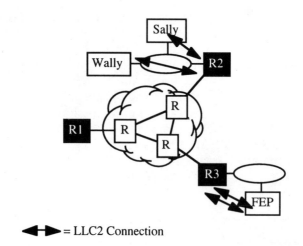

= LLC2 Connection

Figure 15.17:   DLSw and LLC2 Spoofing

Reliable DLSw Connections

DLSw is designed to operate only with LLC2 traffic. If Sally was sending Novell traffic to Laurel or Hardy, then DLSw would ignore the AREs and pass them to a routing or bridging stack.

SNA and NetBIOS both use LLC2 so they can benefit from DLSw caching capabilities.

LLC2 is a reliable Data Link Layer protocol. The reliability is achieved by a windowed acknowledgment procedure and a regular transmission of keepalive frames to maintain the integrity of the connection.

If we pass the keepalive traffic over the IP backbone, we're occupying bandwidth that could be used by other applications. DLSw implements a mechanism to spoof LLC2 sessions locally and prevent keepalive "leakage." In Figure 15.17 I show how this is done.

In an SRB network and in many other encapsulation schemes, the LLC2 connection from Sally to the FEP would actually operate over the IP backbone, as you can see in Figure 15.17.

Once a DLSw connection is formed, then the LLC2 connection operates only between the originating hosts and the nearest DLSw switch. In Figure 15.17, there will be a connection between Sally and R2 and an associated connection between R3 and the FEP.

If Wally now connects to the FEP, there will be an LLC2 connection from Wally to R2 and an associated connection from R3 to the FEP.

These connections are terminated at the DLSw switch, but the reliability of the link is maintained using TCP. There are two very important points to realize about this issue.

First, TCP connections do not generate keepalives. This is currently a point of lively debate within the Internet community [7]. For DLSw, if an LLC2 connection is lost, then the corresponding LLC2 spoofed connection of the far side of the IP backbone is terminated. For the network shown in Figure 15.17, if Wally's PC dies, then his LLC2 connection with R2 is lost. R2 uses SSP to signal to R3 that this connection *and only this connection* should be terminated, so Sally will maintain her session with the FEP.

Implementing Flow Control

Another benefit of DLSw is that LLC2 connection flow control can be signaled over the DLSw network. If the FEP becomes overloaded in a local situation, it would normally use LLC2 Receiver Not Ready (RNR) frames to force the sending station to stop transmitting. RNRs are a negative flow control technique; the transmitting station will stop sending while it receives RNRs. If the sending station stops receiving RNRs, but the connection timeouts have not yet triggered, then it will start sending again. The connection will not timeout if keepalives are received.

In this case, if the FEP becomes overloaded, it will send RNRs to Sally. Since the LLC2 connection is terminated at R3, then R3 must translate the RNR into a DLSw SSP message which is then sent to R2. R2 then regenerates the LLC2 RNR on Sally's ring.

Flow Control is one of several issues that is currently under discussion within the DLSw section of the APPN Working Group (AWG). This is a multivendor forum which is focussed on all aspects of APPN and SNA interoperability.

Session Resilience with DLSw

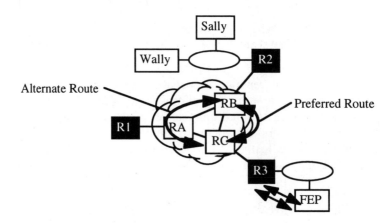

Figure 15.18:   Session Resilience with DLSw

DLSw peers form TCP sessions using the routes chosen by conventional IP routing. In Figure 15.18, there is a one-hop route between RB and RC. There is an alternate route from RB to RA and then from RA to RC. The preferred route will be determined by the specific metric used by the Routing Protocol. Let's assume that the one-hop route is preferred.

If the link between RB and RC "goes away," rerouting may take place within a very short period. For OSPF, this period is likely to be several seconds. For RIP and IGRP, rerouting may take several minutes. Either way, the TCP sessions between DLSw peers will try to re-establish the connection. If alternate routes exist and if routing protocols can react quickly enough, then the DLSw connections will be maintained.

DLSw Is Not SNA Routing

There is a common misconception that DLSw offers a magical solution to the problem of SNA routing. Remember from my earlier descriptions that SNA routing takes place when the session is established. In effect, VTAM is the SNA router today. DLSw can offer a resilient, rerouteable transport path for existing SNA sessions, but it does not represent a form of "routeable SNA."

15.9 Carrying IP Over SNA

Yes, it does sound a little bit crazy, doesn't it? But if we accept the concept of SNA within IP, the reverse option should be considered. In many ways, IP-in-SNA makes a lot more sense than the other way round. Remember that SNA is connection-oriented, so the addressing overhead for the encapsulated traffic will be lower than for SNA-in-IP.

15.9.1 SNAlink

SNAlink is a function in TCP/IP for the VM and MVS operating systems for IBM System 370 and 390 hosts. This function allows the mainframe to route IP datagrams over an SNA network encapsulated in LU0 sessions. By the time you read this, the function may have been enhanced to use LU6.2 sessions, which would allow the feature to migrate to an APPN environment. In Figure 15.19 I show a simple schematic of this system. The hosts in the diagram have the capability to operate with TCP/IP or SNA communications. IP applications can be routed into the mainframe via a conventional IP network or internetwork. The IP applications can also be based on the mainframes themselves.

IBM can combine the SNAlink facility with other packages they have implemented in the mainframe environment. In particular, NFS is available for the SNA mainframes under VM or MVS. In this mode they probably qualify as the world's most expensive file servers. The main drawback with SNAlink in its present form is that it requires VTAM participation; in other words, the mainframe is actually doing the work. One of the things that may happen over the next couple of years is that VTAM functions are moved into the FEP, so leave the mainframe free to do its sums, or its database processing.

15.9.2 Using X.25

There is a natural synergy between SNA, TCP/IP and X.25. In many configurations, X.25 can be a useful catalyst to interconnect these two communications families. IBM's 37XX Communications Controllers (FEPs) have been capable of X.25 communication for several years and in June of 1991 IBM announced the introduction of IP support over an Ethernet connection on the 3745. The combination of NPSI, TCP/IP and X.25 SNA Interconnection (XI) offers some interesting connection configurations.

For SNA over X.25, NPSI tends to use a feature I call "hot" Virtual Circuits. A hot VC is one which is defined as an SVC in X.25 terms. However, when we connect a "hot" DTE device to the X.25 switch, the DTE device will sense that LAPB is up and running and will immediately make an X.25 call to a pre-configured address. This call is never cleared down. This contrasts to IP's use of SVCs, in which the VC should only be up when there is IP data to transmit over the circuit (see Chapter 6).

Table 15.3: Summary of SDLC Support Strategies

Synchronous Passthrough	SDLC Local Acknowledgment	SDLC-LLC2 Conversion
Advantages	**Advantages**	**Advantages**
Transparent to the end devices. No effect on NetVIEW Management Supports all current PUs and LUs. Should support APPN in the future.	Eliminates SDLC keep-alive traffic. Reduction in WAN traffic can be high. Transparent to the end devices. No effect on NetVIEW Management Can offer reduction in FEP ports.	Eliminates serial ports on the FEP. Potential cost savings as a result. Eliminates SDLC keep-alive traffic. SDLC session are multiplexing. Traffic reduction on WAN can be high. Supported by standard NCP at the FEP. Visible to NetVIEW. Can result in overall performance improvements for SNA transactions.
Disadvantages	**Disadvantages**	**Disadvantages**
No reduction of keep-alive traffic on the backbone. Keep-alive traffic must contend for backbone bandwidth with multiprotocol LAN traffic. Check vendor support for NRZI. IP backbone will not be visible to NetView.	Check vendor support for PU2.1 and future APPN strategy. Requires FEP serial ports. Reduction in NetView sensitivity. NetView may not see problems on remote serial link. Certainly, IP backbone will not be NetView-visible.	Check vendor support for PU2.1 and future APPN strategy. External box solution may be more expensive. Integration into router will have non-trivial effect on performance. • Reduction in NetView sensitivity. NetView may not be able to see problems on remote serial link. IP backbone will not be NetView-visible. NetView alerts may contain contradictory information. SDLC converter tells NV that it is LAN-attached, but remote 3X74s claim serial-attached. NV does not cross-check today.
Check vendor support for multidrop.		Check vendor support for NRZI.
No SNA routing over backbone.	No SNA routing over backbone.	No SNA routing over backbone.

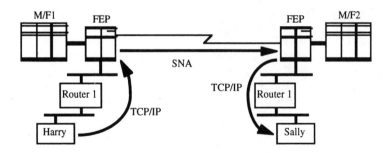

Figure 15.19:   SNAlink Tunnelling of TCP/IP

15.9.3   NPSI

NPSI runs with the Network Control Program (NCP) in a 37XX Communications Controller. In simple terms, NPSI allows a downstream Communications Controller or Cluster Controller to connect to the local Communications Controller over an X.25 Packet Switched Network. In addition, non-SNA X.25 machines can connect to the SNA hosts using standard protocols like X.3, X.28 and X.29. NPSI works in conjunction with the host TCP/IP application support to allow IP to be transported over an X.25 network. Since this support includes RFC877 compliance the IP datagrams may be received by non-IBM X.25 equipment.

15.9.4   SNA Interconnection (XI)

XI, like NPSI, runs with NCP. XI allows pure X.25 communication to "tunnel" across an SNA network in much the same way as SNAlink tunnels IP. IP datagrams that have already been encapsulated by RFC877 devices can take advantage of this facility. XI makes use of subarea virtual routes as described above.

15.9.5   IP-Over-SNA, A General Warning

These TUNnelling feature may sound interesting to those of you with existing SNA networks. By all means consider them as real connectivity options. However, remember that all of these features run either on the mainframe, or on the FEP. Both of these devices are *very* expensive to use as routers. You may come into conflict with your DP manager when you try to actually make use of the features.

15.10 Ethernet Support

Connection to a 3745 using a LAN has normally implied Token Ring connection using NetBIOS or other SNA protocols. In 1991, however, IBM announced Ethernet support for this device and in 1993 FDDI support. Currently the Ethernet support uses only TCP/IP and OSI protocol stacks. SNA is not supported. The 3745 must be using NCP Version 6 or later, which was released by IBM at the end of 1992. The Ethernet support operates in conjunction with SNAlink and allows IP traffic to access host IP applications, or for IP datagrams to be transported over an SNA backbone.

15.10.1   IP Support - The 3172

The 3172 Establishment Controller is a channel-attach, *External Communications Adapter* (XCA) device which allows the user to install Token Ring, Ethernet, FDDI and ATM interfaces. The 3172 appears to the host as a channel-attached Cluster Controller. The 3172 was first shipped as an industrial PC/AT unit in 1989, offering just TCP/IP support. SNA support was added in 1990 and today's model is based on an 80486 CPU with a Microchannel bus. Despite the power boost, the 3172 is still optimized for TCP/IP operation and for SNA use, many customer prefer a channel-attached 3174 or a full Communications Controller. The 3172 is intended as a host "front end," in other words, the traffic flow through the box is LAN-to-host, host-to-LAN. This means that when the 3172 is fitted with more than one LAN connection, it cannot bridge or route traffic between the LANs. In fact, the 3172 does not perform any protocol processing. All communication functions are performed within the host. However for SNA traffic, the 3172 does terminate the LLC2 sessions, which allows the SNA traffic to pass to more than one SNA host. In contrast, TCP/IP sessions are connectionless until they reach the host. In effect this means that all IP communication must terminate inside the host to which the 3172 is attached. The 3172 can support IP and SNA communication simultaneously from the same LAN, but two separate LAN adapters are required. This contrasts with the 3745 situation where the Ethernet connections are unable to support SNA and the Token Ring connections are unable to support TCP/IP.

Channel-Attached Routers

During 1993 and 1994, several companies have been touting the idea of channel-attached router devices as replacements for FEPs, Cluster Controllers or 3172s. These sound like an interesting idea, but I'd just like to add a dash of realism to the marketing hype.

First of all, let's look at what we expect these boxes to do. By channel-attaching the unit, we need to emulate some feature of a normal channel-attached device. Basically we have three options:

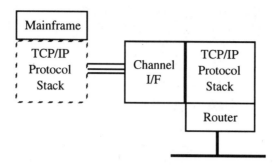

Figure 15.20:   Channel-Attached Router

- Emulate a FEP, PU4

- Emulate a Cluster Controller, PU2.1

- Implement the XGA function

Emulating a FEP is a silly idea. Only IBM knows how FEPs are supposed to work and they obviously make regular changes to VTAM and NCP to keep it that way.

Emulating PU2 or PU2.1 devices is more sensible, but a Cluster Controller is just a Terminal Server. Why should we implement Terminal Server functions in a router? This is especially true because channel-attach cards for routers will only be available in the top end device from a given manufacturer. This means that the channel attach router will actually cost *more* than the equivalent IBM device.

Emulating XGA devices is a much better idea. In effect, we're replacing the 3172 with the router. By implementing protocol stacks in the router, we can offload the mainframe. This is shown in Figure 15.20.

This figure shows a TCP/IP offload, which is probably the only offload that will be offered in the first few years (until APPN stabilizes). There's one technical and one commercial reason why the channel-attached XGA concept may have a limited future. Technically, the channel is such a fragile environment. A mainframe computer will probably have several devices, FEPs, printers, channel extenders,, etc., attached to the channel connector. If any of these devices malfunctions, it can bring down the entire channel. The mainframe will restart! Normally the only devices that are allowed by the Data Processing Manager to connect directly to the channel are built by IBM, or by plug-compatible manufacturers. It's not too likely that a conservative SNA system manager would allow any company less than 50 years old to attach to that channel! The exception is Network Systems, who made this technology their primary focus a few years ago.

The second reason is that, from a commercial point of view, the XGA gateways are the cheapest device you can buy for a mainframe. A high-end router with channel interface will cost over $30,000. A modern 3172 will cost only $20,000 and it's got the "magic" three letters on the front.

15.11   Future SNA - APPN and HPAPPN

Traditional SNA routing is performed by VTAM in the mainframe. It is this restriction that currently causes problems for traditional router vendors. Only IBM can reliably produce a PU5 capability.

However, IBM has been using a form of SNA which is suitable for routing for around eight years now; this is called *Advanced Peer to Peer Communication* (APPC). APPC uses much more intelligent Logical and Physical Units: LU6.2 and PU2.1.

The routing capability of APPC is known as *Advanced Peer-to-Peer Networking* (APPN).

In an IP network, we define hosts and routers. In an APPN network, these devices are known as APPN *End Nodes* and APPN *Network Nodes*. This is shown in Figure 15.21.

APPC/APPN History

APPN was first introduced in 1986 into networks of IBM's popular minicomputer, the System/36. In 1988 this support was extended to the newly introduced AS/400. In 1990, APPN became available for the DPPX operating system and VTAM and in 1991 for OS/2. On March 25th, 1992 IBM officially unveiled its Networking Blueprint in which APPN plays a key role. Mainframe users with VTAM Version 4 or later have the opportunity to move from the hierarchical networks that I've described as "traditional SNA" to a true peer-to-peer system.

APPC/APPN Performance

At the time of writing, it's a bit early to think seriously about APPN performance. The early implementations are likely to be focussed on stability and functionality. As the technology matures, then we should see APPN performance exceeding TCP/IP connectivity for SNA. The real test will be in the performance of the first true APPN Network Node router implementations. At this stage it looks as though Wellfleet may be the first vendor to hit the market with such an implementation, towards the end of 1994.

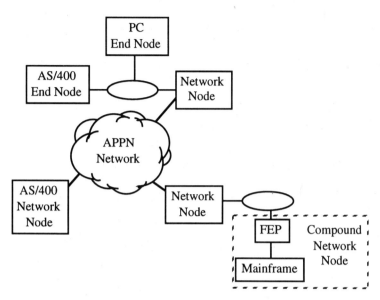

Figure 15.21:   An APPN Network

APPN Scaleability

When APPN was first deployed in the early AS/400 networks, it was intended to offer SNA connectivity in a more dynamic way than traditional SNA, with less operation and maintenance.   The original scope was limited; an APPN network was never intended to be bigger than about 100 nodes.   No real routing protocol was defined. Instead, static routing was configured in each Network Node.   IBM refer to this as *Intermediate Session Routing* (ISR).

A much more important question concerns the scaleability of APPN.   ISR is certainly not scaleable and all early implementations will be based on this static routing technique.

15.11.1   APPN Over IP

At the time of writing, only IBM has offered a *native* APPN Network Node implementation.   This is available for a range of SNA products, but not currently for IBM's router, the 6611.   Instead, the 6611 offer a form of APPN transport over IP. In this configuration the 6611 acts as an APPN End Node.   I show this in Figure

15.22. In this configuration the 6611 just acts as an APPN End Node, encapsulating the APPN traffic in IP for transit over the backbone.

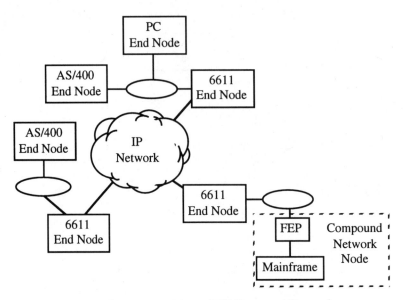

Figure 15.22:   APPN over IP

End Node support for APPN is less demanding of the router than full Network Node support. However, the encapsulation mechanism between IP and APPN has not been made available in the public domain, so interoperability between different vendor offerings is dubious. The APPN Working Group is looking into the encapsulation issue.

The logical future for APPN over IP is simply to define an APPN End Node termination in terms of DLSw.

Future APPN

With APPN not even released, IBM has already made it obsolete. ISR has already been replaced in IBM strategy discussions by a dynamic, connectionless routing protocol known as *High Performance Routing* (HPR). HPR was then put under threat by discussions of ."*APPN+*" and ."*APPN++*." These versions of APPN are intended to scale to ATM speeds in the future. However, with other parts of IBM announcing ATM connectivity products, the future seems to have arrived before APPN is ready to meet it.

For the next couple of years, APPN may be such a rapidly moving target that early adopters will be placing themselves into a very vulnerable position.

15.12   Sharing the Backbone

An obvious way to treat SNA is as "just another protocol" over a multiprotocol backbone. I discuss multiprotocol issues in Chapters 2 and 3, the problem is that, in this context, traditional SNA protocols cannot just be treated as in a similar way to IPX or DECNet.

Prior to the appearance of DLSw, we would have to allow Source Route Bridging to leak out onto our corporate backbone. The uncontrolled spread of bridging is a very bad thing that has a direct impact on the scaleability of the internetwork.

Today we can encapsulate SRB traffic, terminate all the messy keepalives from LLC2 and suppress repeated broadcast discovery frames, all using DLSw.

However, when APPN routing becomes available, I'd be very eager to pilot a dual protocol backbone: IP and APPN in parallel. APPN offers true SNA routing and in the long run this would seem to be the best way to approach SNA.

In the future, I can quite imagine that LAN workgroup protocol will converge on IP (or IPng) and SNA networks converge towards APPN. The combined multiprotocol data streams will then be transported over an ATM backbone.

15.13   Summary

- SNA is an evolving network architecture that presents special challenges to the designer wishing to integrate its traffic within an IP backbone.

- In a pure SNA network with dedicated serial circuits, the performance, reliability and predictability of the system is extremely high. The biggest single challenge is to retain these characteristics during an integration phase.

- Much of the traditional SNA is based on serial protocols and in particular SDLC.

- SDLC can be tunneled over IP internets, or can be converted into a LAN-friendly form using SDLC-LLC2 Converters.

- Whatever way we deal with SDLC, we need to remember that it uses frequent keepalive timers that should be excluded from the IP backbone. Excluding these keepalives means that spoofing intelligence must be installed in our SDLC access layer.

- SNA networks also generate native LAN frames. In contrast to IP, these LAN frames are contained in LLC2, which is a connection-oriented protocol. Sensitive LLC2 timers operate in a similar way to SDLC timers.

- LLC2 termination can be achieved using a standard technique called Data Link Switching (DLSw).

- DLSw encapsulates LLC2 traffic (either SNA or NetBIOS) over a reliable TCP connection.

- No keepalive traffic leaks over a DLSw backbone.

- DLSw also provides several caching features to reduce broadcast discovery traffic from SNA and NetBIOS.

- APPN is a fully routeable form of SNA which may come to dominate SNA backbones over the next five years.

15.14   References

[1]   James Martin. *SNA: IBM's Networking Solution.*   Prentice-Hall, Englewood Cliffs, NJ. 1987.

[2]   IBM. *Local Area Network Technical Reference.* Document number SC30-3383-2, Third Edition, 1988.

[3]   Kevin Tolly. "Playing to Win with IBM's LAN Gateways." *Data Communications* (February 1990).

[4]   Robin Layland. "Token Ring Bridges and Routers: Heirs to the SNA Throne." *Data Communications* (November 21, 1990).

[5]   Kevin Tolly. "Surprise! SNA Gateways Are More Than Mere Child's Play." *Data Communications* (October 1990).

[6]   R. Dixon, D. Kushi, "Data Link Switching: Switch-to-Switch Protocol". *RFC 1434.* March 1993.

CHAPTER 16

Designing for Resilience

> *Failure to complete a task within the allocated time or budget proves that the task was more difficult than expected and requires promotion for those in charge.*
>
> **Pratt's Second Rule, Second Interpretation (IEEE Spectrum)**

16.1 What is Resilience?

Imagine we're walking through the woods one fine spring morning, and we see a small branch on the ground. We pick it up and try to snap it in half (so that we can throw it for the dog to fetch). If the stick is old and dry, it'll just snap straight away. If the stick is young and *resilient*, it might bend a bit, but then will spring back into its original shape. If we now consider the original purpose of our internetwork, it was to support user applications. We can say that a resilient internetwork is one which will continue to support the user applications, even when someone or something tries to break it.

In practical terms, the accepted way to improve network resilience is to eliminate *single points of failure*. This is generally a good technique, but one of my objectives with this chapter is to show you how upper layer protocols and communication systems will react to network redundancy.

It seems logical first to discuss ways that you can quantify investment in resilience, and asses overall improvements to the resilience of your internetwork. This is the subject of Risk Analysis.

16.2 Risk Analysis

Risk Analysis is a remarkably simple concept: we list all the likely risks to the network and assign some kind of value to them. We then consider possible counters to each risk and evaluate the level of protection offered compared to its cost. We end up with a situation similar to the one I show in Figure 16.1. The solutions to various threats compete for the overall budget. Multiple solutions to each threat are weighed against the protection they give. Using this type of model we can trade off a less effective, but cheaper solution to one threat so that we can afford a much more effective, but expensive, solution to another.

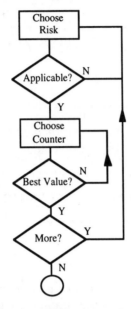

Figure 16.1:   Risk Analysis Flowchart

Flowcharts like this one always seem totally obvious at first glance. But think about a typical situation. Let's say that the CEO of Joe Bloggs Ltd. has lunch with a friend who tells a story about a company that went bankrupt because they lost network connectivity for three days. The CEO rushes back in the afternoon and talks it over with the Network Administrator. The AN sees a good opportunity to improve the network resilience, so suggests a study be made for the most cost-effective way to spend some money on resilience. Three network operations staff, Fred, Helen and Anne, come up with various threats that they see as important. Fred is concerned with WAN outages, Helen with communications hardware failure, and Anne with power supply glitches and surges.

The actual details for their solutions don't matter, but in Figure 16.1 I've sketched out an overview. So, you must choose. Which of the suggestions produces the most benefit? When multiple, competing solutions are presented, we need a more mathematical treatment. For each case, we need to get some idea of the frequency of the event that it protects against. How many power glitches or surges do we suffer per year, for example?

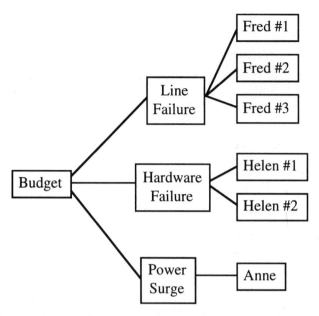

Figure 16.1:   One Interpretation of Risk Analysis

Given that we can come up with such a number, what's the average cost of the damage caused by such an event? This needs to be expressed in hardware damage, and the cost of system downtime. Finally, we need to be realistic about our countermeasures. Even if we install the proposed solution, it won't offer 100% protection. So we need to factor in the number of events that will occur *even with* the proposed resilience features.

First let me define some terminology:

$EVENT_X$ The number of events X that will occur per year if no countermeasures are deployed.

$COST_X$ The financial cost to the company for each event X.

$CEVENT_X$ The number of events X that will occur per year if the countermeasures are deployed.   Remember that no countermeasures are totally effective.

$BENE_X$ The *benefit index* of using the countermeasure for event X.

This is given by the formula:

$$BENE_x = \frac{CEVENT_x \; * \; COST_x}{EVENT_x}$$

This benefit index is only used as a comparative ranking. In a real network, the Risk Analysis will be much more complex, because you won't just have a fixed amount to spend on "resilience," rather the resilience features you build into the network will be paid for from the overall budget.

Given that you now have at least one way to compare different resilience solutions, let me describe some of the tools of resilience.

- Resilience of WAN Services
- Backup of Non-Resilient WAN Links
- Router to Router Resilience
- End System to Router Resilience
- Hardware and Software Resilience

16.3 Resilient WAN Services

Resilient router internetworks typically involve redundant WAN links, with the additional overhead these impose. If the WAN component is the "weak link," is there an alternative solution? Figure 16.2 contrasts two possible WAN topologies. On the left is a router internetwork with redundant leased lines. On the right is a switched service WAN offering resilience inside the cloud.

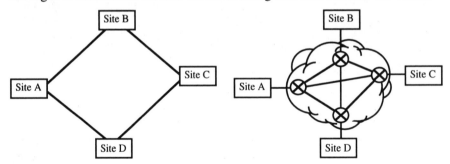

Figure 16.2: Leased Line Resilience, or WAN Service Resilience?

The cloud shown in Figure 16.2 could be X.25, Frame Relay, SMDS or ATM. All four WAN technologies share one thing in common, the core network is built as a resilient system. Any two of these sites are connected by more than one possible route. Packets may be dropped for a short time until the service recovers.

If we look at Site B in this Figure in more detail, we need to understand the effects on the router caused by the leased line failure [3]. In Figure 16.3 I've shown the routing concept for the left hand diagram of Figure 16.2.

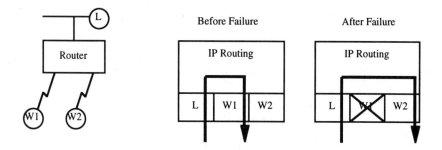

Figure 16.3:   Rerouting Around a Failed Leased Line

Before the failure, *all traffic* is routed down W1. After the failure, the IP routing table will force *all traffic* down W2. The time taken to change over depends on two things:

- The time needed to detect that W1 is down.

- The hold-down time for the routing technique.

16.3.1   Line-Down Detection

This is a very important factor in leased line services. How *can* we detect if a leased line is down? You might think that this is a non-issue. If a telephone connection is down, we tend to realize it. The problem with leased lines is that they don't fail "cleanly." Often, their bit error rate increases, and after a while the line finally gives up. Sometimes the line disappears cleanly, but comes back a second later, only to fail again randomly every few seconds (this effect is called *bouncing*). If a line is bouncing, imagine the effect that this would have on a link state protocol such as OSPF. Every few seconds, the CPU-intensive Dijkstra Algorithm would be forced to recalculate. Whatever detection techniques we use need to be fast-acting, but not so fast that they continually report the line up, then down, then up, then down, and so on.

In general, there are two techniques we can use to determine the line state. The first is to embed some form of handshake protocol in the data stream. The send is to rely on the physical signals on the serial interface.

Data stream handshaking is very common. Proprietary serial protocols implement a *Breath of Life* (BOFL) feature. In this case, special BOFL frames are sent between the routers at each end of the serial connection. For standards-based system we use PPP over serial links. PPP uses a scheme called *Link Quality Monitoring* (LQM) to determine the link state [1].

16.3.2 Routing Hold-down

In Chapter 14 I discussed the concept of hold-down as a way to stabilize the process of convergence in the internetwork. The problem with hold-down is that it increases the amount of time required for rerouting to take place. However, for routing protocols that operate reliable update schemes, such as OSPF, we can eliminate the routing hold-down timer completely. In other words, for an OSPF connection we can assume that a new route will be calculate as soon as the link has been reported as down.

16.3.3 Load Balancing

Another tempting way to reduce the convergence time is to operate load balancing over the redundant serial lines. In this scenario, both lines are used in normal operation, and all traffic is transferred over the remaining line if one or the other connection fails. A few things to remember about load balancing: first, load balancing can be supported as part of a routing protocol, as in the case of IGRP or OSPF, or as part of a transmission group effect. In the former case, only IP traffic can be load-balanced. In the latter case, all traffic can be balanced between any point to point connection group.

Second, load balancing is not always a good thing, for two reasons. First of all, load-balanced traffic can end up arriving at the other end of the connection out of sequence. Some upper layer protocols , like TCP, are able to tolerate out-of-sequence packet, but others (the majority of others) are not. In Chapter 18 I discuss this in more detail. The second disadvantage with load balancing is that users who are able to operate successfully in this mode become accustomed to the additional bandwidth. If they have a link failure, users complain about the performance drop. The only real answer to this question is some form of Bandwidth on Demand (BoD) technique. BoD can also be used for backup purposes, as well as congestion relief.

16.3.4 Multipoint Service Resilience

There is an alternative approach to link backup that allows us to avoid rerouting hold-down, and recalculation. This mechanism requires that we have just one connection into the router. Link resilience is achieve *outside* the router.

In Figure 16.4, I've chosen to consider attachment to a multipoint WAN service such as X.25, Frame Relay, SMDS or ATM. In these services, resilience is assumed to occur *within* the cloud. The connection to the router is through the same physical port, and for routing purposes the "before" and "after" configurations are identical.

However, the weak point in a multipoint service attachment is the access line running between the router and the first service switch; sometimes called the *Point of Presence* (PoP). If this access line fails, then total connection is lost regardless of how much resilience there is inside the cloud. One of the favorite backup options for this connection (outside the US) is ISDN.

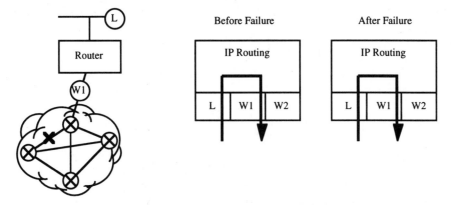

Figure 16.4: External Link Resilience

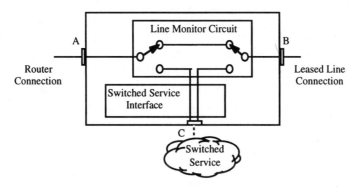

Figure 16.5: ISDN Backup Adapter

In Figure 16.5 you can see an ISDN Backup Adapter such as the one I described in Chapter 6. Using this external device, the router doesn't need any additional ISDN intelligence, and the routing table sees no break in connection.

In this diagram, the normal serial connection comes in from the router at Point A, passes through the backup device, and exits to the leased line at Point B. If the leased line is detected as "down," then the circuits inside the backup device reroute the serial line to exit at Point C, where an ISDN connection has been established automatically. While the ISDN line is operating, diagnostic tests are run on the leased line, and the communication pathway passes back to it when the line is OK. In Europe, ISDN charging is normally made on a per-minute (or multiple minute) basis. So, if a leased line fails, and comes back after a few seconds, we might as well keep it out of service for at least one minute to make sure it's stable.

These backup adapters need to be installed in pairs, which is a bit of a problem in terms of cost, and the logistics of running so many boxes.

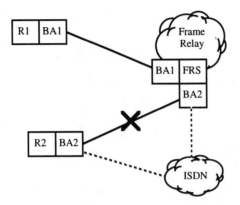

Figure 16.6:   ISDN Backup to Frame Relay

In Figure 16.6, there are two routers connected to a Frame Relay service, with backup via ISDN.   Router R1 connects into the Frame Relay Switch (FRS) through a specific connection port.   The backup adapters BA1 are paired together.   The BA1 adapter at the switch cannot be used to backup R2's connection.   As you can imagine, when the number of Frame Relay subscribers increases, the large number of boxes becomes difficult to manage.

An alternative solution is now possible from the leading routers vendors.   This solution goes by a variety of names, but is essentially an "any for any" backup system using link pools.

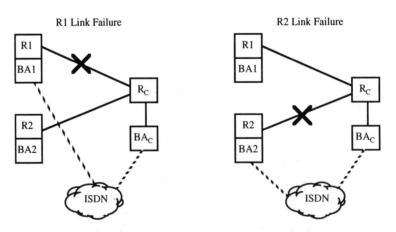

Figure 16.7:   Link Pooling for Backup

In Figure 16.7 you can see a few subtle differences from the earlier examples. On the left, when the R1 leased line fails, the Backup Adapter BA1 calls the central site router, and attaches to Backup Adapter BA$_C$. On the right, when the

R2 access link fails then BA2 also dials BA$_C$. The assumption is that the leased lines will not fail simultaneously.

You might have noticed that the Frame Relay service seems to have disappeared! The problem with the pooling technique is that the port on the central device never knows which of its fellow ports it will be backing up. When the backup connection is established, there needs to be a link handshake to confirm the protocol addresses (e.g., IP addresses) at each end of the link. This kind of handshaking is currently implemented in proprietary ways by router manufacturers, so the technique cannot be used directly to switches.

The other question that springs to mind is what happens if more than one access line fails at the same time? For this we need to look for an "n by m" line pooling technique. In other words, if we have n access lines, we can use m backup adapters at the central site. Not all routers are capable of this, so if you need it, check carefully with the reseller or manufacturer.

16.4 Duplicate LAN Services

WAN services have always been regarded as the Achilles Heel of an internetwork. However, as leased line services have become more reliable, and backup strategies with ISDN have matured, the focus of some organizations has turned towards resilience of LAN connections.

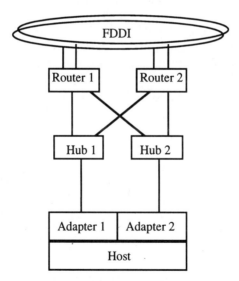

Figure 16.8:   The Ultimate Resilient Network

In Figure 16.8 I show one possible example of a highly resilience LAN system. The host computer is fitted with two LAN Adapters. Each Adapter connects to a separate cable Hub. Two Routers are provided, and each router has two LAN connections; one to each hub. The routers attach to an FDDI backbone, which is itself a dual redundant ring. The only single point of failure in this system is the host itself (or the human operator).

Systems like this are used more frequently today, especially where the host is a server. The problem is, will it work? And what factors do we need to consider if we design a network like this? Finally, are there less resilient (and cheaper) configurations that can still offer greater protection than a conventional internetwork?

These questions are tied up with the notion of the way that TCP/IP software discovers its default router. I'd like to discuss five possible options for the end systems:

- Statically configured routers
- Proxy ARP
- RIP gleaning (aka Wiretapping, Eavesdropping)
- Router Discovery
- Name Server features

16.4.1 Statically Configured Routers

In Chapter 4 I presented the IP Transmission Algorithm, and described how an IP host actually makes the first routing decision by comparing the Source and Destination IP addresses on the packet. If the Network IDs or Subnet IDs are different, the packet is sent to the default router. In simple TCP/IP implementations for PCs or Macs, the default router is statically configured, and there's only one. If the path to the default router goes down (bad cable, hub goes down, router goes down, etc.), the host cannot send traffic off the local LAN.

The first solution to this problem was simple: the Backup Default Router. Some implementations allowed a second IP address to be entered with a timeout value. If the first address could not be reached after a certain time, the Backup Default Router would become active. This mechanism works very well, but requires specific configuration at every host. Moreover, it's not very dynamic. If other routers are added, or router addresses changed, the hosts must be reconfigured.

16.4.2 Proxy ARP

I described Proxy ARP in Chapter 3. Its normal use is to allow hosts that don't know about subnetting to be deployed in a subnetted network. However, it does have an alternative use. In Figure 16.9 I show a subnetted Class B network. Host Harry is set with a default Class B mask of 255.255.0.0.

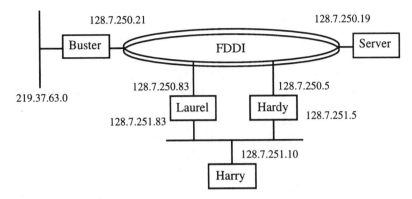

Figure 16.9: Proxy ARP as a Resilience Tool

If Harry wants to send an ARP to the Server, it will assume from the addresses and mask that the Server is on the same LAN, and will ARP *directly* for IP address 128.7.250.19; it will not try to use a Default Router. Laurel and Hardy are both configured for Proxy ARP, and will forward the ARP request onto the FDDI ring. Meanwhile, both routers will respond to the ARP request offering their MAC address. Harry will keep the most recent update (i.e., the last update received *before* transmitting the actual data); let's say Harry keeps Laurel's address.

Later, if Laurel cannot be reached for some reason, application timers will expire and force Harry to ARP again for the Server. This time only Hardy will answer, and Harry is back in business.

Note that the Server must be on the same Class B network as Harry for Proxy ARP to work in this way. However, with careful consideration, the design can be extended a little further. There is another router, Buster, on the FDDI ring that is used to connect to other IP networks (in this case to 219.37.63.0). If Buster is configured as the default router for Harry (i.e., 128.7.25.21) then the connection to the Class C network can operate through Laurel or Hardy, and will be resilient.

There is another problem with Proxy ARP. Imagine now that there are lots of other Hosts on the same LAN as Harry. The laws of chance dictate that roughly half of the hosts will be using Laurel as their Proxy Router, and the other half Hardy. If Laurel fails, all the hosts will eventually timeout and switch over to Hardy. If Laurel comes back on line, the hosts will continue to use Hardy. Unless new ARPs are sent out, Laurel will not be seeing any traffic. Proxy ARP is only dynamic until the ARP is resolved. Hosts will continue to use the MAC address until communication is broken.

16.5 Power and Power Supplies

A study by Safeware, the insurance analysis agency, showed that in 1992, 43% of claims involving computer damage were blamed on power surges. This is a US study. On the one hand, you'd expect US power distribution systems to be very well developed, but on the other hand the climate across the US is much more extreme (more severe thunderstorms, extremes of hot and cold weather, hurricanes and flooding). In Europe, we have a less well developed infrastructure in some areas, but more temperate conditions.

Problems that occur on the power company side of the connection can be broken down into *sags*, *surges*, *spikes*, *brownouts*, *blackouts* and *noise*. Before I describe these in more detail, let me just remind you that mains power operates as alternating current (AC), with a specific *voltage* and *frequency*. In Europe, the voltage norms are 200V (mainland) and 240V (UK and Eire), at a 50Hz supply frequency. North America uses 110V at 60Hz, although heavy-duty equipment (such as high end routers and minicomputers) require a 220V supply even in the US.

Power Sags

A sag is a short period when the supply voltage drops below the recommended level. This can happen when a device is switched on that uses a lot of power. In industrial environments, large electric motors, electromagnets, heaters or powerful lighting systems can cause a sag when they are switched on. Typically the sag should occur only on the same electrical circuit. I've found by experience that the human eye is good enough to detect sags before they're bad enough to effect computers. For example, in our house at 11pm, our electric water heater kicks in and the lights flicker. My PC and Mac carry on happily, and I haven't had data corruption problems (yet). Sags can cause older style hard discs to spin erratically. If you're using modern hard discs, especially those designed for portable machines, you're unlikely to suffer damage.

Power Surges

When the voltage of the supply exceeds the specified level for a short time, this is known as a surge. The period of a surge is typically half of the AC period, or longer. In Europe, this means around 1/100th of a second, and in the US, 1/120th of a second. Surges can occur when a heavy load is removed from the same circuit. A surge is dangerous because, apart from potential data corruption, the overvoltage can cause damage to electrical components. So far I haven't been using my PC at 7am when our water heater switches *off*.

Power Spikes

Spikes are very short overvoltages. Typical everyday spikes are caused by equipment such as photocopiers, fluorescent lighting, and thermostatically controlled devices like heaters and air conditioners. This kind of spike is *relatively* harmless because protection devices are included in the power supply

of modern PCs. More serious spike can happen because of electrical storms.
This kind of spike can destroy a computer, router, or anything with microchips
inside.

Brownouts

A brownout is a power sag that doesn't go away! When a power company grid
becomes overloaded, they react by "diluting" the power to each user. The effect
you'll see is lighting that dims, TV pictures may get smaller (on older TVs),
electric kettles take ages to boil. In Europe, most computer systems are
relatively tolerant to brownouts because the power supplies inside are designed
to operate over in the US at 110V. Providing the brownout is brought on
gradually, with the voltage levels remaining steady, these systems are quite
happy. In the US it's a different matter.

Blackouts

This is where power is lost completely. Blackouts can last anything from a few
seconds to several weeks, but in most "emergency" situations, it's probably tens
of minutes or hours that we're talking about. The effects on unprotected
computer systems are exactly the same as switching the computer off in the
middle of a job. The only real problem with a blackout is that surges, sags or
spikes will often happen just prior to the blackout as the power company
struggles to maintain the supply.

Noise

Noise can be caused by a variety of events: distant lightning strikes, computer
equipment, Radio Frequency Interference (RFI), and many other possibilities.
Minor noise will not even be noticed. In fact, you'd be surprised just how much
noise there is on a "clean" electrical connection. As it gets more serious, noise
has the same effect as surges or spikes; in, effect the noise signal becomes a
series of spikes.

16.5.1 Safeguarding Our Power

Given that all these horrible things can go wrong with the main power, and the
consequences to us can be serious in terms of lost data or even damaged
hardware, what can we do?

There are two aspects to power protection. First, we can *condition* our power
system to prevent damage from overvoltages or noise. Second, we can *augment*
the external power system to overcome brownouts or blackouts.

In addition, we need to consider which of these events is most likely to happen to
us. European figures are difficult to obtain since many European power
companies are in transition from monopoly to commercially open
environments. However, some sample statistics from a Detroit Edison study
(courtesy of [6]) indicate that undervoltages (sags) are responsible for 68% of

recorded power anomalies, and overvoltages (spikes and surges) for 17%. No complete outages occurred during the 14 weeks of study. I've already said that sags don't always have an effect on computer equipment; an AT&T Bell Labs report also quoted in [6] stated that 87% of power problems to computers were caused by sags lasting less tha 0.25 seconds, spikes caused 7.4%, blackouts 4.7% and other overvoltages only 0.7%. For reader outside of North America these results are interesting, because sags at 220V will cause much less of a problem than sags at 110V.

Outsourcing Your Safeguards

For some time in the US, and now just beginning in Europe, we are able to source our power from multiple providers. The theory is that a problem with one supply will not be reproduced in the other. This is a good idea, but in practice you need a third party power consultant to check the integrity and independence of these supplies for a specific installation.

However, a good idea is that power companies are beginning to offer surge protected supplies, and even centralized UPS facilities (for an additional fee, of course). Again, the third party expert view is a good idea if this type of service is your main weapon against power problems.

Outsourced services really cover both conditioning and augmentation of normal power supplies.

Surge Suppressers

As the name suggests, these devices are intended to protect against overvoltage problems such as surges and spikes. There is a wide selection of such products, with an equally wide range of quality and applicability. If possible, look for *recent* reviews of power protection devices in good quality trade magazines.

Remember, surges are a less frequent event. If you spend thousands of dollars installing individual surge protection units on PCs, printers, servers, etc., you may find that this wasn't such an efficient way to approach the problem.

Where does the surge go in a surge suppresser? An interesting question that I hadn't thought about until I read [5]. The energy in the surge is sent to earth, which might seem fine until you remember that most LAN equipment uses the same earth. In other words, the surge can be deflected into your LAN infrastructure. There are specialist devices that will prevent this problem. For up to date information on these devices you should contact your cabling suppliers, or a power consultant.

Voltage Regulators and AC Filters

These are passive devices. Voltage Regulators are designed to damp out temporary voltage variation. However, a passive device cannot create power, so they have difficulty coping with prolonged undervoltage. Some systems include battery support. The batteries trickle charge during normal operation, and then beef up the supply during sags. Generally they're low in cost, although battery systems become much more expensive. Looking at the Detroit Edison figures, short duration sags seem to be something we should be concerned with, so even a non-battery voltage suppresser looks like a worthwhile investment.

AC filters simply smooth out noise in the supply, essentially a less powerful voltage regulator that does not have the option of battery support. Top of the range voltage regulators normally include AC filtering.

Uninterruptable Power Supplies (UPS)

The UPS is normally the first thing we all think of when power supply protection is mentioned. In simple terms a UPS contains a battery system. When the mains power is OK, the battery charges up. If the mains fails, then the battery kicks in and provides some period of emergency power to the attached system. UPSs vary in size, cost and capability. I have a UPS inside my Macintosh Powerbook (it's called *the battery*). I've visited offices in which the entire computer room is protected by a UPS, with massive ranks of lead-acid batteries providing power backup. All UPSs are designed on the assumption that they only need to provide power for the period required to gracefully shut down the system.

Novell Netware servers support a UPS signaling feature. When the UPS goes over to battery power, it will keep the server running for a few minutes (in case power returns). Before the batteries die, the UPS sends a signal to the server over a simple serial connection. The server then performs a graceful shutdown.

Not all of your machines need a UPS. You'll probably choose devices like routers, servers and mail gateways that you'd prefer to keep running permanently. If this is the case, check that the UPS you're planning to use really works the way you think it does. For a Novell Server, perform a benchmark to make sure that the shutdown signaling really works (don't do this on your production server). Make sure that the handover from mains to backup power produces a waveform that your servers and routers can tolerate. In particular this is because many UPSs produce a square wave AC. While this works fine for light bulbs, some switch mode power supplies won't like it.

DC Supply

In telecomms exchanges, you may not find the devices running on AC 110V, or 220V. Instead they may be running on a -48V DC supply. This is because telecomms providers (like RBOCs and PTTs) are serious about uninterruptable service, and DC supplies are easier to back up with batteries. Some larger routers such as Wellfleet's BLN and BCN are available with -48V power. The smallest router I'm aware of with this capability is the Cisco 4000.

16.6 Router Resilience

I've discussed the concepts of LAN and WAN *connection* resilience. Is there a way we improve the resilience of our routers? I'd like to look at the hardware first, and then briefly discuss the software. Let me say one thing first. Resilience in routers costs money. There's no way to avoid it. You're unlikely to find resilience feature in entry level routers. The reason is that these boxes are now so cheap that even to design in the *possibility* of resilience would make the box uncompetitive. When I describe these features, I'm really talking about the latest high end products such as the Cisco 7000, and the Wellfleet Backbone Node. For low end devices, just buy two routers!

16.6.1   Power Supplies

The most obvious resilience feature looking through router manufacturer prices lists is a redundant power supply. Power supplies do contain some AC filtering, and "sag suppressers" in the form of capacitors. However, if the power anomaly causes the supply to fail, then it's nice to know that the router will keep on going. Redundant power is available in two forms.

Dual Supply Configurations

In Figure 16.10 I show a router with two power supplies, and two power cords. This is the configuration you'll find on a Cisco 70X0 and Wellfleet BLN2. The router can function in a fully loaded configuration with only one supply, so if one of the units fails then the router will keep going. The power supplies in the Wellfleet router can be *hot swapped*, which is a nice servicing feature. Unfortunately I can't confirm this about the Cisco 7000 since one of my sources thought it could and the other disagreed. My guess is that it should be possible because the supplies are independent.

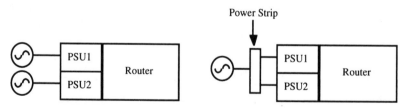

Figure 16.10:   Two Power Cords?

How important is the dual power cord issue? For most people, two power cords is actually an inconvenience. In Figure 16.10 I show the "ideal" situation on the left. Each PSU is powered from a separate mains supply. If one supply fails, the other takes the load. In reality, all of the installations I've seen use a variation on the right hand diagram. Only one mains supply is actually available, so both PSUs operate from it. I've shown the most silly situation, where a power strip is used to provide a socket for each supply. The more common variation is a user who plugs each supply into different sockets around the room. A careful check reveals that both sockets are on the same ring main, with one fuse protecting both!

AC Bus: "N+1" Redundancy

An alternative approach is taken by routers with more than two PSUs. For example, Wellfleet's BCN requires up to 3 PSUs depending on its configuration. A fourth PSU can be added to provide power supply redundancy. During normal operation, the PSUs perform load balancing. If any PSU fails, the remaining three supplies can support the router indefinitely. The faulty supply can be hot-swapped out of the unit and replaced. In this configuration, only one power cord can be provided because any attempt to introduce two cords actually adds a point of failure. Figure 16.11 shows how to provide resilient power to such a device.

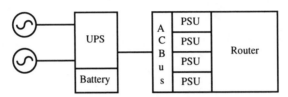

Figure 16.11:   Multiple PSU Router

This type of system is known as *N+1* redundancy because any combination of *N* PSUs can be backed up using an additional supply.

16.6.2   Processors

In Chapter 11 I look at various router architectures. Some of the architectures include multiple CPUs, but not all of these are truly redundant. At this time, only Ascom-Timeplex and Wellfleet have distributed processor architectures. The other multiprocessor architectures all include a centralized CPU that represents a single point of failure.

16.6.3   Interface Cards

All slotted routers contain multiple interfaces, so how can we use them to provide redundancy and resilience? The answer today is that we can't. Figure 16.12 shows a connectivity Device X with two LAN port attachments.

If Device X is a bridge, then the Spanning Tree protocol will operate to shut down one of these ports. In the event of the failure of the remaining port, Spanning Tree will reconfigure and the connection will, indeed, be resilient.

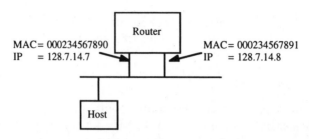

Figure 16.12: Illegal Dual Attachment for Router

However, as I discussed in Chapter 11, if we configure two ports on the same *router* to be connected to the same LAN segment, then the routing table will become confused. Currently no router manufacturers offers "port resilience," but the first implementations of "router resilience" are beginning to appear.

16.6.4 Redundant Routers

The redundant router concept is significantly easier to implement than redundant interfaces, and is generally more robust.

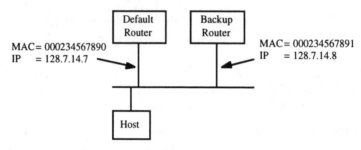

Figure 16.13: Redundant Routers

Figure 16.13 simply shows two separate routers attached to the same LAN segment. As I explained in Chapter 4, the Host will be configured (either statically or dynamically) to use one of the routers as its Default Router. If the Default Router is not available, the host must adopt a new Default. The fastest way to do this is using ICMP Router Discovery, which I described in Chapter 13. The problem is that many applications may restart because their traffic is being redirected, or they may timeout during the changeover. If you have some control over the application, then this simple form of router redundancy is the most reliable and interoperable. In Figure 16.13, the Default and Backup routers can be bought from different manufacturers, for example. If you have more sensitive applications, a new form of standby router function has been announced by both Cisco and Wellfleet.

In Figure 16.14 I show two routers. One is the "primary" device, the other the secondary. Note that, in contrast to the redundant interface configuration, both of these routers have the same IP address and same MAC address on the redundant port. Some type of *Breath of Life* (BOFL) protocol is set up between the primary and secondary routers. While the primary is still "alive" the secondary will keep the backup port in a standby mode. If the primary link fails for any reason, the secondary will activate the port and begin to forward traffic. Note that hosts will not need to modify their default router or ARP cache setting because the backup router has the same IP and MAC addresses as the primary. Sensitive applications are less likely to restart, and the timeout for the BOFL keepalive can be rather short (e.g., single digits of seconds).

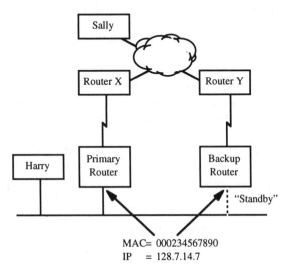

Figure 16.14:   Redundant Routers

Even better news is that the routers on the other end of the links, Routers X and Y in Figure 16.14, don't need to be equipped with the special backup protocol. IP uses a completely connectionless delivery mechanism, so datagrams from Harry to Sally will continue to flow over the intermediate internetwork.

The one problem with redundant routers is the WAN connection. The extra expense of a redundant router might be possible to justify, but the cost of the leased line is likely to be several times more expensive than the router hardware. Dial-up WAN services are likely to be a very attractive solution to this problem.

The redundant router principle is very powerful because it should be possible to back up a large, expensive router using an entry level unit. In Figure 16.15 I show a typical installation.

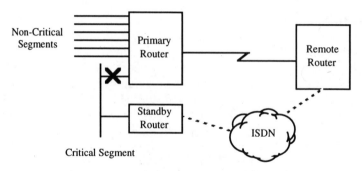

Figure 16.15:   Backup of Critical Segment

In this configuration you can see that the Primary Router is not an entry level device. The Standby router is an entry level device, so will cost between $2-3,000. The Standby router is backing up a Critical segment. The other segments on the Primary Router are assumed to be non-critical.

16.6.5   Load Media

Network devices such as routers and bridges need software to operate. They boot this software from internal storage devices such as PROM, Floppy Disk, or Flash EPROM. Older devices may even boot from network servers. This last option is not really desirable for routers because their load images are often around 1MB or more. Over a LAN this will cause few problems, but devices that boot over a WAN could be a serious problem.

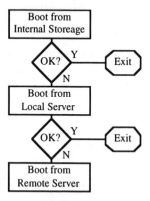

Figure 16.16:   Boot Preference Flowchart

Typically the order of preference should be internal load media, local TFTP server, remote TFTP server.

Some high end routers may offer redundant *internal* load media. This is better again than the network fallback, because TFTP is an insecure application, and many network administrators prefer not to have it operating at all.

16.6.6   Hot Swap

The most interesting resilience feature for high-end devices is the ability to install or service the units while it is fully operational. For small routers, this facility is irrelevant, and would simply add cost to the device. But imagine a router with 30 or more Ethernet LANs connected. Is it reasonable to require that this device is powered down just to install another Ethernet card? The leading vendors are now offering hot-swappable devices. Cisco's 7000 is capable of on-line servicing, in which a faulty interface card can be replaced without switching off the unit and just requiring a software reset. All of Wellfleet's slotted router products can be serviced and upgraded while fully operational, with no software disruption apart from the changed card.

16.7 End System Resilience

Resilience in hosts is an interesting concept. A colleague of mine once joked that the MTBF on a human operator was much lower than a modern computer! When we consider host resilience, we need to be pragmatic. In Figure 16.17 you can see a very resilient system.

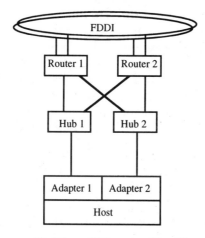

Figure 16.17:   Ultimate Resilience?

The end system has two LAN adapters, which connect over separate cable links to two separate hubs. The hubs are cross-connected to two separate routers, which are connected to a fault-tolerant FDDI backbone. When the user plugs in the computer, the fuse on the monitor blows.

Even if the monitor came up OK, how does the software react to two separate LAN adapters? An interesting example is in the realm of fault-tolerant minicomputers such as Stratus and Tandem. Until recently, the only single point of failure in these systems was the LAN connection. This was because the device drivers into the IP stack were not fault tolerant. When we try to introduce redundant interfaces into a normal computer we have serious problems, unless the applications can be written to cope with the duplicated adapters.

For a more realistic view, we need to ask ourselves this simple question. For host resilience, are we more concerned about failure points *inside* the machine or *outside* the machine?

Internal Failures

What can go wrong *inside* the host? Quite a lot, obviously. Power supplies, disk crashes, hardware failure, software corruption, etc. In general, unless you decide that a specific host application is worth the cost of buying a Stratus or Tandem fault tolerant machine, then there isn't a lot you can do to eliminate the real points of failure in the host.

External Failure

Failures that occur outside of the host are limited to the communication cabling, and power. I've already discussed the issues of redundant power supplies. Cabling is a different matter.

Most LAN technologies are designed to use one transmit path, and one receive path between the host adapter and the cabling concentrator. If the cable breaks, we lose connectivity to the LAN. FDDI can be configured as a redundant system, as I described in Chapter 5. A break in one fiber for a *Dual Attach Station* (DAS) will not cause a break in connectivity. This feature can be taken one stage further by connecting an FDDI DAS to two separate cabling hubs, as I show in the left hand side of Figure 16.18. However, much of the increase in popularity for FDDI is based on the copper variant, CDDI. CDDI hosts are almost always configured as Single Attach Stations (SAS).

For Ethernet and Token Ring, a variety of ingenious products are on offer. In the right hand side of Figure 16.18 I show a typical external device for Token Ring attachment on fiber optic cable.

From the Token Ring host to the external fiber attachment runs a copper Token Ring cable. The external fiber connection is intelligent. If the connection to Hub #1 is in good shape, then the connection to Hub #2 operates in standby mode. However, if the connection to Hub #1 breaks, then the connection Hub #2 is activated. We can do this with Token Ring because the inter-hub connection operates on the same kind of dual ring philosophy as FDDI.

An Alternative Approach

Think about the problem another way. One day you arrive at work, switch on your workstation and something goes wrong: cables, disk drives,, etc.. Exactly how exposed are you at this point? Well, you need to think about the data loss. Right about now you wish you were a bit more diligent about backups. You aren't going to get any work done today; you'll be too busy calling MIS and trying to sort out replacement machines, track down the fault, work out exactly which service contract covers the problem and so on. With a bit of luck, sometime later in the week, you might have been able to borrow an old 286 with an EGA display (look at that phosphor burn-in!). The machine doesn't have the software you need, and obviously the Windows desktop just isn't arranged the way you like it. Plus there's a lot of data restoring to do.

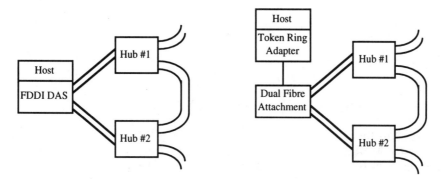

Figure 16.18:   Dual Attachment LANs

If your network makes use of diskless workstations, the situation could be completely different. The Joe Bloggs organization has just such a policy. You arrive at work at 9.00am, switch on your machine and ZAP! You have an urgent proposal to deliver to management by 10am. You walk down to the central MIS dept., and they hand you a portable PC, equipped with a LAN adapter. You go back to your work area and connect the portable to a different wall socket. Even though the portable has a big hard disc, it is configured to perform a network boot if there's an available connection. Five minutes later, you've got access to all your software (the server is backed up every 4 hours), and because of the diskless boot, your Windows desktop and directory structure looks the way it always does.

In effect, you've achieved total fault tolerance for the host system because the hardware is generic. All files are stored on the servers.

The portable PC is a shared resource for three departments in case of a problem such as this. An alternative strategy is shown in Figure 16.19.

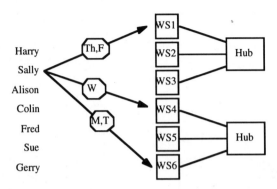

Figure 16.19:   The Generic Workstation

In this organization, workers are often out of the office. When they return, they can use any available workstation because they boot their configuration *after* login (the login runs a script or batch file based on the user name input).

16.7.1   Duplicate Servers

The obvious host to be concerned about is the file server. I've already mentioned fault tolerant system from Stratus and Tandem. Another famous server system is SFT Level III from Novell. The famous demonstration at trade shows is to drop an anvil onto one of the servers and show that no disruption is caused to the attached clients.

On a more modest scale, we can protect servers with UPSs, and perform backups on a very frequent basis. We can also use mirrored disks, duplex discs (duplicated disks and controllers), or even removable disks. Another technique of special interest is the new Redundant Array of Inexpensive Disks (RAID) technology. RAID doesn't really fall within the scope of this book, but let me give a brief overview.

RAID is a technology that makes a series of low cost, PC-style hard disks appear as a single drive. This drive can be viewed as a combined storage capacity, or can be configured for additional performance, or resilience.

RAID Level 0

This is the high speed configuration for RAID. The technique used to achieve the speed is called *striping*. Striping involves laying down consecutive disk blocks on separate drives. The blocks can be read into memory simultaneously to improve performance. This is the only RAID mode that does not offer fault tolerance, but the disk drive capacity of the RAID array equals the sum of disk capacities in the array.

RAID Level 1

This level introduces disk mirroring. Two copies of the disk information are maintained on separate drives, so only half of the aggregate storage is available in the array. Disk striping can also be used with mirroring to increase performance.

RAID Level 2

Basically the same as Level 1, but with error checking distributed around the drives in the array. The technique works best with very large files. For small files, performance can be very poor indeed. Typically about 70% of the aggregate storage is available. Performance is not sufficient for server applications.

RAID Level 3

As Level 2, but now error detection and correction is assigned to a single drive, the *parity disc*. This means that only one write can be performed at a time (the single parity disk being the bottleneck). Performance is not sufficient for most server applications. Around 85% of storage is available.

RAID Level 4

Error correction is improved, and a big performance boost is achieved because calculations are made at the sector level instead of Level 3's bit level.

RAID Level 5

Distributes the parity disk function to all discs, allowing simultaneous reads and writes. Sophisticated controllers are required. Around 85% of total storage is available.

16.8 Summary

- Resilience is the ability of the network to keep delivering service when various elements have failed.

- Resilience costs money, so careful calculation is needed to justify one resilience approach compared to another.

- Wide Area connections are a common resilience candidate. Different network solutions must be considered to get the correct view of the threats.

- Leased lines can be duplicated, or backed up using switched WAN services such as ISDN or X.25.

- Switched service access lines should be treated as a leased line.

- LAN systems can be considered for resilience features. Cabling and power supplies are the most likely areas for treatment.

- For LANs and WANs we need to consider the behavior of upper layer protocols to the resilience features.

- Mains power systems are vulnerable to a range of effects including surges, spikes, sags, brownouts, blackouts and noise. Products and designs exist to combat these effects.

- Redundancy is a feature of modern mid-range and high-end routers. Distributed processors, duplicate power supplies, redundant load media and hot swap capabilities are available.

- Duplicating interfaces or entire routers is possible if we have some control over the behavior of upper layer protocols. Standby router features are available from some manufacturers.

- Duplicating host systems is not usually cost effective, unless the host is a server. Diskless workstations that boot from servers allow workers to move between machines, or for MIS to provide "floating" reserve equipment.

- Server resilience can also be enhanced using disk mirroring systems, or RAID arrays.

16.9 References

[1]   W. Simpson. "PPP Link Quality Monitoring," *RFC 1333*. May 1992.

[2]   R. Braden. "Requirements for Internet hosts - communication layers," *RFC 1122*. October 1989.

[3]   R. Braden. J. Postel. "Requirements for Internet gateways," *RFC 1009*. June 1987.

[4]   D.Stang. S.Moon. *Network Security Secrets*. (IDG , San Mateo, 1993).

[5]   St.Clair, M. "Beyond Batteries," *LAN Magazine*. November 1992 p.137.

CHAPTER 17

Designing for Security

Easy's gettin' harder every day.

Iris DeMent

17.1 Introduction

The subject of security is vast. We typically think of security in terms of hackers entering military networks and attempting to launch nuclear strikes against Cleveland. In the real world of the ubiquitous Internet and the growing "Information Super Highway," we could soon find Internet connections into our electricity meter. In turn our meter is connected over a domestic network to our other electrical appliances, including our home PC.

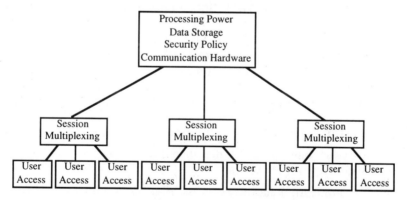

Figure 17.1: Mainframe Security Structure

For computer networks, the subject of security has always been modeled on the terminal/mainframe relationship. Mainframe-centric systems, shown in Figure 17.1, are relatively easy to secure, for the following reasons:

- Complex operating security can be set up and maintained by dedicated professionals. This process is centralized.

- There is only one source of computer intelligence in the network: the mainframe itself. This means that a single, consistent security structure can be applied over the whole organization. This process is centralized.

- The communication hardware is generally located in the computer room, so is physically secure. Hardware that's outside the computer room (such as IBM Cluster Controllers, shown as "Session Multiplexing") has a low status on the security hierarchy. Important hardware is centralized.

- Access into the network can be over dial-up circuits, but everyone must eventually arrive at the mainframe site. I can install sophisticated password controls and dial-back security at this location.

- Data can be protected because it can only exist on those big, expensive hard drives in the computer room. These can be kept secure and can be regularly backed up. Data storage is centralized.

- Power systems in the computer room can be fitted with expensive conditioning equipment. Power systems out in the remote sites don't matter because the worst thing that can happen is for a terminal to be blown up (cost = $450). A dead terminal happens once a year for a large installation.

So the mainframe model of security looks pretty good from my point of view (i.e., the poor dude who actually has to implement the mechanics of security policy). From the use point of view, things look different. The PC revolution has given us all the taste of computing freedom. In fact, this Chapter is being written 30,000 feet over the Atlantic Ocean while I'm enjoying Lufthansa's Business Class service. We can contrast the mainframe-centric view of the security issue with the typical PC environment:

- Complex security is a problem if I have distributed servers and dozens of employees have access to system administrator passwords. I can't train them all on security procedures to a level that I'd prefer.

- Computer intelligence is distributed and different operating systems have different views of security.

- Communication hardware is distributed around the network. The connectionless nature of IP communication means that even a remote office router is effectively a peer of the routers in my computer room.

- Communication pathways actually go all around the network and don't always terminate in centralized or regional server sites. In fact, every machine on the network could be a server if it wanted to. Given the number of communication paths, I can't possibly install the security hardware I'd like to.

- Data is stored all over the damned network. Some users know what a backup is, some even remember the last time they did it. Even worse, data leaves even the distributed corporate sites inside portable PCs.

If the security situation is changing so rapidly, is there a systematic way in which we can analyze the threats against us?

17.2 Threat Analysis

One of the techniques of management is that when you have too much to do, you prioritize. In a similar way, when the security threats against your organization seem to be overwhelming, you must analyze the threats in order to co-ordinate your response to them. In formal terms, this is called *Threat Analysis*. Threat Analysis is considered to be an exact science in the insurance world. For example, if you're trying to insure your car in Boston, USA, or Paris, France, you'll typically pay a higher premium than the same car in Seattle or Avignon. Insurance companies know that certain locations have a higher risk than others. They work from historical data.

When we perform a threat analysis for our own internetworks, we need to consider many factors:

- The most likely threat.

- The most scary threat.

- The total set of threats that we can imagine for the overall company.

I've written these down in the order that we normally think of them during brainstorming sessions. First of all we come up with threats that may have already happened, like theft of portable PCs or power surges. Then we come up with threats that scare the hell out of us, like viruses or fires or visits from the IRS. Eventually we end up with a whiteboard full of threats that we can then use to prioritize a strategy.

17.2.1   Most Likely Threat

What is the most likely threat? In other words, where are we most vulnerable? If we're talking about the subject of security in its broadest sense, then we don't just consider network access. We need to factor in threat from fire, power surges, theft, etc. Unfortunately, very few studies have been undertaken in this area. An excellent summary of these is offered by Stang and Moon in [1]. Figure 17.2 shows the results of a survey by Safeware, the Insurance Agency Inc., of 25,000 of its insured microcomputer sites in 1986. As you can see, power surges seem to be the most common disaster to befall a company. Note that since this information is compiled from an insurance agency, we can assume that the power surges caused enough damage to result in a claim, which was subsequently paid out. Good old fashioned theft is right behind power surges, followed by a range of traditional threats. Some network-related threats are tucked away in "Other," but my guess is that a good chunk were reported as theft.

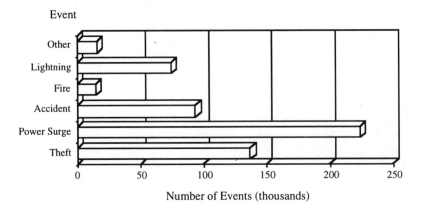

Figure 17.2:   How Many Disasters?

17.2.2   Most Scary Threat

Threats can be scary for two reasons. First, if the event happens it will cause great damage to the company. Second, I *perceive* the threat to be very scary. A good example of the combination of these events is:

"If a virus gets onto our database server, we could lose the entire customer list. It would takes weeks to re-enter the information from printouts, because all of backups would be infected too."

I don't know about you, but I'd be very scared of something like that. The problem with assessing scary risks is one of perception. We are told that viruses are scary. We are told that fire is scary. The problem is that we've lived with fire for thousands of years; it's scary, but we think we understand it (I guess a fire-fighter might disagree). Viruses have only been around for a few years and even the word is scary. Let's look at those statistics again.

Figure 17.3 shows the most expensive threat is Fire and then Theft. So if a Fire or a Theft happens to our company, it's likely to cost us a lot of money. The most frequent occurrence, Power Surge, doesn't seem to actually do much damage when it happens.

17.2.3   Most Expensive Threat

It seems as though threats that happen often don't always do the most damage. The logical way to rank the threats would seem to be to multiply the frequency of the threat by its monetary cost. I show the result in Figure 17.4.

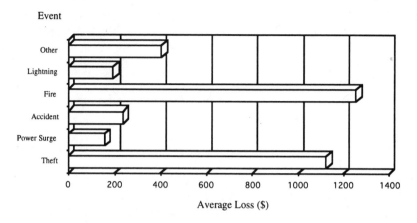

Figure 17.3:   Average Dollar Loss for Specific Threat

So now it seems clear that Theft wins the "Most Scary Threat" award by a long way. Unfortunately the figures don't distinguish network theft, such as hacking into a confidential database, from physical theft such as stealing office supplies.

I think the important thing is that they are essentially the same thing. If you're a jeweler, then you are afraid of physical theft. People can steal your business from under you. If you're a software development company, or an information retrieval company, then your life-blood is sitting on magnetic media somewhere in your company. Intruders and enemies don't need to remove the magnetic media to steal your business.

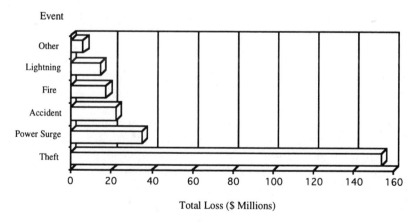

Figure 17.4:   Total Dollar Loss for Specific Threat

The classic synthesis of physical and non-physical theft is the portable PC. Let's say for example that you have a customer database, very useful to your competitor. In terms of the effect on your company, there is no difference between the following two events. First, a competitor gains access to the database through the network. Second, an engineer leaves his LAN analyzer on a customer site. The analyzer is a PC of course and has a copy of the database on it. A competitor salesperson visits the site and has an opportunity to copy the database, or even to steal the PC.

Five years ago, portable PCs were stolen for the PC. Today, they're just as likely to be stolen for the information that's on the PC.

17.2.4   Newly Emerging Threats

Just when we start to get a handle on the traditional threats such as fire and theft, fate comes up with a whole new batch of scary possibilities. Computer viruses are a good example and I talk about these in a moment. We can also introduce new threats by changing the way we do existing procedures. If we have an isolated LAN, or WAN, we might think that it's secure from outside threats. But if we add Internet access, or we use a public WAN as our backbone, then we can't be sure anymore. If we suddenly find that our business has grown to be dependent on information transfer over insecure data circuits, we have a definite problem.

As we develop our threat lists, we need to consider these "invented" threats and "procedural" threats as they emerge.

In Chapter 1 I talked about Service Level Definitions and Service Level Agreements. When designing a secure network, these concepts are very useful. First, we need to lay down of a few Points of Agreement:

- Networks can *never* be totally secure. When we seal up a side door today, some of the most intelligent hackers around will start working on another.

- Information cannot be kept confidential forever.

- New threats will continue to emerge and may bypass our current security strategy.

In other words, we can try to understand a security concept, but we must be prepared to stay up to date. We can try to protect information, but we know that sooner or later it might leak out. We can even come to a total understanding of all the threats that are leveled against our organization today and then tomorrow a new threat will appear.

Is this the time to reach for the whisky bottle? Of course not. I've been speaking in generalizations. Let's look at file encryption as a more specific example.

Our service engineer is reprimanded for leaving his portable with such sensitive information. We implement a new policy that sensitive files on portables must be encrypted. This is how my three Points of Agreement can be interpreted:

- We choose a proprietary file encryption system. After two happy and secure years we find that a bug in the program actually means that the encryption is significantly less secure than we thought. We need to upgrade to the latest fix.

- Even with the fix, we see that a determined hacker using recently introduced PowerZap technology could break the encryption in only three months! In fact, the value of the customer database has mostly to do with current information. If a competitor stole the database and then it took three months to crack the code, then the information would be out of date, or at least significantly devalued.

- As revenge against our super new security policy, one of our competitor's engineers infects one of our machines with a virus.

You can see that, on the whole, we are winning. The virus was a bit of a blow, but let's remember that very few companies would actually be childish enough to do such a thing. Even if the company had no moral standards, they would have to know that they are equally vulnerable to a counter attack (on the unofficial level) or a law suit.

The Points of Agreement have to be used as part of the Service Level Agreement definition process. If you are a network Administrator, then you have responsibility for security. But is that right? In fact you have responsibility for devising a sensible security strategy, preparing policy documents, installing security hardware software and training employees on the systems. If one of your colleagues decides not to carry out security policy, then there isn't much you can do about it without backup from management.

17.3 Threats and Solutions

I'd like to look at threats that are high in the headlines today. I feel that some of these areas are of more concern than others. I think all of these subjects are still poorly understood by many network users. I've chosen to look at:

- Viruses
- Passwords
- Encryption
- Internetwork Firewalls

As you can see, this is not an exhaustive list of topics, but these subjects are the three that occur most often *outside* of the router product area. I'll look at router-based security features later in the Chapter.

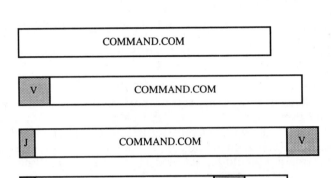

Figure 17.5:   Location of Virus

17.4 Computer Viruses

Viruses certainly have a good PR agency, because they seem to get more press that a lot of more relevant computer activities.   A recent example, the Michelangelo virus, seems to have failed to live up to its reputation.   After ten years of dealing with PCs, this year I finally came across my first hostile virus. Prior to this I'd never even met anyone who had experienced a virus attack.   All my information came third hand.

What Is a Virus?

Viruses are computer programs and are part of a small family of annoying, but technically very clever beasts:

- The virus itself
- Trojan Horse
- Worm

17.4.1   Viruses

A virus is a small piece of computer code that inserts itself into a benign program and stays there until it's triggered.   For example, if a virus enters your PC, it might target the COMMAND.COM file and insert code at the beginning, the end or in some other usable area.   In Figure 17.5 I show the three possibilities.

At the top of the diagram you can see the uninfected COMMAND.COM.   The next line shows a virus (V) that inserted itself at the front of COMMAND.COM. In this type of virus, when you execute COMMAND.COM (i.e., when you boot your PC), the virus code will run.

The next line shows a virus that inserts itself at the *end* of COMMAND.COM. In addition to the virus code, a small Jump (J) instruction. The jump instruction forces the virus code to be executed when COMMAND.COM is run.

These first two examples usually mean that the infected version of COMMAND.COM is longer than the uninfected version. A clever alternative shown in the final line is to insert virus code into rarely used parts of COMMAND.COM. Normally a jump is inserted at the beginning of COMMAND.COM to activate the code, however, the inserted code can be triggered by an infrequently used COMMAND.COM instruction such as "ver" (tells you the version of COMMAND.COM).

Viruses may be very destructive. For example, when their code executes they may damage parts of your *File Allocation Table* (FAT). The FAT is the DOS "road map" of your disk. Without a clean FAT, your data is still somewhere on the disk, but DOS just can't find it. Modern viruses remain dormant until some external event triggers the code. The most famous was the Michelangelo virus, timed to trigger on the artist's birthday.

17.4.2   Trojan Horse

A Trojan Horse is a program that *appears* to have some real function, such as a game or a utility like a fancy clock program. However, the program is actually performing some other function. This secret function could be trivial, or a real security threat. A good example of the latter is that Trojan Horse programs can be used to penetrate through the security in an installation, by posing as a useful utility. Once inside the security, the program will run on the workstations, performing its utility function. At the same time it may be monitoring passwords or collecting context-specific keystrokes.

After some period of activity, the Trojan Horse can send the information it collects out of the site using E-mail. Unlike viruses, Trojan Horses are often tailored to specific company security systems. They will be looking for specific information.

17.4.3   Worm

A Worm is very similar to a virus, but does not normally do specific damage to computer systems. The motive interesting, it's a worm program that has created a good deal of fuss over Internet security.

In November 1988, a *worm* spread around the Internet. The program was written by Robert Tappan Morris, Jr. The Internet worm was derived from long term research that Morris had been able to do in cracking passwords of Internet users at Cornell and Stanford. In simple terms, the worm program made repeated attempts at login and passwords for Internet users, using a combination of brute force and a dictionary of 52,327 commonly used passwords! The worm did no specific damage, but did use large chunks of CPU power and network bandwidth. Unlike a virus, which inserts its code into a benign host program, the worm simply installed itself on the host computers it infected. During the evening of November 2nd, 1988, the worm spread from Cornell to Berkeley, MIT, Harvard, Princeton, Purdue, U. of Illinois, U. of Wisconsin, Stanford, Lawrence Livermore Lab, NASA Ames, Rand Corp., Naval Oceans Systems Center and many other locations. Stang and Moon give a superb account of the spread of the worm [1], including tales of heroic rescue attempts by individuals across the whole Internet.

In fact, it seems that Morris had no real intention to release the worm on the evening of November 2nd. Examination of the code reveals that it was incomplete and Morris himself attempted to warn Internet authorities when he discovered the program was out of control. He was eventually convicted under the Computer Fraud and Abuse Act of 1986 and sentenced to three years probation, a $10,000 fine and 400 hours community service.

17.4.4   What Does This Mean to Me?

For many users, viruses became a problem because they chose to ignore the threat for too long. I guess it's like going to the dentist: we put it off until the pain becomes too bad. The sensible approach is to make a regular check-up and to take corrective action if we find something is amiss.

How Can I Be Attacked?

In terms of viruses and Trojan Horses, the obvious way you can be attacked is by allowing software into the company without checks. Virus-infected files can be transferred when someone inserts a floppy disk into an infected machine. Any machine to use the infected disk may also become infected.

Originally viruses were associated with floppy disk attack. Today, however, there are other ways for these beasts to get inside your defenses. Bulletin Board Systems (BBS) are operated by enthusiastic non-professionals (I don't like the implication of the word "amateur"). You can dial up to a BBS, typically over telephone lines. You enter a user name or a password and are then allowed some time to browse and download files. Most BBSs have an incoming virus check that is actually automated. However, virus scanners are actually at their least effective in a BBS context, for reasons I'll explain below.

Portable PCs, in the form of analyzers or sales tools, may be allowed to attach to the LAN segments of customers, or prospective customers. It's possible that viruses may operate over a LAN. This is a subject on which Stang and Moon [1] have a lot to say. In simple terms, if you're using Netware, then you are in good shape. If you are using UNIX, then you may be much more vulnerable.

In particular I feel that many UNIX systems are very much more vulnerable to Trojan Horse attack.

Whereas a virus pattern can be recognized inside a variety of host programs, a Trojan Horse will often be built for a specific purpose, perhaps even a specific target. It's much more difficult to protect yourself against a specific threat, because the enemy programmer will have spent time and effort to discover your weaknesses. The whole philosophy of our Security Policy relies on the fact that we cannot possibly be perfect in all areas, so by definition we will have weaknesses.

How Likely Is an Attack?

That's a really difficult question. If you pirate software on a regular basis. If you have no procedure for testing disks when they arrive in your organization. If you have a mobile computer base that attaches back to the corporate LAN. As you pile on the if's the chances of virus attack become higher. Stang and Moon provide rough data on the subject [1] in a survey of computer consultants. Around 1 in 10 of the computers in the organizations polled had been infected. Is this a figure we should worry about? Two factors to consider are:

- What percentage of these organizations had *any* form of virus defense?

- Viruses, unlike Trojan Horses, are not a "directed" threat. Whatever damage they do is basically because of our negligence.

How Much Damage Can It Do?

Viruses can only do about the same amount of damage as a fire, or power surge. If you have your entire business records on a computer and a virus scrambles the hard disk, it's just the same effect as if your power supply blows the computer up. In a well prepared organization, you would detect the problem (i.e., the smoking hole where your desk used to be), rectify the situation (i.e., buy a new desk and PC) and restore all of your files from backups.

Virus attack is just the same, with one exception. If you restore from backups, how do you know that they're not infected also? The answer must be that you assume that they are infected and then you see what data can be recovered anyway. You would normally discover a virus attack when it is triggered, like on Michelangelo's birthday. Your infected backup will not have a "triggered" virus on it, so a consultant will make a copy of the backup, remove the trigger stimulus from a clean system (e.g., set the system date to some other value) and restore the backups to that system. He or she can then try to remove the virus using commercially available techniques. If your data isn't absolutely critical, you could even try it yourself. My advice is to get professional help.

How Can I Prevent Attack?

Build virus protection into your Security Policy. Remember, each feature we implement will cost money and will require time from the MIS staff.

You could install virus protection software on every machine on the network. This software runs in conjunction with the operating system, preventing modification of files such as COMMAND.COM, or write access to the disk FAT. Each machine will require time from MIS to install the software, in addition to the expense of the software.

A typical compromise is this:

- Ban all unofficially approved software. This has the double advantage of virus protection and preventing breaches of copyright (i.e., piracy). Make a special case of BBS software, as I explain below.

- Don't *assume* that commercial software is virus-free.

- Make a policy that all floppy disks entering the company must be scanned, no exceptions: violation is a dismissal offense.

- Install virus protection software on all *portable* machines and on fixed machines that are installed in DMZ LAN segments (see below).

- Implement a Firewall policy to protect against network.

There have been a few examples recently of commercial programs containing viruses. Software companies go to great lengths to prevent this happening, but they may suffer a breakdown in procedures and whoops! Take a look at how you distribute software inside the corporation. If you hand out disks to all employees and tell them to go install it themselves, you're in trouble. Network-based installation and Corporate Licenses are allowing MIS managers to thoroughly check new software. BBS software is a special case. The data-only files (clip-art, mail boards, documents, etc.) should be harmless since viruses can only lurk inside executable files, until some lonely genius finds a way to do otherwise. Sometimes we need BBS software urgently because it does a specific job, such as a program that translates .GIF images into .PCX or .BMP format. In this case the policy should allow for *suspected* software to be run on a *DMZ Segment*. A *De-Militarized Zone* (DMZ) is simply a segment, or an interconnected network, that is not trusted.

In the routing context, the DMZ is the network to which we connect ASs that are outside of our control; such as the Internet connection. We use the AS concept and the control we have over routing information that passes from an IGP to an EGP, to prevent route leakage. For security purposes, we might isolate a given LAN segment from the rest of the network and allow suspected software to be run in this segment. The best way to achieve isolation is by literally disconnecting the segment form the rest of the network. Because the segment is contained in this way, we can selectively allocate more MIS resource to clean up machines on a regular basis.

The DMZ concept doesn't mean we abandon virus scans. The issue that I'm trying to address is with BBS utilities. You see, the fastest way for a new virus to enter circulation is via a BBS or network. Existing virus scanners will not be able to detect the new virus patterns, so BBS software represents a real threat. By providing the DMZ LAN for users who absolutely *must* have the latest conversion or compression software, then the DMZ is the answer.

Be aware of the consequences, however! If you allow a new virus into the DMZ, you then need a policy to cover files that are processed *inside* the DMZ and then taken out. If these are executable files, such as a self-extracting archive, they may be infected.

17.5 Passwords

Passwords are difficult to remember. We can force passwords to be set at a certain length, we can use special utilities to generate random passwords, we can force users to change passwords on a regular basis. We can't stop the type of behavior shown in the film "Wargames," where a computer user simply wrote down the latest password on a pull-out panel of his desk. A friend of mine claims he has no difficulty remembering passwords. He uses the names of American cars and includes upper and lower case letters if the O/S allows it. The problem is that he also has posters of American cars around his house and in his office. Even an inexperienced hacker would probably start trying "cadillac," "pontiac," and so on right after he'd exhausted the usual list of family names.

Many system administrators insist on long passwords and even insist on generating passwords centrally and distributing them to users by secure mail. There are several variables tied in together here and by understanding them a little better, we can try to "fine tune" our passwords policy:

- The longer the password, the more difficult it is to determine through a "brute force" approach.

- If the password can be chosen from a larger character set, the "brute force" approach is also more difficult.

- If the password changes regularly, then the problem of "physical discovery" becomes less important.

- If the password is chosen by a randomize utility, then "brute force" may be useless.

So what do we mean by "brute force"? Well, imagine that you know someone's user name. This is not so hard to guess because the convention in most systems is first initial followed by last name, "GBENNETT" or "gbennett" for me, for example. Operating systems are sometimes helpful in this case because they will tell you that "This user is unknown," rather than "Try again or go away." If you give the correct user, but a bad password, the error will be something like "Incorrect password." The "brute force" method simply tries a series of passwords for this user name until it is given access to the system. True "brute force" starts with "a," "b."..."aa," "ab," etc. until it cracks the system. More intelligent systems will try lists of everyday words. They will even modify their approach if you tell them something about the company, using "Einstein," "Fermi," and so on for physics, or "micron," "joggle," and so on for engineering. Brute force approaches will be limited by the number of attempts that can be made in a given time.

If we are trying to protect against a brute force attack, then we could force system passwords to be longer. This will be unpopular with users and will increase the chance of the users writing down the password. Table 17.1 shows the effect of password length, n, for a system which allows the letters "A.".''Z'' and the numbers "0.".''9'' in its alphabet (a total of 36 characters). The table assumes a "cycle time" of 2 seconds, which includes the time to send the users name and password and the time for the host to reject the attempt. The number of password of n characters is given by ((alphabet_size)^n * cycle_time). I'm assuming that the system allows passwords up to and including n characters.

Table 17.1: Effect of Password Size on Brute-Force Method

n	Number of n character passwords	Total number of passwords to guess	Time (secs)	Time (appropriate unit)
1	36	36	7.2E+01	72 secs
2	1.3E+03	1.4E+03	2.7E+03	44 mins
3	4.8E+04	4.9E+04	9.6E+04	27 hours
4	1.7E+06	1.8E+06	3.5E+06	40 days
5	6.2E+07	6.4E+07	1.2E+08	4 years
6	2.2E+09	2.3E+09	4.5E+09	146 years
7	8.1E+10	8.3E+10	1.6E+11	5,241 years
8	2.9E+12	3.0E+12	5.8E+12	188,678 years

From this evidence we might immediately decide that all of our passwords must be 8 characters in length. Well, maybe. In fact there are two things we need to consider in this table. First, we can see that a variable length of password doesn't actually make much difference. For example, I tend to use 6-character passwords with letter/number combinations. Table 17.1 tells me that I have a fairly secure habit; it would take about 146 years to randomly guess my password. However, if the O/S *only allows* 6 character passwords, then this figure falls to about 138 years. In other words, the *cumulative* search time for smaller passwords below 6 characters is small compared to the 6 character time. This is because the length of the password, n, is an *exponent* in the formula. Secondly, we *can* keep passwords down to a reasonable length as long as they are "random." I think that most people are capable of remembering a 6 character password and we can see that this size of password gives us pretty good protection.   Let's look at two other effects now; cycle time and password alphabet.

Cycle time is an important factor. The longer it takes to "guess" each password, the longer a brute force technique will require. Cycle time is a *geometric term*, in other words, if you double the cycle time, you will double the time required to guess the password. Cycle time in a network is quite important. If you combine the transit time of a packet over a busy internet with the response time of a busy host, you are looking at a cycle time of several seconds. However, if a thief has stolen an encrypted file and is able to use a brute force program on a fast computer, the cycle time may drop to a fraction of a second. For our favorite 6 character password size, this means the difference between 146 years for a 2 second cycle time, down to 36 years for 0.5 seconds.

If we look at the formula used to calculate the Table 17.1 values, we see that alphabet size is a part of an *exponential term* along with n. This means that if we increase the alphabet size, we have an exponential effect on the search time. In Table 17.1, I took a typical 36 character alphabet, which only allowed single case characters. If we allow upper case characters too, we end up with a 62 character alphabet. The search time for the same 6 character password increases to 3,750 years!

If you have the opportunity to influence the way a secure application behaves, there are a few tips that you can implement:

- Use encryption methods to avoid sending clear text passwords over the network. This approach is taken by SNMP2, for example.

- To thwart a brute-force attack, allow only three attempts at login before a disconnect is forced. Build in a delay before any further attempts can be made at this port. Have the device send an alert to the NMS when such a counter is exceeded.

- Allow large alphabets.

- If you are using encryption applications, make sure that they include a mechanism to limit the rate at which brute-force attempts can be sent to the application.

- Don't give too much information in login error messages. At the very minimum, don't allow an attacker to know that they have guessed a correct user name.

To sum up, I'd like to list the major tips on password policy:

- Adopt a password policy. Check the legal and industry regulations that apply to your installation and make sure your policy complies with, or exceeds these standards. Document and confirm this with all levels of management and enforce the policy. Include strictly defined penalties for breach of policy.

- Adopt a "Quality of Security" with your policy. Use this to negotiate standards for password size, change frequency and other policy features.

- Use the longest password you can justify for a given instance. Bridge/router passwords can be longer than user passwords, for example.

- Use shorter passwords for read-only access to devices, but these passwords should still comply with user-levels of security.

- Change passwords periodically. Remember that user passwords should be changed on a well-defined regular basis. MIS equipment passwords can be changed more frequently and randomly. Lists of passwords should be stored on a highly secure central system. Removal of this document from the secure site should be treated as a contractual termination offense.

- Avoid using the same password on all of your bridge/routers, but not if this means you have to write down the passwords in an insecure location.

- Change your passwords on a regular basis and especially when knowledgeable employees leave the company, or are moved to other departments.

- Use a password generation utility to ensure randomness. This also allows you to limit the overall length of passwords for users.

Mixing Operating Systems

Modern networks allow us to treat remote hosts as though we are working directly at them. Protocols such as NFS are the first step on the long road to truly distributed computing. Unfortunately, when we begin to use different hosts, we may also end up using different operating systems. Different operating systems use different password formats (e.g., all upper case, all lower case, case sensitive, case insensitive). Different operating systems may offer different form of *access rights*. Access rights are a parameter that ties your login and user name to the way that you can access hosts, directories, or even individual files. Novell Netware is the best example of access right flexibility and security, while DOS is the worst. All other network operating systems lie somewhere along the scale between DOS and Netware. To be fair, they tend to be more like Netware than DOS!

Many security consultants, as well as large systems vendors like IBM and DEC, are promoting the concept of single-password access. The argument goes that a single password is easier to generate, distribute and control than multiple passwords.

In contrast, most of the systems we use have multiple passwords. If we have a portable PC with a security login, we might type Password A. Then when we log onto our Novell server, we type Password B. Then we connect to a UNIX machine that is our Internet Application Host and type Password C. Then we connect to a mail system which is platform-independent and has Password D. These passwords are all generated using randomizer utilities, so are difficult to remember. As a result, we either write them down or store them in login scripts. The scripts are, of course, on our hard disc which is encrypted with a password. The problem is that we've lost the PC manual that tells us which key combination gets us into the password change utility, so we never change the password.

Who's right? Well the single password solution seem the logical way to go. The problem is that different operating systems need to adopt a lowest common denominator for password format and alphabet, which might not be that good. In addition, some systems may store user passwords in less secure ways than others. For example, I would tend to think that a mainframe password storage is a bit more secure than a PC mail package, so the hacker simply targets the mail package and can find out everyone's mainframe passwords too!

17.6 Encryption and Authentication

When we think about security, we inevitably think of encryption. *Encryption* is a technique that disguises the content of a clear message using either a *code* or a *cypher*. If we encode a message, we replace letters, groups of letters, words, or whole phrases with a single *symbol*. When we *decode* the message, we replace the symbols with the original letters from a *dictionary*, or *code book*. Coding is not normally used in communication encryption, but is used extensively in compression techniques such as Lempel-Ziv, that I describe in Chapter 18.

If we encypher a message, we replace each character with a different character in some systematic way. The length of the encyphered message can be the same as the clear text message. However, an encryption header is normally inserted, so the encrypted message is usually longer.

Authentication allows us to verify that a message from a given sender really is from that person and has not been tampered with by some third party. Authentication can tell us if a message has been altered en route, but cannot tell us if the message has been intercepted and copied.

17.6.1   Point-to-Point Encryption

There are two strategies that are normally used for encryption, *point-to-point* encryption and *end-to-end* encryption. In Figure 17.6 I show a typical point-to-point mechanism. Two sites are interconnected over a WAN using routers. The serial line from each router is fed into a "black box" encryption device. Each frame transmitted is encrypted and sent to the other end of the connection. The message is then decrypted by another "black box" and passed up into the other router. The encryption and decryption devices are readily available in many countries and are widely used in banking and government networks. Typically the commercially available units are capable of maintaining a steady throughput

Figure 17.6:   Point-to-Point Encryption

of 2Mbps into a leased line. In addition, there are units available that recognize higher level packet structures such as X.25.

If the encryption device recognizes the packet structure, it may be able to encrypt just the Network Layer portion of the frame, allowing the encrypted message to be passed over a public or private switched network. This is common in X.25 device today.

For Internet attachment, point-to-point encryption is not very well developed. If we encrypt an IP packet before it enters the Internet, then the IP routers in the cloud will just throw it away. Even more complex is that we may wish some of our network traffic to be encrypted, while other traffic remains in the clear for communication with outside organizations. In these case, we may need to resort to end-to-end encryption.

17.6.2   End-to-End Encryption

This form of encryption is installed on host systems. If we have sensitive data to send, we encrypt it in software and insert it into a normal IP packet. To the intermediate routers, it just looks like a normal IP packet. For less sensitive transactions, we don't choose the encryption option.

End-to-end encryption offers us the ultimate in control, but the penalty we pay is CPU power. Software based encryption is heavy on CPU power and hardware coprocessors for encryption are expensive (perhaps $500 per workstation). Obviously we need to install such hardware on all of the machines we expect to ever take part in encrypted conversations. These encryption devices are also proprietary, so we may not be able to obtain such hardware for all possible computing platforms in our internetwork.

A more common approach is to encrypt sensitive files for storage on our hard discs. File-by-file encryption using a third party utility means that we can transfer the encrypted file instead of the clear text version.

Whole-disc encryption is becoming common because of the explosion in the portable PC marketplace. In this scenario, the disc coprocessor of the portable machine is used to encrypt data as it is stored on the disc. Note that in this case, any read operations from the disc result in a clear text file, so this technique cannot be used for secure internetwork communication.

If we use any form of encryption, how does the receiving end know how to decrypt the message?

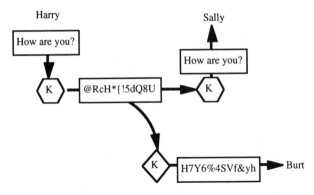

Figure 17.7:   Symmetric Key Encryption

17.6.3   Encryption Algorithms and Key Management

Unfortunately I need to summarize the subject quite dramatically, so I would highly recommend that you consult one of the references quoted for a fuller understanding of this topic [1, 4, 8].

When you read about encryption in these references, you'll keep coming across two important commercial encryption schemes: the Data Encryption Standard (DES) [6] and the Rivest-Shamir-Adleman (RSA) [7] algorithm.

Secret Key Cryptography

DES is a *symmetrical, secret key* encryption system. In other words, the key used to encrypt and decrypt the message is the same (symmetrical). And because it's the same key, you'd better keep it secret!

In Figure 17.7, Harry sends a simple message to Sally. He encrypts the message with a DES package and this uses a specific key that I've represented as a hexagon. Once the message is encrypted, it can be sent over serial lines, or even broadcast over the airwaves. Burt picks up the message and attempts to decypher it using another DES key; I've represented it as a diamond. The result is meaningless. The chances of Burt finding the correct key are mathematically very small.

Symmetrical encryption techniques like DES are CPU-intensive, but chips have been produced to allow this load to be devolved from the main host CPU. In-line encryption of DES at 2Mbps and higher has already been achieved using this kind of hardware.

The problem with symmetric encryption is that to make them truly secure, the keys should be changed on a regular basis. In fact, it would be nice if we could change the key for every message. One way to achieve this is to send the key with the message, but that's a bit of a problem. If we send the key as part of the *encrypted* message, then the receiver has no way to decrypt the key. If we send the key in a clear text part of the message, then we have given away our secret!

To solve the problem, a new type of encryption was described by Diffie and Hellman [8]. This is *asymmetric*, or *Public Key* encryption.

Public Key Cryptography

Using a Public Key cypher, every user has two keys. One of these is their *Public Key* and the other is their *Private Key*. As the names suggest, they keep their Private Key private, but can freely publish their public key. In Figure 17.8, each user is shown with a different "shape" of key. Sally uses hexagonal keys; the white-filled hexagon is her Public Key and the black-filled hexagon is her Private Key.

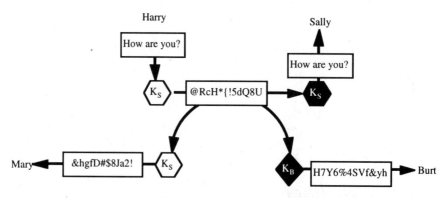

Figure 17.8: Public Key Cryptography

If Harry wants to use Public Key encryption to send a message to Sally, he encrypts the message *using Sally's Public Key*, K_S. Because the key is totally open, Harry can even *include* the key he used for encryption in case Sally is using more than one key. When Sally receives the message, she decrypts the message using the appropriate Private Key, K_S.

Burt intercepts the message and attempts to decrypt it with his own *Private* key, K_B (Burt is using diamond-shaped keys).

Mary intercepts the message and attempts to decrypt it using Sally's *Public* key, which was included in the message. Unfortunately for Mary, the cypher is *asymmetric*. Mary also gets a meaningless output. One of the principles of Public Key Cryptography is that it is "computationally impractical" to derive the Private Key given the Public Key. If we translate this into English it means that if the keys are long enough, it would take a ridiculously long time to calculate the Private Key for any given Public Key (given current CPU power).

RSA is probably the best known Public Key system and it is based on very complex mathematical calculations involving large prime numbers [7, 8]. As

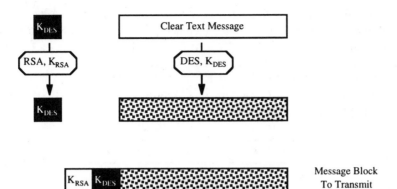

Figure 17.9:   Private/Public Combination without Authentication

I've just mentioned, it's not realistically possible (even using supercomputers) to calculate the value of a *Private* key given the corresponding *Public* key.

Unfortunately one side effect of this mechanism is that Public Key systems are very CPU-intensive: between ten and one thousand times more than a symmetric cypher like DES. For this reason, RSA is not normally used to encrypt the body of a message (bulk encryption). Instead, it is used for two other purposes:

- The transfer of symmetrical cypher keys within the message.

- Authentication based on a *Message Digest*.

I state above that the most obvious way to exchange DES keys was to put them in the message. But we can't do that because DES keys have to be kept secret. In Figure 17.9 you can see how we first encrypt the message using DES. We then encrypt the 56-bit DES key using the Private RSA key for the intended destination. We can then append the encrypted DES key to the front of the message and add on the RSA key we used.

This kind of encryption procedure is used in many secure mail packages. Public Keys for RSA are stored against E-mail names in an openly available mail list.

Authentication

This is a very hot topic at the moment because of the uncertainty over the use of DES outside the USA and the policy of certain PTTs in banning the transmission of encrypted data over WAN connections. Authentication is also becoming vital in a market that accepts electronic confirmation of transactions.

Authentication simply involves a check on a message. For example, we may want to check that the message has not been tampered with in transit. We may want to verify that if the message source address indicates that it was sent by

Sally, that it wasn't really sent by Burt. The former concept involves the use of *message digests* and the latter *digital signatures*. In fact both these techniques involve the same process. An algorithm is used to generate a fixed length message digest from an arbitrary length message. The current favorite algorithm is MD5, devised by Ronald Rivest [9]. MD5 is used, for example, for SNMP2 authentication, as I describe in Chapter 12. Figure 17.10 shows the concept of authentication using MD5.

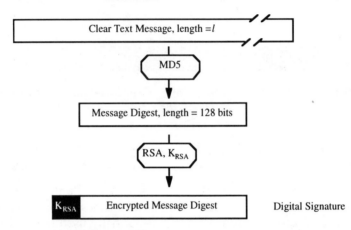

Figure 17.10: Digital Signature / Message Digest Concept

How Secure Are these Codes?

One of the controversial aspects of encryption is that systems such as DES have been "doctored" by certain US security organizations and that export of DES is subject to US controls. DES uses a 56-bit key, although the original inventors of DES, IBM, proposed a 64-bit key. The key length was reduced at the request of the NSA to allow DES communication to be broken by NSA cryptographers. Even in its "weakened" state, DES is a formidable challenge to non-government hackers. The NSA originally endorsed DES as a secure cryptographic standard for Federal Government communications. Recently the NSA have dropped this endorsement and until a replacement standard is available, have suggested that government procurement bodies make DES an optional security mechanism.

For RSA, the key length can be varied quite a bit. The lowest level of protection offered by a commercial RSA product, Mailsafe, uses a 400-bit key. It's estimated that a Cray-1 would take about 10 years to crack a message. Moving up to a more secure key of 700 bits slows down the computation of the encrypted message by a factor of 4 or 5. However, the time required to crack the message on a Cray-1 moves up to 36 million years!

Legal and Standards Positions

The US State Department requires that all US manufacturers or product developers must submit any products that involve encryption for export license approval. The *International Traffic in Arms Regulation* (ITAR) defines cryptographic devices as "munitions." In general, the State Department has been reluctant to grant export license on a general basis and requires end user certification. For authentication, however, the situation is somewhat better. The manufacturer must simply be able to prove that the device cannot be easily adapted for encryption.

In simple terms, the pressure from users is to free encryption and authentication systems from export restrictions. The pressure from security forces is to keep these restrictions in place, or to ensure that key sizes are restricted to allow codes to be broken.

In terms of standards, DES is the favored encryption mechanism because it is a bulk-data cypher which is amenable to hardware implementation. Secure SNMP and SNMP2 both use DES, as does the Kerberos System [10]. DES is officially approved as ANSI X3.92-1981/R1987.

RSA is a product of RSA Laboratories, a commercial organization. However, it has been adopted as an approved authentication mechanism for X.500 Directory Authentication in X.509. It is used in the IETF Privacy Enhanced Mail (PEM) system [11, 12, 13, 14]. The Society for Worldwide Interbank Telecommunications (SWIFT), the French financial industry ETEBAC 5 and the Australian digital signature standard, AS2805.6.5.3, are all based on RSA. In addition, the software industry is looking at the Public Key Cryptography Standard (PKCS) [15] for the validation of software in an effort to thwart piracy.

Portable Computers

A few years ago, we were afraid that our portable PC might be stolen because it was valuable. Today, we're probably more concerned that the software and data on the hard disc are valuable. Just before the Gulf War, a British staff officer had his portable PC stolen from the back of his car when he popped into a shop on the way home from the war room. We seem to have done OK in that war, so hopefully the thief was more interested in playing Lemmings, or fencing the PC to pay for his next fix.

The problem of portables is very real. When these machines are attached to the Corporate Network, they will have the same access rights as any other Network Citizen. When they leave for the night, who knows what data has been downloaded? Of course, we can't insist that portable machines are diskless!

17.7 Firewalls

In US English, a firewall is a specially strengthened wall that is designed to hold back the spread of fire in a building. In networking terms, a firewall is some kind of logical barrier that prevents the spread of some undesirable packet types. Routers are often the focus of firewall techniques because when they were first deployed, the router's main advantage over a bridge was its ability to limit the

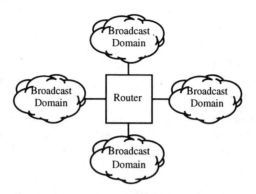

Figure 17.11:   Broadcast Domains and Firewalls

broadcast domain and effectively combat the legendary *broadcast storm*. As I explained earlier in the book, routers limit the spread of broadcasts because the majority of broadcast packets only need to operate within the bounds of a single Network ID. By using IP addressing to route packets from one Network ID to another, routers can simply ignore MAC Layer broadcasts. In Figure 17.11 I show logically how this would work.   Each of the clouds represents a broadcast domain .   This is simply the area in which a broadcast will spread.

The router allows internetwork communication to pass between broadcast domains, but prevents the unwanted spread of broadcast traffic; in other words it acts as a Firewall. If I replaced the router in Figure 17.11 with a multiport bridge or LAN Switch, I'd have to redraw the broadcast domain cloud to cover the whole diagram.

17.7.1   Packet Filters

As router technology developed, packet filtering features were introduced to allow network administrators to override standard IP routing. Packet filters can be used to improve internetwork performance, but are mainly associated with security schemes. By specifying filtering schemes, we can extend the limiting mechanism of Firewalls beyond just broadcast traffic.

A filter must specify some mechanism for the router to select the packets we want to identify. For example, if the MAC Destination address is equal to 00AA00123456 then the router will drop the packet; if the source IP address is equal to 192.32.60.1, then the router will drop the packet; if the packet contains Telnet information then the router will forward the packet and drop all other application types.

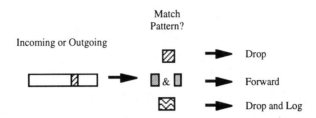

Figure 17.12: Packet Filtering

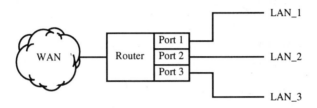

Figure 17.13: Filtering Example

Packet filtering on routers operates in a very simple way. First of all we select a *match pattern* that the router can use to select the traffic that must be filtered. Then we decide upon an *action* that will take place if a successful match is made. Filters can be applied to incoming or outgoing traffic. In Figure 17.13, for example, I show three LAN segments that have access to a WAN through a router.

Some typical filtering requirements are:

1. LAN_1 can access LAN_2, LAN_3 and the WAN.

2. LAN_2 can access the other LANs, but not the WAN.

3. LAN_3 can access LAN_1 and LAN_2, but can only run Telnet over the WAN.

4. Incoming WAN connections are not allowed, only outbound connections should be forwarded.

5. All security breaches must be immediately reported to the Network Administrator.

This example fits many security requirements, in that some departments have more trust than others, while outsiders have no trust at all! How can we build filters to achieve this degree of access control?

For the first requirement, we don't need to install filters, do we? This is just default routing. Except that Requirement 4 says that incoming calls *to* LAN_1 must be dropped. Well, I'll deal with that in a moment because it's the same condition for all the segments.

For the second requirement, it's simple. We can set two filters on the receiving port at LAN_2 that say:

- "If the destination address is LAN_1 or LAN_3, then forward the packet."

- "If the destination address is anything else, send a message to the log and drop the packet."

When any security breaches occur (i.e., dropped packets), then a message appears in the router's event log. Most routers allow you to immediately convert log entries into SNMP traps and these can alert the Network Administrator. So we're satisfying the fifth requirement too.

For the third requirement, we need filters that are configured on the incoming side of LAN_3, saying something like:

- "If the destination address is LAN_1 or LAN_2, then forward the packet."

- "If the destination address is anything else and the packet is Telnet, then forward the packet."

- "If neither of these filters applies, send a message to the log and drop the packet."

How do we tell if the packet is Telnet? Remember from Chapter 3 that each IP application uses either UDP or TCP as its Transport Layer service. Furthermore, different IP applications have reserved port numbers and I list the most common of these in Table 3.1. As you can see from this table, the Telnet server process operates at port 23. The problem is that the actual Telnet session will use *dynamically* assigned port numbers [4]. By definition we can't know what these are, but we do know that dynamic port numbers lie above 1024 (these are the ports reserved for application server daemons like *telnetd*, *ftpd* and *smtpd*). By blocking the original request at port 23, we prevent the dynamic port from being established and thus we block the telnet session.

If we want to allow the subsequent non-server port numbers to pass, the router must allow a filter statement something like:

- "If the destination port number is greater than 1023 then forward the packet."

RFC Question:	Describe the filtering capabilities of your router software.

The fourth requirement is an even more interesting one. How can we distinguish between *incoming* Telnet requests and *outgoing* Telnet requests?

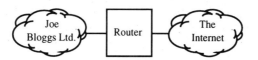

Figure 17.14:   The FTP Problem

17.7.2   Filtering Problems

Packet filtering firewalls can only do as much as the protocol stack will allow. So while it's easy to filter on a specific address, or range of addresses, it's less easy to filter on application types.   NFS is used as the basis for many applications today, but it doesn't used the convenient fixed port numbers as do other traffic types [4].   Even "well-behaved" traffic types like FTP may be a problem.   In Figure 17.14 I show a simple security example.

The Network Administrator at Joe Bloggs wants to set up some security filtering through the router that provides access into the Internet.   Amongst the other requirements is that FTP file transfers are restricted in some way.   A Joe Bloggs employee should be able to FTP data *into* the company from the Internet, but should not be able to FTP information *out*.   It's possible to prevent FTP session requests passing *from* the Internet into Joe Bloggs hosts using simple traffic filters.   However, it's not possible (using simple traffic filters) to prevent a Joe Bloggs host from connecting via FTP to an Internet host and then performing an FTP "put."   To provide this level of sophistication in a *router* is probably inappropriate for several reasons:

- Not every router user needs this level of control and adding intelligent packet filtering will raise the cost of routing for all users.

- This kind of packet filtering requires iterative, conditional testing of packet patterns.   Without doubt, such processing in the router will have a major impact on performance.

- The trend is for routers to become easier to install and maintain. Complex filtering semantics will be a major obstacle to user friendliness.

17.7.3   Filtering and Fragmentation

There is another, very obvious limitation to packet filtering for more complex patterns: fragmentation.   If we are trying to filter on information *above* the IP layer; what happens if packets are fragmented en route?   Obviously fragments have full IP addressing but the second and subsequent fragments don't have port information.   We could try preventing fragmentation, which is undesirable for performance reasons, but this might limit the choices for rerouting.   In addition, if we refuse to fragment, we're not behaving like a proper router.

192.32.60.5

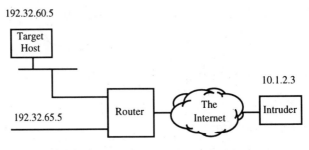

Figure 17.15:   Impersonation

17.7.4   Filtering and Impersonation

For simple source/destination traffic filters, the classic attack technique is for the intruder to impersonate some known, allowed address.

In Figure 17.15 I show an intruder trying to access some Target Host inside a corporate network that is "protected" by a router configured with traffic filters. The simplest way to bypass the filter option is for the Intruder to claim that its source address belongs to an "allowed" IP address, say on 192.32.65.0.

Obviously when the router sends back the IP traffic from the Target Host, the router will forward the traffic back *into* the corporate network.   But if the Intruder specifies *Strict Source Routing* [16] on the original traffic, then the router will override the Routing Table and forward the traffic into the Internet. Unless some other non-address filter in operating in the router, the Intruder has just gained free access to the network.

But how could the Intruder possibly know the IP addresses inside the corporate network? Well this kind of information is published, perhaps not openly, but my business card has my Internet name on it. It's a simple process to perform a reverse name translation given a host name.

Does this mean we should disable Source Routing? Possibly. You have to decide this based on your own circumstances. The point is that if we keep on disabling fundamental IP features to try and secure our network we will eventually run out of options. Surely there must be a better way?

17.7.5   Application Hosts and Access Gateways

In Chapter 13 I raised the subject of Internet address registration and described a means to implement private network addressing using Application Hosts (also known as *Access Gateways*). Address convenience is only one use for these beasts; network access security is their primary function.

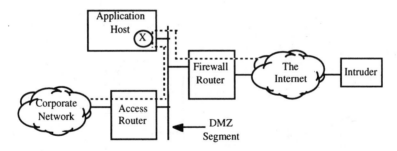

Figure 17.16: The Application Host Mechanism

In Figure 17.16 I show the classic Application Host configuration. Traffic from the Internet flows through the Firewall Router. At this router, strict filtering is maintained. In effect, the only place that traffic can go is to one or more Application Hosts in the *DeMilitarised Zone* (DMZ) LAN segment. A DMZ is a place where military action is discouraged, but you go there at your own risk. In internetworking terms, the DMZ is a place where we need to be very suspicious.

The only route for traffic in the DMZ is into one of the Application Hosts. In this case I've only shown one, but you could maintain several if you need to distribute application load. The traffic that enters the Application Host can suffer several fates, depending on your configuration.

- At point X, the IP traffic may not be processed by the host, but may just have its address changed. In this case, the host is acting as an *Address Translation Gateway*. Translation Gateways are not security devices.

- At point X, we terminate the traffic in a session, with user name and login requirements.

Assuming we're using the second mechanism, we immediately receive several benefits:

- Incoming sessions are required to login.

- Incoming traffic streams are reassembled if any fragmentation has taken place.

- Address Translation can still occur.

We can achieve Address Translation by configuring the Application Host with more than one IP address. Typically the host will have two addresses; one is an Internet registered address, the other is an address within the Corporate addressing scheme. Traffic can only pass through the Access Router if it has been assigned an address within the Corporate addressing scheme. These internal addresses are never advertised outside the Firewall Router.

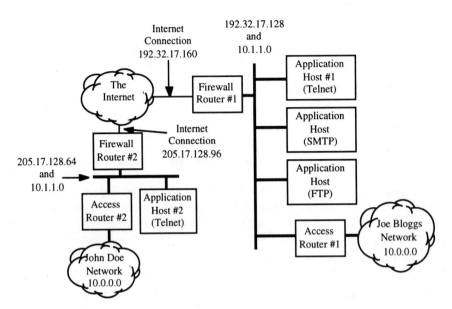

Figure 17.17:   An Application Host Example

In Figure 17.17 I show a similar diagram to the one I included in Chapter 13, which contains specific IP addresses and multiple Application Hosts.

Attacks on the Application Host

Put yourself in the position of a hacker, trying to penetrate your network. From external Domain Name Servers, you can assume that your Internet addresses will soon be known to whomever would like to know them. So our hacker can find out the *Internet* address of the Firewall Router and maybe take a guess at the addresses of the Application Servers on the access LAN segment. From there it's a simple job to say:

telnet 192.32.17.130 (let's assume this is the address of the Telnet server)

The server happily responds with a "login, user name" barrier. In theory the hacker is locked out. It's possible to install "secure" versions of UNIX on these servers that will be difficult for the average hacker to penetrate. A secure version of UNIX will, for example:

- Have various "system utilities" removed.

- Enforce a minimum password length, format, frequency of change and number of unsuccessful login attempts.

- Have various "side doors" in applications like SMTP, FTP and Telnet firmly closed.

The password features will make "brute force" login attempts rather difficult. I look at some of the mathematics of this later on in the chapter.

Protecting the Application Host

The Application Host is likely to be a UNIX machine. You have two choices to ensure that this host is secure. First, you can buy a secure UNIX version, or a packages access gateway. Second, you can configure an existing UNIX system and plug the most obvious holes.

The first choice is relatively simple. UNIX System V.4.2 has been awarded an NSA B2 security classification (see below on *Orange Book*). This classification basically means that access control labels are associated with any element within the operating system. The "B" classification makes this labeling mandatory and the "2" indicates that the protection falls within the control of a structured security policy document. The document describes which elements are critical and which are non-critical from a security standpoint.

Another aspect of System V.4.2 is that the most obvious sidedoors in UNIX applications are removed.

We can look at a few of these sidedoors briefly. For a more detailed view, you should refer to [4], or subscribe to a CERT mailing list (see Glossary).

UNIX can be made more secure by diligent system administration. Note that you can never be sure that this homemade approach is sufficient for a secure Application Host, but it should stop the casual hacker.

- Check your system logs on a regular basis. Especially check for entries from unexpected sources, in the syslog and accounting log. If you are using an Orange Book UNIX, there is a C2 log also. Unfortunately this can only pick up casual hackers, or intruders who've been interrupted for some reason. An experienced intruder would be quite capable of editing the logs to remove evidence of tampering.

- I explained the concept of a Trojan Horse program earlier. These are often found in common UNIX utilities such as telnet, login and ftp. Check the integrity of these files on a regular basis against secure backups, or stored checksum values.

- Check your search path as part of your Trojan Horse hunt. Entries at the beginning of the path entry will be found in preference to the files you *think* should be executing.

- Check for hidden files. These may contain non-printable characters.

- Beware of any files that set the user ID to a privileged account, or even root (e.g., the mail demon!). Shell copies with root access are especially suspicious.

- Remove any software that isn't specifically needed. Applications like sed, emacs, cc, awk and any other software development tools are a gift for the hacker.

- Remove unwanted daemons.

- Modify the kernel to limit TCP connections to a known range of ports. Especially eliminate support for TFTP, sunrpc, printer or any of the BSD "r" commands.

- Isolate the machine so the only way to reconfigure it is from its own keyboard.

- Change access rights in all system directories to mode 711. This means that ordinary users will not be able to view filenames. Make chmod unavailable to users to prevent attempts to change the attributes back.

- Select a random password for the Application Host and change it regularly.

Attacks on the Internal Addresses

If the hacker draws a blank at the Application Host, they could try to log directly onto a Corporate host using its private IP address. In the Joe Bloggs network, all of these hosts will have an IP address of 10.X.X.X. From *outside* of the Joe Bloggs Autonomous System, the Network ID 10.0.0.0 should never even be advertised (remember it's one of the private IP addresses reserved by RFC 1597). Hacker attempts at a direct 10.X.X.X address should be answered by an ICMP "Network Unreachable" message.

Direct attempts *from within* the Joe Bloggs AS are a different matter. The private 10.X.X.X addresses are advertised throughout the Joe Bloggs network. At this point we must clarify the problem:

- A penetration attempt from within the AS by a non-employee is indistinguishable from the same attempt made by an employee. However, the non-employee must have physical access to the LANs in the AS.

- Penetration attempts made from *within* the organization are a matter of Security Policy.

In other words, using the Application Host method, we can pretty well seal our organization from security attempts from *outside* the organization.

"Donating" Chosen Information

In the Joe Bloggs network, there may be specific information that we want to be made public. For example, Joe Bloggs may manufacture some kind of communications equipment. If pricing and licensing policies allow it, Joe Bloggs may make software updates freely available on an Internet "Anonymous

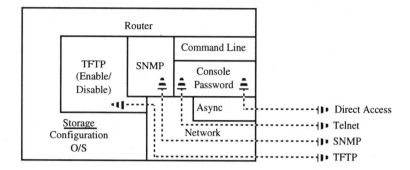

Figure 17.18:   Access Methods to Typical Router

FTP" server. In this case, the FTP Application Host would be configured to allow anonymous FTP to be made from a specified directory on the UNIX Application Server. To prevent corruption of these images, a read-only access right could be configured on the directory.

Other public directories might be used to contain publicity materials such as brochures, application notes, newsletters or any other public domain documentation.

Other directories might be locked up with passwords. Technical bulletins, bug lists or competitive information would require a valid user name and password.

17.7.6   Securing Bridges and Routers

We should look upon modern bridges and routers as network hosts also. These devices have operating systems and store valuable data. They must be secured just like a host. Fortunately, routers and bridges have limited application content. Typically these are limited to TFTP (for the transfer of configuration and O/S) and Telnet (for configuration and management). SNMP is also a standard application, but I'll deal with SNMP security below.

TFTP Security

TFTP is a simple file transfer utility that has absolutely no security. If you have TFTP enabled on a bridge or router, you should be prepared for potential problems. Obviously you do need the features of TFTP to transfer configuration files and to allow you to upgrade software on remote devices. Unlike TFTP in a host environment, the file system in a typical router is rather simple, more like DOS than UNIX. In particular it may not be possible to mark configuration files as "read-only" and it's certainly not possible to assign access rights according to user name.

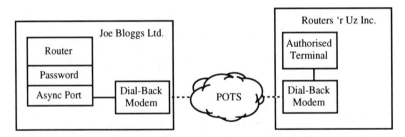

Figure 17.19:   Secure Third Party Terminal Access

The best way to maintain security with TFTP is to enable the feature just before you use it and disable it right after you finish.   The enable and disable commands are protected by Telnet or SNMP security.

Async Port Security

Most routers are designed with simple asynchronous terminal ports to allow local configuration of the router.   The terminal gives us access to whatever user interface is implemented inside the router itself.   Most implementations are command-line based and are not widely known for their user-friendliness.

Many network users today have contracted third party maintenance organizations for all, or parts of their network.   In Figure 17.19 I show the situation in which Joe Bloggs Ltd. have a contract with Routers 'r Uz Inc.   The service company obviously needs access to the routers for diagnostic purposes and the best way to achieve this is to use a conventional dial-up telephone connection.   Dial-up security is very well developed.   In the diagram, for example, I show that the Joe Bloggs router is protected by a console password. Even better, the service company provides dial-back modems.   These work as follows:

- All of the routers at Joe Bloggs are equipped with dial-back modems.   Each modem at Joe Bloggs Ltd. is configured with the same telephone number of the service contractor, Routers 'r Uz Inc.

- When the service technician needs access to the Joe Bloggs network, she dials the appropriate number for the router she needs to service.

- When the modem on this router accepts the call, it immediately hangs up and dials the stored number for Routers 'r Uz.

- The technician is attached to the async port of the router and must give a password, if one is configured.

For really secure sites, we can even use encrypted modems, although by using V.34 compression modems, we can achieve some level of protection from the casual hacker.

Telnet Security

In a typical router implementation, Telnet is used to allow console access over the network. In other words, whatever you can do at the console, you can do with Telnet. Ideally we should have the same safeguards on our Telnet connection as our async connection, but this is not the case. Dial-back Telnet does not exist and even if it did, Source Routing would offer a tempting sidedoor.

Like TFTP, Telnet should be disabled during the normal operation of the router. You would enable Telnet during a debugging phase, or while commissioning a system.

SNMP Security

In Chapter 12 I described the basics of SNMP and that the original SNMP system lacked any serious security features. If we use an insecure SNMP, what exactly is our exposure?

Remember that SNMP is a database system that allows multiple routers to be monitored and configured simultaneously. In contrast, Telnet is session-based and only one router at a time can be managed. Since SNMP was first introduced in 1988, all the major vendors have operated SNMP in a "read-only" mode. In effect, SNMP is used to monitor the system and to transmit asynchronous alerts (traps). If modification is required, then a Telnet session is opened.

There have been two separate initiatives towards improving the security of SNMP: Secure SNMP and SNMP2, both of which I describe in Chapter 12. The problem was that the need within the marketplace could not wait for these standards to be finished. The response by leading manufacturers Cisco and Wellfleet has been to replace the user-hostile Telnet interface with a session-oriented, Windows-driven interface. Cisco's CiscoWorks uses a proprietary real-time and batch transfer protocol. Wellfleet have actually enabled the SNMP *set* capability, with an optional authentication mechanism based on a pre-release SNMP2. Figure 17.20 shows how this mechanism operates for a user of the leading NMS package, HP OpenView.

OpenView has no encryption or authentication mechanism, so the SNMP dialogue between the Wellfleet router and the UNIX NMS must only involve SNMP *get* and SNMP *trap*. Configuration messages from SNMP are generated by Wellfleet's Site Manager application which runs with OpenView. The SNMP dialogue between Site Manager and the Wellfleet router is covered by an encrypted counter authentication tag. If the router receives and SNMP *set* command which does not have an appropriate counter entry, it will ignore the *set* and generate an authentication failure *trap* which is sent to OpenView.

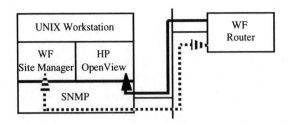

Figure 17.20: Wellfleet's SNMP Authentication

Wellfleet's system *does not* encrypt the entire SNMP message. Some countries, including France, forbid the transmission of encrypted messages over their WAN connections. Authentication messages can be sent over these links because authentication does not represent "data."

17.8 Security Policy

The Security Policy document should be the central focus for your efforts. This document should describe the issues that you've considered. It should contain background references and product information as well as the basic policy statements.

Security policy should be linked to employee terms and conditions. In effect, deliberate abuse of the policy is an act of misconduct. You need to discuss exactly how that relates to your own company terms and conditions of employment. Remember that unions are very sympathetic to security policies for three reasons:

- It's in the best interest of the company and therefore helps to secure the jobs of their members.

- There is a bilateral obligation on the part of the company. In other words, the privacy of the employee is also protected by the Security Policy.

- A good Security Policy actually gives their members guidelines in which to work. If a member is ever accused of a security violation, the Security Policy can work as much in the employee's favor as the company.

Figure 17.21:   Dynamic Effects on Security Policy

Don't rely on legislation for help with computer crime. The record to date has been lousy [1]. Without exception, the offended party has come off worse because of the time and expense of going to court. The penalties meted out today are illogical for all crime, so why should we expect computer crime to be different?

17.9 Summary

- Security is a central part of any network design.

- The nature of modern networks makes them far more vulnerable to security penetration than older, mainframe-centric systems.

- Even mainframe system are less secure today because the "dumb" terminals we use to attach to them are no longer that dumb!

- Traditional threats are still a major concern for network administrators. Security and Resilience should be considered at the same time.

- Viruses represent one of several new threats. Although the impact of viruses may be overstated, the means of dealing with the problem are straightforward.

- Adopting a sensible password policy is one of the easiest and cheapest forms of security.

- Password policy is made more difficult for the Network Administrator because of the diversity of operating systems and application packages.

- Encryption can be a useful technique to protect sensitive data transfer over private WANs.

- Encryption can be performed on a point-to-point basis over serial lines, or end-to-end from one application to another.

- Two main forms of encryption are in use: Symmetric Key and Asymmetric Key. These are also known as Secret Key and Public Key encryption respectively.

- DES is the best known form of symmetric key encryption. It is a fast technique that is suited to the encryption of the entire message. However, the key is the same for the sender and receiver, so must be exchanged by some other, secure technique.

- RSA is the best known form of asymmetric encryption. RSA is slower than DES and is normally used to encrypt only parts of the message, or to send DES secret keys over the network.

- RSA is also used for authentication. In this technique, the receiver can verify that a message has not been modified in transit and can verify the sender's identity.

- All form of encryption techniques are subject to export control by the US State Department. Authentication systems are not subject to such stringent controls.

- Encryption utilities for portable PCs are a useful part of a security policy.

17.10   References

[1]   D. Stang. S. Moon. *Network Security Secrets*. (IDG, San Mateo, 1993).

[2]   S. Fisher. "DARPA Sets Up Response Teams to Tackle ARPANET Emergencies," *InfoWorld*, March 1989, p43.

[3]   S. Salamone. "Internetwork Security: Unsafe at Any Node?," *Data Communications*, September 1993, p60.

[4]   W. Cheswick, S. Bellovin. *Firewalls and Internet Security*. (Addison-Wesley, Reading MA, 1994).

[5]   D. Brent Chapman. "Network (in)security through IP packet filtering," Proceedings of the Third Usenix UNIX Security Symposium, pp63-76, Baltimore MD, 1992. This document can be downloaded by anonymous FTP from FTP.GREATCIRCLE.COM as "/pub/firewalls/pkt.filtering.ps.Z."

[6]   National Bureau of Standards, "Data Encryption Standard," *FIPS Publication 46-1*, January 1988.

[7]   RSA Data Security Inc., "PKCS#1: RSA Encryption Standard, Version 1.4," June 1991.

[8]   W. Diffie, M. E. Hellman. "New Directions in Cryptography." *IEEE Transactions on Information Theory*, IT-22:644-654, 1976.

[9]   R. Rivest. "The MD5 Message-Digest Algorithm." *RFC 1321*. April 1992

[10] J. Kohl, B. Neuman. "The Kerberos Network Authentication Service (V5)," *RFC 1510*. September 1993.

[11] J. Linn. "Privacy Enhancement for Internet Electronic Mail: Part I: Message Encryption and Authentication Procedures," *RFC1421*. February 1993.

[12] S. Kent. "Privacy Enhancement for Internet Electronic Mail: Part II: Certificate-Based Key Management," *RFC1422*. February 1993.

[13] D. Balenson. "Privacy Enhancement for Internet Electronic Mail: Part III: Algorithms, Modes and Identifiers," *RFC 1423* February 1993.

[14] B. Kaliski. "Privacy Enhancement for Internet Electronic Mail: Part IV: Key Certification and Related Services," *RFC 1424*. February 1993.

[15] B. Kaliski. "An Overview of Public-Key Cryptography Standards." *Connexions*. May 1992.

[16] Sidnie Feit. *TCP/IP; Architecture, Protocols and Implementation.* McGraw-Hill. 1993.

CHAPTER 18

Designing for Performance

> *Don't ask the barber if he thinks you need a haircut.*
>
> **Expert Advice, First Law Of**

18.1 Selecting Service Level Definitions

In Chapter 1 I discussed the concept of Service Level Agreements. Using these agreements, the Network Administrator is able to control the terms under which they will design the network. Service Level Definitions within the Agreements can be used to tightly define performance, reliability or security elements. Using the Definitions, we also define how these properties are measured and how they should be recorded. The overall effect is that we were the original controllers of how the network was designed and we remain in control of how the network is judged by its users.

Please don't get the idea that we are using Service Level Definitions to tip the user/provider balance in our favor. We are simply making sure that the scales are balanced at the start and that we have a scientific way to determine if they've shifted.

If we're looking at the general concept of "performance" as a quality metric, we need to be even more careful. There are at least a dozen parameters that we could choose to measure and still claim that they have something to do with performance. Here are some examples:

- Packet forwarding rate (for switches, bridges and routers)
- Throughput
- Packet loss rate
- Transaction handling rate (for application servers)
- Response time (for any acknowledged transaction)
- Network latency
- Data Transfer Rate

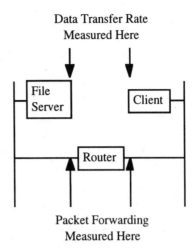

Data Transfer Rate
Measured Here

Packet Forwarding
Measured Here

Figure 18.1:   Where Do We Measure?

18.1.1   Simple and Compound Parameters

I don't really want to spend time defining all of these parameters, because I could then write down another dozen or so that are relevant to a particular system. It would be a never-ending task. Scott Bradner has defined a number of these parameters that relate to specific IP internetwork performance [10] and I recommend a quick browse through RFC1242 as good background material from one of the original benchmarking veterans.

Let's take a look at this list of parameters at a higher level. What's the difference between, for example, "Packet Forwarding Rate" and "Data Transfer Rate." You might think that one is measured in packets and the other in bytes and you can just convert between the two if you know the packet size. Not really true.

Packet Forwarding is normally a *simple parameter*. This means that the result of the measurement has been produced by a single system or subsystem performance capability.

The way that Data Transfer is normally defined means that the result is actually the *synthesis* of the performance of several systems or subsystems.

I've shown this concept in Figure 18.1.

For Packet Forwarding, we simply measure the output rate of the router. In benchmark tests, the output rate normally cannot be greater than the input rate, because any processes that generate data within the router are switched off (e.g., routing protocols, network management, etc.). The resulting measurement should only be a result of the router performance and doesn't involve any other systems (in this case the client or server). If we wanted to compare Packet

Forwarding rates between different routers, or different version of software on the same router, we know that external factors (like upgrading the server performance) shouldn't matter.

18.2 Measurement Tools

The typical measurement tool for benchmarking is the *Network Analyzer*. Probably the most famous of these is Network General's "Sniffer" product, but the market includes other hardware-based products from Wandel and Goltermann, Tekelec and Hewlett-Packard. Software based analyzers that use popular PCs and LAN adapter are available from Azure Technologies, Protocols Inc. and Triticom. One of the most interesting benchmarks of analyzers was published by Data Communications in their LAN Interconnect edition in January 1994 [12]. This test was actually designed to test the accuracy of analyzers, but it gives a good idea of functionality and pricing.

18.2.1   Outsourcing Your Benchmarks

Every networking vendor will, at some stage (i.e., when their latest benchmark shows them beaten by their biggest rival) admit that benchmarking is a "black art" and the overall topic so complex that it should only be undertaken by professional labs. Benchmarking information is actually available from a number of third party sources:

The Harvard Test Lab

Probably the most famous benchmarker of all, Scott Bradner's Lab at Harvard U. performs public domain testing on any bridge/router products that are provided by the manufacturers.

For the public testing, Bradner's lab produces its own test schedule; it's not influenced by individual manufacturers. You submit your product and you take your chance. The results are targeted for publication just before Interop shows, although since these are now virtually continuous around the world, I guess the lab just tests as fast as it can.

The Harvard lab pioneered some of the first automated test procedures. These used switching hubs like the Alantec Powerbits to generate reproducible traffic streams on multiple ports at the same time. One of the Harvard test beds is shown in Figure 18.2.

In this test, data is generated *by the hub itself* using a pre-programmed packet buffer. Six *streams* of Ethernet traffic are sent through the router under test *simultaneously*.

Bradner's tests are widely distributed by manufacturers to show the performance of their products. If a manufacturer does not provide Bradner data, the customer will demand it, or will just FTP the information off of the Harvard

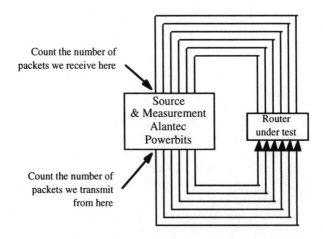

Figure 18.2:   Harvard "e2e6.*" Test Bed

server (hsdndev.harvard.edu, 128.103.202.40).   You can download test descriptions and even scripts for the automated test devices from the same server.

The Benchmark Working Group, chaired by Bradner, stresses that benchmarking is just one factor to consider, both in terms of the overall system performance and the purchase of equipment. The public testing done by the lab *must* be of a generic nature, in order to test the widest range of products.

Over the years, the Harvard lab has adapted its tests to mimic real world situations, but can never duplicate an individual customer network. The changes in the test suits include:

- The use of multiple data streams to load down routers.

- Inclusion of non-IP protocols such as IPX, DECnet and AppleTalk.

- Examination of packet loss rates; how much of this data *really* gets through?

Customized Benchmarks

The ultimate reassurance for customers is a customized benchmark. Logically this is the only way to be sure that a given device will perform as required. There are three variations on this theme:

- Pay a third party lab to perform a benchmark.

- Ask a manufacturer to demonstrate a custom test bed.

- Do it yourself.

Third party labs will gladly emulate any environment you like; you pay more money the more complex the test. In reality, the third party labs are only an economical proposition if you want them to perform a well-known test. For example, in the latest edition of Data Communications, you see a Tolly Group benchmark on Joe Bloggs GigaGateway. You are just about to buy a similar product, the Jane Doe HyperPortal and you'd really like to see the comparative performance. You can pay the Tolly Group to reproduce their previous test on the HyperPortal. Because they already have test scripts and layouts, this kind of third party test will cost much less than a completely customized benchmark.

Manufacturers or system integrators are often willing to demonstrate the performance of their equipment in specific environments. Do not ask a manufacturer to reproduce Bradner or Tolly Group tests, it's a waste of time. In general the third party labs will do a much better job for the tests that they undertake. Let's face it, manufacturers should know how to get even better results out of their kit; a third party lab is in the same position you'll be in. For manufacturer-sponsored tests, keep it simple. Even though the *salesperson* wants your business, he or she may not have access to unlimited equipment and engineering resources. By focusing the objectives of your test, manufacturers, reseller and customer are more likely to be happy. Remember to set goals for the benchmark, otherwise why are you performing it? What happens if the equipment *does not* pass the test? The salesperson will probably ask for the order if the equipment passes, so you should have some objective prepared for a fail result.

If you decide to test the equipment yourself, there are two possible approaches. First, you borrow the equipment for a limited time period. You'll find that this period will be around one month, so plan your test schedule accordingly. Bear in mind that for one month, you will probably get good backup support from the reseller or manufacturer presales engineers. If you try to drag the tests on beyond this, you'll find the salesperson losing interest, they've got sales targets to fill within specific timescales.

The second option applies to very large network projects. In such projects you should *always* include a pilot phase. Piloting a system is simple, you just install a smaller version of the real thing and see what happens. Piloting is *the* best way to find out how this equipment will behave. By definition, at the end of the pilot phase, you should be prepared to throw the equipment away and try something else if the pilot does not meet its objectives. In Figure 18.3 I show a flowchart for a pilot project system.

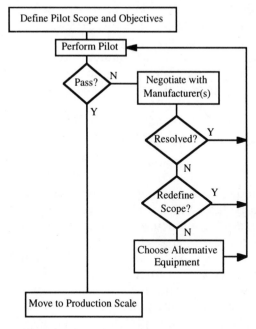

Figure 18.3:   Pilot Project Flowchart

18.3 Understanding Limiting Processes (Bottlenecks)

Benchmarks generally tell us about the performance of individual subsystems. When we construct Service Level Definitions and agreements, we need to understand the performance of the end-to-end process.

For example, if we are using an old 286 PC as a file server, what's the use of installing Pentium clients all around the network? Similarly, we can't expect the same level of performance from a WAN service compared to the same service operating on a LAN.

In Figure 18.4 you can see a PC File Server, two routers and a portable PC client. We can obtain benchmarking information on all of these components as follows:

- File server performance; capable of maintaining 8Mbps into buffered disc controller.

- Routers; 14,000 pps onto Ethernet.

- Portable PC; 1Mbps parallel port Ethernet adapter.

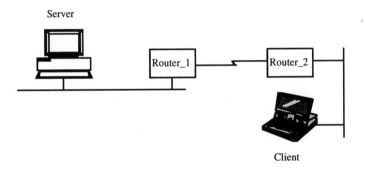

Figure 18.4:   Where Is the Bottleneck?

Obviously the first point to note is that the two routers are connected by a serial line, let's say a 64kbps connection. Since 64kbps is by far the lowest number we can see, we ought to be able to be certain of getting this throughput between the client and server.

When we perform a pilot test, we see about 8kbps of performance. Why?

To detect performance bottlenecks we need to go through a performance checklist. Here is a simplified checklist. As we progress through the chapter, we can hopefully narrow down the cause of the bottleneck:

- What is the slowest device in the data path?
- Is my end-to-end performance slower than this device?
- Is the device benchmark valid for the protocols I'm using?
- Am I sharing the data path, i.e., am I using multiple streams?
- Are there software effects?

I'd like to consider a few of these points now.

18.4 Sharing Effects

When we talk about LAN and WAN speeds, one of the important things to remember is that these channels are usually shared between many users.

Sharing LANs

Benchmark numbers are often misleading because they are performed with single devices on the network. For example, a single Ethernet segment is capable of forwarding a maximum of 14,880 frames per second. This figure is derived as follows:

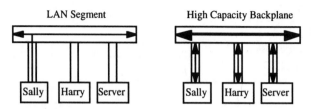

Figure 18.5: LAN Switch Performance Boost

- Ethernet has a data transmission rate of 10Mbps.

- The minimum frame size allowed by the IEEE 802.3 standard is 64 bytes. This number excludes the 64-bit preamble and 9.6µs interframe gap.

- The total length of a *minimum* sized Ethernet frame is therefore (64x8)+64+96 = 672 bits.

- The number of 672-bit frames that can fit on a 10Mbps LAN is 14880.

However, this calculation assumes that the transmitting station has exclusive access to the Ethernet. What happens if two or more stations aretransmitting? In fact, the accepted throughput for Ethernet is between 3 and 4Mbps for multiple stations. This is the equivalent of 5,900 minimum-sized Ethernet frames per second.

On Token Ring or FDDI, the sharing algorithm is *much* more efficient. On a 4Mbps Token Ring, multiple users actually get an aggregate of about 3.9Mbps. On a 16 Mbps Token Ring, the aggregate is about 15.9Mbps and on FDDI it's over 95Mbps.

Nevertheless, if we have *n* users on a LAN, we will receive 1/*n* time the overall bandwidth to each user, even if the sharing algorithm is 100% efficient.

The switched LANs that I describe in Chapter 5 are the most efficient way to overcome LAN sharing issues. In these systems, the shared LAN segment is replaced by a high speed backplane in a multiport bridge.

In Figure 18.5, you can see on the left hand side, a traditional LAN segment. If Sally gains access to the LAN for communication with the Server, not only does she block Harry's channel, she also prevents the Server from simultaneously replying. Full Duplex LANs solve the latter problem. On the right hand side of the diagram is a typical LAN switch. In this system, every user has a "private" LAN segment so the traditional access control sharing effects are eliminated. In reality, of course, all of the users still want access to the server so it turns out that the server LAN connection becomes the bottleneck. At this stage, we can add multiple LAN cards into the server (if the operating system supports such a capability) until something *inside* the server becomes the bottleneck.

Sharing WANs

WAN bandwidth is especially precious for two reasons. First there is (and will always be) a lot less of it than on a LAN. Second, we have to pay a lot more for WAN bandwidth.

WAN-attached devices such as routers normally make use of RAM buffers to smooth out the massive difference between local and remote bandwidth. The assumption is that bursts of data from a LAN-attached host will last only a few tenths of a second before some form of response is required from the destination. For example, in Figure 15.4, the portable PC might be using a UDP-based file transfer protocol. UDP will typically transmit up to 8kB of data before some kind of far end acknowledgment is required. In former times, perhaps 8kB of high speed memory was an expensive luxury for interconnection devices, but now it is virtually free. Remote routers should be able to buffer multiple 8kB data blocks and "trickle" them over a 64kbps pipe. The result will be a reduced file transfer rate, but what do you expect?

For multiple data streams over a WAN, the accepted efficiency level for queuing is around 80-90%. In other words, we can expect around 57kbps of real throughput from our 64kbps line and about 50kbps from a 56kbps line.

Sharing Routers

Typical benchmarks for routers operate between one analyzer and another. Or, in the case of the Bradner test rig shown in Figure 15.2, between one port and another on the same hub. What happens if we put more than one data stream through the router? To fully appreciate this explanation, you might like to read through my description of router architectures in Chapter 11.

If the router has one CPU, then each data stream has to share the switching power. So a router CPU that's capable of 30,000 pps switching (e.g., a good AMD 29000 implementation) should be capable of switching 6 Ethernet streams at 5000 pps per stream.

What is a "Data Stream?"

LANs are half-duplex communication channels. In other words, if I'm transmitting on an Ethernet, Token Ring or FDDI, the data has to go somewhere. For a router test, the idea is to count the number of packets that go through the router each second. For a packet to go through the router, it must enter on one port and exit on another. So, for a six-stream test, we need twelve ports on the router.

If the router has *multiple* CPUs, you need to understand how the load is distributed between CPUs. Systems such as the Cisco 7000 and the Proteon CNX600 have an auxiliary CPU to handle routing updates and management. The auxiliary CPU takes no part in packet switching.

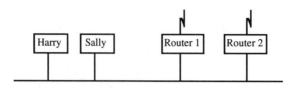

Figure 18.6:   Routers on the Same LAN Segment

Systems such as the Wellfleet ASN, LN, BLN, CN, BCN routers, the DECNIS 600 and the Ascom-Timeplex ER have a distributed switching architecture. In this case, each slot has dedicated CPU power. If the slot has four Ethernet connections, then a maximum of four Ethernet streams can flow off this slot to another slot. The CPU must be capable of around 60,000 pps (14880 x 4) to maintain wire speed Ethernet performance. Note that a good 68040 implementation delivers about 90,000 pps.

Over the past two or three years, Bradner and other benchmarkers have introduced multiple stream tests for Ethernet, Token Ring and FDDI to push routers to their limits.

Another way to think about sharing routers is shown in Figure 18.6. On this LAN segment, two routers are installed. Traffic can be load-balanced over the two WAN connections and if one of the connections fails, then we have a backup. In Chapter 13 I talk about ways that hosts discover routers. In this case, you would need to be using ICMP Router Discovery to get the benefit of load balancing *and* resilience.

Sharing Protocols

Company X claims that they can switch 50,000 IP packets per second. Does this also mean that they can switch 50,000 IPX or DECnet or AppleTalk packets per second? Does it mean that if we send a *mixed* stream of IP, IPX, DECnet and AppleTalk packets at the router that it will continue to switch a *total* of 50,000 pps? The answer is definitely no. Not one single router on the market today can do this.

First of all, IP is quite easy to switch. For example, an IP address is only 32 bits long so it's possible to put an entire address into a single 32-bit CPU register. DECnet is easy too, with its tiny 16-bit addresses. Bridging is harder because of the 48-bit addresses, but there is less checking to do during the forwarding process so you'd expect a shorter code path. IPX uses 80-bit addresses so is harder to switch. AppleTalk is a less popular protocol and is not usually associated with high performance. It's forté is friendliness.

In addition to the different properties of the protocol, we need to consider the efficiency of the protocol multiplexer. In other words, does the router lose time in deciding which protocol is actually in this packet?

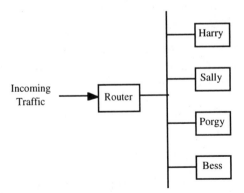

Figure 18.7: Transmission to Multiple Destinations

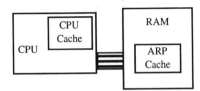

Figure 18.8: Where Are the Addresses Cached?

So another way to load the router is to test for different protocols in isolation and then to mix protocols within a single data stream. Currently the Bradner tests have included the first part of this, but not the second.

Sharing Destinations

An interesting point that is often overlooked in benchmarks is that the outbound packets are often all sent to the same destination address. This is not a limitation of the measuring technique; the capture device is probably operating promiscuously. It is a deficiency in the data generator. Most current scripts don't generate more than a couple of possible destinations. In Figure 15.5 I show the problem.

In this diagram, the router will cache the MAC addresses of Harry, Sally, Porgy and Bess.

The incoming traffic would be switched to lots of different local LAN addresses. In a benchmark, the router can do some sneaky caching of IP against MAC address to maximize performance. In Figure 18.8, you can see that there is a *CPU Cache* that is very closely associated with the chip. In most modern CPUs, the cache is actually on the chip, with an option to extend the cache externally. The ARP cache is in general purpose DRAM, which is much slower to access than the CPU cache. LAN end-points that are accessed frequently are kept in the CPU cache. Less frequently used end-points are not and must be fetched from the ARP cache when needed.

Modern chips will have room for quite a few entries in their CPU caches so the real world performance may approach the benchmark speed. Check with your prospective vendor. Beware, though: CPU cache is expensive compared to ordinary DRAM. For entry level devices, you might want to see if the manufacturer offers this feature as an option. Even without the CPU cache, a decent router should be able to switch tens of thousands of packets per second.

Sharing CPU Time

Switching packets is only one of the things that the router CPU has to do. The other possibilities are:

- Routing updates
- Network management
- Console updates
- DLSw encapsulation and caching
- Data compression
- X.25 encapsulation

Each of these is a CPU-intensive task, such as packet switching. Benchmarks are performed with every possible "background" task switched off. It is not possible to perform a fair comparison in a benchmark environment with any of these features activated. The only way to assess the impact of these activities on your installation is during a pilot test. Routers with auxiliary CPUs or multiple processors will obviously stand up better to these tests than single CPU models.

18.4.1   Improve Router Performance

Routers are designed to operate as Network Layer packet switches. If we use them for other things, we're taking away CPU power that should be switching IP traffic for us. Let me describe some of the features that you might like to consider *not* using in a router.

Telnet

Most routers offer a Telnet server capability. In other words, you can log onto the router and use console commands as though you were directly attached to the unit with a terminal. The problem with Telnet is that it operates over TCP, which is quite demanding protocol. During benchmark testing, router manufacturers will always ensure that Telnet is disabled on their units.

Console Statistics Display

Routers can offer the Network Administrator quite a lot of useful information about traffic flow and internal counters. Usually specific screens of statistics can be displayed on the router console, but these screens must be continuously updated and this takes CPU power. Statistics screens are only required for debugging purposes so there's no harm in switching off this facility for normal router operation.

Packet Capture

Another debugging feature of the mainstream routers is the ability to capture and display received packets. Once again this feature requires CPU power and potentially a significant amount of buffer memory so should only be used when there are problems on the network.

Event Logging

Router event logs are an excellent aid for the Network Administrator to discover what's going on in the network. However, event logging needs to be treated carefully. First of all, it should be possible to select the range of events that are written to the log. In a stable internetwork, only true errors need to be reported. During commissioning or debugging, other events (such as specific packet types, or buffer overflows) may be useful. The more events that you ask the router to report, the busier it will be and the more RAM is used up to buffer the log. The second factor to consider is what the router should do with its log. Some routers are fitted with disc drives that can be used to store larger logs. Since the write time for a disc drive is rather long, the router may end up being rather busy. Some routers may allow the log to be sent to a file server. Once again, the sensitivity level of the event log is a critical factor because individual events may be translated into data transfer transactions over the network.

Bridging

One of the most common causes of router performance degradation is the use of combined bridging and routing. Consider the network I've shown in Figure 18.9.

The diagram shows a simple WAN connection for a single LAN segment. When the early router manufacturers started to implement bridging on their platforms, a very interesting effect showed up. Let's say the LAN segment is running TCP/IP and LAT and the WAN connection is a standard 2Mbps line. With routing only turned on, the router is easily able to fill the 2Mbps line. When bridging is switched on, the WAN line utilization drops to about 75%.

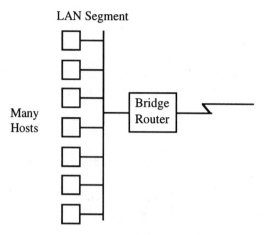

Figure 18.9:   Potential Bridge/Router Bottlenecks

The reason is simple: Ethernet bridges operate in *promiscuous mode*. In this mode, the Ethernet chipset on the router will interrupt the router CPU for every single frame that passes on the Ethernet, even if the frame is passing between two stations on the LAN segment. With bridging switched off, the router chipset is operating in *unicast mode* and sees only traffic that is addressed to the router's MAC address (plus broadcasts and multicast group addresses to which the router belongs). So in routing mode, the router CPU might be interrupted 100 times per second. In bridging mode, the CPU might be interrupted 5,000 times per second! Each time a CPU is interrupted, it wastes a small amount of time transferring its register contents to the stack, services the interrupt and then retrieves the registers from the stack. Even for an interrupt that requires only a few instructions, the overhead time remains the same. With thousands of useless interrupts every second, the router loses processing efficiency. This was the situation around 1988 when router manufacturers first started offering combined bridging and routing. I'd like to describe the approach taken by the two largest router vendors to this problem.

When Cisco introduced their Multiport Communication Interface (MCI) card, it was specifically designed to add bridging capabilities to the CGS, MGS and AGS router platforms. The MCI card had a logical structure as shown in Figure 18.10. The new feature that Cisco introduced with this card was to include a "pseudo processor," the AMD 2900. The 2900 is not a general purpose CPU, like the 68000 or 29000. Instead, it is designed as a fast "bit mover." However, for simple code paths such as bridging, the 2900 can be used to offload the main CPU.

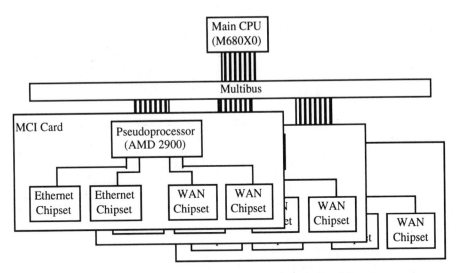

Figure 18.10:   The Cisco MCI Card Architecture

Originally the MCI architecture offered only port-to-port bridging on the same card. However, with the introduction of the C-bus to the AGS+ in 1989, slot-to-slot bridging achieved a similar performance level to the on-card bridging.

Wellfleet shipped their first product two years after Cisco and were able to include integrated bridging support into their VME-bus multiprocessor architecture. Originally, Wellfleet was able to guarantee bridging performance by simply dedicating an entire CPU to one or two Ethernet ports. However, when a four-port interface was introduced in 1991, it was evident that some form of hardware assistance would be required.

Rather than add more CPUs to their architecture, Wellfleet decided to design each interface slot as though it were a true MAC level bridge. Bridges are fitted with high speed memory circuits called Content Addressable Memory (CAM). CAMs allow specific addresses to be found in large tables with no additional processor support. Wellfleet produced a circuit called a *High Speed Filter* by adding a simple *Application Specific Integrated Circuit* (ASIC) to the CAM. The basic format for the HSF circuit is shown in Figure 18.11.

The HSF works by using a property of the Ethernet chipset. When the chipset is operating in promiscuous mode, it will clock the MAC Destination Address on a received frame into a special address buffer on the chip. Even while the rest of the frame is being received, the ASIC can compare this Destination Address to the existing CAM entries (these are learned just as a conventional bridge does). If the Destination Address exists in the same CAM column that is assigned to the receiving port, this means that the frame is a purely local frame. The ASIC then forces the chip to generate an internal collision condition. This forces the

Ethernet chip to "forget" that it is receiving a frame and prevents the CPU from being interrupted.

Another method is becoming popular today and is typified by the Proteon CNX600 FDDI adapter. In this architecture, a true general purpose CPU (in Proteon's case, an Intel i960) is included on the appropriate expansion card. This is shown in Figure 18.12.

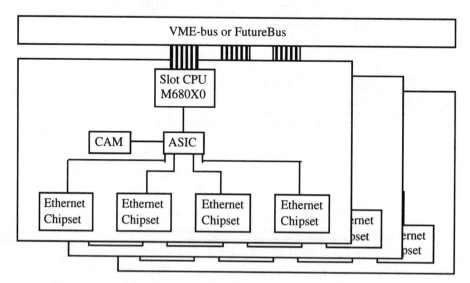

Figure 18.11:   The Wellfleet HSF Solution

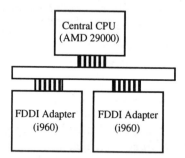

Figure 18.12:   General Purpose CPU on Expansion Card

The i960 is responsible for filtering at high packet rates when the card is used in Translation Bridging mode, as well as running FDDI "housekeeping" tasks such as Station Management (SMT).

If you are using a router which does not have these assisted bridging capabilities, then enabling bridging *will* have a direct impact on performance.

18.5 Protecting WAN Bandwidth

Since WAN bandwidth is so precious, we need to make use of every possible router function to preserve it.

I can summarize these functions as:

- Limit the broadcast domain.
- Use efficient routing protocols.
- Eliminate poll-based management.
- Implement caching features.
- Over-ride routing using filters.
- Implement data compression.

I've dealt with most of these features elsewhere in the book, so let me just give you the pointers.

Limiting Broadcast Domains

ARP, RARP, BOOTP and Routing Protocol broadcasts are stopped dead at the router. I discussed this feature in Chapters 3, 4 and 11.

Efficient Routing Protocols

We can use Static Routes for sites with very limited bandwidth. OSPF is an efficient IGP if dynamic routing is needed and route filters allow us to limit the size of BGP4 routing updates if we need to implement an AS boundary function. All of these points are discussed in Chapters 11, 13 and 14.

Poll Based Management

This technique is simple, but doesn't scale to large numbers of devices. Routers are an excellent candidate to allow us to implement the Poll-on-Trap paradigm of SNMP. I discussed this procedure in Chapter 12.

Caching

In this context, I'm talking about the router caching broadcast discovery packets the first time they are sent out. Subsequent transmission of broadcasts by other hosts can be answered from the cache by the router. The broadcast does not leak out onto the WAN connection. In the TCP/IP world, the most common caching technique today is *Data Link Switching* (DLSw),, discussed in Chapter 15.

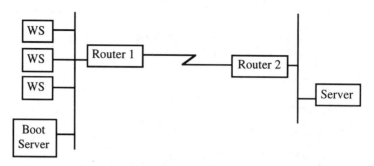

Figure 18.13:   Possible Application for Filters

18.5.1   Applying Filters

Another way of protecting bandwidth is the use of manually constructed *Traffic Filters*. In Figure 18.13 I show two sites connected by a leased line, with routers providing the connection. On the left hand site is a group of diskless workstations. On the right hand site, a Server. The workstations use the Server to run a character-oriented application. Telnet is the application.

After a few months of happy operation, the Network Administrator receives a complaint that the required response times (as outlined in the Service Level Agreement) are not always being met. the Network Administrator takes a quick look at the situation and decides to put in an analyzer to record a typical day's traffic flow. When she examines the data, she finds that some NFS traffic is going over the link as well. The next day, she sets up the analyzer to capture the NFS traffic. After two days, she gets some capture data and immediately discovers the problem. On the right hand site, the Server also contain some games. During the coffee break (which staff on the left hand site are required to stagger over a one-hour period), some of the workstation users are downloading games from the Server to their workstations. The remaining Telnet users who are not on their break then suffer a drastic drop in performance.

As an immediate solution to the problem, the Network Administrator installs a Port filter on the router on the left hand site. In fact there are several combinations of filters that could be used to stop this traffic. For example, since NFS uses Remote Procedure Calls [8, 9], she could block the *portmapper* function that operates at well-known port 111[1]. Since Telnet uses TCP as its Transport Layer protocol, it will be unaffected by the portmapper block. Note that portmapper will block *all* use of NFS so it's a fairly non-specific filter and may not be the right choice in a larger and more diverse environment. Filter patterns, especially port filters, must be chosen carefully so that you block the appropriate traffic without blocking any essential datagrams. Cheswick and

---

[1]Portmapper is a multiplexing function that responds to an RPC request.

Bellovin is an ideal introduction to the complexity of filtering systems [11], though their primary focus is security, rather than performance.

By the way, the longer term solution was to install the games on the local boot server for the diskless workstation. After all, the users were playing games on their coffee break.

Data Compression

An obvious way to squeeze more out of limited line bandwidth is to use *Data Compression*. The de facto standard compression algorithm in use today is the Lempel-Ziv, or Lempel-Ziv-Welsch (LZW) algorithm. The basics behind the algorithm are simple. The compression device examines the incoming bitstream looking for patterns. Common patterns are stored in a *dictionary*. If a dictionary item is found, then the block of bytes is replaced by a symbol marking the specific dictionary entry. It's a bit like the macro keys we used to use in DOS for formatting disks, or performing other repetitive tasks. LZW compression on an ASCII bitstream can be very impressive, delivering compression of 4:1 or even higher. This is because ASCII text files are full of repeated words or phrases. In addition, LZW dictionaries are *dynamic*. If the algorithm sees that you keep using the phrase "in these circumstances," or "would you like to come out with me tonight," it will insert the repeating pattern as a single symbol into the dictionary.

Binary files, such as programs, may not be as spectacular; it depends on the operating system and the compiler options. 2:1 compression is pretty good in these circumstances.

If you are sending data that has already been compressed by a program such as PKZIP, or CompactPro, then you're unlikely to get any additional compression at all.

If your data stream contains repeated patterns such as TCP connection headers, you could be in for a nice surprise.

Today, the mainstream router manufacturers such as Cisco and Wellfleet are offering software based compression on even entry level devices. Software based compression is usually able to operate up to line speeds of 64kbps; quite adequate for an entry level router. Hardware-based compression is no more efficient than software, but can operate up to T1 or E1 line speeds.

Compression schemes should offer the option to compress only the data portion of the frame. In Figure 18.14 I show an IP datagram, with the header and trailer portions shaded. Compression is performed only on the data portion of the frame, with IP header information and MAC trailer information being recalculated so that the compressed packet can be routed through a conventional IP network. In other words, with this technique you can achieve data compression, but still send traffic over the Internet.

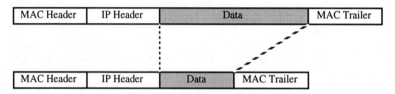

Figure 18.14:   Data Field Compression

The routers at each end of the conversation need to be from the same vendor, because LZW compression is not currently the subject of an RFC.

Data compression works best if the algorithm can examine large blocks of sample data (e.g., 10kB) and store large dictionaries. Data field compression doesn't give the algorithm much of a data block to look at; at most about 1450 bytes on Ethernet. However, the benefit of being able to switch the compressed frames over a multivendor network is often worth the reduced efficiency.

A drawback of general data stream compression with large block sizes is the added latency that this buffering produces on the data flow. For example, a 10kB buffer takes 8ms to fill on Ethernet, so this is 8ms of added latency. In contrast, data field compression will never wait longer than about 1ms.

18.6 Tuning Host Applications for the WAN

Most TCP/IP applications operate over either UDP or TCP. TCP has the sophistication required to operate over connections with variable delay. TCP will dynamically tune its timeout values until they are appropriate for the link. UDP, however, operates with a fixed timeout value. By default this is 700ms.

If we connect two sites over a 64kbps line, we can transmit about 5 600 bytes in 700ms. That's enough time for several complete Ethernet frames to be sent and an *acknowledgment* (ack) to return to the sending station. The problem is that the *default* UDP message size is 8,000 bytes [7]. To operate successfully over even a 64kbps link, it seems that some host tuning is required. In fact the situation is worse than it seems, because we're assuming here that no other hosts are using the 64kbps link at the same time. So in a real network, we would have to reduce the default message block size, or increase the timeout.

What Happens after a Timeout?

Timeouts cause packets to be retransmitted. In fact we need to know three parameters to predict the effect of retransmissions on the network:

- Protocol timeout value
- Retry count

•   Retransmission block size

The retry count is the number of times a host will retransmit a packet before it reports an error to higher levels of software. Retransmission counts may be configurable, but are sometimes "hard coded" into lower levels of firmware. A typical count would be 3, 4 or 5. Normally, each retransmission is identical so an acknowledgment will not differentiate between retransmissions. In other words, if you transmit 5 times and receive one ack, you don't know which of the 5 retransmission made it through (and you don't care actually). The first four may have been lost due to congestion, or network reconfiguration for example. On the other hand, the first transmission may have made it through, but the path delay is so long that you timed out four times before the ack arrived.

The retransmission block size is a vital piece of information. For example, let's say that we have a default UDP message block of 8kB and we want to send this over an Ethernet LAN. The block is broken down into 6 Ethernet frames and these are blasted out onto the LAN. The third frame is dropped by the receiving host. UDP will normally time out (after 700ms) and then retransmit all 6 frames.

By reducing the block size, we can reduce the amount of data that is retransmitted in the event of a lost frame. So by understanding a little bit more about the application characteristics, we can now conclude that:

•   If we have slow links, it is better to increase the timeout, but keep the block size the same.

•   If we have noisy or unreliable links, it is better to decrease the block size.

18.7 Bandwidth on Demand

One of the biggest problems we can face when designing a LAN/WAN internetwork is that the WAN connections usually have to be dimensioned for *peak* demand and not *average* demand. A startling statistic from the US is that the average utilization level of T1 lines for a major provider is only 8%! Since customers are paying for 100% usage, it seems that they're not getting their money's worth.

Why is the utilization so low? The reason is that LAN traffic levels can vary dramatically. For example, let's say I'm running a wordprocessing application on a diskless workstation. In the morning when I arrive, there is a burst of LAN activity while my machine boots and loads the application. I start work on a file and the LAN is silent. Every 10 minutes, my auto-save sends the file to my server and the LAN has a burst of activity.

If I could adjust my LAN speed to the *average* data rate of the LAN, it might take my machine an hour or so to boot in the morning!

If we now consider WAN activity, there is a lot of pressure on me, as a network designer, to minimize my line costs. In general, line costs still account for over 80% of the total cost of an internetwork during a five year period. Wouldn't it be wonderful if I could install a WAN connection that could cope with typical burst demand, but that would kick in additional bandwidth for occasional heavy demand? This is *Bandwidth on Demand* (BoD)

18.7.1   BoD with Frame Relay

In Chapter 6 I discuss the benefits of Frame Relay with its CIR feature. For most people, Frame Relay offers the closest thing yet to BoD. You install a T1 or E1 connection to your site, but only pay for a 128kbps CIR. Anything you send beyond 128kbps may or may not get through (remember it will have the Discard Eligibility bit set).

Frame Relay is not generally available in Europe. In fact, many of the PTTs that have it seem to be good at keeping it secret. Is there another way to achieve BoD?

18.7.2   BoD with ISDN

Also in Chapter 6 I discussed ISDN and its possible applications. In Figure 6.12 I show two sites connected with an ISDN Backup Adapter. In normal operation, this adapter will only connect the ISDN circuit if the leased line goes down. It is such a small step to allow the adapter to nail up the call if the leased line becomes *congested*.

In Figure 18.15 I show a possible design for a BoD circuit on a router. Traffic flow passes through a Queue Multiplexer circuit and normally out to Queue 1 for transmission onto the leased line. If Queue 1 becomes congested (let's say more than 70%), the Queue Multiplexer starts to push traffic into Queue 2. As soon as frames appear in this queue, a signal is sent to the dial circuit. This could be a native ISDN TA within the router, or a V.25*bis* signal to an external TA. The advantage of an internal TA is that both ISDN B channels could be used for BoD, whereas only one can be used with V.25*bis*.

The Queue Multiplexer monitors the levels of the two queues and if the *combined* level falls below 60% of the depth of Queue 1, then the BoD line can be dropped.

The 70% and 60% levels are usually referred to as *high* and *low watermarks*. Watermarks are used to prevent the BoD line from being connected too soon, or from being cleared too soon. In effect, they damp out bandwidth demand irregularity. A timer can also be associated with these watermarks for additional stability. For example we could say:

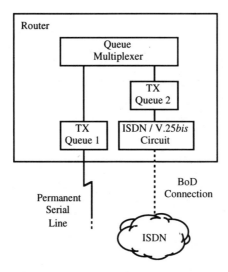

Figure 18.15: BoD with ISDN

- If the Queue 1 depth exceeds 70% for 1 second or more, then connect the BoD circuit.

- If Queue 1 + Queue 2 depth is less than 60% for more than 3 seconds, then clear the BoD circuit.

18.7.3 Packet Sequencing

As soon as we have multiple paths between two locations, we take the risk that packets will be delivered out of sequence to their destination. Some protocols are tolerant of out of sequence traffic. Some are not. Routers can buffer packets to re-sequence on behalf of the end stations, but this requires additional buffer space and CPU power in the router and if packets get lost it can result in delays to the application.

A clever technique is known as *address hashing*. In Figure 15.8 I show two routers connected by four data paths. Four workstations on Site 1 are connected to a server on Site 2. The routers are configured to load balance traffic between the four data paths, but to apply address hashing.

An incoming packet from Harry is examined. The Source and Destination addresses are added together and the resulting number is divided by the number of data paths operating between the two sites. The remainder represents the number of the data path to be used by this traffic. Let's take a simplified example:

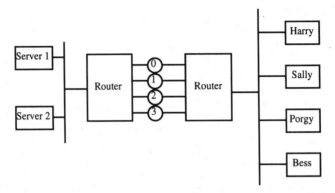

Figure 18.16:   Address Hashing Between Multiple Data Paths

Harry has an address of 12 (hashing can be done on IP address, MAC address, etc.), Server 1 has an address of 52. We add the two addresses together and get 64, we divide by 4 and we get exactly 16, remainder 0. Harry's traffic always passes over data path 0.

Sally has an address of 9. Added to Server 1's address of 52 we get 61. Divide by 4 we get 15, remainder 1, so Sally's traffic all passes over data path 1.

Let's now say that Sally wants to send traffic to Server 2. Server 2 has an address of 53. Add this to Sally's address of 9 and we get 62. Divide by 4 we get 15 remainder 2. So traffic between Sally and Server 2 always passes over data path 2.

The vital point to notice is that traffic between Sally and Server 2 (or between Harry and Server 1) will always pass over the same circuit so cannot be delivered out of sequence.

Address hashing is a simple approach that requires very little router CPU and no additional buffering. With a small number of end systems, the technique does not provide a good load balancing capability. It really shines in internetworks with a medium to large number of active sessions, where statistical distribution over the circuits makes all the difference.

18.8 Optimizing LAN Internetworks

In some ways, LAN performance can be harder to improve than WAN performance. In LANs, we are normally searching for ways to squeeze that last 10% out of the system. Occasionally we come across a real gem of a way to improve our system performance.

18.8.1 MTU Discovery

One of the biggest killers in LAN internetworking is if we encounter fragmentation and reassembly. I discussed this in Chapter 11, but I'd just like to remind you of the problem.

If we are using mixed LAN types, usually Ethernet and FDDI, we may see large frames of up to 4kB generated on the FDDI and these must be broken down into smaller units; maximum 1.5kB for transmission on Ethernet. In fact, this is something that routers were designed to be able to handle. However, the assumption was that this would only be necessary on slow WAN links, not between LANs. Fragmentation is a real performance hog in most router systems.

In Chapter 11 I discussed a wonderful mechanism known as *MTU Discovery*. This simple technique should allow us to forget about MTU problems. Any two hosts will automatically discover the minimum MTU for the specific route they are using and throttle back to this MTU size. This avoids fragmentation completely, yet allows us to use the optimum MTU for the route.

18.8.2 The Effects of Latency

Connection devices operate in two possible modes: *store and forward* or *fast packet*. In store and forward mode, a connecting device will wait for the entire frame to be received and the CRC to be verified, before beginning to transmit the frame. In fast packet (or "on the fly switch") device, the switching decision is made and the frame is transmitted on the outbound interface after only a few bytes have clocked in. This is possible because fast packet devices normally make their switching decision based on the MAC address of the frame, which is located in the first 6 bytes.

Strictly speaking, *latency* is the additional delay imposed in a switching operation by the connecting device circuitry so excludes the store and forward delay. For that reason, devices which operate in a fast packet mode may actually exhibit *negative* latencies.

Note that the application for fast packet devices is strictly limited for two reasons. First, fast packet operation means that connection devices cannot detect bad frames using the CRC. Second, fast packet mode can only be used between two dedicated channels operating at the same speed. This latter restriction comes about because fast packet devices cannot buffer frames to allow for speed differences. In addition, if fast packet mode is used on a conventional LAN connection, the access control delay may prevent the frame from being correctly transmitted. In fact, there is only a handful of true fast packet devices on the market and the most common examples are in the Ethernet switch product family.

In theory, the less software processing required by the connecting device, the lower the latency on the frame. For equivalent software operations, the efficiency of the software and the overall design of the hardware will all effect overall latency.

The general view in the industry is that a high latency is a "bad thing," but at the time of writing, only a handful of latency tests have been performed. Nobody can tell you how high latency can rise before it becomes a measurable problem, for example. Data Communications at the Interlab test lab were one of the first magazines to include a comprehensive latency benchmark [5], but the industry feedback from this single example was surprisingly hostile. It's true that some of the figures from this test were rather dubious, but this was one of the first tests of its kind and I would personally support additional research into the real world effects of latency.

Bridges

MAC bridges offer fairly low latency levels for most traffic because they have a very simple decision to make. Using Content Addressable Memory (CAM) chips, bridges can make address recognition decisions in only one or two microseconds. Bridges always operate in store and forward mode since they must abide by the access control technology for the output LAN or WAN.

Routers

Routers have a good deal more work to do than a typical bridge. Routers operate as store and forward devices, but they must also strip the MAC and LLC wrappers from any incoming frame and rebuild the appropriate MAC and LLC headers for an outgoing frame. In fact, if we fully switch an IP datagram through a router it will require around 1,000 machine instructions for the transaction.

Switches

LAN switches are a relatively new development. These devices are designed to prolong the useful life of conventional LANs like Ethernet by allowing dedicated 10Mbps connections to be made into individual hosts. Instead of collision access method being implemented on the LAN, switches use high speed busses, or non-blocking matrix backplanes to increase total LAN bandwidth without modifying the host software in any way. Most switches operate as store and forward devices. All switches perform segment traffic management by acting as high speed multiport MAC bridges. However, at least one of these products, the Kalpana Etherswitch, acts as a true fast packet device. In a Data Communications benchmark test [6], the Kalpana had a measured latency of 40µs for a 64 byte frame, whereas the Lannet LANswitch (a store and forward device) was measured at 51.2µs. The highest latency in the test was 770µs so it seems as though the improvement for a fast packet device is really not that much.

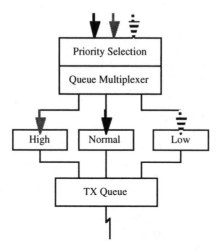

Figure 18.17:   Simplified Priority System

18.8.3   Priority Features

When performance is a real issue, we can find that certain kinds of priority traffic are not getting through the network as fast as we'd like.

In a TCP/IP network the typical examples are Telnet versus FTP traffic. Telnet is an interactive traffic type, whereas FTP can be pipelined. If you have a limited WAN connection speed and Telnet response time is important to you, then you might want to prioritize the Telnet traffic over the FTP. This should be possible using priority selection features of a good quality router.

Figure 18.17 shows a simplified priority system. Some form of selection procedure is used to transfer packets to the High, Normal or Low priority queues. A simple algorithm allocates traffic from each queue to the TX queue. It goes something like this:

- Is there traffic in the High Queue? If there is, pass it to the TX queue if there is room in the TX Queue.

- If there's no traffic left in the High Queue, check the Normal Queue. If there's traffic there, pass it to the TX Queue if there's room.

- If there's no traffic in the High or Normal Queue, look at the Low Queue. If there's traffic there, pass it to the TX Queue if there's room.

- If there's no room in the TX Queue, then hold the traffic in the appropriate Queue until there is room.

This form of the algorithm actually can mean that the Normal and Low Queues can be "locked out" of access to the TX Queue by heavy traffic in the High Queue. A modified version of the algorithm uses a *leaky bucket* technique. When a frame is inserted into the Normal or Low Queue, a timer is started. If this Queue has not been serviced when the timer expires, then the next queued frame is forced into the TX Queue, even if there is traffic in the High Queue.

18.9 Increasing LAN Bandwidth

In Chapter 5 I discussed various LAN technologies and ways in which these technologies were developing.

The key to maintaining performance as the demand on LAN bandwidth increases is to understand the traffic patterns in your networks. For example, in the good old days when bridges were first deployed, we used to say that bridges would separate traffic from different segments on a LAN. If the bridge was forwarding more that 50% of the received traffic, then the bridge was in the wrong place!

Server Segmentation

Ideally, in a client/server environment, the clients and servers should be on the same segment. But what happens when you get more clients attached to a server than one LAN segment can carry? For example, 200 high performance PCs attached to a Super Server? One possibility is to insert multiple cards in the server, as shown in Figure 18.18, in the left hand diagram.

This approach has been used since the early 1980s with Novell and Banyan servers. The problem is that the server spends quite a lot of time routing traffic between segments. Ideally you want to save all the server bandwidth for its primary job. Recently both Cisco and Wellfleet have announced deals with Network Operating System vendors to develop "Router Coprocessor" cards for servers. In this scenario, shown on the right hand side of Figure 18.20, the router would be a "parasite" interface inside the server, simply using it for power and perhaps a configuration console. Routing functions would not impact the server performance in any way.

Generic Segmentation

An alternative approach is segmentation. I show this in Figure 18.19. Here, a Collapsed Backbone has been built using a mid-range router with a high performance backplane. The servers are given their own dedicated LAN segments and the number of clients on each of the access LANs can be controlled by adding more ports to the router. Collapsed Backbone internetworks are still very popular today, since they offer the highest performance from conventional LAN technology, but at a very competitive price compared to conventional campus backbones.

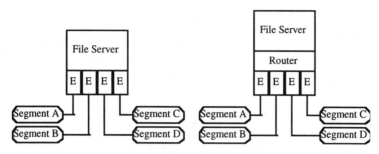

Figure 18.18: Multiple LAN Segments in Server

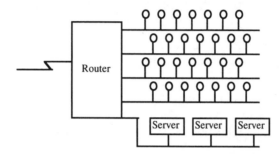

Figure 18.19: LAN Segmentation

More recently, switching hubs have been attacking the Collapsed Backbone market. Switching hubs are essentially multiport bridges, but are much cheaper than high performance routers. In Chapter 5, Figure 5.13 and 5.14, I showed the danger of meshing switching hubs and the way that the architecture can be scaled using routers. In fact the topology I show in Figure 5.14 combines the traffic control benefits of routers and the economy of switching hubs in the best possible way. The danger of this architecture is that 100% of traffic will pass from the LAN clients to the servers *through the router*. Routers will add more delay to the connection than switches. To overcome the problem, the router in Figure 18.19 could be replaced by a Virtual LAN Switch, as described in Chapter 5. Virtual LANs can be used to ensure that all the clients are within the same workgroups as their servers.

18.10 Charging for Performance

Most people think of their IP networks as "free." For corporate backbones, the cost may be shared between departments and charged on the basis of the number of hosts connected. Thus a small department will pay less than a large department. But what happens if the small department is using applications that are very heavy on LAN bandwidth? You may find that an Engineering department will be using several times more network bandwidth per user than an

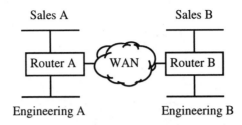

Figure 18.20:   Likely Candidate for IP Accounting

Accounts or Sales department. Wouldn't it be nice if we could bill departments by usage?

It sounds like a wonderful idea, but it means a little extra work for your routers. Figure 18.20 presents a possible example.

Two sites are linked over a WAN. The Sales department on each site only want to pay for as much of the network bandwidth as they actually use, as do the Engineering departments. As you'd expect, most of the traffic flow between sites is between the same departments, with a small amount of interdepartmental traffic.

By using an accounting process on the routers, you can monitor how much of the WAN link is used by Engineering and how much by Sales. The problem lies with the way that IP is switched. Each packet is routed in its own right; that's what connectionless communication is about. This means that the router must explicitly account for every source/destination pairing. How do you bill for cross-department traffic? If someone in Sales A sends traffic to someone on Engineering B, do we bill Sales or Engineering? Can we include a "reverse charge" facility?

In most cases, users find that strict accounting functions actually cause more hassle for the administrator. Instead, the leading router vendors tend to offer a bandwidth reservation system for WAN connections. Bandwidth reservation is based on the priority mechanism I described in Figure 18.17. In this case, each queue is allocated a fixed CIR on the WAN connection. For example, if there's a 64kbps link between the two sites, Sales can be allocated 32kbps and Engineering 32kbps. Most of these implementations allow traffic to burst beyond the CIR *if there is bandwidth available*. However, each department is guaranteed a minimum service level and can be charged for that level. No complicated calculations, no fuss, just get on with the job!

18.11   Summary

- Network performance is a vague term and can better be described in terms of measurable parameters such as packet forwarding, throughput, latency, etc. These terms are described in RFC 1242.

- Measurement of individual performance parameters at specific points in the internetwork will help us to build up Service Level Definitions.

- The overall system performance is actually a function of the slowest part of the overall system. This is known as the bottleneck.

- In a real network, benchmark results are never achieved due to a variety of sharing effects.

- Some sharing effects are external to the router, but some are internal. Some router architectures are better at dealing with sharing effects than others.

- A key factor in optimizing internetwork performance is to understand the behavior of higher level protocols and to tune their packet size and timeout parameters to suite the network conditions.

- Bandwidth on Demand is one obvious way to improve performance in the network, but problems may be encountered with packet sequencing effects in a multipath network.

- Latency effects should logically have a severe effect on network performance. Whilst this is accepted as "common sense," it seems to be very difficult to measure under realistic conditions.

- In general, bridges have a lower latency than routers. LAN Switches have a lower latency than bridges. Fast Packet devices have the lowest latency of all, but can only be used between non-blocking and identical network types.

- The ultimate solution to performance problems is to increase the network bandwidth. Typically the limiting factor here is the cost of higher speed LAN technologies.

- The fairest solution is to create service environments in which users are charged for the internetwork bandwidth that they consume. In practice, this is one of the most fundamental challenges of connectionless internetworking.

18.12   References

[1]   R. Finlayson, T. Mann, J. Mogul, M. Theimer. "Reverse Address Resolution Protocol," *RFC 903*. June 1984.

[2]   W. Wimer. "Clarifications and Extensions for the Bootstrap Protocol," *RFC 1542*. October 1993.

[3] W. Simpson. "The Point-to-Point Protocol (PPP)," *RFC 1548*. December 1993.

[4] F. Baker. "Point-to-Point Protocol Extensions for Bridging," *RFC 1220*. April 1991.

[5] Data communications Token Ring benchmark edition.

[6] Robert Mandeville. "Ethernet Switches Evaluated," Data Communications , March 1994.

[7] J. Postel. "User Datagram Protocol," *RFC 768*. August 1980.

[8] Sun Microsystems, Inc, "NFS: Network File System Protocol specification," *RFC 1094*. March 1989.

[9] Sidnie Feit. "TCP/IP Architectures, Protocols and Implementation." McGraw-Hill 1993. ISBN 0-07-020346-6.

[10] S. Bradner. "Benchmarking Terminology for Network Interconnection Devices," *RFC 1242*. July 1991.

[11] W. Cheswick. S. Bellovin. *Firewalls and Internet Security*. (Addison-Wesley, Reading MA, 1994).

[12] K. Tolly. D. Newman. "How Accurate is Your LAN Analyzer?." Data Communications, January 1994.

CHAPTER 19

Designing for the Future

> *The moment you forecast you know you're going to be wrong. You just
> don't know by how much and in which direction.*
>
> **Fiedler's Third Rule of Forecasting**

19.1 Introduction

Back in 1988, many industry observers thought that IP's days were numbered;
OSI was about to spring into action and take over the world. SNMP was a stop-
gap that would be embarrassed into retirement by CMIS/CMIP. Six years later
we can see that this just didn't happen. It's true that IP is beginning to fray a
little at the seams and SNMP has its faults. But IP address space has been
remarkably durable, and it's the SNMP *applications* that are much worse than
the protocol upon which they are built.

This Chapter is *not* about the future (I just put the title there to fool you). It's
about possibilities and attempts to solve *perceived* problems. Here are some of
the problems:

- Pressure on IPv4 address space.

- The changing character of The Internet.

- The Multiprotocol Dilemma, including the advent of ATM.

19.2 IP Address Pressures

IP addresses are 32 bits long. That means we could address 4,294,967,296, *4.3
billion* individual end stations. In 1988, there were around 5.2 billion people on
Earth. Since a good proportion cannot even afford their next meal, we can
assume that IP address space would be sufficient. The problem arises because of
allocation efficiency. Figure 19.1 shows a simple pie chart of IP addresses.

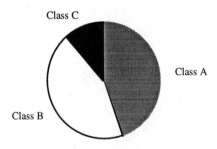

Figure 19.1:   Where Are the Addresses?

This diagram excludes Class D and E addresses and reserved address patterns (such as all-1s, etc.). As you can see, close to half of the *real* IP addresses lie within Class A address space.   The problem is that only 128 different organizations can own a Class A address. If any of these organizations have less than 16 million hosts, they are wasting *our* addresses.

Figure 19.2 shows a different view. The data is taken from [1].

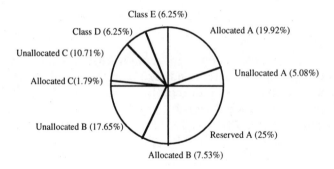

Figure 19.2:   IP Address Allocation in Early '94

These graphs tell us a few things for certain. First, the IP address class structure is very wasteful of address space. Second, we haven't actually allocated so many addresses, though the predictions around 1990 were that demands for IP Class B address space would double around every 14 months (source: IPv4 Address Lifetime Expectation working group).

19.2.1   Registered Address Issues

I already discussed the concept of private addressing schemes in Chapter 13. Even where private addressing isn't *consciously* used, we can still assume that users in the real world have significantly high rations of hosts to registered addresses. The reason for this can be understood looking at Figure 19.3.

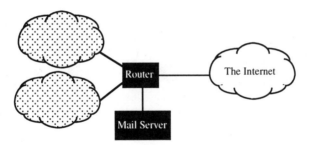

Figure 19.3: Address Ratio Issues

Each of the clouds is filled with dots. These dots are PCs or Macs running IPX or AppleTalk stacks respectively. Their only need to access the Internet is for mail. They contact their Mail Server using the native IPX or AppleTalk protocol. The Mail Server is running a dual stack and communicates with TCP/IP into the Internet. How many of these device need IP addresses? Just the Router and the Mail Server. Potentially this is a problem, because one day we might change the nature of the applications running on the PCs. Maybe we need to assign each of them an IP address. This kind of pent-up demand could be triggered by a new application. For example, if someone at Lotus decided to write Notes to a TCP/IP interface, we might see an explosive increase in the demand for registered IP addresses.

19.2.2 CIDR and BGP-4

The reason that we are still in good shape is that in 1990, the NIC began to resist requests for Class B addresses (the most flexible address structure). To get such an address, you had to put a very strong case to the NIC. As an alternative, contiguous blocks of Class C address space were offered instead. At first glance you might think that lots of Class C addresses were at least as good as a Class B address. For the user, you'd be right. For the router, it's not the case.

Figure 19.4 shows a router, R2, in the Joe Bloggs organization. If Joe Bloggs were able to use a Class B address, then R2 could advertise a single address out to the Internet (DMZ). The router, R3, in Jane Doe's organization would then see all end-points in Joe Bloggs as a single table entry. In contrast, if LANs A..D are actually Class C addresses, then R3 would need four separate entries in its routing table: one for each Network ID.

To overcome this problem, the IETF proposed an address agglomeration mechanism called Classless Inter Domain Routing (CIDR). In a CIDR network, an *address prefix* is transmitted along with each route: overriding the "natural" Class mask. For example, let's say that Joe Bloggs is allocated 15 Class C addresses: 192.32.1.0 to 192.32.15.0. The *natural* subnet mask for a Class C address is 255.255.255.0. Here are the binary digits of the 3rd byte of these Network IDs:

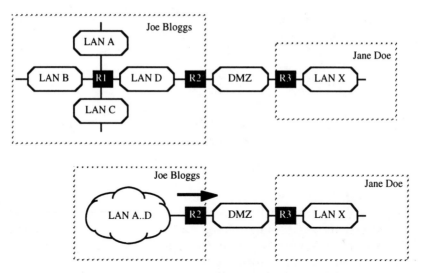

Figure 19.4:   Address Agglomeration Effects

192.32.1.0	00000001
192.32.2.0	00000010
192.32.3.0	00000011
192.32.4.0	00000100
192.32.5.0	00000101
192.32.6.0	00000110
192.32.7.0	00000111
192.32.8.0	00001000
192.32.9.0	00001001
192.32.10.0	00001010
192.32.11.0	00001011
192.32.12.0	00001100
192.32.13.0	00001101
192.32.14.0	00001110
192.32.15.0	00001111

If all of these Network IDs were on Joe Bloggs' site, we could agglomerate the addresses because they lie on a binary boundary (4 bits). So a *prefix* of 00001111 would allow us to group the first 16 Class C addresses in a range and economize on routing table space. This prefix system is the basis of CIDR [2] and CIDR is actually implemented first as a part of BGP-4 [3].

The interesting thing is that, while the NIC began allocating addresses in this way several years ago, CIDR and BGP4 are only rolling out this year (1994). The

NIC were prepared to tolerate additional load on routing tables for a short period in order to reap the benefits when full CIDR capability became available.

Do I Need CIDR in All My Routers?

CIDR is obviously a radical change in the way that routing information is passed around because we need to insert the prefix in routing updates and routers need to be able to manipulate agglomerated addresses in their routing tables. The good news is that CIDR is only needed in routers that attach an organization to the Internet itself. In Figure 19.3, only R2 needs to have CIDR and BGP4 capability.

The address savings that CIDR has brought have certainly put off any immediate threat to IP address space. In addition, increasing numbers of users are not using registered IP addresses. Instead they are using one of the private IP addresses reserved in RFC 1597 and connecting to the Internet (if at all) through address translation gateways or Application Hosts (see Chapter 13).

19.2.3   IP, The Next Generation

One of the great things about CIDR is that it's given the IETF breathing space to create a new generation of IP, now known as *IPng*, or IPv6, to take the Internet into the mid to long-term future. The choice for the new IP is a controversial one. Everyone seems to agree that this kind of change can only be considered once in a generation, so we may as well include as much future functionality as possible. This obviously includes a larger address space offering greater flexibility, but there are also demands for additional functionality from the new IP. These include:

- Graceful transition capability.

- Quality of service, targeted squarely at real-time video and voice support.

- Self-configuration.

- Support for mobile computing.

We could argue that all of these capabilities can be lashed onto the existing IP architecture, but the reality is that these temporary kludges will not stand up to the scaleability problems of the new Internet. The situation in mid-1994 is that no firm decision has been made about IPng.

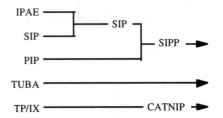

Figure 19.5:   IPng Candidate Family Tree

Figure 19.5 shows the "family tree" of IPng candidates and how various proposals have been merged to produce the current set of candidates:

- Simple IP Plus (SIPP).

- TCP and UDP over Big Addresses (TUBA).

- Common Architecture for the Next Generation Internet Protocol (CATNIP).

And the Winner Is...

The actual winner of this contest is "none of the above!" Deficiencies were found in all of these suggestions. For SIPP, the variable length addressing was thought to be too complex and basically unnecessary. Addressing for the new IP was limited to 16 bytes.

TUBA was rejected because it was based on OSI CLNP. There are basic problems with CLNP that were identified by the IETF working group. However, the IETF has no right to "fix" the protocol (CLNP "belongs" to ISO).

CATNIP was thought to have some good ideas, but was an architectural description and lacked implementation details.

IPv6 is mostly based on SIPP, but with fixed addressing. A lot of work has been done in the host-router arena (i.e., ESIS). The 16 bytes address has been justified as having about the same addressing capability as a 20-byte ISO NSAP. ISO addresses waste a lot of space at the head of the address and a single byte at the end (the Selector field)[7]. The result is that IPv6 addresses can be expressed much more efficiently, so require only 16 bytes.

When Do I Change?

When should you consider changing to the new IP? Eric Fleischman of Boeing [6] talks about the *Inertia Factor*. This is the situation where companies will continue to use "obsolete" protocols for many years. IBM bisync and NetBIOS are excellent examples. These protocols continue to haunt the modern network designer for many years after they have been officially replaced. In contrast, I hung onto my old favorite Word Perfect 4.2 because the newer versions were too clunky, or too complicated for what I needed. I only changed when I changed companies and moved from PCs to Macs. Users hate upgrading. The new software might *seem* exciting at first, but then you get tired of the fact that all those familiar things you used to do happen differently. For network designers and administrators, the implications of the new IP are rather frightening.

All of the current proposals include some migratory step, although some are better than others in this respect.

The simple answer to the question is:

- Wait for stable protocol stacks.

- Wait until the protocol offers you a service you need.

- Design your current networks with migration in mind.

I would love to write another chapter about the final bullet, but each of the migratory strategies is slightly different so we'll have to wait for the Second Edition!

19.3 The Changing Internet

If we consider the situation of the Internet when it began and then look at where we are today, it seems incredible that people could design such a versatile and resilient protocol system. While the obvious change in the Internet is its dramatic growth, there are many other changes from the user perspective that are just as significant.

19.3.1 Who Owns It?

It's true to say that every Internet user today is directly subsidized by the US taxpayer. The vast US Internet infrastructure is currently the lure that attracts other users to join. Access may not be free, but today only carries the price tag of the link between your premises and the first Internet node.

In the future, it's likely that Internet Providers will spring up offering access services over existing WAN infrastructure. Instead of leasing clear channel lines, the provider will offer an IP access service. Charges could be made based on the volume of traffic. Access charges are already springing up to private databases and these providers are finding it difficult to compete with the quality and quantity of public domain Internet data and services.

Figure 19.6 shows one possible view of how Internet providers might enter the market.

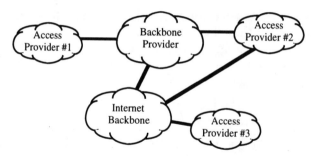

Figure 19.6:   The Future Internet?

In this scheme, we still have the "original" Internet, made up of non-profit organizations and funded from government. Commercial Backbone Providers may spring up. These would be international communication suppliers such as MCI, Sprint, AT&T or British Telecom. Local Access Providers would contract for Internet access to these backbones. The local providers may be RBOCs in the US, private companies, or smaller national PTTs around the world. The Access Providers may have contracts with more than one Backbone Provider and the Backbone Providers will have mutual contracts to allow data to pass from specific Access Providers across their backbones. These transit policies will be controlled by ever more sophisticated EGPs and even higher level *Policy Routing* paradigms.

19.3.2   Virtual Private Networks

One of the key features of the new Internet will be the formation of *Virtual Private Networks* (VPN) over the shared backbone.

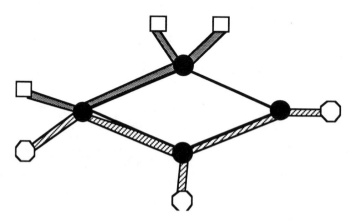

Figure 19.7:   Virtual Private Networks

Figure 19.7 shows the very basic VPN concept. The black-filled circles represent the Access Provider. Traffic from the Square Nodes and traffic from the Hexagonal Nodes shares this bandwidth. Individual IP packets from Squares and Hexagons may pass sequentially over the same backbone cable. The users of this network are concerned about two things:

- I don't want someone else reading my data!
- I don't want to lose service quality if someone else overloads the network.

If you think about the current IP architecture, we can't ensure either of these things, but modified systems have been proposed to offer security, including encryption or private header formats. Quality of service features are offered today in proprietary ways.

19.3.3   Videoconferencing

Part of the quality of service requirement is provoked by the need to support real time video traffic over the Internet. Packet video systems have been available for several years now and IETF meetings are telecast over the Internet backbone using such systems. One of the obvious uses for Videoconferencing is that of Distance Learning. In this application, a teacher lectures to local students and the lesson is telecast out to remote locations. These locations will initially be clusters of students to justify the expense of the system, but eventually this technology could be applied in the home. In the UK, the Open University has been operating a distributed learning system for many years using TV broadcasts, video and audio tapes and specially prepared printed course materials. To provide the interactive aspect of learning, summer schools allow students to meet and local tutorial groups provide backup for detailed questions. In the modern view, students would simply go to extended classrooms and be able to ask questions in real time.

Desktop videoconferencing is a very hyped-up concept today. While it's true that the technique could offer some significant opportunities for desk-bound workers, I am very concerned that the bandwidth available to us today *between* premises will not be able to cope with the demands of any-to-any video. The market is in its infancy, but I certainly see an opportunity for Video Gateway devices such as the one I show in Figure 19.8.

This device allows contact with the Gateway over traditional frame-based LANs. These may be Ethernet and Token Ring, but are more likely to be Switched Ethernet or Fast Ethernet. The Gateway confirms the LAN user's authority to use the WAN video service, sets up a secure channel (if necessary), compresses the video in real time and bills the call to the appropriate department. This technology is possible today.

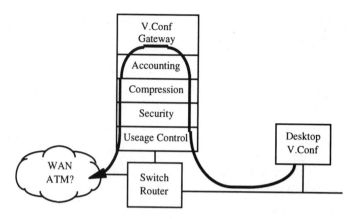

Figure 19.8:   Desktop Videoconferencing

19.3.4   Multicast Information Services

IP routing is fundamentally a unicast service. However, there are ways in which multicast information can be supported. This support can be broken down into two parts. First, we need to include support in the router so that it will recognize and forward multicast traffic, rather than drop it (which is the "natural" behavior for a router). Second, we need to implement extensions to our routing protocols to allow them to distribute the multicast information around the internetwork [4, 5].

The Internet Group Management Protocol (IGMP) describes the support for static and dynamic formation of multicast groups. In simple terms, IGMP allows a host to register its membership of a multicast group on a specific port of a router. Hosts belonging to the same multicast group can register on the same, or different ports of the same router. By using the *Distance-Vector Multicast Routing Protocol* (DVMRP) or *Multicast OSPF* (M-OSPF) [4], membership of multicast groups can be extended to ports on other routers.

Figure 19.9 shows a typical use for a multicast system. Information is generated on the Info Server. One copy of the information is sent to Router 1, which duplicates as many copies as are needed to reach all users belonging to the multicast group. Router 1 sends one copy each to Router 2, Router 3, and Router 4. Router 3 has, for example, three users attached. If these users are attached to the same LAN, one copy of the message is sent onto the LAN and all three users receive it. If they are on three different LANs attached to Router 3, one copy is sent onto each LAN. If Routers 2, 3, and 4 each had three users attached on different LAN segments, then a total of nine copies are generated at the User level (plus the intermediate copies). If we were to use a unicast delivery technique, then the Info Server would have to generate one message copy for each user and explicitly address the message. Nine copies would be sent from the Info Server to Router 1. Now think of a typical stocks and shares information delivery system, with thousands of users! The savings by using multicast are enormous.

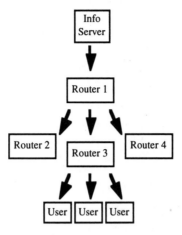

Figure 19.9:   Multicast Update Scheme

Why don't we just send out broadcast traffic? That's a possibility, although routers should always drop broadcasts too! If we were able to forward broadcasts (by using an all-subnets broadcast, for example), then we would dramatically restrict the flexibility of the application. The Info Server could send to everyone, or individuals and nothing in between. What if we wanted to generate separate information streams for Stocks, Bonds, Futures, Commodities, etc.? This can only be achieved using multicast.

Note that Videoconferencing and especially Distance Learning also require multicast support. News provider services such as Reuters or CNN are prime candidates. In fact, once you have taken the lid off the multicast issue, it's difficult to get it back on!

19.4 The Role of ATM

ATM poses the biggest questions for the network designer and for the protocol engineers. For years, US-based developers have specialized in connectionless protocols like IP and DECnet, while in Europe and other parts of the world, connection-oriented protocols like X.25 and Q.931 (the signaling protocol for N-ISDN) have dominated the WAN scene.

Since router products are developed by US companies, they have always lagged behind in terms of X.25 and ISDN support. Even worse, the communication protocols in the workgroup were fundamentally incompatible because of their basic design assumptions (try using Novell over ISDN, for example, and see the 6th Rule of Application Development at the start of Chapter 4). So the integration capabilities of mainstream routers for X.25 and ISDN have been rather lacking until recently.

ATM is also a connection oriented transport system. So, to run connectionless Network Layer protocols that rely on broadcast discovery mechanisms requires LAN Emulation. However, LAN Emulation is a MAC Layer function that suffers from the same scaleability issues as Transparent or Translation Bridging. ATM may offer huge amounts of bandwidth, but the behavior of our current communication protocols will ensure that this bandwidth is used up in useless overhead unless the network is carefully designed.

To support multicast or broadcast protocols in a scaleable way requires an intelligent routing between LAN Emulation domains. This is shown in Figure 19.10. In this case, the router has only a single connection: a high speed ATM link with multiple Virtual Circuits (VC). Groups of these VCs connect into the individual LAN Emulation Domains. Broadcasts or multicasts only spread *within* a LAN Emulation Domain. Communication *between* LAN Emulation Domains is made through conventional Network Layer addressing.

The detailed operation of this architecture are still being decided, although the first pass of LAN Emulation was approved by the ATM Forum in the Autumn of 1994.

Let's assume that Harry, Sally, Porgy, and Bess are all ATM-attached workstations. They all use an IP protocol stack, which requires broadcast and multicast support. In this architecture, Harry and Sally belong to the same MAC broadcast domain (i.e., the same LAN Emulation Domain). LAN Emulation domains may be grouped, for example, within a cluster of ATM Virtual Circuits. ATM has a shorthand way of describing such a group: they share a *Virtual Path Identifyr* (VPI) address[1]. I've denoted this in the diagram by the smaller pipe passing through the router ATM connection.

Broadcasts between hosts in the same domain are handled by a MAC emulation function inside the router, or even within the ATM switches in the cloud. This is the function of LAN Emulation. To the Router, the VCs that belong to the "MAC1" group appear as though they were a single LAN connection. In IP terms this means that they must use the same Network or Subnet ID. The hosts will ARP directly for each other and LAN Emulation handles the transaction.

Between domains, the Network or Subnet IDs are different, so the hosts will look for a router. Conventional IP routing is used to move the IP packets between domains. Currently this requires the router to reassemble ATM cells into a recognizable IP packet. However, in the future, *Virtual Network Routers* (VNR) will simply establish the association between IP address and ATM address. At the time of writing, no standard protocol exists to allow communication between a router and an ATM switch.

---

[1]Sharing a VPI may not be a requirement for a single LAN Emulation Domain.

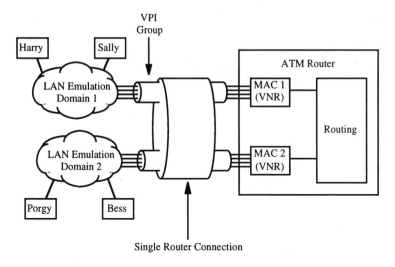

Figure 19.10:   Scaling LAN Emulation

19.5 Multiprotocol or Convergence?

When the Internet first formed, it was an IP network. Today it officially supports IP, and OSI CLNS. IPX access is possible in certain areas. When routers first arrived as discrete products (rather than a host or server function), they became successful because they were cheaper than the things they replaced and they offered concurrent multiprotocol support. Today, the LAN world is converging. Already we can say that XNS is effectively a dead protocol. DECNet Phase IV is terminally ill and VINES IP has a fixed user base that will soon decline in favor of IP. AppleTalk will disappear as Power PC Macs and PCs become mixed on the same LAN segments. Bridging protocols of all kinds should be wiped out, or restricted to local segments. The short-term winners of the protocol race are:

- IP (and IPng)
- IPX
- SNA (including APPN)

In the longer term, we need to consider the following: will our backbone internetworks still be multiprotocol and if they converge on a single protocol which will it be? The choices are:

- IPv4 (using Private Addressing to overcome address space limits)
- IPv6
- ATM

Don't expect an answer to this! Looking at historical trends, there will ᵤᵤ considerable inertia for IPv4. In other words, the protocol will be with us for many years yet. IPv6 offers advantages in scaleability, but at first glance, it doesn't seem to be the ideal protocol to use with ATM backbones (a good deal of emulation is still required and ATM Quality of Service doesn't map into the IPv6 scheme).

ATM as an internetworking protocol is at the very beginning of its development. LAN Emulation is a start, but takes us back to bridging. ATM internetworking in the form of the *Private Network to Network Interface* (PNNI) is just beginning and a *stable, interoperable* PNNI implementation will not be ready before 1996.

The real key to ATM deployment as a native protocol (i.e., instead of a transport mechanism for IP) is the development of an API that can use ATM features directly.

What Do I do?

Don't panic! Designing networks to support these frame-based protocols is a challenge, but at least people have been doing it for the past 20 years or so and there's a bit of experience to be tapped. In the future, the concept of multiprotocol will change dramatically. The only protocols that will matter in the future are:

- Frames
- Cells

In other words, designing truly long-lived internetworks is about understanding the role of cell-switching techniques such as ATM in relation to the frame-based protocols we use today.

ATM is *the* cell-based technology, but is in its infancy. A modern network design should take scaleability as its primary goal. Migration to ATM will occur initially by LAN Emulation, with scaleability maintained using Virtual Network Routing. ATM workgroups may bypass the IP backbone using native ATM APIs, but cannot become a mainstream technique for many years yet.

Even when ATM internetworking is stable, interoperable and affordable, there will still be an inertia effect to continue with known technologies.

19.6 References

[1]   P. Gross. "Charge to IPng Area: A Direction for IPng." *Connexions*. May 1994.

[2]   A selection of RFCs describe and comment upon CIDR. These include RFC 1517, 1518 and 1519 (the most recent documents). The original concept of "Supernetting" (as CIDR was first named) is described in RFC 1338, some architectural comments can be found in RFC 1467.

[3]   Y. Rekhter, T. Li.   "A Border Gateway Protocol 4 (BGP-4)." *Internet Draft*. January 1994.

[4]   A selection of RFCs describe multicasting. IGMP is described in RFC 1112.   Route propagation for multicasts by DVMRP is described in RFC 1075. Multicast OSPF is described in RFC 1584.

[5]   D. Comer. "Internetworking with TCP/IP. Volume 1." Prentice-Hall, 1991.

[6]   E. Fleischman.   "A User's View of the Next Generation of IP (IPng)." *Connexions*. May 1994.

Section 4

APPENDICES

Glossary

4B/5B. A Physical Layer encoding scheme used on FDDI LANs to represent binary information as analog transitions. In FDDI, a 4 bit data progression is encoded into a 5 bit symbol. The symbol transformations are chosen so that an alternating "one/zero" relationship can be guaranteed in the data stream, allowing the FDDI adapters to maintain the synchronous clock on the ring.

ABR. Area Border Router. An OSPF router that has interfaces belonging to more than one OSPF area.

Access method. The arbitration mechanism used to allow an individual user to access a shared data channel while avoiding interference with other users. The two most common access methods in use today are CSMA/CD, used by Ethernet and IEEE 802.3 LANs, and Token Passing used by IEEE 802.5 and FDDI LANs.

Active loop. Loops (i.e., redundant paths) within internetworks are a great way to provide resilience. An active loop is one in which more than one path is allowed to forward traffic. In Transparent Bridging, if there are multiple paths between two LAN segments, multiple copies of the same LAN frame will appear on LAN segments if more than one path is allowed between segments. Spanning Tree is used by Transparent Bridges to block paths between segments until only one active path remains (i.e., active loops are removed). In Source Route Bridging, multiple active paths can be maintained because the frames carry their own routes. In routing, active loops are also allowed since the routers will agree the optimum route amongst themselves.

Address. An identifier used to assign a data unit to a specific end point. Addresses are used at several layers within communication stacks, allowing unique reference to an individual end station, or a specific software process operating within the end station.

ARP. Address Resolution Protocol. The Internet protocol used to dynamically discover the hardware (MAC) address of an end system assuming its IP address is known. ARP may be used on any network technology that supports broadcast operation, or emulation.

Adjacency. An OSPF term. OSPF routers on the same LAN will discover each other using multicast routing updates. When two or more routers are exchanging acknowledged routing updates, they are said to have formed an adjacency.

Address mask. A binary mask used to denote the portion of an IP address that will be used to represent network and subnet addressing. The mask is 32 bits long and is normally written in dotted decimal notation. Also known as the subnet mask.

Age. Many different communication techniques use a process called aging to ensure that information that has not been updated is removed from decision tables.

Agent. The process that resides on a managed device, allowing management parameters to be passed between the managed device and the NMS. In SNMP, the agent is responsible for interpreting the get, get_next, set and trap primitives.

ANSI. American National Standards Institute. The US representative to ISO.

API. Application programming interface. A set of programming functions defining how a specific service can be invoked from software. An example of an API is NetBIOS.

ARPANET. The original Internet. Dissolved in 1989.

Asynchronous transmission. A transmission system which sends data as individual characters, wrapped in specific start and stop bits. Using these bits, the receiver is able to resolve bytes within the data stream without needing to be synchronized with the sender.

AS. Autonomous system. Internet and TCP/IP term to describe a collection of IP routers that are controlled by a single administrative entity. Routers within an AS exchange routing information using a common IGP such as RIP or OSPF.

ASBR. Autonomous System Boundary Router. An OSPF router used to connect the OSPF Autonomous System to other Autonomous Systems.

ASN.1. Abstract Syntax Notation 1. An ISO standard describing data syntax and representation. A subset of ASN.1 is used in SNMP and SNMP2 Structure of Management Information.

ATM. Asynchronous Transfer Mode. A combination of a cell-based transmission technology and a high speed switching system. ATM will be able to scale to much higher speeds than the equivalent frame-based technologies. In addition, the shorter cell transmission units potentially allow voice and data streams to be multiplexed over the same channel.

BECN. Backwards Explicit Congestion Notification. A congestion control mechanism used in Frame Relay WANs.

BER. Bit Error Rate. BER is normally quoted by simply measuring how many bad bits there were in a given time period over a given transmission system. For example, a digital leased line may have a stated BER of one bit in 10,000,000000 (one in ten to the power of nine). However, if there is one bad bit in an IP packet, the whole packet must be retransmitted. If there are ten bad bits in a packet, we still only have to retransmit one packet.

BER. Basic Encoding Rules. The set of rules used to encode information in an ASN.1 format.

Bennett's Law. If a cable has one end, it probably has another.

BGP. Border gateway protocol. BGP is an External Gateway Protocol used to advertise the reachability of network outside of the Autonomous System. It contains a number of improvements over EGP and is designed to support Policy Routing, and address agglomeration using CIDR.

Bottleneck. The point in the overall data path with the lowest communication bandwidth. For example, if a communication path includes a 10Mbps Ethernet, followed by a 64kbps leased line, and then an FDDI LAN, data can only flow at a maximum of 64kbps between the LANs. Bottlenecks exist within individual communication channels, and within any active device in the communication path.

Bridge ID. In an extended Token Ring network interconnected by Source Routing Bridges, each bridge is assigned a 4-bit address known as the Bridge ID. A Bridge ID of 0 is illegal. Bridges may be assigned the same ID unless multiple bridges are connected between the same rings. In this case, each parallel bridge must be given a different Bridge ID.

BPDU. Bridge protocol data unit. The name for the Spanning Tree protocol packets that are used to detect loops in a Transparent Bridge network. Defined by IEEE 802.1.

BR. Backbone Router. An OSPF router in which all of the interfaces belong to the OSPF backbone area (0.0.0.0).

BRI. Basic Rate Interface (ISDN). The original 2B+D ISDN interface. Internationally the B channels operate at 64kbps with a 16kbps signaling channel. The physical interface for ISDN BRI is a single RJ-45 jack connector. The B and D channels are multiplexed over this link.

Broadcast. A data delivery system, such as Ethernet, in which a copy of a given data unit is delivered to all end systems attached to a common medium.

Broadcast. An address pattern applied to a data unit used on a multi access network so that all end systems on this network will copy the data unit.

Broadcast domain. The scope of the network within which a MAC Layer broadcast (or multicast) will spread. In other words, if two hosts are in the same broadcast domain, they will be able to hear each other's broadcasts.

Broadcast storm. An effect seen in early bridge networks, when loops were introduced into the network topology. A single broadcast on any LAN within the loop was effectively continued to travel around the network continuously, and at each bridge was duplicated onto all segments connected to the bridge. Broadcast storms result in the entire network bandwidth being consumed by copies of the original broadcast within a few seconds. The storm can only be cleared by manually removing loops form the network topology. The Spanning Tree protocol was specifically intended to perform this process automatically. Today, routers are used to create network firewalls to prevent the formation and propagation of broadcast storms.

Brouter. Originally a device which concurrently performs bridging and routing functions. The device will route packets whose Network Layer protocol is recognized (and configured within the brouter). All other packets are bridged. Today this term has become misused by manufacturers offering "value-added" bridge functionality. Within this book I have substituted the phrase "bridge/router."

Bus. The internal data pathway of a computer system, or subsystem. Examples include the PC bus, Multibus, VME bus and EISA bus.

Bus. One of several possible LAN implementations. A bus-based LAN typically operates over a bidirectional coaxial cable. Examples include the original Ethernet Version 1.0 and 2.0; IEEE 10BASE5; IEEE 10BASE2; IEEE 802.4 Token Bus.

Byte. Unit of measurement of binary data. A byte is traditionally 8 bits in length, however some older computer architectures have used different values for the byte. To avoid confusion, the word octet is beginning to replace byte in most international literature.

Cache. A store. In communication terms, a cache is a storage area in dynamic memory in which address associations are stored once they are learned from the network. The efficient use of caches means that hosts only need to generate discovery packets or frames when they have no cache entry. Several caches may be maintained by a host, bridge or router, e.g., ARP cache, Name cache, etc.

CCITT. International Consultative Committee for Telegraphy and Telephony. Part of the International Telecommunications Union (ITU) of the United Nations. CCITT consists of representative members from PTTs around the world. In early 1993, the CCITT became officially known as the ITU-TSS..

CERT. Computer Emergency Response Team. Initiative started after the Internet Worm attack of 1988. CERT teams keep a regular watch on security threats to specific areas. In addition, you may find specific CERT advisory documents that can be obtained by mail list subscription.

CHAP. Challenged Handshake Authentication Protocol. CHAP is defined as part of PPP. In contrast to PAP, a CHAP authentication is performed at the connection setup, and periodically during the connection. CHAP authentication is encrypted to prevent impersonation.

CIDR. Classless Interdomain Routing. An address agglomeration technique that frees IP addresses from the concept of class structure. CIDR requires that an address prefix is used to form the subnet structure of any IP address. In this way, contiguous blocks of Class C addresses can be treated as a single address and combined within the routing table. CIDR is an interim technique that can help in conserving IP address space until the next generation IP protocol is deployed.

CIR. Committed Information Rate. A Frame Relay term. CIR is the minimum amount of bandwidth that a specific virtual circuit can use on a given physical connection. For example, let's say that we rent a 2Mbps Frame Relay circuit from a carrier. We set up 4 PVCs on this circuit, and we allocate each PVC a CIR of 128kbps. Each PVC can transmit above its CIR, but the frames that exceed CIR are marked by setting the D/E bit, and can be discarded by the network in the event of congestion. As long as we keep the sum of CIRs on a given access link to be less than or equal to the line speed, then the CIR is equivalent to a guaranteed bandwidth. Note that the bandwidth guarantee only applies to our physical link. The Frame Relay provider must perform a similar summation to ensure that the CIR is significant end-to-end over the Frame Relay service.

CLID. Calling Line Identification. An ISDN term, the CLID is the telephone number of the calling party, which is sent to the called device as part of ISDN signaling. CLID is an excellent security feature.

CLNP. Connectionless Network Protocol. Defined in ISO 8473, CLNS is the Network Layer protocol for the ISO Connectionless Network Service. It is sometimes known as "ISO IP," and uses a 40 character, variable format address known as an NSAP. Since the IETF decision on the Next Generation IP, the future for CLNP looks bleak.

CMIS/CMIP.   Common Management Information Service/Protocol. CMIS/CMIP is the ISO equivalent of SNMP. Although offering many scaleability advantages over SNMP, CMIS/CMIP is fundamentally hampered by its perceived dependence on CLNP. Today, this management system seems to be used only by telecom providers in the management of large switching systems.

CMOT. Common Management Over TCP. CMOT was an early attempt to implement ISO Common Management Services over a non-ISO Transport

Layer, specifically TCP. At the time of writing, CMOT had been abandoned in favor of SNMP, SNMP2 and potentially full CMIS/CMIP.

Connectionless. A system in which communication takes place between two end systems without a specific connection establishment phase. Most LAN protocols in use today operate in a connectionless mode at the Physical, Data Link and Network Layers. The UDP protocol is an example of a connectionless Transport Layer protocol.

Connection oriented. A system in which communication takes place between two end systems in three clearly defined phases; connection establishment; data transfer; connection release.   Some LAN protocols, such as TCP, offer connection oriented operation.   Some protocol stacks, such as X.25, SNA, and the current APPN proposal are connection oriented at all layers.

Core gateway. An Internet terms for the routers that are directly attached to the NSFNET backbone.

COS. Corporation for Open Systems. A manufacturer, vendor, and user group committed to conformance testing, certification and promotion of OSI and TCP/IP protocols and products. At the time of writing, COS is hosting the OIG test lab.

CRC. Cyclic Redundancy Check. An error check mechanism used by LAN and WAN transmission technologies. The IEEE CRC is a 32-bit value which is calculated using a standard mathematical function. The CRC is calculated on the contents of the frame and appended by the transmitter. The *local receiver* (e.g., a router in an internetwork conversation) will receive the frame and will recalculate the CRC. The calculated value is compared to the received value, and if they are different the receiver assumes that the frame is corrupted. Internetwork routers will recalculate the CRC when they forward the frame (since the local wire addresses will have changed and the original CRC will be invalid). Translation and Source Route bridges

CSMA/CD. Carrier Sense Multiple Access with Collision Detection. The access control method for Ethernet, IEEE 802.3 and Fast Ethernet.

Data Link Layer. The second layer of the OSI model. The Data Link Layer is normally implemented in dedicated communication hardware, such as an Ethernet or Token Ring chipset, or an HDLC line driver. The Data Link Layer is normally divided into two sub-layers. The lower sublayer - the Media Access Control (MAC) sublayer, interfaces directly with the Physical Layer. The upper sublayer, the Logical Link Control (LLC) sublayer, interfaces with the Network Layer. Within the Data Link Layer, communication bitstreams are resolved into frames by using indicators in the bitstream known as flags. The frames may contain addressing information, and verification information, typically in the form of a CRC.

DCE. Data Circuit-terminating Equipment. The equipment that forms the network connection for a DTE. By convention, DCEs must offer network clock, and present a female connector to the DTE. For example, a modem will normally offer a DCE interface to the attaching DTE device.

Default Gateway. Default Router. These terms have two meanings, depending on the device function. In both cases the word "router" and "gateway" are functionally equivalent. For an IP host, the Default Router/Gateway is the address of an IP router that is used by the host to transmit datagrams out of the host's Broadcast Domain. For an IP router, the Default Router/Gateway is the IP address of a router to which datagrams should be forwarded if no other route is known. The older term, "gateway" is still used (thanks to "legacy" documentation and user interfaces). Since a gateway is now generally accepted as an Application Layer protocol conversion device, it is quite misleading, and strictly speaking inaccurate, to retain the older phrase.

D/E. Discard Eligible. This is a reserved bit in the header of a Frame Relay frame. Frames that have the D/E bit set should be discarded before frames with D/E clear in the event that the Frame Relay network becomes congested.

DECnet. Digital Equipment Corporation's proprietary networking architecture.

DES. Data Encryption Standard. The de facto encryption standard currently approved by the US government. Defined by the National Bureau of Standards in FIPS Publication 46-1, January 1988.

DDN. Defense Data Network. A group of US military networks. The term DDN is also used to describe a form of IP tunneling over X.25. The DDN method uses a group of IP addresses originally allocated to BBN to dynamically map the IP address to a special format of X.25 DTE address.

Digital Envelope. Digital enveloping is the process of encrypting the *body* of a message using a symmetric or asymmetric cypher.

Digital Signature. Take a clear text message and calculate a fixed length (typically 128 bit) message digest that is essentially unique to that message. Then encrypt the message digest using (typically) an asymmetric (Public Key) cypher. The result is a digital signature. See also MD5.

DMZ. De-Militarized Zone. A phrase that describes a section of LAN or WAN that is known to be insecure. In this context the word "trusted" is more appropriate than "secure" since DMZs can be Autonomous Systems that are outside of our own control. In this case it is the routing information that is not "secure." We can tolerate DMZs, or connection to them by installing Firewalls.

DNS. Domain Name System. A distributed database system used to resolve client name requests into IP addresses.

Domain. A term with both generic and specific uses to describe a separate logical or administrative partition.

Dotted decimal notation. The syntactic representation used in IP addressing. A 32 bit IP address is split into four 8-bit fields, each of which is evaluated as a decimal number with no leading zeros. The decimal numbers are separated by dots, e.g., 128.7.192.66.

DTE. Data Terminal Equipment. The source or destination of data over the internetwork. By convention, DTEs offer male connectors to the DCE. Usually the DTE will take at least the receive clock form the DCE, and may optionally take transmit clock. The V.35 standard, for example, prohibits the DTE from providing transmit clock.

Encapsulation. Generally the concept of using a protocol "wrapper" to allow information from one protocol stack to be transported over a network which supports a different, and incompatible protocol stack. Two examples of standards-based encapsulation include tunneling IP datagrams over X.25 using RFC877 or RFC 1356 procedures, and transport of SNA or NetBIOS over an IP backbone using Data Link Switching. Many other forms of encapsulation are proprietary.

ES. End system. A computer system containing communication software and hardware which is capable of communicating through all seven layers of the OSI model. In this book, I have used the term end system to refer to IP devices. In earlier literature, the term was often reserved to describe ISO-base communication systems.

ESIS. End System to Intermediate System. ESIS is the ISO protocol by which end systems discover other end systems, and intermediate systems. In some ways, ESIS provides the equivalent functionality of ARP and ICMP for ISO communication systems.

Ethernet. A 10Mbps, baseband LAN using a CSMA/CD access method. Ethernet was developed by an industry consortium consisting of Digital Equipment Corp., Intel and Xerox. The original Ethernet 1.0 specification was published in September 1980, with Version 2.0 (the current version) published in November 1982. The IEEE 802.3 10BASE5, 10BASE2, 10BASET and 10BASEF LANs are all derivations of the original Ethernet specification.

EtherTalk. The implementation of AppleTalk over Ethernet Version 2.0 (for AppleTalk Phase 1) or IEEE 802.3 (for AppleTalk Phase 2).

EGP. Exterior Gateway Protocol. EGP is a reachability protocol used between Autonomous Systems. Currently there are two inter-AS protocols approved for use on the Internet - EGP and the newer BGP.

Extended network. Extended Token Ring. Extended Ethernet. These are all phrases that I use to describe homogeneous LAN segments that are interconnected by bridges. The common concept is that two bridged LANs will use identical Network or Subnet IDs, and so will use conventional ARP to resolve IP/MAC addresses. For this reason, broadcast (and multicast) traffic must be passed by the bridges. This has an impact on the scaleability of the extended network.

External Data Representation (XDR). A standard originally developed by Sun as part of the NFS system. Analogous to (but much simpler compared to) ASN.1.

Fast packet. Networking devices such as Bridges and Routers operate on the "store and forward" principle. Originally, the concept of fast packet operation implied that the device was designed to initiate its forwarding process as soon as enough "addressing" bits had been received to allow it to make an appropriate decision. In the cast of a rhetorical "Ethernet fast packet bridge," this would mean that the first 48 address bits (the MAC destination) would be received into the bridge, at which point the bridge would decide whether or not to forward the frame. This original definition was lost when Stratacom registered the fast packet name (using upper case "f" and "p"). The Stratacom IPX Fast Packet switch is still a store and forward device, but the marketing impetus behind this, and other similar devices effectively killed off the original meaning of the term. Ethernet switches such as those made by Kalpana and Alantec are true fast packet devices.

Fat Pipe. A general expression that implies a higher speed connection (LAN or WAN) into (typically) shared resource. A currently popular example is the use of half-duplex (i.e., conventional) Ethernet by LAN clients, while the servers and routers are fitted with Full Duplex Ethernet.

FCS. Frame Check Sequence. See CRC.

FDDI. Fiber Distributed Data Interface. A 100Mbps, baseband LAN using a Token Passing access method. FDDI is defined by ANSI committee X3T9.5.

FDE. Full Duplex Ethernet. A twisted pair (10 BASET) Ethernet variant in which hosts are allowed to transmit and receive simultaneously.

FECN. Forward Explicit Congestion Notification. A congestion control mechanism used in Frame Relay WANs.

Fragmentation. The process by which a Network Layer packet is broken down into smaller, Network Layer packets to fit the requirements of a given physical network. An example would be the fragmentation of a 4000 byte FDDI packet into three smaller packets for transmission over Ethernet, which support a maximum packet size of 1500 bytes. Fragmentation is generally an inefficient process which reduces overall throughput in a router network. It can be avoided by static MTU configuration, or by the implementation of MTU Discovery.

FTP. File Transfer Protocol. An Internet file transfer protocol implemented over TCP. FTP includes a session login in which a user name and password are provided.

Gateway. The original Internet term for router. The term began to lose favor around 1988, but it still appears in RFCs and other Internet documentation.

Gateway. An End System which is used to translate an Application Process implemented over a specific communication stack into a similar Application Process implemented over another stack. Examples include Telnet/X.25, LAT/Telnet, X.400/RFC822.

GOSIP. Government OSI Profile. Government guidelines for the procurement of OSI products. Two versions of GOSIP exist. In the US, GOSIP has concentrated on connectionless ISO protocol stacks, and may now introduce TCP/IP as an officially recognized option. In the UK, GOSIP originally specified connection oriented operation, but since Version 3.1 (1992) has given equal weighting to both operating modes. TCP/IP is not currently a part of UK GOSIP.

HDLC. High Level Data Link Control. HDLC is a Data Link Layer protocol design for use over serial communication circuits.

Infinity. In routing, a concept whereby routes with high costs can be regarded as unreachable. In RIP, infinity is represented by a route with a hop cost of 16 or higher.

Internetwork. Intranetwork. The Latin words "intra" and "inter" mean respectively "within" and "between" respectively. Something that is described as *intra*network occurs *within* the network, such as a conversation passing between two hosts on the same network. *Inter*network conversations would be those passing *between* hosts on different networks. Note the Latin word "infra" (as in infrared) means "below" or "beneath."

Integrated PNNI. The Integrated Private Network to Network Interface. An initiative of the ATM Forum, IPNNI is intended to allow "legacy" internetworks using IP to fully route over ATM clouds. In effect, full address and quality of service can be passed from the LAN domain into the ATM domain. IPNNI should be presented to the ATM Forum in late 1995, and if all goes well it should begin trials in 1996.

IR. Internal Router. An OSPF router in which all interfaces belong only to one area.

IS.   Intermediate System.   An intermediate system is a device in the communication path through which traffic will pass, but not terminate.   In ISO terms, an IS is a Network Layer router.

ISIS. Intermediate System to Intermediate System routing protocol. A Link State ISO routing protocol similar to OSPF, but designed to route ISO Connectionless Network Layer Protocol networks.   Integrated ISIS is a development of ISIS which is capable of determining routes for ISO CLNP or DoD IP.

ISDN. Integrated Services Digital Network.   A digital telephone system with special adaptations that make it useful for transaction-oriented data applications. See also BRI, PRI.

ISO.   The Organization for International Harmonization.

LAPB. Link Access Protocol - Balanced.   LAPB is a connection oriented LLC protocol used by the X.25 communication stack.   LAPB includes the concept of acknowledgments and sliding window flow control.

LLC1. Logical Link Control Type 1.   IBM's term for IEEE 802.2 Class 1. Used by most LAN protocol stacks, including Novell IPX and TCP/IP SNAP.

LLC2. Logical Link Control Type 2.   IBM's term for the IEEE 802.2 Class 2 protocol.   Used by most SNA protocols on LANs.   Also used by "native" NetBIOS.

Manchester Encoding.   A Physical Layer encoding scheme used to represent binary signals as voltage transitions on an electrical circuit.   Manchester encoding uses up to two transitions to encode one binary symbol.   Thus a 16Mbps Token Ring may use a clock speed up to 32MHz.   Higher speed LAN technologies (such as FDDI or ATM Fiberchannel) have opted to use other encoding techniques such as 4B/5B or 8B/10B.

MD5. Message Digest Algorithm 5.   A message digest, or digital signature algorithm developed by Ron Rivest at MIT, and defined in RFC 1321.   MD5 takes an input data stream of arbitrary length and produces a 128-bit digital signature.   The signature allows transmitting or receiving stations to detect modification or corruption of the data.   MD5 is the specified digital signature mechanism for Secure SNMP.

Message Digest. Message Digest Algorithm. See MD5.

MIB.   Management Information Base.   A tree structured database used by SNMP managed devices and management systems to represent management parameters within the managed device.

MIB2. The specific MIB defined in RFC 1213.

MLM. Mid-Level Manager. A management information concentrator. MLMs are software processes located in active network devices such as hubs or routers. They concentrate and summarize local management information for forwarding to the central NMS.

NetBIOS. Network Basic I/O System. A software extension to the BIOS of a PC to allow distributed LAN functions to be accessed by applications. Originally implemented by Sytek in their PC LAN Adapter, NetBIOS is now only implemented as a variety of emulation packages. IBM's own NetBIOS is a NetBIOS API (NETBEUI) implemented over LLC2. NetBIOS emulators are also available for TCP/IP, IPX, XNS and VINES. Note that NetBIOS implementations written over different protocol stacks cannot interoperate.

NLPID. Network Layer Protocol ID. A field used in X.25 (RFC1256), Frame Relay (RFC1490) and ATM (RFC1483) as an analogy to the SNAP or Type field in LANs. In other words, the number in this field identifies the Network Layer protocol contained inside the encapsulation unit. An NLPID of CCh indicates "IP" and 80h indicates "SNAP."

NMS. Network Management System. A generic name for the workstation on which the Network Management client software operates. Server software operates in the managed device.

NRZ. NRZI. Non-Return to Zero and Non-Return to Zero Inverted respectively. Physical level encoding methods used on IBM SDLC connections to represent binary signals in terms of electrical voltage transitions. NRZ and NRZI are analogous to LAN-style methods such as Manchester Encoding or 4B/5B encoding.

OSI. Open Systems Interconnection. A reference model, originally drawn with 7 Layers. Each has a defined function, or set of functions. An interface is defined between layers to enforce a structured design paradigm. Today, the OSI model is drawn with additional layers to adapt it more closely to modern systems.

PAD. Packet Assembler/Disassembler. Although this term sounds rather generic, the accepted form of PAD device used in the industry today is to allow an asynchronous (start/stop) terminal to communicate over an X.25 switched network. This operation is defined in the Triple X standards.

PAP. The Password Authentication Protocol. Defined for PPP connections, PAP is a one-time password exchange in which a clear text password is sent over the connection.

PNNI. Private Network to Network Interface. An ATM Forum initiative, PNNI is the ATM routing protocol. PNNI operate only within ATM clouds, and has no concept of IP or IPX address space.

PRI. Primary Rate Interface (ISDN). Higher capacity ISDN interface based on a 22B+D (USA) or 30B+D (International) carrier. Each B channel is offered at 64kbps, with a 64kbps D channel reserved for signaling. PRI was designed to interconnect telephone PABX equipment, offering a high quality of service with additional distributed telephone facilities. Now widely deployed in Europe using an E1 (G.703) interface, PRI is of great interest for internetworking applications.

Reliable. In communication terms, a protocol which includes error detection and possibly error correction (normally by retransmission request). It is quite possible (in fact, it is usual) to implement a reliable protocol over an unreliable protocol stack. TCP is a reliable Transport Layer protocol that runs over unreliable Network, Data Link and Physical Layers.

Ring ID. In an extended Token Ring network interconnected by Source Routing Bridges, each ring is assigned a unique, 12-bit address known as the Ring ID. A Ring ID of 0 is illegal.

SAR. Segmentation and Reassembly. *Segmentation* is the process of breaking down a LAN or WAN frame into smaller, fixed length units called cells. These cells are then transmitted over a cell based transport system such as ATM or SMDS, and then *Reassembled* into their original frame structure.

Service Level Agreement. A document which summarizes the agreed values that are acceptable for quality criteria defined by Service Level Definitions. Typically such an agreement will be between the users of the internetwork, and the providers of the internetwork.

Service Level Definition. A systematic definition of the quality of a very specific system function. Service Level Definitions should include a unique description of the subsystem being measured, a complete test method and recommendations for data treatment.

Secure SNMP. A revised version of SNMP in which authentication and encryption mechanisms are defined. Secure SNMP is defined RFCs 1321, 1351, 1352 and 1353.

SDLC. Synchronous Data Link Control. A derivation of HDLC used by IBM to connect many types of SNA communication devices. SDLC is a connection oriented version of HDLC, and includes a connection setup and maintenance protocol.

Silently discard. This phrase is now in common usage in standards documents such as RFCs. If a device such as a host or router receives a network packet which causes the receiving device a problem (such as an unknown IP address, or an inappropriate protocol type), the device should discard the packet. If possible, devices should signal to the transmitter that there is a problem (failure to do so normally results in a retransmission of the problem packet). In some circumstances, protocol designers may feel it's better *not* to signal an error, and will specify that the device should *silently discard* the offending packet.

SMI. The Structure of Management Information. A components of the SNMP architecture that describes the way that management data is represented.

SNAP. Sub Network access Protocol. SNAP is a specially reserved variant of IEEE 802.2 LSAP encoding. LSAPs are designed to allow Link Layer protocol multiplexing. SNAP was introduced because LSAP are only 8 bits long, and do no allow all possible Type numbers to be expressed. In effect, SNAP indicates to the protocol multiplexer to look further into the packet, where it will find a Type field.

SNMP. The Simple Network Management Protocol is a management protocol which is designed to operate over UDP over IP.

SNMP2. SNMPv2. A revised management protocol which is designed to address problems found with the original SNMP architecture. SNMP2 is defined in RFCs 1441, 1442, 1443, 1444, 1445, 1446, 1447, 1448, 1449, 1450 and 1451.

Spanning Tree. The concept, defined in IEEE 802.1d, of converting a redundant meshed network into a loop-free tree. Spanning Tree is a protocol used by Transparent and Translation Bridges to prevent the infinite looping of bridge frames. In Source Route Bridges, Spanning Tree is used to discover a single, most efficient interconnection path between two given rings.

SRA. Source Route Accelerator. In Token Ring, a Source Route Accelerator is a piece of hardware that allows Source Route Bridges to examine RIF entries and make frame forwarding decision at wire speed.

SSCP. System Services Control Point. An SNA term for the control point within an IBM mainframe used to establish, monitor and terminate remote sessions. SSCP is normally provided by a program called VTAM.

Striping. If two (typically equal cost) paths exist between two networks, striping is a process of frame distribution between paths to achieve some form of load balancing.

Stripping. On a ring-based LAN, frames are sent by one station, pass around the ring, and are copied by another station. The frame continues around the ring, and must be removed by the originating station. This process is known as stripping. Safeguards exist within Token Ring and FDDI to ensure that frames are stripped from the ring if their originating stations fail to do so.

Synchronous transmission. A transmission system which sends data as a block of continuous bits, rather than individually marked bytes. In synchronous transmission, the sender and receiver must maintain synchronization so that the position of individual bytes in the block can be determined.

Tap. Transceiver Attachment Point. The boxes used to attach to the backbone cable in an IEEE 802.3 10BASE5 network.

Telnet. The Network Terminal protocol. Telnet provides a terminal emulation API over TCP over IP. Various terminal emulations have been implemented over Telnet. These include the VT terminals (VT52, VT100, VT3XX), and the TN3270(for IBM 327X synchronous terminals). Using Telnet, a networked workstation can log onto a host system on the network and emulate an appropriate terminal type.

TFTP. Trivial File Transfer Protocol. Defined in RFC 1350. A session-less file transfer protocol which operates over UDP over IP. TFTP is often used by diskless devices to boot operating systems. It is also used extensively by bridges and routers to upload new versions of software, or to transfer configuration information for storage on the Network Management System.

Transport Layer Interface. TLI. An enhanced API introduced by AT&T in UNIX System V in 1986.

Token Ring. A ring-based access technique based on a Token Passing access technique. The two most common examples of this technology being IEEE 802.5 and FDDI.

Triple X. X.3, X.28, X.29. The so-called "Triple X" protocols are used to define the operation of terminals into an X.25 PAD.

UDP. User Datagram Protocol. Defined in RFC 768, UDP is a connectionless, unreliable Transport Layer protocol available to TCP/IP program developers. Higher level applications based on UDP include TFTP, SNMP and NFS.

Unreliable. This term sometimes worries a newcomer to internetworking. If a protocol is described as unreliable, it simply means that no form of error correction is performed by the protocol at this layer. Many reliable communication system are implemented over unreliable lower layers. For example, all TCP/IP applications operate over an unreliable Network Layer (IP), yet a Transport Layer protocol such as TCP can be used to provide reliable service to higher level applications. Even reliable systems such as X.25 were designed to operate over unreliable Physical Layer networks.

V.21. A venerable old CCITT standard for modems allowing transmission speeds up to 300bps.

V.22. V.22*bis*. CCITT modem standard allowing transmission up to 1200bps. V.22*bis* doubles this to 2400 bps.

V.23. CCITT standard allowing transmission up to 1200 bps in half-duplex mode. In the UK, British Telecom used this standard for its Prestel service.

V.25. V.25*bis***.** A synchronous modem signaling standard. V.25 allows a modem answering an incoming call to determine the appropriate modulation standard. V.25*bis* allows the DTE device to transfer a connection identifier (usually a telephone number) into the DCE device (usually a modem or DSU) prior to a connection command.

V.32, V.32*bis***, V.32***ter***.** CCITT modem standard for devices transmitting at 4800 bps or 9600 bps. V.32*bis* extends the standard to include speeds of 7200, 12 000 and 14 400 bps. Due to delays in the finalizing of the V.34 standard, a consortium of manufacturers increased the base line rate for V.32 to 19.2kbps, and this system is known as V.32*ter*.

V.34. A CCITT modem modulation standard, currently unfinalized. In effect, V.34 is the standard designation for the V.Fast initiative.

V.42. V.42*bis***.** The CCITT standard protocol for error correction between modems. This standard includes MNP up to Level 4. V.42*bis* extends V.42 to include data compression.

V.35. A serial connection standard. V.35 is a part-balanced synchronous interface that can operate at data rates up to 8Mbps. V.35 is also a common connection type in Europe for 64kbps services.

VPN. Virtual Private Network. A closed group of network segments whose communication is kept separate, even though their traffic shares a backbone with open groups, or other VPNs.

VTAM. Virtual telecommunications Access Method. One of several communication access methods used by SNA.

X.21. A serial connection standard that is implemented over a V.11 electrical interface. X.21 is a balanced, differential, synchronous serial interface that can operate at data rates up to 10Mbps. In much of Europe, X.21 is the standard connection provided for 64kbps services by the PTT. It is also the standard interface for X.25 switched public services.

X.25. A packet layer protocol originally defined in the CCITT Blue Book standards. X.25 is a connection oriented, packet based protocol which was designed to operate over unreliable data circuits. The protocol is losing popularity today as its error detection and correction routines are regarded as unnecessary for modern digital circuits. However, X.25 in its latest forms (the 1984 and 1988 versions of the standard) are an integral form of the GOSIP recommendations.

Diskette Tutorials

Along with this book, you should have received two floppy discs containing some additional material that I thought might be useful.

Since I'm actually finishing off this material *after* the deadline for the manuscript, I'm not going to describe the contents in too much detail. However, I can state that one of my main goals was to make the tutorials accessable for PC users and for Mac users.

PC Users

You should get the most out of the tutorials, because the disks contain a Windows 3.1 program. To install the tutorials, start Windows, and from the Program Manager window, select File / Run, and in the dialog box type:

a:\setup

Hit **OK** and just follow the instructions.

Setup will install some custom drivers into your WINDOWS\SYSTEM directory, and will create a directory called SEMPAI on your hard disc. My target for the disc useage is less than 5 MB.

Setup will create a Windows program group called SEMPAI, and in it you'll find an icon called SEMPAI. When the installation routine finishes, you simpy double-click the icon to get going.

The program contains two basic modules:

- A set of additional tutorials on various networking subjects.
- A simple expert system that can help you diagnose IP connectivity problems in hosts and routers.

Apple Mac Users

As I am a Mac user myself, I wanted people like us to get at least something out of the diskettes. For that reason, I wrote the tutorials as Powerpoint 3.0

presentations. You might be aware that Microsoft Powerpoint 3.0 files for the Mac and PC are interchangeable with two important caveats:

1.   The versions of Powerpoint must be identical.   YOU NEED VERSION 3.0 on your Mac to view these presentations. If you have a later version of Powerpoint then you're out of luck, because at least at the time I wrote this Microsoft had not included the cross-platform compatibility code in Version 4. Dig out those old 3.0 diskettes and reinstall it (personally I never bothered upgrading).

2.   You need to borrow a PC to decompress the tutorials, then transfer them to a DOS diskette and make sure youe have a DOS reader utility on your Mac.

The expert system and program shell is written with Microsoft Visual Basic, the only reason I still use a PC. I can see why Microsoft don't port VB to the Mac, they'd never sell another copy of Windows!

Index